The Power of Your Subconscious Mind

Win Riches and Prosperity
Free yourself of the negative attitudes that block your path to wealth. Master the three simple steps employed by successful businesspersons around the world.

Regain Former Youthfulness and Vigor
Find out why the mental and physical deterioration associated with aging is not natural, and how you can retain your youth.

Work Real Miracles in the Lives of Others
Learn how to use Mental Transference to will health and vitality to a far-off loved one or friend in great need.

Find New Peace of Mind
Discover how to use the Spiritual Law of Communion to bring yourself into radiant union with God.

ABOUT THE AUTHOR

DR. JOSEPH MURPHY, D.R.S., PH.D., L.L.D., has been teaching, writing, counseling, and lecturing thousands of men and women all over the world for over a quarter of a century. He is internationally respected as a metaphysician and religious counselor. Hundreds of thousands have attended his classes on the Laws of the Mind and the inner meaning of life. A Doctor of Religious Science of the Bible University of Ambur, India, and a Fellow of the Andhra Research University, India, he was associated with the late Dr. Ernst Holmes, founder of Religious Science. He is the author of scores of books.

The POWER of
Your Subconscious Mind

Joseph Murphy

D.R.S., D.D., Ph.D., LL.D.
Fellow of the Andhra Research
University of India

BANTAM BOOKS
TORONTO · NEW YORK · LONDON · SYDNEY

THE POWER OF YOUR SUBCONSCIOUS MIND
A Bantam Book / published by arrangement with Prentice-Hall, Inc.

PRINTING HISTORY
Prentice-Hall edition published June 1963
13 printings through June 1980
A Selection of SCIENCE OF MIND MAGAZINE, September 1980
Bantam Edition / April 1982

ISBN 0-553-13672-0

Published simultaniously in the United States and Canada

Bantam Books are published by Bantam Books, Inc. Its trademark, consisting of the words "Bantam Books" and the portrayal of a rooster, is Registered in U.S. Patent and Trademark office and in other countries. Marca Registrada. Bantam Books, Inc., 666 Fifth Avenue, New York, New York 10103.

PRINTED IN THE UNITED STATES OF AMERICA

0 9 8 7 6 5 4 3

How This Book Can Work Miracles in Your Life

I have seen miracles happen to men and women in all walks of life all over the world. Miracles will happen to you, too—when you begin using the magic power of your subconscious mind. This book is designed to teach you that your habitual thinking and imagery mold, fashion, and create your destiny; for as a man thinketh in his subconscious mind, so is he.

• Do you know the answers?

Why is one man sad and another man happy? Why is one man joyous and prosperous and another man poor and miserable? Why is one man fearful and anxious and another full of faith and confidence? Why does one man have a beautiful, luxurious home while another man lives out a meager existence in a slum? Why is one man a great success and another an abject failure? Why is one speaker outstanding and immensely popular and another mediocre and unpopular? Why is one man a genius in his work or profession while the other man toils and moils all his life without doing or accomplishing anything worth while? Why is one man healed of a so-called incurable disease and another isn't? Why is it so many good, kind religious people suffer the tortures of the damned in their mind and body? Why is it many immoral and irreligious people succeed and prosper and enjoy radiant health? Why is one woman happily married and her sister very unhappy and frustrated? Is there an answer to these questions in the workings of your conscious and subconscious minds? There most certainly is.

5

• Reason for writing this book

It is for the express purpose of answering and clarifying the above questions and many others of a similar nature that motivated me to write this book. I have endeavored to explain the great fundamental truths of your mind in the simplest language possible. I believe that it is perfectly possible to explain the basic, foundational, and fundamental laws of life and of your mind in ordinary everyday language. You will find that the language of this book is that used in your daily papers, current periodicals, in your business offices, in your home, and in the daily workshop. I urge you to study this book and apply the techniques outlined therein; and as you do, I feel absolutely convinced that you will lay hold of a miracle-working power that will lift you up from confusion, misery, melancholy, and failure, and guide you to your true place, solve your difficulties, sever you from emotional and physical bondage, and place you on the royal road to freedom, happiness, and peace of mind. This miracle-working power of your subconscious mind can heal you of your sickness, make you vital and strong again. In learning how to use your inner powers, you will open the prison door of fear and enter into a life described by Paul as the glorious liberty of the sons of God.

• Releasing the miracle-working power

A personal healing will ever be the most convincing evidence of our subconscious powers. Over forty-two years ago I resolved a malignancy—in medical terminology it was called a sarcoma—by using the healing power of my subconscious mind which created me and still maintains and governs all my vital functions. The technique I applied is elaborated on in this book, and I feel sure that it will help others to trust the same Infinite Healing Presence lodged in the subconscious depths of all men. Through the kindly offices of my doctor friend, I suddenly realized that it was natural to assume that the Creative Intelligence which made all my organs, fashioned my body, and started my heart, could heal its own handiwork. The ancient proverb says, "The doctor dresses the wound and God heals it."

• Wonders happen when you pray effectively

Scientific prayer is the harmonious interaction of the conscious and subconscious levels of mind scientifically directed for a specific purpose. This book will teach you the scientific way to tap the realm of infinite power within you enabling you to get what you really want in life. You desire a happier, fuller, and richer life. Begin to use this miracle-working power and smooth your way in daily affairs, solve business problems, and bring harmony in family relationships. Be sure that you read this book several times. The many chapters will show you how this wonderful power works, and how you can draw out the hidden inspiration and wisdom that is within you. Learn the simple techniques of impressing the subconscious mind. Follow the new scientific way in tapping the infinite storehouse. Read this book carefully, earnestly, and lovingly. Prove to yourself the amazing way it can help you. It could be and I believe it will be the turning point of your life.

• Everybody prays

Do you know how to pray effectively? How long is it since you prayed as part of your everyday activities? In an emergency, in time of danger or trouble, in illness, and when death lurks, prayers pour forth—your own and friends. Just read your daily newspaper. It is reported that prayers are being offered up all over the nation for a child stricken with a so-called incurable ailment, for peace among nations, for a group of miners trapped in a flooded mine. Later it is reported that when rescued, the miners said that they prayed while waiting for rescue; an airplane pilot says that he prayed as he made a successful emergency landing. Certainly, prayer is an ever-present help in time of trouble; but you do not have to wait for trouble to make prayer an integral and constructive part of your life. The dramatic answers to prayer make headlines and are the subject of testimonies to the effectiveness of prayer. What of the many humble prayers of children, the simple thanksgiving of grace at the table daily, the faithful devotions wherein the individual seeks only communion with God? My work with people has made it necessary for me to study the various approaches to prayer. I have experienced the power of prayer in my own life, and I have talked and worked with many people who also have enjoyed the help of prayer. The problem usually is how to tell others how to pray. People who are in trouble have difficulty in thinking and acting reasonably. They need an easy formula to follow, an obviously workable pattern that is simple and specific. Often they must be led to approach the emergency.

• Unique feature of this book

The unique feature of this book is its down-to-earth practicality. Here you are presented with simple, usable techniques and formulas which you can easily apply in your workaday world. I have taught these simple processes to men and women all over the world, and recently over a thousand men and women of all religious affiliations attended a special class in Los Angeles where I presented the highlights of what is offered in the pages of this book. Many came from distances of two hundred miles for each class lesson. The special features of this book will appeal to you because they show you why oftentimes you get the opposite of what you prayed for and reveal to you the reasons why. People have asked me in all parts of the world and thousands of times, "Why is it I have prayed and prayed and got no answer?" In this book you will find the reasons for this common complaint. The many ways of impressing the subconscious mind and getting the right answers make this an extraordinarily valuable book and an ever-present help in time of trouble.

• What do you believe?

It is not the thing believed in that brings an answer to man's prayer; the answer to prayer results when the individual's subconscious mind responds to the mental picture or thought in his mind. This law of belief is operating in all religions of the world and is the reason why they are psychologically true. The Buddhist, the Christian, the Moslem, and the Hebrew all may get answers to their prayers, not because of the particular creed, religion, affiliation, ritual, ceremony, formula, liturgy, incantation, sacrifices, or offerings, but solely because of belief or mental acceptance and receptivity about that for which they pray. The law of life is the law of belief, and belief could be summed up briefly as a thought in your mind. As a man thinks, feels, and believes, so is the condition of his mind, body, and circumstances. A technique, a methodology based on an understanding of what you are doing and why you are doing it will help you to bring about a subconscious embodiment of all the good things of life. Essentially, answered prayer is the realization of your heart's desire.

• Desire is prayer

Everyone desires health, happiness, security, peace of mind, true expression, but many fail to achieve clearly defined results. A university professor admitted to me recently, "I know that if I changed my mental pattern and redirected my emotional life, my ulcers would not recur, but I do not have any technique, process, or modus operandi. My mind wanders back and forth on my many problems, and I feel frustrated, defeated, and unhappy." This professor had a desire for perfect health; he needed a knowledge of the way his mind worked which would enable him to fulfill his desire. By practicing the healing methods outlined in this book, he became whole and perfect.

• There is one mind common to all individual men (Emerson)

The miracle-working powers of your subconscious mind existed before you and I were born, before any church or world existed. The great eternal truths and principles of life antedate all religions. It is with these thoughts in mind that I urge you in the following chapters to lay hold of this wonderful, magical, transforming power which will bind up mental and physical wounds, proclaim liberty to the fear-ridden mind, and liberate you completely from the limitations of poverty, failure, misery, lack, and frustration. All you have to do is unite mentally and emotionally with the good you wish to embody, and the creative powers of your subconscious will respond accordingly. Begin now, today, let wonders happen in your life! Keep on, keeping on until the day breaks and the shadows flee away.

Contents

11

4. Mental Healings in Ancient Times . . . 55

- Bible accounts on the use of the subconscious powers—
Miracles at various shrines throughout the world—One
universal healing principle—Widely different theories—
Views of Paracelsus—Bernheim's experiments—Producing
a blister by suggestion—The cause of bloody stigmata—
Healing points in review.

5. Mental Healings in Modern Times . . . 66

- One process of healing—The law of belief—Prayer therapy
is the combined function of the conscious and subconscious
mind scientifically directed—Faith healing, what it means,
and how blind faith works—Subjective faith and what it
means—The meaning of absent treatment—Releasing the
kinetic action of the subconscious mind—Summary of your
aids to health.

6. Practical Techniques in Mental Healings . . . 75

- The passing-over technique for impregnating the subconscious—Your subconscious will accept your blueprint—
The science and art of true prayer—The visualization
technique—Mental movie method—The Baudoin technique—The sleeping technique—The "thank-you" technique—The affirmative method—The argumentative
method—The absolute method is like modern sound wave
therapy—A cripple walks—The decree method—Serve
yourself with scientific truth.

7. The Tendency of the Subconscious Is Lifeward . . . 90

- How the body portrays the workings of the mind—There
is an intelligence which takes care of the body—The subconscious mind works continually for the common good—
How man interferes with the innate principle of harmony
—Why it's normal to be healthy, vital, and strong—It's
abnormal to be sick—Pott's disease cured—How faith in
your subconscious powers makes you whole—Pointers to
review.

The POWER of
Your Subconscious Mind

1

The Treasure House Within You

Infinite riches are all around you if you will open your mental eyes and behold the treasure house of infinity within you. There is a gold mine within you from which you can extract everything you need to live life gloriously, joyously, and abundantly.

Many are sound asleep because they do not know about this gold mine of infinite intelligence and boundless love within themselves. Whatever you want, you can draw forth. A magnetized piece of steel will lift about twelve times its own weight, and if you demagnetize this same piece of steel, it will not even lift a feather. Similarly, there are two types of men. There is the magnetized man who is full of confidence and faith. He knows that he is born to win and to succeed. Then, there is the type of man who is demagnetized. He is full of fears and doubts. Opportunities come, and he says, "I might fail; I might lose my money; people will laugh at me." This type of man will not get very far in life because, if he is afraid to go forward, he will simply stay where he is. Become a magnetized man and discover the master secret of the ages.

• The master secret of the ages

What, in your opinion, is the master secret of the ages? The secret of atomic energy? Thermonuclear energy? The neutron bomb? Interplanetary travel? No—not any of these. Then, what is this master secret? Where can one find it, and how can it be contacted and brought into action? The answer is extraordinarily simple. This secret is the marvelous, miracle-working power found in your own subconscious mind, the last place that most people would seek it.

• The marvelous power of your subconscious

You can bring into your life more power, more wealth, more health, more happiness, and more joy by learning to contact and release the hidden power of your subconscious mind.

You need not acquire this power; you already possess it. But, you want to learn how to use it; you want to understand it so that you can apply it in all departments of your life.

As you follow the simple techniques and processes set forth in this book, you can gain the necessary knowledge and understanding. You can be inspired by a new light, and you can generate a new force enabling you to realize your hopes and make all your dreams come true. Decide now to make your life grander, greater, richer, and nobler than ever before.

Within your subconscious depths lie infinite wisdom, infinite power, and infinite supply of all that is necessary, which is waiting for development and expression. Begin now to recognize these potentialities of your deeper mind, and they will take form in the world without.

The infinite intelligence within your subconscious mind can reveal to you everything you need to know at every moment of time and point of space provided you are open-minded and receptive. You can receive new thoughts and ideas enabling you to bring forth new inventions, make new discoveries, or write books and plays. Moreover, the infinite intelligence in your subconscious can impart to you wonderful kinds of knowledge of an original nature. It can reveal to you and open the way fo perfect expression and true place in your life.

Through the wisdom of your subconscious mind you can attract the ideal companion, as well as the right business associate or partner. It can find the right buyer for your home, and provide you with all the money you need, and the financial freedom to be, to do, and to go as your heart desires.

It is your right to discover this inner world of thought, feel ing, and power, of light, love, and beauty. Though invisible, its forces are mighty. Within your subconscious mind you will find the solution for every problem, and the cause for every effect. Because you can draw out the hidden powers, you come into actual possession of the power and wisdom necessary to move forward in abundance, security, joy, and dominion.

I have seen the power of the subconscious lift people up out of crippled states, making them whole, vital, and strong once more, and free to go out into the world to experience happiness, health, and joyous expression. There is a miraculous healing power in your subconscious that can heal the troubled mind and the broken heart. It can open the prison door of the mind and liberate you. It can free you from all kinds of material and physical bondage.

• Necessity of a working basis

Substantial progress in any field of endeavor is impossible in the absence of a working basis which is universal in its application. You can become skilled in the operation of your subconscious mind. You can practice its powers with a certainty of results in exact proportion to your knowledge of its principles and to your application of them for definite specific purposes and goals you wish to achieve.

Being a former chemist, I would like to point out that if you combine hydrogen and oxygen in the proportions of two atoms of the former to one of the latter, water will be the result. You are very familiar with the fact that one atom of oxygen and one atom of carbon will produce carbon monoxide, a poisonous gas. But, if you add another atom of oxygen, you will get carbon dioxide, a harmless gas, and so on throughout the vast realm of chemical compounds.

You must not think that the principles of chemistry, physics, and mathematics differ from the principles of your subconscious mind. Let us consider a generally accepted principle: "Water seeks its own level." This is a universal principle which is applicable to water everywhere.

Consider another principle: "Matter expands when heated."

This is true anywhere, at any time, and under all circumstances. You can heat a piece of steel, and it will expand regardless whether the steel is found in China, England, or India. It is a universal truth that matter expands when heated. It is also a universal truth that whatever you impress on your subconscious mind is expressed on the screen of space as condition, experience, and event.

Your prayer is answered because your subconscious mind is principle, and by principle I mean the way a thing works. For example, the principle of electricity is that it works from a higher to a lower potential. You do not change the principle of electricity when you use it, but by co-operating with nature, you can bring forth marvelous inventions and discoveries which bless humanity in countless ways.

Your subconscious mind is principle and works according to the law of belief. You must know what belief is, why it works, and how it works. Your Bible says in a simple, clear, and beautiful way: *Whosoever shall say unto this mountain, Be thou removed, and be thou cast into the sea; and shall not doubt in his heart, but shall believe that those things which he saith shall come to pass; he shall have whatsoever he saith.* MARK 11:23.

The law of your mind is the law of belief. This means to believe in the way your mind works, to believe in belief itself. The belief of your mind is the thought of your mind—that is simple—just that and nothing else.

All your experiences, events, conditions, and acts are the reactions of your subconscious mind to your thoughts. Remember, it is not the thing believed in, but the belief in your own mind which brings about the result. Cease believing in the false beliefs, opinions, superstitions, and fears of mankind. Begin to believe in the eternal verities and truths of life which never change. Then, you will move onward, upward, and Godward.

Whoever reads this book and applies the principles of the subconscious mind herein set forth, will be able to pray scientifically and effectively for himself and for others. Your prayer is answered according to the universal law of action and reaction. Thought is incipient action. The reaction is the response from your subconscious mind which corresponds with the nature of your thought. Busy your mind with the concepts of harmony, health, peace, and good will, and wonders will happen in your life.

• The duality of mind

You have only one mind, but your mind possesses two distinctive characteristics. The line of demarcation between the two is well known to all thinking men and women today. The two functions of your mind are essentially unlike. Each is endowed with separate and distinct attributes and powers. The nomenclature generally used to distinguish the two functions of your mind is as follows: The objective and subjective mind, the conscious and subconscious mind, the waking and sleeping mind, the surface self and the deep self, the voluntary mind and the involuntary mind, the male and the female, and many other terms. You will find the terms "conscious" and "subconscious" used to represent the dual nature of your mind throughout this book.

• The conscious and subconscious minds

An excellent way to get acquainted with the two functions of your mind is to look upon your own mind as a garden. You are a gardener, and you are planting seeds (thoughts) in your subconscious mind all day long, based on your habitual thinking. As you sow in your subconscious mind, so shall you reap in your body and environment.

Begin now to sow thoughts of peace, happiness, right action, good will, and prosperity. Think quietly and with interest on these qualities and accept them fully in your conscious reasoning mind. Continue to plant these wonderful seeds (thoughts) in the garden of your mind, and you will reap a glorious harvest. Your subconscious mind may be likened to the soil which will grow all kinds of seeds, good or bad. *Do men gather grapes of thorns, or figs of thistles?* Every thought is, therefore, a cause, and every condition is an effect. For this reason, it is essential that you take charge of your thoughts so as to bring forth only desirable conditions.

When your mind thinks correctly, when you understand the truth, when the thoughts deposited in your subconscious mind are constructive, harmonious, and peaceful, the magic working power of your subconscious will respond and bring about harmonious conditions, agreeable surroundings, and the best of everything. When you begin to control your thought processes, you can apply the powers of your subconscious to any problem or difficulty. In other words, you will actually be consciously co-operating with the infinite power and omnipotent law which governs all things.

Look around you wherever you live and you will notice that the vast majority of mankind lives in the world without; the more enlightened men are intensely interested in the world within. Remember, it is the world within, namely, your thoughts, feelings, and imagery that makes your world without. It is, therefore, the only creative power, and everything which you find in your world of expression has been created by you in the inner world of your mind consciously or unconsciously.

A knowledge of the interaction of your conscious and subconscious minds will enable you to transform your whole life. In order to change external conditions, you must change the cause. Most men try to change conditions and circumstances by working with conditions and circumstances. To remove discord, confusion, lack, and limitation, you must remove the cause, and the cause is the way you are using your conscious mind. In other words, the way you are thinking and picturing in your mind.

You are living in a fathomless sea of infinite riches. Your subconscious is very sensitive to your thoughts. Your thoughts form the mold or matrix through which the infinite intelligence, wisdom, vital forces, and energies of your subconscious flow. The practical application of the laws of your mind as illustrated in each chapter of this book will cause you to experience abundance for poverty, wisdom for superstition and ignorance, peace for pain, joy for sadness, light for darkness, harmony for discord, faith and confidence for fear, success for failure, and freedom from the law of averages. Certainly, there can be no more wonderful blessing than these from a mental, emotional, and material standpoint.

Most of the great scientists, artists, poets, singers, writers, and inventors have a deep understanding of the workings of the conscious and subconscious minds.

One time Caruso, the great operatic tenor, was struck with stage fright. He said his throat was paralyzed due to spasms caused by intense fear which constricted the muscles of his throat. Perspiration poured copiously down his face. He was ashamed because in a few minutes he had to go out on the stage, yet he was shaking with fear and trepidation. He said, "They will laugh at me. I can't sing." Then he shouted in the presence of those behind the stage, "The Little Me wants to strangle the Big Me within."

He said to the Little Me, "Get out of here, the Big Me wants to sing through me."

By the Big Me, he meant the limitless power and wisdom of his subconscious mind, and he began to shout, "Get out, get out, the Big Me is going to sing!"

His subconscious mind responded releasing the vital forces within him. When the call came, he walked out on the stage and sang gloriously and majestically, enthralling the audience.

It is obvious to you now that Caruso must have understood the two levels of mind—the conscious or rational, and the subconscious or irrational level. Your subconscious mind is reactive and responds to the nature of your thoughts. When your conscious mind (the Little Me) is full of fear, worry, and anxiety, the negative emotions engendered in your subconscious mind (the Big Me) are released and flood the conscious mind with a sense of panic, foreboding, and despair. When this happens, you can, like Caruso, speak affirmatively and with a deep sense of authority to the irrational emotions generated in your deeper mind as follows: "Be still, be quiet, I am in control, you must obey me, you are subject to my command, you cannot intrude where you do not belong."

It is fascinating and intensely interesting to observe how

you can speak authoritatively and with conviction to the irrational movement of your deeper self bringing silence, harmony, and peace to your mind. The subconscious is subject to the conscious mind, and that is why it is called subconscious or subjective.

• Outstanding differences and modes of operation

You will perceive the main differences by the following illustrations: The conscious mind is like the navigator or captain at the bridge of a ship. He directs the ship and signals orders to men in the engine room, who in turn control all the boilers, instruments, gauges, etc. The men in the engine room do not know where they are going; they follow orders. They would go on the rocks if the man on the bridge issued faulty or wrong instructions based on his findings with the compass, sextant, or other instruments. The men in the engine room obey him because he is in charge and issues orders which are automatically obeyed. Members of the crew do not talk back to the captain; they simply carry out orders.

The captain is the master of his ship, and his decrees are carried out. Likewise, your conscious mind is the captain and the master of your ship, which represents your body, environment, and all your affairs. Your subconscious mind takes the orders you give it based upon what your conscious mind believes and accepts as true.

When you repeatedly say to people, "I can't afford it," then your subconscious mind takes you at your word and sees to it that you will not be in a position to purchase what you want. As long as you persist in saying, "I can't afford that car, that trip to Europe, that home, that fur coat or ermine wrap," you can rest assured that your subconscious mind will follow your orders, and you will go through life experiencing the lack of all these things.

Last Christmas Eve a beautiful young university student looked at an attractive and rather expensive traveling bag in a store window. She was going home to Buffalo, New York, for the holidays. She was about to say, "I can't afford that bag," when she recalled something she had heard at one of my lectures which was, "Never finish a negative statement; reverse it immediately, and wonders will happen in your life."

She said, "That bag is mine. It is for sale. I accept it mentally, and my subconscious sees to it that I receive it."

At eight o'clock Christmas Eve her fiancé presented her with a bag exactly the same as the one she had looked at and mentally identified herself with at ten o'clock the same morning. She had filled her mind with the thought of expectancy and released the whole thing to her deeper mind which has the "know-how" of accomplishment.

This young girl, a student at the University of Southern California, said to me, "I didn't have the money to buy that bag, but now I know where to find money and all the things I need, and that is in the treasure house of eternity within me."

Another simple illustration is this: When you say, "I do not like mushrooms," and the occasion subsequently comes that you are served mushrooms in sauces or salads, you will get indigestion because your subconscious mind says to you, "The boss (your conscious mind) does not like mushrooms." This is an amusing example of the outstanding differences and modes of operation of your conscious and subconscious minds.

A woman may say, "I wake up at three o'clock, if I drink coffee at night." Whenever she drinks coffee, her subconscious mind nudges her, as if to say, "The boss wants you to stay awake tonight."

Your subconscious mind works twenty-four hours a day and makes provisions for your benefit, pouring all the fruit of your habitual thinking into your lap.

● **How her subconscious responded**

A woman wrote me a few months ago as follows: "I am seventy-five years old, a widow with a grown family. I was living alone and on a pension. I heard your lectures on the powers of the subconscious mind wherein you said that ideas could be conveyed to the subconscious mind by repetition, faith, and expectancy.

"I began to repeat frequently with feeling, 'I am wanted. I am happily married to a kind, loving, and spiritual-minded man. I am secure!'

"I kept on doing this many times a day for about two weeks, and one day at the corner drugstore, I was introduced to a retired pharmacist. I found him to be kind, understanding, and very religious. He was a perfect answer to my prayer. Within a week he proposed to me, and now we are on our honeymoon in Europe. I know that the intelligence within my subconscious mind brought both of us together in divine order."

This woman discovered that the treasure house was within her. Her prayer was felt as true in her heart, and her affirmation sank down by osmosis into her subconscious mind, which is the creative medium. The moment she succeeded in bringing about a subjective embodiment, her subconscious mind brought about the answer through the law of attraction. Her deeper mind, full of wisdom and intelligence, brought both of them together in divine order.

Be sure that you think on *whatsoever things are true, whatsoever things are honest, whatsoever things are just, whatsoever things are pure, whatsoever things are lovely, whatsoever things are of good report; if there be any virtue, and if there be any praise, think on these things.* PHIL. 4:8.

• Brief summary of ideas worth remembering

1. The treasure house is within you. Look within for the answer to your heart's desire.

2. The great secret possessed by the great men of all ages was their ability to contact and release the powers of their subconscious mind. You can do the same.

3. Your subconscious has the answer to all problems. If you suggest to your subconscious prior to sleep, "I want to get up at 6 A.M.," it will awaken you at that exact time.

4. Your subconscious mind is the builder of your body and can heal you. Lull yourself to sleep every night with the idea of perfect health, and your subconscious, being your faithful servant, will obey you.

5. Every thought is a cause, and every condition is an effect.

6. If you want to write a book, write a wonderful play, give a better talk to your audience, convey the idea lovingly and feelingly to your subconscious mind, and it will respond accordingly.

7. You are like a captain navigating a ship. He must give the right orders, and likewise, you must give the right orders (thoughts and images) to your subconscious mind which controls and governs all your experiences.

8. Never use the terms, "I can't afford it" or "I can't do this." Your subconscious mind takes you at your word and sees to it that you do not have the money or the ability to do what you want to do. Affirm, "I can do all things through the power of my subconscious mind."

9. The law of life is the law of belief. A belief is a thought in your mind. Do not believe in things to harm or hurt you. Believe in the power of your subconscious to heal, inspire, strengthen, and prosper you. According to your belief is it done unto you.

10. Change your thoughts, and you change your destiny.

2

How Your Own Mind Works

You have a mind, and you should learn how to use it. There are two levels of your mind—the conscious or rational level, and the subconscious or irrational level. You think with your conscious mind, and whatever you habitually think sinks down into your subconscious mind, which creates according to the nature of your thoughts. Your subconscious mind is the seat of your emotions and is the creative mind. If you think good, good will follow; if you think evil, evil will follow. This is the way your mind works.

The main point to remember is once the subconscious mind accepts an idea, it begins to execute it. It is an interesting and subtle truth that the law of the subconscious mind works for good and bad ideas alike. This law, when applied in a negative way, is the cause of failure, frustration, and unhappiness. However, when your habitual thinking is harmonious and constructive, you experience perfect health, success, and prosperity.

Peace of mind and a healthy body are inevitable when you begin to think and feel in the right way. Whatever you claim mentally and feel as true, your subconscious mind will accept and bring forth into your experience. The only thing necessary for you to do is to get your subconscious mind to accept your idea, and the law of your own subconscious mind will bring forth the health, peace, or the position you desire. You give the command or decree, and your subconscious will faithfully reproduce the idea impressed upon it. The law of your mind is this: You will get a reaction or response from your subconscious mind according to the nature of the thought or idea you hold in your conscious mind.

Psychologists and psychiatrists point out that when thoughts are conveyed to your subconscious mind, impressions are made in the brain cells. As soon as your subconscious accepts any idea, it proceeds to put it into effect immediately. It works by association of ideas and uses every bit of knowledge that you have gathered in your lifetime to bring about its purpose. It draws on the infinite power, energy, and wisdom within you. It lines up all the laws of nature to get its way. Sometimes it seems to bring about an immediate solution to your difficulties, but at other times it may take days, weeks, or longer. . . . *Its ways are past finding out.*

• Conscious and subconscious terms differentiated

You must remember that these are not two minds. They are merely two spheres of activity within one mind. Your conscious mind is the reasoning mind. It is that phase of mind which chooses. For example, you choose your books, your home, and your partner in life. You make all your decisions with your conscious mind. On the other hand, without any conscious choice on your part, your heart is kept functioning automatically, and the process of digestion, circulation, and breathing are carried on by your subconscious mind through processes independent of your conscious control.

Your subconscious mind accepts what is impressed upon it or what you consciously belie.re. It does not reason things out like your conscious mind, and it does not argue with you controversially. Your subconscious mind is like the soil which accepts any kind of seed, good or bad. Your thoughts are active and might be likened unto seeds. Negative, destructive thoughts continue to work negatively in your subconscious mind, and in due time will come forth into outer experience which corresponds with them.

Remember, your subconscious mind does not engage in proving whether your thoughts are good or bad, true or false, but it responds according to the nature of your thoughts or suggestions. For example, if you consciously assume something as true, even though it may be false, your subconscious mind will accept it as true and proceed to bring about results which must necessarily follow, because you consciously assumed it to be true.

• Experiments by psychologists

Innumerable experiments by psychologists and others on persons in the hypnotic state have shown that the subconscious mind is incapable of making selections and comparisons which are necessary for a reasoning process. They have shown repeatedly that your subconscious mind will accept any suggestions, however false. Having once accepted any suggestion, it responds according to the nature of the suggestion given.

To illustrate the amenability of your subconscious mind to suggestion, if a practiced hypnotist suggests to one of his subjects that he is Napoleon Bonaparte, or even a cat or a dog, he will act out the part with inimitable accuracy. His personality becomes changed for the time being. He believes himself to be whatever the operator tells him he is.

A skilled hypnotist may suggest to one of his students in the hypnotic state that his back itches, to another that his nose is bleeding, to another that he is a marble statue, to another that he is freezing and the temperature is below zero. Each one will follow out the line of his particular suggestion, totally oblivious to all his surroundings which do not pertain to his idea.

These simple illustrations portray clearly the difference between your conscious reasoning mind and your subconscious mind which is impersonal, non-selective, and accepts as true whatever your conscious mind believes to be true. Hence, the importance of selecting thoughts, ideas, and premises which bless, heal, inspire, and fill your soul with joy.

• The terms objective and subjective mind clarified

Your conscious mind is sometimes referred to as your objective mind because it deals with outward objects. The objective mind takes cognizance of the objective world. Its media of observation are your five physical senses. Your objective mind is your guide and director in your contact with your environment. You gain knowledge through your five senses. Your objective mind learns through observation, experience, and education. As previously pointed out, the greatest function of the objective mind is that of reasoning.

Suppose you are one of the thousands of tourists who come to Los Angeles annually. You would come to the conclusion that it is a beautiful city based upon your observation of the parks, pretty gardens, majestic buildings, and lovely homes. This is the working of your objective mind.

Your subconscious mind is oftentimes referred to as your subjective mind. Your subjective mind takes cognizance of its environment by means independent of the five senses. Your subjective mind perceives by intuition. It is the seat of your emotion and the storehouse of memory. Your subjective mind performs its highest functions when your objective senses are in abeyance. In a word, it is that intelligence which makes itself manifest when the objective mind is suspended or in a sleepy, drowsy state.

Your subjective mind sees without the use of the natural organs of vision. It has the capacity of clairvoyance and clairaudience. Your subjective mind can leave your body, travel to distant lands, and bring back information oftentimes of the most exact and truthful character. Through your subjective mind you can read the thoughts of others, read the contents of sealed envelopes and closed safes. Your subjective mind has the ability to apprehend the thoughts of others without the use of the ordinary objective means of communication. It is of the greatest importance that we understand the interaction of the objective and subjective mind in order to learn the true art of prayer.

• The subconscious cannot reason like your conscious mind

Your subconscious mind cannot argue controversially. Hence, if you give it wrong suggestions, it will accept them as true and will proceed to bring them to pass as conditions, experiences, and events. All things that have happened to you are based on thoughts impressed on your subconscious mind through belief. If you have conveyed erroneous concepts to your subconscious mind, the sure method of overcoming them is by the repetition of constructive, harmonious thoughts frequently repeated which your subconscious mind accepts, thus forming new and healthy habits of thought and life, for your subconscious mind is the seat of habit.

The habitual thinking of your conscious mind establishes deep grooves in your subconscious mind. This is very favorable for you if your habitual thoughts are harmonious, peaceful, and constructive.

If you have indulged in fear, worry, and other destructive forms of thinking, the remedy is to recognize the omnipotence of your subconscious mind and decree freedom, happiness, and perfect health. Your subconscious mind, being creative and one with your divine source, will proceed to create the freedom and happiness which you have earnestly decreed.

• The tremendous power of suggestion

You must realize by now that your conscious mind is the "watchman at the gate," and its chief function is to protect your subconscious mind from false impressions. You are now aware of one of the basic laws of mind: Your subconscious mind is amenable to suggestion. As you know, your subconscious mind does not make comparisons, or contrasts, neither does it reason and think things out for itself. This latter function belongs to your conscious mind. It simply reacts to the impressions given to it by your conscious mind. It does not show a preference for one course of action over another.

The following is a classic example of the tremendous power of suggestion. Suppose you approach a timid-looking passenger on board ship and say to him something like this: "You look very ill. How pale you are! I feel certain you are going to be seasick. Let me help you to your cabin." The passenger turns pale. Your suggestion of seasickness associates itself with his own fears and forebodings. He accepts your aid down to the berth, and there your negative suggestion, which was accepted by him, is realized.

• Different reactions to the same suggestion

It is true that different people will react in different ways to the same suggestion because of their subconscious conditioning or belief. For example, if you go to a sailor on the ship and say to him sympathetically, "My dear fellow, you're looking very ill. Aren't you feeling sick? You look to me as if you were going to be seasick."

According to his temperament he either laughs at your "joke," or expresses a mild irritation. Your suggestion fell on deaf ears in this instance because your suggestion of seasickness was associated in his mind with his own immunity from it. Therefore, it called up not fear or worry, but self-confidence.

The dictionary says that a suggestion is the act or instance of putting something into one's mind, the mental process by which the thought or idea suggested is entertained, accepted, or put into effect. You must remember that a suggestion cannot impose something on the subconscious mind against the will of the conscious mind. In other words, your conscious mind has the power to reject the suggestion given. In the case of the sailor, he had no fear of seasickness. He had convinced himself of his immunity, and the negative suggestion had absolutely no power to evoke fear.

The suggestion of seasickness to the other passenger called forth his indwelling fear of seasickness. Each of us has his own inner fears, beliefs, opinions, and these inner assumptions rule and govern our lives. A suggestion has no power in and of itself except it is accepted mentally by you. This causes your subconscious powers to flow in a limited and restricted way according to the nature of the suggestion.

• How he lost his arm

Every two or three years I give a series of lectures at the London Truth Forum in Caxton Hall. This is a Forum I founded a number of years ago. Dr. Evelyn Fleet, the director, told me about an article which appeared in the English newspapers dealing with the power of suggestion. This is the suggestion a man gave to his subconscious mind over a period of about two years: "I would give my right arm to see my daughter cured." It appeared that his daughter had a crippling form of arthritis together with a so-called incurable form of skin disease. Medical treatment had failed to alleviate the condition, and the father had an intense longing for his daughter's healing, and expressed his desire in the words just quoted.

Dr. Evelyn Fleet said that the newspaper article pointed out that one day the family was out riding when their car collided with another. The father's right arm was torn off at the shoulder, and immediately the daughter's arthritis and skin condition vanished.

You must make certain to give your subconscious only suggestions which heal, bless, elevate, and inspire you in all your ways. Remember that your subconscious mind cannot take a joke. It takes you at your word.

• How autosuggestion banishes fear

Illustrations of autosuggestion: Autosuggestion means suggesting something definite and specific to oneself. Herbert Parkyn, in his excellent manual of autosuggestion,* records the following incident. It has its amusing side, so that one remembers it. "A New York visitor in Chicago looks at his watch, which is set an hour ahead of Chicago time, and tells a Chicago friend that it is twelve o'clock. The Chicago friend, not considering the difference in time between Chicago and New York, tells the New Yorker that he is hungry and that he must go to lunch."

Autosuggestion may be used to banish various fears and other negative conditions. A young singer was invited to give an audition. She had been looking forward to the interview, but on three previous occasions she had failed miserably due to fear

---

* Herbert Parkyn, *Autosuggestion* (London: Fowler, 1916).

of failure. This young lady had a very good voice, but she had been saying to herself, "When the time comes for me to sing, maybe they won't like me. I will try, but I'm full of fear and anxiety."

Her subconscious mind accepted these negative autosuggestions as a request and proceeded to manifest them and bring them into her experience. The cause was an involuntary autosuggestion, i.e., silent fear thoughts emotionalized and subjectified.

She overcame it by the following technique: Three times a day she isolated herself in a room. She sat down comfortably in an armchair, relaxed her body, and closed her eyes. She stilled her mind and body as best she could. Physical inertia favors mental passivity and renders the mind more receptive to suggestion. She counteracted the fear suggestion by saying to herself, "I sing beautifully. I am poised, serene, confident, and calm." She repeated this statement slowly, quietly, and with feeling from five to ten times at each sitting. She had three such "sittings" every day and one immediately prior to sleep. At the end of a week she was completely poised and confident. When the invitation to audition came, she gave a remarkable, wonderful audition.

• How she restored her memory

A woman, aged seventy-five, was in the habit of saying to herself, "I am losing my memory." She reversed the procedure and practiced induced autosuggestion several times a day as follows: "My memory from today on is improving in every department. I shall always remember whatever I need to know at every moment of time and point of space. The impressions received will be clearer and more definite. I shall retain them automatically and with ease. Whatever I wish to recall will immediately present itself in the correct form in my mind. I am improving rapidly every day, and very soon my memory will be better than it has ever been before." At the end of three weeks, her memory was back to normal, and she was delighted.

- **How he overcame a nasty temper**

Many men who complained of irritability and bad temper proved to be very susceptible to autosuggestion and obtained marvelous results by using the following statements three or four times a day—morning, noon, and at night prior to sleep for about a month. "Henceforth, I shall grow more good-humored. Joy, happiness, and cheerfulness are now becoming my normal states of mind. Every day I am becoming more and more lovable and understanding. I am now becoming the center of cheer and good will to all those about me, infecting them with good humor. This happy, joyous, and cheerful mood is now becoming my normal, natural state of mind. I am grateful."

- **The constructive and destructive power of suggestion**

Some illustrations and comments on heterosuggestion: Heterosuggestion means suggestions from another person. In all ages the power of suggestion has played a part in the life and thought of man in every period of time and in each country of the earth. In many parts of the world it is the controlling power in religion.

Suggestion may be used to discipline and control ourselves, but it can also be used to take control and command over others who do not know the laws of mind. In its constructive form it is wonderful and magnificent. In its negative aspects it is one of the most destructive of all the response patterns of the mind, resulting in patterns of misery, failure, suffering, sickness, and disaster.

- **Have you accepted any of these?**

From infancy on the majority of us have been given many negative suggestions. Not knowing how to thwart them, we unconsciously accepted them. Here are some of the negative suggestions: "You can't." "You'll never amount to anything." "You mustn't." "You'll fail." "You haven't got a chance." "You're all wrong." "It's no use." "It's not what you know, but who you know." "The world is going to the dogs." "What's the use, nobody cares." "It's no use trying so hard." "You're too old now." "Things are getting worse and worse." "Life is an endless grind." "Love is for the birds." "You just can't win." "Pretty soon you'll be bankrupt." "Watch out, you'll get the virus." "You can't trust a soul," etc.

Unless, as an adult, you use constructive autosuggestion, which is a reconditioning therapy, the impressions made on you in the past can cause behavior patterns that cause failure in your personal and social life. Autosuggestion is a means releasing you from the mass of negative verbal conditioning that might otherwise distort your life pattern, making the development of good habits difficult.

• You can counteract negative suggestions

Pick up the paper any day, and you can read dozens of items that could sow the seeds of futility, fear, worry, anxiety, and impending doom. If accepted by you, these thoughts of fear could cause you to lose the will for life. Knowing that you can reject all these negative suggestions by giving your subconscious mind constructive autosuggestions, you counteract all these destructive ideas.

Check regularly on the negative suggestions that people make to you. You do not have to be influenced by destructive heterosuggestion. All of us have suffered from it in our childhood and in our teens. If you look back, you can easily recall how parents, friends, relatives, teachers, and associates contributed in a campaign of negative suggestions. Study the things said to you, and you will discover much of it was in the form of propaganda. The purpose of much of what was said was to control you or instill fear into you.

This heterosuggestion process goes on in every home, office, factory, and club. You will find that many of these suggestions are for the purpose of making you think, feel, and act as others want you to and in ways that are to their advantage.

• How suggestion killed a man

Here is an illustration of heterosuggestion: A relative of mine went to a crystal gazer in India who told him that he had a bad heart and predicted that he would die at the next new moon. He began to tell all members of his family about this prediction, and he arranged his will.

This powerful suggestion entered into his subconscious mind because he accepted it completely. My relative also told me that this crystal gazer was believed to have some strange occult powers, and he could do harm or good to a person. He died as predicted not knowing that he was the cause of his own death. I suppose many of us have heard similar stupid, ridiculous, superstitious stories.

Let us look at what happened in the light of our knowledge of the way the subconscious mind works. Whatever the conscious, reasoning mind of man believes, the subconscious mind will accept and act upon. My relative was happy, healthy, vigorous, and robust when he went to see the fortuneteller. She gave him a very negative suggestion which he accepted. He became terrified, and constantly dwelt upon the fact that he was going to die at the next new moon. He proceeded to tell everyone about it, and he prepared for the end. The activity took place in his own mind, and his own thought was the cause. He brought about his own so-called death, or rather destruction of the physical body, by his fear and expectation of the end.

The woman who predicted his death had no more power than the stones and sticks in the field. Her suggestion had no power to create or bring about the end she suggested. If he had known the laws of his mind, he would have completely rejected the negative suggestion and refused to give her words any attention, knowing in his heart that he was governed and controlled by his own thought and feeling. Like tin arrows aimed at a battleship, her prophecy could have been completely neutralized and dissipated without hurting him.

The suggestions of others in themselves have absolutely no power whatever over you except the power that you give them through your own thoughts. You have to give your mental consent; you have to entertain the thought. Then, it becomes your thought, and you do the thinking. Remember, you have the capacity to choose. Choose life! Choose love! Choose health!

• The power of an assumed major premise

Your mind works like a syllogism. This means that whatever major premise your conscious mind assumes to be true determines the conclusion your subconscious mind comes to in regard to any particular question or problem in your mind. If your premise is true, the conclusion must be true as in the following example:

> Every virtue is laudable;
> Kindness is a virtue;
> Therefore, kindness is laudable.

Another example is as follows:

> All formed things change and pass away;
> The Pyramids of Egypt are formed things;
> Therefore, some day the Pyramids will pass away.

The first statement is referred to as the major premise, and the right conclusion must necessarily follow the right premise.

A college professor, who attended some of my science of mind lectures in May, 1962, at Town Hall, New York, said to me, "Everything in my life is topsy-turvy, and I have lost health, wealth, and friends. Everything I touch turns out wrong."

I explained to him that he should establish a major premise in his thinking, that the infinite intelligence of his subconscious mind was guiding, directing, and prospering him spiritually, mentally, and materially. Then, his subconscious mind would automatically direct him wisely in his investments, decisions, and also heal his body and restore his mind to peace and tranquillity.

This professor formulated an over-all picture of the way he wanted his life to be, and this was his major premise:

"Infinite intelligence leads and guides me in all my ways.

Perfect health is mine, and the Law of Harmony operates in my mind and body. Beauty, love, peace, and abundance are mine. The principle of right action and divine order govern my entire life. I know my major premise is based on the eternal truths of life, and I know, feel, and believe that my subconscious mind responds according to the nature of my conscious mind thinking."

He wrote me as follows: "I repeated the above statements slowly, quietly, and lovingly several times a day knowing that they were sinking deep down into my subconscious mind, and that results must follow. I am deeply grateful for the interview you gave me, and I would like to add that all departments of my life are changing for the better. It works!"

• The subconscious does not argue controversially

Your subconscious mind is all-wise and knows the answers to all questions. It does not argue with you or talk back to you. It does not say, "You must not impress me with that." For example, when you say, "I can't do this." "I am too old now." "I can't meet this obligation." "I was born on the wrong side of the tracks." "I don't know the right politician," you are impregnating your subconscious with these negative thoughts, and it responds accordingly. You are actually blocking your own good, thereby bringing lack, limitation, and frustration into your life.

When you set up obstacles, impediments, and delays in your conscious mind, you are denying the wisdom and intelligence resident in your subconscious mind. You are actually saying in effect that your subconscious mind cannot solve your problem. This leads to mental and emotional congestion, followed by sickness and neurotic tendencies.

To realize your desire and overcome your frustration, affirm boldly several times a day: "The infinite intelligence which gave me this desire leads, guides, and reveals to me the perfect plan for the unfolding of my desire. I know the deeper wisdom of my subconscious is now responding, and what I feel and claim within is expressed in the without. There is a balance, equilibrium, and equanimity."

If you say, "There is no way out; I am lost; there is no way out of this dilemma; I am stymied and blocked," you will get no answer or response from your subconscious mind. If you want the subconscious to work for you, give it the right request, and attain its co-operation. It is always working for you. It is controlling your heart beat this minute and also your breathing. It heals a cut on your finger, and its tendency is lifeward, forever seeking to take care of you and preserve you. Your subconscious has a mind of its own, but it accepts your patterns of thought and imagery.

When you are seeking an answer to a problem, your subconscious will respond, but it expects you to come to a decision and to a true judgment in your conscious mind. You must acknowledge the answer is in your subconscious mind. However, if you say, "I don't think there is any way out; I am all mixed up and confused; why don't I get an answer?" you are neutralizing your prayer. Like the soldier marking time, you do not get anywhere.

Still the wheels of your mind, relax, let go, and quietly affirm: "My subconscious knows the answer. It is responding to me now. I give thanks because I know the infinite intelligence of my subconscious knows all things and is revealing the perfect answer to me now. My real conviction is now setting free the majesty and glory of my subconscious mind. I rejoice that it is so."

• **Review of highlights**

1. Think good, and good follows. Think evil, and evil follows. You are what you think all day long.

2. Your subconscious mind does not argue with you. It accepts what your conscious mind decrees. If you say, "I can't afford it," it may be true, but do not say it. Select a better thought, decree, "I'll buy it. I accept it in my mind."

3. You have the power to choose. Choose health and happi-

ness. You can choose to be friendly, or you can choose to be unfriendly. Choose to be co-operative, joyous, friendly, lovable, and the whole world will respond. This is the best way to develop a wonderful personality.

4. Your conscious mind is the "watchman at the gate." Its chief function is to protect your subconscious mind from false impressions. Choose to believe that something good can happen and is happening now. Your greatest power is your capacity to choose. Choose happiness and abundance.

5. The suggestions and statements of others have no power to hurt you. The only power is the movement of your own thought. You can choose to reject the thoughts or statements of others and affirm the good. You have the power to choose how you will react.

6. Watch what you say. You have to account for every idle word. Never say, "I will fail; I will lose my job; I can't pay the rent." Your subconscious cannot take a joke. It brings all these things to pass.

7. Your mind is not evil. No force of nature is evil. It depends how you use the powers of nature. Use your mind to bless, heal, and inspire all people everywhere.

8. Never say, "I can't." Overcome that fear by substituting the following, "I can do all things through the power of my own subconscious mind."

9. Begin to think from the standpoint of the eternal truths and principles of life and not from the standpoint of fear, ignorance, and superstition. Do not let others do your thinking for you. Choose your own thoughts and make your own decisions.

10. You are the captain of your soul (subconscious mind) and the master of your fate. Remember, you have the capacity to choose. Choose life! Choose love! Choose health! Choose happiness!

11. Whatever your conscious mind assumes and believes to be true, your subconscious mind will accept and bring to pass. Believe in good fortune, divine guidance, right action, and all the blessings of life.

3

The Miracle-Working Power
of Your Subconscious

The power of your subconscious is enormous. It inspires you, it guides you, and it reveals to you names, facts, and scenes from the storehouse of memory. Your subconscious started your heartbeat, controls the circulation of your blood, regulates your digestion, assimilation, and elimination. When you eat a piece of bread, your subconscious mind transmutes it into tissue, muscle, bone, and blood. This process is beyond the ken of the wisest man who walks the earth. Your subconscious mind controls all the vital processes and functions of your body and knows the answer to all problems.

Your subconscious mind never sleeps, never rests. It is always on the job. You can discover the miracle-working power of your subconscious by plainly stating to your subconscious prior to sleep that you wish a certain specific thing accomplished. You will be delighted to discover that forces within you will be released, leading to the desired result. Here, then, is a source of power and wisdom which places you in touch with omnipotence or the power that moves the world, guides the planets in their course, and causes the sun to shine.

Your subconscious mind is the source of your ideals, aspirations, and altruistic urges. It was through the subconscious mind that Shakespeare perceived great truths hidden from the average man of his day. Undoubtedly, it was the response of his subconscious mind that caused the Greek sculptor, Phidias, to portray beauty, order, symmetry, and proportion in marble and bronze. It enabled the Italian artist, Raphael, to paint Madonnas, and Ludwig van Beethoven to compose symphonies.

In 1955 I lectured at the Yoga Forest University, Rishikesh, India, and there I chatted with a visiting surgeon from Bombay. He told me about Dr. James Esdaille, a Scotch surgeon, who worked in Bengal before ether or other modern methods of anesthesia were discovered. Between 1843 and 1846, Dr. Esdaille performed about four hundred major operations of all kinds, such as amputations, removal of tumors and cancerous growths, as well as operations on the eye, ear, and throat. All operations were conducted under mental anesthesia only. This Indian doctor at Rishikesh informed me that the postoperative mortality rate of patients operated on by Dr. Esdaille was extremely low, probably two or three percent. Patients felt no pain, and there were no deaths during the operations.

Dr. Esdaille suggested to the subconscious minds of all his patients, who were in a hypnotic state, that no infection or septic condition would develop. You must remember that this was before Louis Pasteur, Joseph Lister, and others who pointed out the bacterial origin of disease and causes of infection due to unsterilized instruments and virulent organisms.

This Indian surgeon said that the reason for the low mortality rate and the general absence of infection, which was reduced to a minimum, was undoubtedly due to the suggestions of Dr. Esdaille to the subconscious minds of his patients. They responded according to the nature of his suggestion.

It is simply wonderful, when you conceive how a surgeon, over one hundred twenty years ago, discovered the miraculous wonder-working powers of the subconscious mind. Doesn't it cause you to be seized with a sort of mystic awe when you stop and think of the transcendental powers of your subconscious mind? Consider its extrasensory perceptions, such as its capacity for clairvoyance and clairaudience, its independence of time and space, its capacity to render you free from all pain and suffering, and its capacity to get the answer to all problems, be they what they may. All these and many more reveal to you that there is a power and an intelligence within you that far transcends your intellect, causing you to marvel at the wonders of it all. All these experiences cause you to rejoice and believe in the miracle-working powers of your own subconscious mind.

• Your subconscious is your Book of Life

Whatever thoughts, beliefs, opinions, theories, or dogmas you write, engrave, or impress on your subconscious mind, you shall experience them as the objective manifestation of circumstances, conditions, and events. What you write on the inside, you will experience on the outside. You have two sides to your life, objective and subjective, visible and invisible, thought and its manifestation.

Your thought is received by your brain, which is the organ of your conscious reasoning mind. When your conscious or objective mind accepts the thought completely, it is sent to the solar plexus, called the brain of your mind, where it becomes flesh and is made manifest in your experience.

As previously outlined, your subconscious cannot argue. It acts only from what you write on it. It accepts your verdict or the conclusions of your conscious mind as final. This is why you are always writing on the book of life, because your thoughts become your experiences. The American essayist, Ralph Waldo Emerson said, "Man is what he thinks all day long."

• What is impressed in the subconscious is expressed

William James, the father of American psychology, said that the power to move the world is in your subconscious mind. Your subconscious mind is one with infinite intelligence and boundless wisdom. It is fed by hidden springs, and is called the law of life. Whatever you impress upon your subconscious mind, the latter will move heaven and earth to bring it to pass. You must, therefore, impress it with right ideas and constructive thoughts.

The reason there is so much chaos and misery in the world is because people do not understand the interaction of their conscious and subconscious minds. When these two principles work in accord, in concord, in peace, and synchronously together, you will have heath, happiness, peace and joy. There is no sickness or discord when the conscious and subconscious work together harmoniously and peacefully.

The tomb of Hermes was opened with great expectancy and a sense of wonder because people believed that the greatest secret of the ages was contained therein. The secret was *as within, so without; as above, so below.*

In other words, whatever is impressed in your subconscious mind is expressed on the screen of space. This same truth was proclaimed by Moses, Isaiah, Jesus, Buddha, Zoroaster, Laotze, and all the illumined seers of the ages. Whatever you feel as true subjectively is expressed as conditions, experiences, and events. Motion and emotion must balance. *As in heaven* [your own mind], *so on earth* [in your body and environment]. This is the great law of life.

You will find throughout all nature the law of action and reaction, of rest and motion. These two must balance, then there will be harmony and equilibrium. You are here to let the life principle flow through you rhythmically and harmoniously. The intake and the outgo must be equal. The impression and the expression must be equal. All your frustration is due to unfulfilled desire.

If you think negatively, destructively, and viciously, these thoughts generate destructive emotions which must be expressed and find an outlet. These emotions, being of a negative nature, are frequently expressed as ulcers, heart trouble, tension, and anxieties.

What is your idea or feeling about yourself now? Every part of your being expresses that idea. Your vitality, body, financial status, friends, and social status represent a perfect reflection of the idea you have of yourself. This is the real meaning of what is impressed in your subconscious mind, and which is expressed in all phases of your life.

We injure ourselves by the negative ideas which we entertain. How often have you wounded yourself by getting angry, fearful, jealous, or vengeful? These are the poisons that enter your subconscious mind. You were not born with these negative attitudes. Feed your subconscious mind life-giving thoughts, and you will wipe out all the negative patterns lodged therein. As you continue to do this, all the past will be wiped out and remembered no more.

• The subconscious heals a malignancy of the skin

A personal healing will ever be the most convincing evidence of the healing power of the subconscious mind. Over forty years ago I resolved a malignancy of the skin through prayer. Medical therapy had failed to check the growth, and it was getting progressively worse.

A clergyman, with a deep psychological knowledge, explained to me the inner meaning of the 139th Psalm wherein it says, *In thy book all my members were written, which in continuance were fashioned, when as yet there was none of them.* He explained that the term *book* meant my subconscious mind which fashioned and molded all my organs from an invisible cell. He also pointed out that inasmuch as my subconscious mind made my body, it could also recreate it and heal it according to the perfect pattern within it.

This clergyman showed me his watch and said, "This had a maker, and the watchmaker had to have the idea first in mind before the watch became an objective reality, and if the watch was out of order, the watchmaker could fix it." My friend reminded me that the subconscious intelligence which created my body was like a watchmaker, and it also knew exactly how to heal, restore, a. direct all the vital functions and processes of my body, but that I had to give it the perfect idea of health. This would act as cause, and the effect would be a healing.

I prayed in a very simple way as follows: "My body and all its organs were created by the infinite intelligence in my subconscious mind. It knows how to heal me. Its wisdom fashioned all my organs, tissues, muscles, and bones. This infinite healing presence within me is now transforming every atom of my being making me whole and perfect now. I give thanks for the healing I know is taking place now. Wonderful are the works of the creative intelligence within me."

I prayed aloud for about five minutes two or three times a day repeating the above simple prayer. In about three months my skin was whole and perfect.

As you can see, all I did was give life-giving patterns of wholeness, beauty, and perfection to my subconscious mind, thereby obliterating the negative images and patterns of thought lodged in my subconscious mind which were the cause of all my trouble. Nothing appears on your body except when the mental equivalent is first in your mind, and as you change your mind by drenching it with incessant affirmatives, you change your body. This is the basis of all healing. . . . *Marvellous are thy works; and that my soul* [subconscious mind] *knoweth right well.* PSALM 139:14.

• How the subconscious controls all functions of the body

While you are awake or sound asleep upon your bed, the ceaseless, tireless action of your subconscious mind controls all the vital functions of your body without the help of your conscious mind. For example, while you are asleep your heart continues to beat rhythmically, your lungs do not rest, and the process of inhalation and exhalation, whereby your blood absorbs fresh air, goes on just the same as when you are awake. Your subconscious controls your digestive processes and glandular secretions, as well as all the other mysterious operations of your body. The hair on your face continues to grow whether you are asleep or awake. Scientists tell us that the skin secretes much more perspiration during sleep than during the waking hours. Your eyes, ears, and other senses are active during sleep. For instance, many of our great scientists have received answers to perplexing problems while they were asleep. They saw the answers in a dream.

Oftentimes your conscious mind interferes with the normal rhythm of the heart, lungs, and functioning of the stomach and intestines by worry, anxiety, fear, and depression. These patterns of thought interfere with the harmonious functioning of your subconscious mind. When mentally disturbed, the best procedure is to let go, relax, and still the wheels of your thought processes. Speak to your subconscious mind, telling it to take over in peace, harmony, and divine order. You will find that all the functions of your body will become normal again. Be sure to speak to your subconscious mind with authority and conviction, and it will conform to your command.

Your subconscious seeks to preserve your life and restore you to health at all costs. It causes you to love your children which also illustrates an instinctive desire to preserve all life. Let us suppose you accidentally ate some bad food. Your subconscious mind would cause you to regurgitate it. If you inadvertently took some poison, your subconscious powers would proceed to neutralize it. If you completely entrusted yourself to its wonder-working power, you would be entirely restored to health.

• How to get the subconscious to work for you

The first thing to realize is that your subconscious mind is always working. It is active night and day, whether you act upon it or not. Your subconscious is the builder of your body, but you cannot consciously perceive or hear that inner silent process. Your business is with your conscious mind and not your subconscious mind. Just keep your conscious mind busy with the expectation of the best, and make sure the thoughts you habitually think are based on whatsoever things are lovely, true, just, and of good report. Begin now to take care of your conscious mind, knowing in your heart and soul that your subconscious mind is always expressing, reproducing, and manifesting according to your habitual thinking.

Remember, just as water takes the shape of the pipe it flows through, the life principle in you flows through you according to the nature of your thoughts. Claim that the healing presence in your subconscious is flowing through you as harmony, health, peace, joy, and abundance. Think of it as a living intelligence, a lovely companion on the way. Firmly believe it is continually flowing through you vivifying, inspiring, and prospering you. It will respond exactly this way. It is done unto you as you believe.

- **Healing principle of the subconscious restores atrophied optic nerves**

There is the well-known, duly authenticated case of Madame Bire of France, recorded in the archives of the medical department of Lourdes, France. She was blind, the optic nerves were atrophied and useless. She visited Lourdes and had what she termed a miraculous healing. Ruth Cranston, a Protestant young lady who investigated and wrote about healings at Lourdes in *McCall's* magazine, November, 1955, writes about Madame Bire as follows: "At Lourdes she regained her sight incredibly, with the optic nerves still lifeless and useless, as several doctors could testify after repeated examinations. A month later, upon re-examination, it was found that the seeing mechanism had been restored to normal. But at first, so far as medical examination could tell, she was seeing with 'dead eyes.' "

I have visited Lourdes several times where I, too, witnessed some healings, and of course, as we shall explain in the next chapter, there is no doubt that healings take place at many shrines throughout the world, Christian and non-Christian.

Madame Bire, to whom we just referred, was not healed by the waters of the shrine, but by her own subconscious mind which responded to her belief. The healing principle within her subconscious mind responded to the nature of her thought. Belief is a thought in the subconscious mind. It means to accept something as true. The thought accepted executes itself automatically. Undoubtedly, Madame Bire went to the shrine with expectancy and great faith, knowing in her heart she would receive a healing. Her subconscious mind responded accordingly, releasing the ever present healing forces. The subconscious mind which created the eye can certainly bring a dead nerve back to life. What the creative principle created, it can recreate. *According to your belief is it done unto you.*

- **How to convey the idea of perfect health to your subconscious mind**

A Protestant minister I knew in Johannesburg, South Africa, told me the method he used to convey the idea of perfect health to his subconscious mind. He had cancer of the lung. His technique, as given to me in his own handwriting, is exactly as follows: "Several times a day I would make certain that I was completely relaxed mentally and physically. I relaxed my body by speaking to it as follows, 'My feet are relaxed, my ankles are relaxed, my legs are relaxed, my abdominal muscles are relaxed, my heart and lungs are relaxed, my head is relaxed, my whole being is completely relaxed.' After about five minutes I would be in a sleepy drowsy state, and then I affirmed the following truth, 'The perfection of God is now being expressed through me. The idea of perfect health is now filling my subconscious mind. The image God has of me is a perfect image, and my subconscious mind recreates my body in perfect accordance with the perfect image held in the mind of God.'" This minister had a remarkable healing. This is a simple easy way of conveying the idea of perfect health to your subconscious mind.

Another wonderful way to convey the idea of health to your subconscious is through disciplined or scientific imagination. I told a man who was suffering from functional paralysis to make a vivid picture of himself walking around in his office, touching the desk, answering the telephone, and doing all the things he ordinarily would do if he were healed. I explained to him that this idea and mental picture of perfect health would be accepted by his subconscious mind.

He lived the role and actually felt himself back in the office. He knew that he was giving his subconscious mind something definite to work upon. His subconscious mind was the film upon which the picture was impressed. One day, after several weeks of frequent conditioning of the mind with this mental picture, the telephone rang by prearrangement and kept ringing while his wife and nurse were out. The telephone was about twelve feet away, but nevertheless he managed to answer it. He was healed at that hour. The healing power of his subconscious mind responded to his mental imagery, and a healing followed.

This man had a mental block which prevented impulses from the brain reaching his legs, therefore, he said he could not walk. When he shifted his attention to the healing power within him, the power flowed through his focused attention, enabling him to walk. *Whatsoever ye shall ask in prayer, believing, ye shall receive.* MATT. 21:22.

• **Ideas worth remembering**

1. Your subconscious mind controls all the vital processes of your body and knows the answer to all problems.

2. Prior to sleep, turn over a specific request to your subconscious mind and prove its miracle-working power to yourself.

3. Whatever you impress on your subconscious mind is expressed on the screen of space as conditions, experiences, and events. Therefore, you should carefully watch all ideas and thoughts entertained in your conscious mind.

4. The law of action and reaction is universal. Your thought is action, and the reaction is the automatic response of your subconscious mind to your thought. Watch your thoughts!

5. All frustration is due to unfulfilled desires. If you dwell on obstacles, delays, and difficulties, your subconscious mind responds accordingly, and you are blocking your own good.

6. The Life Principle will flow through you rhythmically and harmoniously if you consciously affirm: "I believe that the subconscious power which gave me this desire is now fulfilling it through me." This dissolves all conflicts.

7. You can interfere with the normal rhythm of your heart, lungs, and other organs by worry, anxiety, and fear. Feed your subconscious with thoughts of harmony, health, and peace, and all the functions of your body will become normal again.

8. Keep your conscious mind busy with the expectation of the best, and your subconscious will faithfully reproduce your habitual thinking.

9. Imagine the happy ending or solution to your problem, feel the thrill of accomplishment, and what you imagine and feel will be accepted by your subconscious mind and bring it to pass.

4

Mental Healings in Ancient Times

Down through the ages men of all nations have somehow instinctively believed that somewhere there resided a healing power which could restore to normal the functions and sensations of man's body. They believed that this strange power could be invoked under certain conditions, and that the alleviation of human suffering would follow. The history of all nations presents testimony in support of this belief.

In the early history of the world the power of secretly influencing men for good or evil, including the healing of the sick, was said to be possessed by the priests and holy men of all nations. Healing of the sick was supposed to be a power derived directly by them from God, and the procedures and processes of healing varied throughout the world. The healing processes took the form of supplications to God attended by various ceremonies, such as the laying on of hands, incantations, the application of amulets, talismans, rings, relics, and images.

For example, in the religions of antiquity priests in the ancient temples gave drugs to the patient and practiced hypnotic suggestions prior to the patient's sleep, telling him that the gods would visit him in his sleep and heal him. Many healings followed. Obviously, all this was the work of potent suggestions to the subconscious mind.

After the performance of certain mysterious rites, the devotees of Hecate would see the goddess during sleep, provided that before going to sleep they had prayed to her according to weird and fantastic instructions. They were told to mix lizards with resin, frankincense, and myrrh, and pound all this together in the open air under the crescent moon. Healings were reported in many cases following this grotesque procedure.

It is obvious that these strange procedures, as mentioned in the illustrations given, favored suggestion and acceptance by the subconscious mind of these people by making a powerful appeal to their imagination. Actually, in all these healings, the subconscious mind of the subject was the healer.

In all ages unofficial healers have obtained remarkable results in cases where authorized medical skill has failed. This gives cause for thought. How do these healers in all parts of the world effect their cures? The answer to all these healings is due to the blind belief of the sick person which released the healing power resident in his subconscious mind. Many of the remedies and methods employed were rather strange and fantastic which fired the imagination of the patients, causing an aroused emotional state. This state of mind facilitated the suggestion of health, and was accepted both by the conscious and subconscious mind of the sick. This will be elaborated on further in the next chapter.

- **Biblical accounts on the use of the subconscious powers**

What things soever ye desire, when ye pray believe that ye receive them, and ye shall have them. MARK 11:24.

Note the difference in tenses. The inspired writer tells us to believe and accept as true the fact that our desire has already been accomplished and fulfilled, that it is already completed, and that its realization will follow as a thing in the future.

The success of this technique depends on the confident conviction that the thought, the idea, the picture is already a fact in mind. In order for anything to have substance in the realm of mind, it must be thought of as actually existing there.

Here in a few cryptic words is a concise and specific direction for making use of the creative power of thought by impressing upon the subconscious the particular thing which you desire. Your thought, idea, plan, or purpose is as real on its own plane as your hand or your heart. In following the Biblical technique, you completely eliminate from your mind all consideration of conditions, circumstances, or anything which might imply adverse contingencies. You are planting a seed (concept) in the mind which, if you leave it undisturbed, will infallibly germinate into external fruition.

The prime condition which Jesus insisted upon was faith. Over and over again you read in the Bible, *According to your faith is it done unto you.* If you plant certain types of seeds in the ground, you have faith they will grow after their kind. This is the way of seeds, and trusting the laws of growth and agriculture, you know that the seeds will come forth after their kind. Faith as mentioned in the Bible is a way of thinking, an attitude of mind, an inner certitude, knowing that the idea you fully accept in your conscious mind will be embodied in your subconscious mind and made manifest. Faith is, in a sense, accepting as true what your reason and senses deny, i.e., a shutting out of the little, rational, analytical, conscious mind and embracing an attitude of complete reliance on the inner power of your subconscious mind.

A classical instance of Bible technique is recorded in MATTHEW 9:28-30. *And when he was come into the house, the blind men came to him: and Jesus saith unto them, Believe ye that I am able to do this? They said unto him, Yea, Lord. Then touched he their eyes, saying, according to your faith be it unto you. And their eyes were opened; and Jesus straitly charged them, saying, see that no man know it.*

In the words *according to your faith be it unto you,* you can see that Jesus was actually appealing to the co-operation of the subconscious mind of the blind men. Their faith was their great expectancy, their inner feeling, their inner conviction that something miraculous would happen, and that their prayer would be answered, and it was. This is the time-honored technique of healing, utilized alike by all healing groups throughout the world regardless of religious affiliation.

In the words *see that no man know it,* Jesus enjoins the newly healed patients not to discuss their healing because they might be subjected to the skeptical and derogatory criticisms of the unbelieving. This might tend to undo the benefits they had received at the hand of Jesus by depositing thoughts of fear, doubt, and anxiety in the subconscious mind.

. . . for with authority and power he commandeth the unclean spirits, and they came out. LUKE 4:36.

When the sick came to Jesus to be healed, they were healed by their faith together with his faith and understanding of the healing power of the subconscious mind. Whatever he decreed, he felt inwardly to be true. He and the people needing help were in the one universal subjective mind, and his silent inner knowing and conviction of the healing power changed the negative destructive patterns in the patients' subconscious. The resultant healings were the automatic response to the internal mental change. His command was his appeal to the subconscious mind of the patients plus his awareness, feeling, and absolute trust in the response of the subconscious mind to the words which he spoke with authority.

• Miracles at various shrines throughout the world

It is an established fact that cures have taken place at various shrines throughout the world, such as in Japan, India, Europe, and America. I have visited several of the famous shrines in Japan. At the world famous shrine called Diabutsu is a gigantic divinity of bronze where Buddha is seated with folded hands, and the head is inclined in an attitude of profound contemplative ecstasy. It is 42 feet in height and is called the great Buddha. Here I saw young and old making offerings at its feet. Money, fruit, rice, and oranges were offered. Candles were lit, incense was burned, and prayers of petition recited.

The guide explained the chant of a young girl as she murmured a prayer, bowed low, and placed two oranges as an offering. She also lit a candle. He said she had lost her voice, and it was restored at the shrine. She was thanking Buddha for restoring her voice. She had the simple faith that Buddha would give her back her singing voice if she followed a certain ritual, fasted, and made certain offerings. All this helped to kindle faith and expectancy, resulting in a conditioning of her mind to the point of belief. Her subconscious mind responded to her belief.

To illustrate further the power of imagination and blind belief I will relate the case of a relative of mine who had tuberculosis. His lungs were badly diseased. His son decided to heal his father. He came home to Perth, Western Australia, where his father lived, and said to him that he had met a monk who had returned from one of the healing shrines in Europe. This monk sold him a piece of the true cross. He said that he gave the monk the equivalent of $500 for it.

This young man had actually picked up a splinter of wood from the sidewalk, went to the jeweler's, and had it set in a ring so that it looked real. He told his father that many were healed just by touching the ring or the cross. He inflamed and fired his father's imagination to the point that the old gentleman snatched the ring from him, placed it over his chest, prayed silently, and went to sleep. In the morning he was healed. All the clinic's tests proved negative.

You know, of course, it was not the splinter of wood from the sidewalk that healed him. It was his imagination aroused to an intense degree, plus the confident expectancy of a perfect healing. Imagination was joined to faith or subjective feeling, and the union of the two brought about a healing. The father never learned of the trick that had been played upon him. If he had, he probably would have had a relapse. He remained completely cured and passed away fifteen years later at the age of 89.

• One universal healing principle

It is a well-known fact that all of the various schools of healing effect cures of the most wonderful character. The most obvious conclusion which strikes your mind is that there must be some underlying principle which is common to them all, namely, the subconscious mind, and the one process of healing is faith.

It will now be in order to recall to your mind once more the following fundamental truths:

First, that you possess mental functions which have been

distinguished by designating one the conscious mind and the other the subconscious mind.

Secondly, your subconscious mind is constantly amenable to the power of suggestion. Furthermore, your subconscious mind has complete control of the functions, conditions, and sensations of your body.

I venture to believe that all the readers of this book are familiar with the fact that symptoms of almost any disease can be induced in hypnotic subjects by suggestion. For example, a subject in the hypnotic state can develop a high temperature, flushed face, or chills according to the nature of the suggestion given. By experiment, you can suggest to the person that he is paralyzed and cannot walk: it will be so. By illustration, you can hold a cup of cold water under the nose of the hypnotic subject and tell him, "This is full of pepper; smell it!" He will proceed to sneeze. What do you think caused him to sneeze, the water or the suggestion?

If a man says he is allergic to Timothy grass, you can place a synthetic flower or an empty glass in front of his nose, when he is in a hypnotic state, and tell him it is Timothy grass. He will portray the usual allergic symptoms. This indicates that the cause of the disease is in the mind. The healing of the disease can also take place mentally.

You realize that remarkable healings take place through osteopathy, chiropractic medicine, and naturopathy, as well as through all the various religious bodies throughout the world, but it is obvious that all of these healings are brought about through the subconscious mind—the only healer there is.

Notice how it heals a cut on your face caused by shaving. It knows exactly how to do it. The doctor dresses the wound and says, "Nature heals it!" Nature refers to natural law, the law of the subconscious mind, or self-preservation which is the function of the subconscious mind. The instinct of self-preservation is the first law of nature. Your strongest instinct is the most potent of all autosuggestions.

• Widely different theories

It would be tedious and unprofitable to discuss to any great extent the numerous theories advanced by different religious sects and prayer therapy groups. There are a great number who claim that because their theory produces results it is, therefore, the correct one. This, as explained in this chapter, cannot be true.

You are aware that there are all types of healing. Franz Anton Mesmer, an Austrian physician (1734–1815) who practiced in Paris, discovered that by applying magnets to the diseased body, he could cure that disease miraculously. He also performed cures with various other pieces of glass and metals. He discontinued this form of healing and claimed that his cures were due to "animal magnetism," theorizing that this substance was projected from the healer to the patient.

His method of treating disease from then on was by hypnotism which was called mesmerism in his day. Other physicians said that all his healings were due to suggestion and nothing else.

All of these groups, such as psychiatrists, psychologists, osteopaths, chiropractors, physicians, and all the churches are using the one universal power resident in the subconscious mind. Each may proclaim the healings are due to their theory. The process of all healing is a definite, positive, mental attitude, an inner attitude, or a way of thinking, called faith. Healing is due to a confident expectancy which acts as a powerful suggestion to the subconscious mind releasing its healing potency.

One man does not heal by a different power than another. It is true he may have his own theory or method. There is only one process of healing and that is faith. There is only one healing power, namely, your subconscious mind. Select the theory and method you prefer. You can rest assured, if you have faith, you shall get results.

• Views of Paracelsus

Philippus Paracelsus, a famous Swiss alchemist and physician, who lived from 1493 to 1541, was a great healer in his day. He stated what is now an obvious scientific fact when he uttered these words, "Whether the object of your faith be real or false, you will nevertheless obtain the same effects. Thus, if I believed in Saint Peter's statue as I should have believed in Saint Peter himself, I shall obtain the same effects that I should have obtained from Saint Peter. But that is superstition. Faith, however, produces miracles; and whether it is true or false faith, it will always produce the same wonders."

The views of Paracelsus were also entertained in the sixteenth century by Pietro Pomponazzi, an Italian philosopher and contemporary of Paracelsus, who said, "We can easily conceive the marvelous effects which confidence and imagination can produce, particularly when both qualities are reciprocated between the subjects and the person who influences them. The cures attributed to the influence of certain relics are the effect of their imagination and confidence. Quacks and philosophers know that if the bones of any skeleton were put in place of the saint's bones, the sick would none the less experience beneficial effects, if they believed that they were veritable relics."

Then, if you believe in the bones of saints to heal, or if you believe in the healing power of certain waters, you will get results because of the powerful suggestion given to your subconscious mind. It is the latter that does the healing.

• Bernheim's experiments

Hippolyte Bernheim, professor of medicine at Nancy, France, 1910–1919, was the expounder of the fact that the suggestion of the physician to the patient was exerted through the subconscious mind.

Bernheim, in his *Suggestive Therapeutics,* page 197, tells a story of a man with paralysis of the tongue which had yielded to no form of treatment. His doctor told the patient that he had a new instrument with which he promised to heal him. He introduced a pocket thermometer into the patient's mouth. The patient imagined it to be the instrument which was to save him. In a few moments he cried out joyfully that he could once more move his tongue freely.

"Among our cases," continues Bernheim, "facts of the same sort will be found. A young girl came into my office, having suffered from complete loss of speech for nearly four weeks. After making sure of the diagnosis, I told my students that loss of speech sometimes yielded instantly to electricity, which might act simply by its suggestive influence. I sent for the induction apparatus. I applied my hand over the larynx and moved a little, and said, 'Now you can speak aloud.' In an instant I made her saw 'a,' then 'b,' then 'Maria.' She continued to speak distinctly; the loss of voice had disappeared."

Here Bernheim is showing the power of faith and expectancy on the part of the patient which acts as a powerful suggestion to the subconscious mind.

• **Producing a blister by suggestion**

Bernheim states that he produced a blister on the back of a patient's neck by applying a postage stamp and suggesting to the patient that it was a fly-plaster. This has been confirmed by the experiments and experiences of many doctors in many parts of the world, which leave no doubt that structural changes are a possible result of oral suggestion to patients.

• **The cause of bloody stigmata**

In Hudson's *Law of Psychic Phenomena,* page 153, he states, "Hemorrhages and bloody stigmata may be induced in certain subjects by means of suggestion.

"Dr. M. Bourru put a subject into the somnambulistic condition, and gave him the following suggestion: 'At four o'clock this afternoon, after the hypnosis, you will come into my office, sit down in the armchair, cross your arms upon your breast, and your nose will begin to bleed.' At the hour appointed the young man did as directed. Several drops of blood came from the left nostril.

"On another occasion the same investigator traced the patient's name on both his forearms with the dull point of an instrument. Then when the patient was in the somnambulistic condition, he said, 'At four o'clock this afternoon you will go to sleep, and your arms will bleed along the lines which I have traced, and your name will appear written on your arms in letters of blood.' He was watched at four o'clock and seen to fall asleep. On the left arm the letters stood out in bright relief, and in several places there were drops of blood. The letters were still visible three months afterward, although they had gradually grown faint."

These facts demonstrate at once the correctness of the two fundamental propositions previously stated, namely, the constant amenability of the subconscious mind to the power of suggestion and the perfect control which the subconscious mind exercises over the functions, sensations, and conditions of the body.

All the foregoing phenomena dramatize vividly abnormal conditions induced by suggestion, and are conclusive proof that *as a man thinketh in his heart* [subconscious mind] *so is he.*

• **Healing points in review**

1. Remind yourself frequently that the healing power is in your own subconscious mind.

2. Know that faith is like a seed planted in the ground; it grows after its kind. Plant the idea (seed) in your mind, water and fertilize it with expectancy, and it will manifest.

3. The idea you have for a book, new invention, or play is real in your mind. This is why you can believe you have it now. Believe in the reality of your idea, plan, or invention, and as you do, it will become manifest.

4. In praying for another, know that your silent inner knowing of wholeness, beauty, and perfection can change the negative patterns of the other's subconscious mind and bring about wonderful results.

5. The miraculous healings you hear about at various shrines

are due to imagination and blind faith which act on the subconscious mind, releasing the healing power.

6. All disease originates in the mind. Nothing appears on the body unless there is a mental pattern corresponding to it.

7. The symptoms of almost any disease can be induced in you by hypnotic suggestion. This shows you the power of your thought.

8. There is only one process of healing and that is faith. There is only one healing power, namely, your subconscious mind.

9. Whether the object of your faith is real or false, you will get results. Your subconscious mind responds to the thought in your mind. Look upon faith as a thought in your mind, and that will suffice.

5

Mental Healings in Modern Times

Everyone is definitely concerned with the healing of bodily conditions and human affairs. What is it that heals? Where is this healing power? These are questions asked by everyone. The answer is that this healing power is in the subconscious mind of each person, and a changed mental attitude on the part of the sick person releases this healing power.

No mental or religious science practitioner, psychologist, psychiatrist, or medical doctor ever healed a patient. There is an old saying, "The doctor dresses the wound, but God heals it." The psychologist or psychiatrist proceeds to remove the mental blocks in the patient so that the healing principle may be released, restoring the patient to health. Likewise, the surgeon removes the physical block enabling the healing currents to function normally. No physician, surgeon, or mental science practitioner claims that "he healed the patient." The one healing power is called by many names—Nature, Life, God, Creative Intelligence, and Subconscious Power.

As previously outlined, there are many different methods used to remove the mental, emotional, and physical blocks which inhibit the flow of the healing life principle animating all of us. The healing principle resident in your subconscious mind can and will, if properly directed by you or some other person, heal your mind and body of all disease. This healing principle is operative in all men regardless of creed, color, or race. You do not have to belong to some particular church in order to use and participate in this healing process. Your subconscious will heal the burn or cut on your hand even though you profess to be an atheist or agnostic.

The modern mental therapeutic procedure is based on the truth that the infinite intelligence and power of your subconscious mind responds according to your faith. The mental science practitioner or minister follows the injunction of the Bible, i.e., he goes into his closet and shuts the door, which means he stills his mind, relaxes, lets go, and thinks of the infinite healing presence within him. He closes the door of his mind to all outside distractions as well as appearances, and then he quietly and knowingly turns over his request or desire to his subconscious mind, realizing that the intelligence of his mind will answer him according to his specific needs.

The most wonderful thing to know is this: Imagine the end desired and feel its reality; then the infinite life principle will respond to your conscious choice and your conscious request. This is the meaning of *believe you have received, and you shall receive.* This is what the modern mental scientist does when he practices prayer therapy.

• One process of healing

There is only one universal healing principle operating through everything—the cat, the dog, the tree, the grass, the wind, the earth—for everything is alive. This life principle operates through the animal, vegetable, and mineral kingdoms as instinct and the law of growth. Man is consciously aware of this life principle, and he can consciously direct it to bless himself in countless ways.

There are many different approaches, techniques, and methods in using the universal power, but there is only one process of healing, which is faith, for *according to your faith is it done unto you.*

• The law of belief

All religions of the world represent forms of belief, and these beliefs are explained in many ways. The law of life is belief. What do you believe about yourself, life, and the universe? *It is done unto you as you believe.*

Belief is a thought in your mind which causes the power of your subconscious to be distributed into all phases of your life according to your thinking habits. You must realize the Bible is not talking about your belief in some ritual, ceremony, form, institution, man, or formula. It is talking about belief itself. The belief of your mind is simply the thought of your mind. *If thou canst believe, all things are possible to him that believeth.* MARK 9:23.

It is foolish to believe in something to hurt or harm you. Remember, it is not the thing believed in that hurts or harms you, but the belief or thought in your mind which creates the result. All your experiences, all your actions, and all the events and circumstances of your life are but the reflections and reactions to your own thought.

• Prayer therapy is the combined function of the conscious and subconscious mind scientifically directed

Prayer therapy is the synchronized, harmonious, and intelligent function of the conscious and subconscious levels of mind specifically directed for a definite purpose. In scientific prayer or prayer therapy, you must know what you are doing and why you are doing it. You trust the law of healing. Prayer therapy is sometimes referred to as mental treatment, and another term is scientific prayer.

In prayer therapy you consciously choose a certain idea, mental picture, or plan which you desire to experience. You realize your capacity to convey this idea or mental image to your subconscious by feeling the reality of the state assumed. As you remain faithful in your mental attitude, your prayer will be answered. Prayer therapy is a definite mental action for a definite specific purpose.

Let us suppose that you decide to heal a certain difficulty by prayer therapy. You are aware that your problem or sickness, whatever it may be, must be caused by negative thoughts charged with fear and lodged in your subconscious mind, and that if you can succeed in cleansing your mind of these thoughts, you will get a healing.

You, therefore, turn to the healing power within your own subconscious mind and remind yourself of its infinite power and intelligence and its capacity to heal all conditions. As you dwell on these truths, your fear will begin to dissolve, and the recollection of these truths also corrects the erroneous beliefs.

You give thanks for the healing that you know will come, and then you keep your mind off the difficulty until you feel guided, after an interval, to pray again. While you are praying, you absolutely refuse to give any power to the negative conditions or to admit for a second that the healing will not come. This attitude of mind brings about the harmonious union of the conscious and subconscious mind, which releases the healing power.

- **Faith healing, what it means, and how blind faith works**

What is popularly termed faith healing is not the faith mentioned in the Bible, which means a knowledge of the interaction of the conscious and subconscious mind. A faith healer is one who heals without any real scientific understanding of the powers and forces involved. He may claim that he has a special gift of healing, and the sick person's blind belief in him or his powers may bring results.

The voodoo doctor in South Africa and other parts of the world may heal by incantations, or a person may be healed by touching the so-called bones of saints, or anything else which cause the patients to honestly believe in the method or process.

Any method which causes you to move from fear and worry to faith and expectancy will heal. There are many persons, each of whom claims that because his personal theory produces results, it is, therefore, the correct one. This, as already explained in this chapter, cannot be true.

To illustrate how blind faith works: You will recall our discussion of the Swiss physician, Franz Anton Mesmer. In 1776 he claimed many cures when he stroked diseased bodies with artificial magnets. Later on he threw away his magnets and evolved the theory of animal magnetism. This he held to be a fluid which pervades the universe, but is most active in the human organism.

He claimed that this magnetic fluid which was going forth from him to his patients healed them. People flocked to him, and many wonderful cures were effected.

Mesmer moved to Paris, and while there the Government appointed a commission composed of physicians and members of the Academy of Science, of which Benjamin Franklin was a member, to investigate his cures. The report admitted the leading facts claimed by Mesmer, but held that there was no evidence to prove the correctness of his magnetic fluid theory, and said the effects were due to the imagination of the patients.

Soon after this, Mesmer was driven into exile, and died in 1815. Shortly afterwards, Dr. Braid of Manchester undertook to show that magnetic fluid had nothing to do with the production of the healings of Dr. Mesmer. Dr. Braid discovered that patients could be thrown into hypnotic sleep by suggestion, during which many of the well-known phenomena ascribed to magnetism by Mesmer could be produced.

You can readily see that all these cures were undoubtedly brought about by the active imagination of the patients together with a powerful suggestion of health to their subconscious minds. All this could be termed blind faith as there was no understanding in those days as to how the cures were brought about.

• **Subjective faith and what it means**

You will recall the proposition, which need not be repeated at length, that the subjective or subconscious mind of an individual is as amenable to the control of his own conscious or objective mind as it is by the suggestions of another. It follows that whatever may be your objective belief, if you will assume to have faith actively or passively, your subconscious mind will be controlled by the suggestion, and your desire will be fulfilled.

The faith required in mental healings is a purely subjective faith, and it is attainable upon the cessation of active opposition on the part of the objective or conscious mind.

In the healing of the body it is, of course, desirable to secure the concurrent faith of both the conscious and subconscious mind. However, it is not always essential if you will enter into a state of passivity and receptivity by relaxing the mind and the body and getting into a sleepy state. In this drowsy state your passivity becomes receptive to subjective impression.

Recently, I was asked by a man, "How is it that I got a healing through a minister? I did not believe what he said when he told me that there is no such thing as disease and that matter does not exist."

This man at first thought his intelligence was being insulted, and he protested against such a palpable absurdity. The explanation is simple. He was quieted by soothing words and told to get into a perfectly passive condition, to say nothing, and think of nothing for the time being. His minister also became passive, and affirmed quietly, peacefully, and constantly for about one half hour that this man would have perfect health, peace, harmony, and wholeness. He felt immense relief and was restored to health.

It is easy to see that his subjective faith had been made manifest by his passivity under treatment, and the suggestions of perfect healthfulness by the minister were conveyed to his subconscious mind. The two subjective minds were then *en rapport*.

The minister was not handicapped by antagonistic autosuggestions of the patient arising from objective doubt of the power of the healer or the correctness of the theory. In this sleepy, drowsy state the conscious mind resistance is reduced to a minimum, and results followed. The subconscious mind of the patient being necessarily controlled by such suggestion exercised its functions in accordance therewith, and a healing followed.

• **The meaning of absent treatment**

Suppose you learned that your mother was sick in New York City and you lived in Los Angeles. Your mother would not be physically present where you are, but you could pray for her. *It is the Father within which doeth the work.*

The creative law of mind (subconscious mind) serves you and will do the work. Its response to you is automatic. Your treatment is for the purpose of inducing an inner realization of health and harmony in your mentality. This inner realization, acting through the subconscious mind, operates through your mother's subconscious mind as there is but one creative mind. Your thoughts of health, vitality, and perfection operate through the one universal subjective mind, and set a law in motion on the subjective side of life which manifests through her body as a healing.

In the mind principle there is no time or space. It is the same mind that operates through your mother no matter where she may be. In reality there is no absent treatment as opposed to present treatment for the universal mind is omnipresent. You do not try to send out thoughts or hold a thought. Your treatment is a conscious movement of thought, and as you become conscious of the qualities of health, well-being, and relaxation, these qualities will be resurrected in the experience of your mother, and results will follow.

The following is a perfect example of what is called absent treatment. Recently, a listener of our radio program in Los Angeles prayed as follows for her mother in New York who had a coronary thrombosis: "The healing presence is right where my mother is. Her bodily condition is but a reflection of her thought-life like shadows cast on the screen. I know that in order to change the images on the screen I must change the projection reel. My mind is the projection reel, and I now project in my own mind the image of wholeness, harmony, and perfect health for my mother. The infinite healing presence which created my mother's body and all her organs is now saturating every atom of her being, and a river of peace flows through every cell of her body. The doctors are divinely guided and directed, and whoever touches my mother is guided to do the right thing. I know that disease has no ultimate reality; if it had, no one could be healed. I now align myself with the infinite principle of love

and life, and I know and decree that harmony, health, and peace
are now being expressed in my mother's body."

She prayed in the above manner several times daily, and
her mother had a most remarkable recovery after a few days,
much to the amazement of her specialist. He complimented her
on her great faith in the power of God.

The conclusion arrived at in the daughter's mind set the
creative law of mind in motion on the subjective side of life,
which manifested itself through her mother's body as perfect
health and harmony. What the daughter felt as true about her
mother was simultaneously resurrected in the experience of her
mother.

• Releasing the kinetic action of the subconscious mind

A psychologist friend of mine told me that one of his lungs
was infected. X rays and analysis showed the presence of tuberculosis. At night before going to sleep he would quietly affirm,
"Every cell, nerve, tissue, and muscle of my lungs are now being
made whole, pure, and perfect. My whole body is being restored
to health and harmony."

These are not his exact words, but they represent the essence of what he affirmed. A complete healing followed in about
a month's time. Subsequent X rays showed a perfect healing.

I wanted to know his method, so I asked him why he repeated the words prior to sleep. Here is his reply, "The kinetic
action of the subconscious mind continues throughout your
sleep-time period. Hence, give the subconscious mind something
good to work on as you drop off into slumber." This was a very
wise answer. In thinking of harmony and perfect health, he
never mentioned his trouble by name.

I strongly suggest that you cease talking about your ailments or giving them a name. The only sap from which they
draw life is your attention and fear of them. Like the above
mentioned psychologist, become a mental surgeon. Then your
troubles will be cut off like dead branches are pruned from a tree.

If you are constantly naming your aches and symptoms,
you inhibit the kinetic action, which means the release of the

healing power and energy of your subconscious mind. Further-more, by the law of your own mind, these imaginings tend to take shape, *As the thing I greatly feared*. Fill your mind with the great truths of life and walk forward in the light of love.

• **Summary of your aids to health**

1. Find out what it is that heals you. Realize that correct directions given to your subconscious mind will heal your mind and body.

2. Develop a definite plan for turning over your requests or desires to your subconscious mind.

3. Imagine the end desired and feel its reality. Follow it through, and you will get definite results.

4. Decide what belief is. Know that belief is a thought in your mind, and what you think you create.

5. It is foolish to believe in sickness and something to hurt or to harm you. Believe in perfect health, prosperity, peace, wealth, and divine guidance.

6. Great and noble thoughts upon which you habitually dwell become great acts.

7. Apply the power of prayer therapy in your life. Choose a certain plan, idea, or mental picture. Mentally and emotionally unite with that idea, and as you remain faithful to your mental attitude, your prayer will be answered.

8. Always remember, if you really want the power to heal, you can have it through faith, which means a knowledge of the working of your conscious and subconscious mind. Faith comes with understanding.

9. Blind faith means that a person may get results in healing without any scientific understanding of the powers and forces involved.

10. Learn to pray for your loved ones who may be ill. Quiet your mind, and your thoughts of health, vitality, and perfection operating through the one universal subjective mind will be felt and resurrected in the mind of your loved one.

6

Practical Techniques in Mental Healings

An engineer has a technique and a process for building a bridge or an engine. Like the engineer, your mind also has a technique for governing, controlling, and directing your life. You must realize that methods and techniques are primary.

In building the Golden Gate bridge, the chief engineer understood mathematical principles, stresses and strains. Secondly, he had a picture of the ideal bridge across the bay. The third step was his application of tried and proven methods by which the principles were implemented until the bridge took form and we drive on it. There also are techniques and methods by which your prayers are answered. If your prayer is answered, there is a way in which it is answered, and this is a scientific way. Nothing happens by chance. This is a world of law and order. In this chapter you will find practical techniques for the unfolding and nurture of your spiritual life. Your prayers must not remain up in the air like a balloon. They must go somewhere and accomplish something in your life.

When we come to analyze prayer we discover there are many different approaches and methods. We will not consider in this book the formal, ritual prayers used in religious services. These have an important place in group worship. We are immediately concerned with the methods of personal prayer as it is applied in your daily life and as it is used to help others.

Prayer is the formulation of an idea concerning something we wish to accomplish. Prayer is the soul's sincere desire. Your desire is your prayer. It comes out of your deepest needs and it reveals the things you want in life. *Blessed are they that hunger and thirst after righteousness: for they shall be filled.* That is really prayer, life's hunger and thirst for peace, harmony, health, joy, and all the other blessings of life.

• The passing-over technique for impregnating the subconscious

This consists essentially in inducing the subconscious mind to take over your request as handed it by the conscious mind. This passing-over is best accomplished in the reverie-like state. Know that in your deeper mind is Infinite Intelligence and Infinite Power. Just calmly think over what you want; see it coming into fuller fruition from this moment forward. Be like the little girl who had a very bad cough and a sore throat. She declared firmly and repeatedly, "It is passing away now. It is passing away now." It passed away in about an hour. Use this technique with complete simplicity and naïveté.

• Your subconscious will accept your blueprint

If you were building a new home for yourself and family, you know that you would be intensely interested in regard to the blueprint for your home; you would see to it that the builders conformed to the blueprint. You would watch the material and select only the best wood, steel, in fact, the best of everything. What about your mental home and your mental blueprint for happiness and abundance? All your experiences and everything that enters into your life depend upon the nature of the mental building blocks which you use in the construction of your mental home.

If your blueprint is full of mental patterns of fear, worry, anxiety, or lack, and if you are despondent, doubtful, and cynical, then the texture of the mental material you are weaving into your mind will come forth as more toil, care, tension, anxiety, and limitation of all kinds.

The most fundamental and the most far-reaching activity in life is that which you build into your mentality every waking hour. Your word is silent and invisible; nevertheless, it is real.

You are building your mental home all the time, and your thought and mental imagery represent your blueprint. Hour by hour, moment by moment, you can build radiant health, success, and happiness by the thoughts you think, the ideas which you harbor, the beliefs that you accept, and the scenes that you rehearse in the hidden studio of your mind. This stately mansion, upon the construction of which you are perpetually engaged, is your personality, your identity in this plane, your whole life story on this earth.

Get a new blueprint; build silently by realizing peace, harmony, joy, and good will in the present moment. By dwelling upon these things and claiming them, your subconscious will accept your blueprint and bring all these things to pass. *By their fruits ye shall know them.*

• The science and art of true prayer

The term "science" means knowledge which is co-ordinated, arranged, and systematized. Let us think of the science and art of true prayer as it deals with the fundamental principles of life and the techniques and processes by which they can be demonstrated in your life, as well as in the life of every human being when he applies them faithfully. The art is your technique or process, and the science behind it is the definite response of creative mind to your mental picture or thought.

Ask, and it shall be given you; seek, and ye shall find; knock, and it shall be opened unto you. MATTHEW 7:7.

Here you are told you shall receive that for which you ask. It shall be opened to you when you knock, and you shall find that for which you are searching. This teaching implies the definiteness of mental and spiritual laws. There is always a direct response from the Infinite Intelligence of your subconscious mind to your conscious thinking. If you ask for bread, you will not receive a stone. You must ask *believing*, if you are to receive. Your mind moves from the thought to the thing. Unless there is first an image in the mind, it cannot move, for there would be nothing for it to move toward. Your prayer, which is your mental act, must be accepted as an image in your mind before the power from your subconscious will play upon it and make it productive. You must reach a point of acceptance in your mind, an unqualified and undisputed state of agreement.

This contemplation should be accompanied by a feeling of joy and restfulness in foreseeing the certain accomplishment of your desire. The sound basis for the art and science of true prayer is your knowledge and complete confidence that the movement of your conscious mind will gain a definite response from your subconscious mind which is one with boundless wisdom and infinite power. By following this procedure, your prayers will be answered.

• The visualization technique

The easiest and most obvious way to formulate an idea is to visualize it, to see it in your mind's eye as vividly as if it were alive. You can see with the naked eye only what already exists in the external world; in a similar way, that which you can visualize in your mind's eye already exists in the invisible realms of your mind. Any picture which you have in your mind is *the substance of things hoped for and the evidence of things not seen.* What you form in your imagination is as real as any part of your body. The idea and the thought are real and will one day appear in your objective world if you are faithful to your mental image.

This process of thinking forms impressions in your mind; these impressions in turn become manifested as facts and experiences in your life. The builder visualizes the type of building he wants; he sees it as he desires it to be completed. His imagery and thought-processes become a plastic mold from which the building will emerge—a beautiful or an ugly one, a skyscraper or a very low one. His mental imagery is projected as it is drawn on paper. Eventually, the contractor and his workers gather the essential materials, and the building progresses until it stands finished, conforming perfectly to the mental patterns of the architect.

I use the visualization technique prior to speaking from the platform. I quiet the wheels of my mind in order that I may present to the subconscious mind my images of thought. Then, I picture the entire auditorium and the seats filled with men and women, and each one of them illumined and inspired by the infinite healing presence within each one. I see them as radiant, happy, and free.

Having first built up the idea in my imagination, I quietly sustain it there as a mental picture while I imagine I hear men and women saying, "I am healed," "I feel wonderful," "I've had an instantaneous healing," "I'm transformed." I keep this up for about ten minutes or more, knowing and feeling that each person's mind and body are saturated with love, wholeness, beauty, and perfection. My awareness grows to the point where in my mind I can actually hear the voices of the multitude proclaiming their health and happiness; then I release the whole picture and go onto the platform. Almost every Sunday some people stop and say that their prayers were answered.

• Mental movie method

The Chinese say, "A picture is worth a thousand words." William James, the father of American psychology, stressed the fact that the subconscious mind will bring to pass any picture held in the mind and backed by faith. *Act as though I am, and I will be.*

A number of years ago I was in the Middle West lecturing in several states, and I desired to have a permanent location in the general area from which I could serve those who desired help. I traveled far, but the desire did not leave my mind. One evening, while in a hotel in Spokane, Washington, I relaxed completely on a couch, immobilized my attention, and in a quiet, passive manner imagined that I was talking to a large audience, saying in effect, "I am glad to be here; I have prayed for the ideal opportunity." I saw in my mind's eye the imaginary audience, and I felt the reality of it all. I played the role of the actor, dramatized this mental movie, and felt satisfied that this picture was being conveyed to my subconscious mind, which would bring it to pass in its own way. The next morning, on awakening, I felt a great sense of peace and satisfaction, and in a few days' time I received a telegram asking me to take over an organization in the Midwest, which I did, and I enjoyed it immensely for several years.

The method outlined here appeals to many who have described it as "the mental movie method." I have received numerous letters from people who listen to my radio talks and weekly public lectures, telling me of the wonderful results they get using this technique in the sale of their property. I suggest to those who have homes or property for sale that they satisfy themselves in their own mind that their price is right. Then, I claim that the Infinite Intelligence is attracting to them the buyer who really wants to have the property and who will love it and prosper in it. After having done this I suggest that they quiet their mind, relax, let go, and get into a drowsy, sleepy state which reduces all mental effort to a minimum. Then, they are to picture the check in their hands, rejoice in the check, give thanks for the check, and go off to sleep feeling the naturalness of the whole mental movie created in their own mind. They must act as though it were an objective reality, and the subconscious mind will take it as an impression, and through the deeper currents of the mind the buyer and the seller are brought together. A mental picture held in the mind, backed by faith, will come to pass.

• The Baudoin technique

Charles Baudoin was a professor at the Rousseau Institute n France. He was a brilliant psychotherapist and a research director of the New Nancy School of Healing, who in 1910 taught that the best way to impress the subconscious mind was to enter into a drowsy, sleepy state, or a state akin to sleep in which all effort was reduced to a minimum. Then in a quiet, passive, receptive way, by reflection, he would convey the idea to the subconscious. The following is his formula: "A very simple way of securing this (impregnation of the subconscious mind) is to condense the idea which is to be the object of suggestion, to sum it up in a brief phrase which can be readily graven on the memory, and to repeat it over and over again as a lullaby."

Some years ago, a young lady in Los Angeles was engaged in a prolonged bitter family lawsuit over a will. Her husband had bequeathed his entire estate to her, and his sons and daughters by a previous marriage were bitterly fighting to break the will. The Baudoin technique was outlined to her, and this is what she did: She relaxed her body in an armchair, entered into the sleepy state and, as suggested, condensed the idea of her need into a phrase consisting of six words easily graven on the memory. "It is finished in Divine Order." The significance to her of these words meant that Infinite Intelligence operating through the laws of her subconscious mind would bring about a harmonious adjustment through the principle of harmony. She continued this procedure every night for about ten nights. After she got into a sleepy state, she would affirm slowly, quietly, and feelingly the statement: "It is finished in Divine Order," over and over again, feeling a sense of inner peace and an all-pervading tranquility; then she went off into her deep, normal sleep.

On the morning of the eleventh day, following the use of the above technique, she awakened with a sense of well-being, a conviction that *it was finished*. Her attorney called her the same day, saying that the opposing attorney and his clients were willing to settle. A harmonious agreement was reached, and litigation was discontinued.

• **The sleeping technique**

By entering into a sleepy, drowsy state, effort is reduced to a minimum. The conscious mind is submerged to a great extent when in a sleepy state. The reason for this is that the highest degree of outcropping of the subconscious occurs prior to sleep and just after we awaken. In this state the negative thoughts, which tend to neutralize your desire and so prevent acceptance by your subconscious mind, are no longer present.

Suppose you want to get rid of a destructive habit. Assume a comfortable posture, relax your body, and be still. Get into a sleepy state, and in that sleepy state, say quietly, over and over again as a lullaby, "I am completely free from this habit; harmony and peace of mind reign supreme." Repeat the above slowly, quietly, and lovingly for five or ten minutes night and morning. Each time you repeat the words the emotional value becomes greater. When the urge comes to repeat the negative habit, repeat the above formula out loud by yourself. By this means you induce the subconscious to accept the idea, and a healing follows.

• The "thank-you" technique

In the Bible, Paul recommends that we make known our requests with praise and thanksgiving. Some extraordinary results follow this simple method of prayer. The thankful heart is always close to the creative forces of the universe, causing countless blessings to flow toward it by the law of reciprocal relationship, based on a cosmic law of action and reaction.

For instance, a father promises his son a car for graduation; the boy has not yet received the car, but he is very thankful and happy, and is as joyous as though he had actually received the car. He knows his father will fulfill his promise, and he is full of gratitude and joy even though he has not yet received the car, objectively speaking. He has, however, received it with joy and thankfulness in his mind.

I shall illustrate how Mr. Broke applied this technique with excellent results. He said, "Bills are piling up, I am out of work, I have three children and no money. What shall I do?" Regularly every night and morning, for a period of about three weeks, he repeated the words, "Thank you, Father, for my wealth," in a relaxed, peaceful manner until the feeling or mood of thankfulness dominated his mind. He imagined he was addressing the infinite power and intelligence within him knowing, of course, that he could not see the creative intelligence or infinite mind. He was seeing with the inner eye of spiritual perception, realizing that his thought-image of wealth was the *first cause*, relative to the money, position, and food he needed. His thought-feeling was the substance of wealth untrammeled by antecedent conditions of any kind. By repeating, "Thank you, Father," over and over again, his mind and heart were lifted up to the point of acceptance, and when fear, thoughts of lack, poverty, and distress came into his mind, he would say, "Thank you, Father," as often as necessary. He knew that as he kept up the thankful attitude he would recondition his mind to the idea of wealth, which is what happened.

The sequel to his prayer is very interesting. After praying in the above mentioned manner, he met a former employer of his on the street whom he had not seen for twenty years. The man offered him a very lucrative position and advanced him $500 on a temporary loan. Today, Mr. Broke is vice-president of the company for which he works. His recent remark to me was, "I shall never forget the wonders of 'Thank you, Father.' It has worked wonders for me."

• The affirmative method

The effectiveness of an affirmation is determined largely by your understanding of the truth and the meaning back of the words, *"In praying use not vain repetition."* Therefore, the power of your affirmation lies in the intelligent application of definite and specific positives. For example, a boy adds three and three and puts down seven on the blackboard. The teacher affirms with mathematical certainty that three and three are six; therefore, the boy changes his figures accordingly. The teacher's statement did not make three and three equal six because the latter was already a mathematical truth. The mathematical truth caused the boy to rearrange the figures on the blackboard. It is abnormal to be sick; it is normal to be healthy. Health is the truth of your being. When you affirm health, harmony, and peace for yourself or another, and when you realize these are universal principles of your own being, you will rearrange the negative patterns of your subconscious mind based on your faith and understanding of that which you affirm.

The result of the affirmative process of prayer depends on your conforming to the principles of life, regardless of appearances. Consider for a moment that there is a principle of mathematics and none of error; there is a principle of truth but none of dishonesty. There is a principle of intelligence but none of ignorance; there is a principle of harmony and none of discord. There is a principle of health but none of disease, and there is a principle of abundance but none of poverty.

The affirmative method was chosen by the author for use on his sister who was to be operated on for the removal of gallstones in a hospital in England. The condition described was based on the diagnosis of hospital tests and the usual X-ray procedures. She asked me to pray for her. We were separated geographically about 6,500 miles, but there is no time or space in the mind principle. Infinite mind or intelligence is present in its entirety at every point simultaneously. I withdrew all thought from the contemplation of symptoms and from the corporeal personality altogether. I affirmed as follows: "This prayer is for my sister Catherine. She is relaxed and at peace, poised, balanced, serene, and calm. The healing intelligence of her subconscious mind which created her body is now transforming every cell, nerve, tissue, muscle, and bone of her being according to the perfect pattern of all organs lodged in her subconscious mind. Silently, quietly, all distorted thought patterns in her subconscious mind are removed and dissolved, and the vitality, wholeness, and beauty of the life principle are made manifest in every atom of her being. She is now open and receptive to the healing currents which are flowing through her like a river, restoring her to perfect health, harmony, and peace. All distortions and ugly images are now washed away by the infinite ocean of love and peace flowing through her, and it is so."

I affirmed the above several times a day, and at the end of two weeks my sister had an examination which showed a remarkable healing, and the X ray proved negative.

To affirm is to state that it is so, and as you maintain this attitude of mind as true, regardless of all evidence to the contrary, you will receive an answer to your prayer. Your thought can only affirm, for even if you deny something, you are actually affirming the presence of what you deny. Repeating an affirmation, knowing what you are saying and why you are saying it, leads the mind to that state of consciousness where it accepts that which you state as true. Keep on affirming the truths of life until you get the subconscious reaction which satisfies.

• The argumentative method

This method is just what the word implies. It stems from the procedure of Dr. Phineas Parkhurst Quimby of Maine. Dr. Quimby, a pioneer in mental and spiritual healing, lived and practiced in Belfast, Maine, about one hundred years ago. A book called *The Quimby Manuscripts,* published in 1921 by Thomas Y. Crowell Company, New York City, and edited by Horatio Dresser, is available in your library. This book gives newspaper accounts of this man's remarkable results in prayer treatment of the sick. Quimby duplicated many of the healing miracles recorded in the Bible. In brief, the argumentative method employed according to Quimby consists of spiritual reasoning where you convince the patient and yourself that his sickness is due to his false belief, groundless fears, and negative patterns lodged in his subconscious mind. You reason it out clearly in your mind and convince your patient that the disease or ailment is due only to a distorted, twisted pattern of thought which has taken form in his body. This wrong belief in some external power and external causes has now externalized itself as sickness, and can be changed by changing the thought patterns.

You explain to the sick person that the basis of all healing is a change of belief. You also point out that the subconscious mind created the body and all its organs; therefore, it knows how to heal it, can heal it, and is doing so now as you speak. You argue in the courtroom of your mind that the disease is a shadow of the mind based on disease-soaked, morbid thought-imagery. You continue to build up all the evidence you can muster on behalf of the healing power within, which created all the organs in the first place, and which has a perfect pattern of every cell, nerve, and tissue within it. Then, you render a verdict in the courthouse of your mind in favor of yourself or your patient. You liberate the sick one by faith and spiritual understanding. Your mental and spiritual evidence is overwhelming; there being but one mind, what you feel as true will be resurrected in the experience of the patient. This procedure is essentially the argumentative method used by Dr. Quimby of Maine from 1849 to 1869.

• The absolute method is like modern sound wave therapy

Many people throughout the world practice this form of prayer treatment with wonderful results. The person using the absolute method mentions the name of the patient, such as John Jones, then quietly and silently thinks of God and His qualities and attributes, such as, God is all bliss, boundless love, infinite intelligence, all-powerful, boundless wisdom, absolute harmony, indescribable beauty, and perfection. As he quietly thinks along these lines he is lifted up in consciousness into a new spiritual wave length, at which times he feels the infinite ocean of God's love is now dissolving everything unlike itself in the mind and body of John Jones for whom he is praying. He feels all the power and love of God are now focused on John Jones, and whatever is bothering or vexing him is now completely neutralized in the presence of the infinite ocean of life and love.

The absolute method of prayer might be likened to the sound wave or sonic therapy recently shown me by a distinguished physician in Los Angeles. He has an ultra sound wave machine which oscillates at a tremendous speed and sends sound waves to any area of the body to which it is directed. These sound waves can be controlled, and he told me of achieving remarkable results in dissolving arthritic calcareous deposits, as well as the healing and removal of other disturbing conditions.

To the degree that we rise in consciousness by contemplating qualities and attributes of God, do we generate spiritual electronic waves of harmony, health, and peace. Many remarkable healings follow this technique of prayer.

• A cripple walks

Dr. Phineas Parkhurst Quimby, of whom we spoke previously in this chapter, used the absolute method in the latter years of his healing career. He was really the father of psychosomatic medicine and the first psychoanalyst. He had the capacity to diagnose clairvoyantly the cause of the patient's trouble, pains, and aches.

The following is a condensed account of the healing of a cripple as recorded in Quimby's Manuscripts:

Quimby was called on to visit a woman who was lame, aged, and bedridden. He states that her ailment was due to the fact that she was imprisoned by a creed so small and contracted that she could not stand upright and move about. She was living in the tomb of fear and ignorance; furthermore, she was taking the Bible literally, and it frightened her. "In this tomb," Quimby said, "was the presence and power of God trying to burst the bands, break through the bonds, and rise from the dead." When she would ask others for an explanation of some passage of the Bible, the answer would be a stone; then she would hunger for the bread of life. Dr. Quimby diagnosed her case as a mind cloudy and stagnated, due to excitation and fear, caused by the inability to see clearly the meaning of the passage of the Bible which she had been reading. This showed itself in the body by her heavy and sluggish feeling which would terminate as paralysis.

At this point Quimby asked her what was meant in the Bible verses: *Yet a little while am I with you, and then I go unto Him that sent me. Ye shall seek me, and shall not find me: and where I am, thither ye cannot come.* JOHN 7:33-34. She replied that it meant Jesus went to heaven. Quimby explained what it really meant by telling her that *being with her a little while* meant his explanation of her symptoms, feelings, and their causes; i.e., he had compassion and sympathy for her momentarily, but he could not remain in that mental state. The next step was *to go to Him that sent us which,* as Quimby pointed out, was the creative power of God in all of us.

Quimby immediately traveled in his mind and contemplated the divine ideal; i.e., the vitality, intelligence, harmony, and power of God functioning in the sick person. This is why he said to the woman, "Therefore, where I go you cannot come,

for you are in your narrow, restricted belief, and I am in health."
This prayer and explanation produced an instantaneous sensation, and a change came over her mind. She walked without
her crutches! Quimby said it was one of the most singular of
all his healings. She was, as it were, dead to error, and to bring
her to life or truth was to raise her from the dead. Quimby
quoted the resurrection of Christ and applied it to her own Christ
or health; this produced a powerful effect on her. He also explained to her that the truth which she accepted was the angel
or idea which rolled away the stone of fear, ignorance, and
superstition, thereby, releasing the healing power of God which
made her whole.

• The decree method

Power goes into our word according to the feeling and faith
behind it. When we realize the power that moves the world is
moving on our behalf and is backing up our word, our confidence
and assurance grow. You do not try and add power to power;
therefore, there must be no mental striving, coercion, force, or
mental wrestling.

A young girl used the decree method on a young man who
was constantly phoning her, pressing her for dates, and meeting
her at her place of business; she found it very difficult to get rid
of him. She decreed as follows: "I release .... unto God.
He is in his true place at all times. I am free, and he is free.
I now decree that my words go forth into infinite mind and it
brings it to pass. It is so." She said he vanished and she has
never seen him since, adding, "It was as though the ground
swallowed him up."

*Thou shalt decree a thing, and it shall be established unto
thee: and the light shall shine upon thy ways.* JOB 22:28.

• Serve yourself with scientific truth

1. Be a mental engineer and use tried and proven techniques
   in building a grander and greater life.
2. Your desire is your prayer. Picture the fulfillment of your

desire now and feel its reality, and you will experience the joy of the answered prayer.

3. Desire to accomplish things the easy way—with the sure aid of mental science.

4. You can build radiant health, success, and happiness by the thoughts you think in the hidden studio of your mind.

5. Experiment scientifically until you personally prove that there is always a direct response from the infinite intelligence of your subconscious mind to your conscious thinking.

6. Feel the joy and restfulness in foreseeing the certain accomplishment of your desire. Any mental picture which you have in your mind is the substance of things hoped for and the evidence of things not seen.

7. A mental picture is worth a thousand words. Your subconscious will bring to pass any picture held in the mind backed by faith.

8. Avoid all effort or mental coercion in prayer. Get into a sleepy, drowsy state and lull yourself to sleep feeling and knowing that your prayer is answered.

9. Remember that the thankful heart is always close to the riches of the universe.

10. To affirm is to state that it is so, and as you maintain this attitude of mind as true, regardless of all evidence to the contrary, you will receive an answer to your prayer.

11. Generate electronic waves of harmony, health, and peace by thinking of the love and the glory of God.

12. What you decree and feel as true will come to pass. Decree harmony, health, peace, and abundance.

7

The Tendency of the Subconscious Is Lifeward

Over 90 percent of your mental life is subconscious, so men and women who fail to make use of this marvelous power live within very narrow limits.

Your subconscious processes are always lifeward and constructive. Your subconscious is the builder of your body and maintains all its vital functions. It is on the job 24 hours a day and never sleeps. It is always trying to help and preserve you from harm.

Your subconscious mind is in touch with infinite life and boundless wisdom, and its impulses and ideas are always lifeward. The great aspirations, inspirations, and visions for a grander and nobler life spring from the subconscious. Your profoundest convictions are those you cannot argue about rationally because they do not come from your conscious mind; they come from your subconscious mind. Your subconscious speaks to you in intuitions, impulses, hunches, intimations, urges, and ideas, and it is always telling you to rise, transcend, grow, advance, adventure, and move forward to greater heights. The urge to love, to save the lives of others comes from the depths of your subconscious. For example, during the great San Francisco earthquake and fire of April 18, 1906, invalids and cripples who had been confined to bed for long periods of time, rose up and performed some of the most amazing feats of bravery and endurance. The intense desire welled up within them to save others at all costs, and their subconscious responded accordingly.

Great artists, musicians, poets, speakers, and writers tune in with their subconscious powers and become animated and inspired. For example, Robert Louis Stevenson, before he went to sleep, used to charge his subconscious with the task of evolving stories for him while he slept. He was accustomed to ask his subconscious to give him a good, marketable thriller when his bank account was low. Stevenson said the intelligence of his deeper mind gave him the story piece by piece, like a serial. This shows how your subconscious will speak lofty and wise sayings through you which your conscious mind knows nothing about.

Mark Twain confided to the world on many occasions that he never worked in his life. All his humor and all his great writings were due to the fact that he tapped the inexhaustible reservoir of his subconscious mind.

• How the body portrays the workings of the mind

The interaction of your conscious and subconscious mind requires a similar interaction between the corresponding system of nerves. The cerebrospinal system is the organ of the conscious mind, and the sympathetic system is the organ of the subconscious mind. The cerebrospinal system is the channel through which you receive conscious perception by means of your five physical senses and exercise control over the movement of your body. This system has its nerves in the brain, and it is the channel of your volitional and conscious mental action.

The sympathetic system, sometimes referred to as the involuntary nervous system, has its center in a ganglionic mass at the back of the stomach known as the solar plexus, and is sometimes spoken of as the abdominal brain. It is the channel of that mental action which unconsciously supports the vital functions of the body.

The two systems may work separately or synchronously. Judge Thomas Troward * says, "The vagus nerve passes out of the cerebral region as a portion of the voluntary system, and

* *The Edinburgh Lectures on Mental Science* (New York: Robert McBride & Co., 1909).

through it we control the vocal organs; then it passes onward to
the thorax sending out branches to the heart and lungs; finally,
passing through the diaphragm, it loses the outer coating which
distinguishes the nerves of the voluntary system and becomes
identified with those of the sympathetic system, so forming a
connecting link between the two and making the man physically
a single entity.

"Similarly different areas of the brain indicate their connection with the objective and subjective activities of the mind
respectively, and speaking in a general way we may assign the
frontal portion of the brain to the former and the posterior
portion to the latter, while the intermediate portion partakes of
the character of both."

A rather simple way of looking at the mental and physical
interaction is to realize that your conscious mind grasps an idea
which induces a corresponding vibration in your voluntary system of nerves. This in turn causes a similar current to be generated in your involuntary system of nerves, thus handling the
idea over to your subconscious mind which is the creative medium. This is how your thoughts become things.

Every thought entertained by your conscious mind and accepted as true is sent by your brain to your solar plexus, the
brain of your subconscious mind, to be made into your flesh,
and to be brought forth into your world as a reality.

● **There is an intelligence which takes care of the body**

When you study the cellular system and the structure of the
organs, such as eyes, ears, heart, liver, bladder, etc., you learn
they consist of groups of cells which form a group intelligence
whereby they function together and are able to take orders and
carry them out in deductive function at the suggestion of the
master mind (conscious mind).

A careful study of the single-celled organism shows you
what goes on in your complex body. Though the mono-cellular
organism has no organs, it still gives evidence of mind action
and reaction performing the basic functions of movement, ali-
mentation, assimilation, and elimination.

Many say there is an intelligence which will take care of your body if you let it alone. That is true, but the difficulty is that the conscious mind always interferes with its five-sense evidence based on outer appearances, leading to the sway of false beliefs, fears, and mere opinion. When fear, false beliefs, and negative patterns are made to register in your subconscious mind through psychological, emotional conditioning, there is no other course open to the subconscious mind except to act on the blueprint specifications offered it.

• The subconscious mind works continually for the common good

The subjective self within you works continuously for the general good, reflecting an innate principle of harmony behind all things. Your subconscious mind has its own will, and it is a very real something in itself. It acts night and day whether you act upon it or not. It is the builder of your body, but you cannot see, hear, or feel it building, as all this is a silent process. Your subconscious has a life of its own which is always moving toward harmony, health, and peace. This is the divine norm within it seeking expression through you at all times.

• How man interferes with the innate principle of harmony

To think correctly, scientifically, we must know the "Truth." To know the truth is to be in harmony with the infinite intelligence and power of your subconscious mind which is always moving lifeward.

Every thought or action which is not harmonious, whether through ignorance or design, will result in discord and limitation of all kinds.

Scientists inform us that you build a new body every eleven months; so you are really only eleven months old from a physical standpoint. If you build defects back into your body by thoughts of fear, anger, jealousy, and ill will, you have no one to blame but yourself.

You are the sum total of your own thoughts. You can keep

from entertaining negative thought and imagery. The way to get rid of darkness is with light; the way to overcome cold is with heat; the way to overcome the negative thought is to substitute the good thought. Affirm the good, and the bad will vanish.

• Why it's normal to be healthy, vital, and strong— it's abnormal to be sick

The average child born into the world is perfectly healthy with all its organs functioning perfectly. This is the normal state, and we should remain healthy, vital, and strong. The instinct of self-preservation is the strongest instinct of your nature, and it constitutes a most potent, ever-present, and constantly operative truth, inherent in your nature. It is, therefore, obvious that all your thoughts, ideas, and beliefs must operate with greater potentiality when they are in harmony with the innate life-principle in you, which is forever seeking to preserve and protect you along all lines. It follows from this that normal conditions can be restored with greater ease and certainty than abnormal conditions can be induced.

It is abnormal to be sick; it simply means you are going against the stream of life and thinking negatively. The law of life is the law of growth; all nature testifies to the operation of this law by silently, constantly expressing itself in the law of growth. Where there is growth and expression, there must be life; where there is life there must be harmony, and where there is harmony, there is perfect health.

If your thought is in harmony with the creative principle of your subconscious mind, you are in tune with the innate principle of harmony. If you entertain thoughts which are not in accordance with the principle of harmony, these thoughts cling to you, harass you, worry you, and finally bring about disease, and if persisted in, possibly death.

In the healing of disease, you must increase the inflow and distribution of the vital forces of your subconscious mind throughout your system. This can be done by eliminating thoughts of fear, worry, anxiety, jealousy, hatred, and every other destructive thought which tends to tear down and destroy your nerves and glands—body tissue which controls the elimination of all waste material.

• Pott's disease cured

In the *Nautilus* magazine of March, 1917, there appears an article about a boy suffering from Pott's disease, or tuberculosis of the spine, who had a remarkable healing. His name was Frederick Elias Andrews of Indianapolis, now minister of Unity School of Christianity, Kansas City, Missouri. His physician pronounced him incurable. He began to pray, and from a crooked, twisted cripple going about on hands and knees, he became a strong, straight, well-formed man. He created his own affirmation, mentally absorbing the qualities he needed.

He affirmed over and over again many times a day, "I am whole, perfect, strong, powerful, loving, harmonious, and happy." He persevered and said that this prayer was the last utterance on his lips at night and the first in the morning. He prayed for others also by sending out thoughts of love and health. This attitude of mind and way of prayer returned to him multiplied many times. His faith and perseverance paid off with big dividends. When thoughts of fear, anger, jealousy, or envy drew his attention, he would immediately start his counteracting force of affirmation going in his mind. His subconscious mind responded according to the nature of his habitual thinking. This is the meaning of the statement in the Bible, *Go thy way, thy faith hath made thee whole*. MARK 10:52.

• How faith in your subconscious powers makes you whole

A young man, who came to my lectures on the healing power of the subconscious mind, had severe eye trouble which his doctor said necessitated an operation. He said to himself, "My subconscious made my eyes, and it can heal me."

Each night, as he went to sleep, he entered into a drowsy, meditative state, the condition akin to sleep. His attention was immobilized and focused on the eye doctor. He imagined the doctor was in front of him, and he plainly heard, or imagined he heard, the doctor saying to him, "A miracle has happened!" He heard this over and over again every night for perhaps five minutes or so before going to sleep. At the end of three weeks he again went to the ophthalmologist who had previously examined his eyes, and the physician said to this man, "This is a miracle!" What happened? This man impressed his subconscious mind using the doctor as an instrument or a means of convincing it or conveying the idea. Through repetition, faith, and expectancy he impregnated his subconscious mind. His subconscious mind made his eye; within it was the perfect pattern, and immediately it proceeded to heal the eye. This is another example of how faith in the healing power of your subconscious can make you whole.

• Pointers to review

1. Your subconscious is the builder of your body and is on the job 24 hours a day. You interfere with its life-giving patterns by negative thinking.

2. Charge your subconscious with the task of evolving an answer to any problem, prior to sleep and it will answer you.

3. Watch your thoughts. Every thought accepted as true is sent by your brain to your solar plexus—your abdominal brain—and is brought into your world as a reality.

4. Know that you can remake yourself by giving a new blueprint to your subconscious mind.

5. The tendency of your subconscious is always lifeward. Your job is with your conscious mind. Feed your subconscious mind with premises which are true. Your subconscious is always reproducing according to your habitual mental patterns.

6. You build a new body every eleven months. Change your body by changing your thoughts and keeping them changed.

7. It is normal to be healthy. It is abnormal to be ill. There is within the innate principle of harmony.

8. Thoughts of jealousy, fear, worry, and anxiety tear down and

destroy your nerves and glands bringing about mental and physical diseases of all kinds.

9. What you affirm consciously and feel as true will be made manifest in your mind, body and affairs. Affirm the good and enter into the joy of living.

8

How to Get the Results You Want

The principle reasons for failure are: Lack of confidence and too much effort. Many people block answers to their prayers by failing to fully comprehend the workings of their subconscious mind. When you know how your mind functions, you gain a measure of confidence. You must remember whenever your subconscious mind accepts an idea, it immediately begins to execute it. It uses all its mighty resources to that end and mobilizes all the mental and spiritual laws of your deeper mind. This law is true for good or bad ideas. Consequently, if you use it negatively, it brings trouble, failure, and confusion. When you use it constructively, it brings guidance, freedom, and peace of mind.

The right answer is inevitable when your thoughts are positive, constructive, and loving. From this it is perfectly obvious that the only thing you have to do in order to overcome failure is to get your subconscious to accept your idea or request by feeling its reality now, and the law of your mind will do the rest. Turn over your request with faith and confidence, and your subconscious will take over and answer for you.

You will always fail to get results by trying to use mental coercion—your subconscious mind does not respond to coercion, it responds to your faith or conscious mind acceptance.

Your failure to get results may also arise from such statements as: "Things are getting worse." "I will never get an answer." "I see no way out." "It is hopeless." "I don't know what to do." "I'm all mixed up." When you use such statements, you get no response or co-operation from your subconscious mind. Like a soldier marking time, you neither go forward nor backward; in other words, you don't get anywhere.

If you get into a taxi and give a half dozen different directions to the driver in five minutes, he would become hopelessly confused and probably would refuse to take you anywhere. It is the same when working with your subconscious mind. There must be a clear-cut idea in your mind. You must arrive at the definite decision that there is a way out, a solution to the vexing problem in sickness. Only the infinite intelligence within your subconscious knows the answer. When you come to that clear-cut conclusion in your conscious mind, your mind is then made up, and according to your belief is it done unto you.

• Easy does it

A house owner once remonstrated with a furnace repairman for charging two hundred dollars for fixing the boiler. The mechanic said, "I charged five cents for the missing bolt and one hundred ninety-nine dollars and ninety-five cents for knowing what was wrong."

Similarly, your subconscious mind is the master mechanic, the all-wise one, who knows ways and means of healing any organ of your body, as well as your affairs. Decree health, and your subconscious will establish it, but relaxation is the key. "Easy does it." Do not be concerned with details and means, but know the end result. Get the *feel* of the happy solution to your problem whether it is health, finances, or employment. Remember how you felt after you had recovered from a severe state of illness. Bear in mind that your feeling is the touchstone of all subconscious demonstration. Your new idea must be felt subjectively in a finished state, not the future, but as coming about now.

• Infer no opponent, use imagination and not will power

In using your subconscious mind you infer no opponent, you use no will power. You imagine the end and the freedom state. You will find your intellect trying to get in the way, but persist in maintaining a simple, childlike, miracle-making faith. Picture yourself without the ailment or problem. Imagine the emotional accompaniment of the freedom state you crave. Cut out all red tape from the process. The simple way is the best.

• How disciplined imagination works wonders

A wonderful way to get a response from your subconscious mind is through disciplined or scientific imagination. As previously pointed out, your subconscious mind is the builder of the body and controls all its vital functions.

The Bible says, *Whatsoever ye shall ask in prayer, believing, ye shall receive.* To believe is to accept something as true, or to live in the state of being it. As you sustain this mood, you shall experience the joy of the answered prayer!

• The three steps to success in prayer

The usual procedure is as follows:

1. Take a look at the problem.
2. Turn to the solution or way out known only to the subconscious mind.
3. Rest in a sense of deep conviction that it is done.

Do not weaken your prayer by saying, "I wish I might be healed." "I hope so." Your feeling about the work to be done is "the boss." Harmony is yours. Know that health is yours. Become intelligent by becoming a vehicle for the infinite healing power of the subconscious mind. Pass on the idea of health to your subconscious mind to the point of conviction; then relax. Get yourself off your hands. Say to the condition and circumstance, "This, too, shall pass." Through relaxation you impress your subconscious mind enabling the kinetic energy behind the idea to take over and bring it into concrete realization.

• The law of reversed effort and why you get the opposite of what you pray for

Coué, the famous psychologist from France who visited America about forty years ago, defined the law of reversed effort as follows: "When your desires and imagination are in conflict your imagination invariably gains the day."

If, for example, you were asked to walk a plank on the floor, you would do so without question. Now suppose the same plank were placed twenty feet up in the air between two walls, would you walk it? Your desire to walk it would be counteracted by your imagination or fear of falling. Your dominant idea which would be the picture of falling would conquer. Your desire, will, or effort to walk on the plank would be reversed, and the dominant idea of failure would be reinforced.

Mental effort is invariably self-defeated, eventuating always in the opposite of what is desired. The suggestions of powerlessness to overcome the condition dominate the mind; your subconscious is always controlled by the dominant idea. Your subconscious will accept the strongest of two contradictory propositions. The effortless way is the better.

If you say, "I want a healing, but I can't get it;" "I try so hard;" "I force myself to pray;" "I use all the will power I have," you must realize that your error lies in your effort. Never try to compel the subconscious mind to accept your idea by exercising will power. Such attempts are doomed to failure, and you get the opposite of what you prayed for.

The following is a rather common experience. Students, when taking examinations and reading through their papers, find that all their knowledge has suddenly deserted them. Their minds become appalling blanks, and they are unable to recall one revelant thought. The more they grit their teeth and summon the powers of the will, the further the answers seem to flee. But, when they have left the examination room and the mental pressure relaxes, the answers they were seeking flow tantalizingly back into their minds. Trying to force themselves to remember was the cause of their failure. This is an example of the law of reversed effort whereby you get the opposite of what you asked or prayed for.

• The conflict of desire and imagination must be reconciled

To use mental force is to presuppose that there is opposition. When your mind is concentrated on the means to overcome a problem, it is no longer concerned with the obstacle. MATT. 18:19 says, *If two of you shall agree on earth as touching anything that they shall ask, it shall be done for them of my Father which is in heaven.* Who are these two? It means the harmonious union or agreement between your conscious and subconscious on any idea, desire, or mental image. When there is no longer any quarrel in either part of your mind, your prayer will be answered. The two agreeing may also be represented as you and your desire, your thought and feeling, your idea and emotion, your desire and imagination.

You avoid all conflict between your desires and imagination by entering into a drowsy, sleepy state which brings all effort to a minimum. The conscious mind is submerged to a great extent when in a sleepy state. The best time to impregnate your subconscious is prior to sleep. The reason for this is that the highest degree of outcropping of the subconscious occurs prior to sleep and just after we awaken. In this state the negative thoughts and imagery which tend to neutralize your desire and so prevent acceptance by your subconscious mind no longer present themselves. When you imagine the reality of the fulfilled desire and feel the thrill of accomplishment, your subconscious brings about the realization of your desire.

A great many people solve all their dilemmas and problems by the play of their controlled, directed, and disciplined imagination, knowing that whatever they imagine and feel as true *will* and *must* come to pass.

The following will clearly illustrate how a young girl overcame the conflict between her desire and her imagination. She desired a harmonious solution to her legal problem, yet her mental imagery was constantly on failure, loss, bankruptcy, and poverty. It was a complicated lawsuit and there was one postponement after another with no solution in sight.

At my suggestion, she got into a sleepy, drowsy state each night prior to sleep, and she began to imagine the happy ending, feeling it to the best of her ability. She knew that the image in her mind had to agree with her heart's desire. Prior to sleep she began to dramatize as vividly as possible her lawyer having an animated discussion with her regarding the outcome. She would ask him questions, and he would answer her appropriately. He would say to her over and over again, "There has been a perfect, harmonious solution. The case has been settled out of court." During the day when fear thoughts came into her mind, she would run her mental movie with gestures, voice, and sound equipment. She could easily imagine the sound of his voice, smile, and mannerism. She ran this mental picture so often, it became a subjective pattern, a regular train track. At the end of a few weeks her attorney called her and confirmed objectively what she had been imagining and feeling as true subjectively.

This is really what the Psalmist meant when he wrote, *Let the words of my mouth* [your thoughts, mental images, good] *and the meditations of my heart* [your feeling, nature, emotion] *be acceptable in thy sight, O Lord* [the law of your subconscious mind], *my strength, and my redeemer* [the power and wisdom of your subconscious mind can redeem you from sickness, bondage, and misery]. PSALM 19:14.

• **Ideas worth recalling**

1. Mental coercion or too much effort shows anxiety and fear which block your answer. Easy does it.
2. When your mind is relaxed and you accept an idea, your subconscious goes to work to execute the idea.
3. Think and plan independently of traditional methods. Know that there is always an answer and a solution to every problem.
4. Do not be overly concerned with the beating of your heart, with the breathing of your lungs, or the functions of any part of your anatomy. Lean heavily upon your subconscious and proclaim frequently that Divine right action is taking place.
5. The feeling of health produces health, the feeling of wealth produces wealth. How do you feel?
6. Imagination is your most powerful faculty. Imagine what is

lovely and of good report. You are what you imagine yourself
to be.

7. You avoid conflict between your conscious and subconscious
in the sleepy state. Imagine the fulfillment of your desire over
and over again prior to sleep. Sleep in peace and wake in joy.

9

How to Use the Power
of Your Subconscious for Wealth

If you are having financial difficulties, if you are trying to make ends meet, it means you have not convinced your subconscious mind that you will always have plenty and some to spare. You know men and women who work a few hours a week and make fabulous sums of money. They do not strive or slave hard. Do not believe the story that the only way you can become wealthy is by the sweat of your brow and hard labor. It is not so; the effortless way of life is the best. Do the thing you love to do, and do it for the joy and thrill of it.

I know an executive in Los Angeles who receives a salary of $75,000 yearly. Last year he went on a nine-month cruise seeing the world and its beauty spots. He said to me that he had succeeded in convincing his subconscious mind that hc is worth that much money. He told me that many men in his organization getting about one hundred dollars a week knew more about thc business than he did, and could manage it better, but they had no ambition, no creative ideas, and were not interested in the wonders of their subconscious mind.

• **Wealth is of the mind**

Wealth is simply a subconscious conviction on the part of the individual. You will not become a millionaire by saying, "I am a millionaire, I am a millionaire." You will grow into a wealth consciousness by building into your mentality the idea of wealth and abundance.

• Your invisible means of support

The trouble with most people is that they have no invisible means of support. When business falls away, the stock market drops, or they lose their investments, they seem helpless. The reason for such insecurity is that they do not know how to tap the subconscious mind. They are unacquainted with the inexhaustible storehouse within.

A man with a poverty type mind finds himself in poverty-stricken conditions. Another man with a mind filled with ideas of wealth is surrounded with everything he needs. It was never intended that man should lead a life of indigence. You can have wealth, everything you need, and plenty to spare. Your words have power to cleanse your mind of wrong ideas and to instill right ideas in their place.

• The ideal method for building a wealth consciousness

Perhaps you are saying as you read this chapter, "I need wealth and success." This is what you do: Repeat for about five minutes to yourself three or four times a day, "Wealth—Success." These words have tremendous power. They represent the inner power of the subconscious mind. Anchor your mind on this substantial power within you; then conditions and circumstances corresponding to their nature and quality will be manifested in your life. You are not saying, "I am wealthy," you are dwelling on real powers within you. There is no conflict in the mind when you say, "Wealth." Furthermore, the feeling of wealth will well up within you as you dwell on the idea of wealth.

The feeling of wealth produces wealth; keep this in mind at all times. Your subconscious mind is like a bank, a sort of universal financial institution. It magnifies whatever you deposit or impress upon it whether it is the idea of wealth or of poverty. Choose wealth.

• Why your affirmations for wealth fail

I have talked to many people during the past thirty-five years whose usual complaint is, "I have said for weeks and months, 'I am wealthy, I am prosperous,' and nothing has happened." I discovered that when they said, "I am prosperous, I am wealthy," they felt within that they were lying to themselves.

One man told me, "I have affirmed that I am prosperous until I am tired. Things are now worse. I knew when I made the statement that it was obviously not true." His statements were rejected by the conscious mind, and the very opposite of what he outwardly affirmed and claimed was made manifest.

Your affirmation succeeds best when it is specific and when it does not produce a mental conflict or argument; hence the statements made by this man made matters worse because they suggested his lack. Your subconscious accepts what you really feel to be true, not just idle words or statements. The dominant idea or belief is always accepted by the subconscious mind.

• How to avoid mental conflict

The following is the ideal way to overcome this conflict for those who have this difficulty. Make this practical statement frequently, particularly prior to sleep: "By day and by night I am being prospered in all of my interests." This affirmation will not arouse any argument because it does not contradict your subconscious mind's impression of financial lack.

I suggested to one businessman whose sales and finances were very low and who was greatly worried, that he sit down in his office, become quiet, and repeat this statement over and over again: "My sales are improving every day." This statement engaged the co-operation of the conscious and subconscious mind; results followed.

• Don't sign blank checks

You sign blank checks when you make such statements as, "There is not enough to go around." "There is a shortage." "I will lose the house because of the mortgage," etc. If you are full of fear about the future, you are also writing a blank check and attracting negative conditions to you. Your subconscious mind takes your fear and negative statement as your request and proceeds in its own way to bring obstacles, delays, lack, and limitation into your life.

• Your subconscious gives you compound interest

To him that hath the feeling of wealth, more wealth shall be added; to him that hath the feeling of lack, more lack shall be added. Your subconscious multiplies and magnifies whatever you deposit in it. Every morning as you awaken deposit thoughts of prosperity, success, wealth, and peace. Dwell upon these concepts. Busy your mind with them as often as possible. These constructive thoughts will find their way as deposits in your subconscious mind, and bring forth abundance and prosperity.

• Why nothing happened

I can hear you saying, "Oh, I did that and nothing happened." You did not get results because you indulged in fear thoughts perhaps ten minutes later and neutralized the good you had affirmed. When you place a seed in the ground, you do not dig it up. You let it take root and grow.

Suppose, for example, you are going to say, "I shall not be able to make that payment." Before you get further than, "I shall—" stop the sentence and dwell on a constructive statement, such as, "By day and by night I am prospered in all my ways."

• True source of wealth

Your subconscious mind is never short of ideas. There are within it an infinite number of ideas ready to flow into your conscious mind and appear as cash in your pocketbook in countless ways. This process will continue to go on in your mind regardless of whether the stock market goes up or down, or whether the pound sterling or dollar drops in value. Your wealth is never truly dependent on bonds, stocks, or money in the bank; these are really only symbols necessary and useful, of course, but only symbols.

The point I wish to emphasize is that if you convince your

subconscious mind that wealth is yours, and that it is always circulating in your life, you will always and inevitably have it, regardless of the form it takes.

• Trying to make ends meet and the real cause

There are people who claim that they are always trying to make ends meet. They seem to have a great struggle to meet their obligations. Have you listened to their conversation? In many instances their conversation runs along this vein. They are constantly condemning those who have succeeded in life and who have raised their heads above the crowd. Perhaps they are saying, "Oh, that fellow has a racket; he is ruthless; he is a crook." This is why they lack; they are condemning the thing they desire and want. The reason they speak critically of their more prosperous associates is because they are envious and covetous of the others prosperity. The quickest way to cause wealth to take wings and fly away is to criticize and condemn others who have more wealth than you.

• A common stumbling block to wealth

There is one emotion which is the cause of the lack of wealth in the lives of many. Most people learn this the hard way. It is envy. For example, if you see a competitor depositing large sums of money in the bank, and you have only a meager amount to deposit, does it make you envious? The way to overcome this emotion is to say to yourself, "Isn't it wonderful! I rejoice in that man's prosperity. I wish for him greater and greater wealth."

To entertain envious thoughts is devastating because it places you in a very negative position; therefore, wealth flows *from* you instead of *to* you. If you are ever annoyed or irritated by the prosperity or great wealth of another, claim immediately that you truly wish for him greater wealth in every possible way. This will neutralize the negative thoughts in your mind and cause an ever greater measure of wealth to flow to you by the law of your own subconscious mind.

• Rubbing out a great mental block to wealth

If you are worried and critical about someone whom you claim is making money dishonestly, cease worrying about him. You know such a person is using the law of mind negatively; the law of mind takes care of him. Be careful not to criticize him for the reasons previously indicated. Remember: The block or obstacle to wealth is in your own mind. You can now destroy that mental block. This you may do by getting on mental good terms with everyone.

• Sleep and grow rich

As you go to sleep at night, practice the following technique. Repeat the word, "Wealth," quietly, easily, and feelingly. Do this over and over again, just like a lullaby. Lull yourself to sleep with the one word, "Wealth." You should be amazed at the result. Wealth should flow to you in avalanches of abundance. This is another example of the magic power of your subconscious mind.

• Serve yourself with the powers of your mind

1. Decide to be wealthy the easy way, with the infallible aid of your subconscious mind.
2. Trying to accumulate wealth by the sweat of your brow and hard labor is one way to become the richest man in the graveyard. You do not have to strive or slave hard.
3. Wealth is a subconscious conviction. Build into your mentality the idea of wealth.
4. The trouble with most people is that they have no invisible means of support.
5. Repeat the word, "Wealth," to yourself slowly and quietly for about five minutes prior to sleep and your subconsciou° will bring wealth to pass in your experience.
6. The feeling of wealth produces wealth. Keep this in mind at all times.
7. Your conscious and subconscious mind must agree. Your subconscious accepts what you really feel to be true. The

dominant idea is always accepted by your subconscious mind. The dominant idea should be *wealth,* not *poverty.*

8. You can overcome any mental conflict regarding wealth by affirming frequently, "By day and by night I am being prospered in all of my interests."

9. Increase your sales by repeating this statement over and over again, "My sales are improving every day; I am advancing, progressing, and getting wealthier every day."

10. Stop writing blank checks, such as, "There is not enough to go around," or "There is a shortage," etc. Such statements magnify and multiply your loss.

11. Deposit thoughts of prosperity, wealth, and success in your subconscious mind, and the latter will give you compound interest.

12. What you consciously affirm, you must not mentally deny a few moments later. This will neutralize the good you have affirmed.

13. Your true source of wealth consists of the ideas in your mind. You can have an idea worth millions of dollars. Your subconscious will give you the idea you seek.

14. Envy and jealousy are stumbling blocks to the flow of wealth. Rejoice in the prosperity of others.

15. The block to wealth is in your own mind. Destroy that block now by getting on good mental terms with everyone.

10

Your Right to Be Rich

It is your right to be rich. You are here to lead the abundant life and be happy, radiant, and free. You should, therefore, have all the money you need to lead a full, happy, and prosperous life.

You are here to grow, expand, and unfold spiritually, mentally, and materially. You have the inalienable right to fully develop and express yourself along all lines. You should surround yourself with beauty and luxury.

Why be satisfied with just enough to go around when you can enjoy the riches of your subconscious mind? In this chapter you can learn to make friends with money, and you should always have a surplus. Your desire to be rich is a desire for a fuller, happier, more wonderful life. It is a cosmic urge. It is not only good, but very good.

• Money is a symbol

Money is a symbol of exchange. It means to you not only freedom from want, but beauty, luxury, abundance, and refinement. It is merely a symbol of the economic health of the nation. When your blood is circulating freely in your body, you are healthy. When money is circulating freely in your life, you are economically healthy. When people begin to hoard money, to put it away in tin boxes, and become charged with fear, there is economic illness. Money has taken many forms as a medium of exchange down through the centuries, such as, salt, beads, and trinkets of various kinds. In early times a man's wealth was determined by the number of sheep and oxen he had. Now we use currency, and other negotiable instruments, as it is much more convenient to write a check than carry some sheep around with you to pay bills.

• How to walk the royal road to riches

Knowledge of the powers of your subconscious mind is the means to the royal road to riches of all kinds—spiritual, mental, or financial. The student of the laws of mind believes and knows definitely that regardless of economic situations, stock market fluctuation, depression, strikes, war, other conditions or circumstances, he will always be amply supplied, regardless of what form money takes. The reason for this is that he has conveyed the idea of wealth to his subconscious mind, and it keeps him supplied wherever he may be. He has convinced himself in his mind that money is forever flowing freely in his life and that there is always a wonderful surplus. Should there be a financial collapse of government tomorrow and all the man's present holdings become valueless, as the German marks did after the first World War, he would still attract wealth and be cared for, regardless of the form the new currency took.

• Why you do not have more money

As you read this chapter, you are probably saying, "I am worthy of a higher salary than I am receiving." I believe most people are inadequately compensated. One of the causes many people do not have more money is that they are silently or openly condemning it. They refer to money as "filthy lucre" or "the love of money is the root of all evil." Another reason they do not prosper is that they have a sneaky subconscious feeling there is some virtue in poverty. This subconscious pattern may be due to early childhood training, superstition, or it could be based on a false interpretation of scriptures.

• Money and a balanced life

One time a man said to me, "I am broke. I do not like money. It is the root of all evil." These statements represent a confused neurotic mind. Love of money to the exclusion of everything else will cause you to become lopsided and unbalanced. You are here to use your power or authority wisely. Some men crave power, others crave money. If you set your heart on money exclusively and say, "Money is all I want; I am going to give all my attention to amassing money; nothing else matters," you can get money and attain a fortune, but you have forgotten that you are here to lead a balanced life. You must also satisfy the hunger for peace of mind, harmony, love, joy, and perfect health.

By making money your sole aim, you simply made a wrong choice. You thought that was all you wanted, but you found after all your efforts that it was not only the money you needed. You also desired true expression of your hidden talents, true place in life, beauty, and the joy of contributing to the welfare and success of others. By learning the laws of your subconscious mind, you could have a million dollars or many millions, if you wanted them, and still have peace of mind, harmony, perfect health, and perfect expression.

• Poverty is a mental disease

There is no virtue in poverty; it is a disease like any other mental disease. If you were physically ill, you would think there was something wrong with you. You would seek help and do something about the condition at once. Likewise, if you do not have money constantly circulating in your life, there is something radically wrong with you.

The urge of the life principle in you is toward growth, expansion, and the life more abundant. You are not here to live in a hovel, dress in rags, and go hungry. You should be happy, prosperous, and successful.

• Why you must never criticize money

Cleanse your mind of all weird and superstitious beliefs about money. Do not ever regard money as evil or filthy. If you do, you cause it to take wings and fly away from you. Remember that you lose what you condemn. You cannot attract what you criticize.

• Getting the right attitude toward money

Here is a simple technique you may use to multiply money in your experience. Use the following statements several times a day, "I like money, I love it, I use it wisely, constructively, and judiciously. Money is constantly circulating in my life. I release it with joy, and it returns to me multiplied in a wonderful way. It is good and very good. Money flows to me in avalanches of abundance. I use it for good only, and I am grateful for my good and for the riches of my mind."

• How the scientific thinker looks at money

Suppose, for example, you found gold, silver, lead, copper, or iron in the ground. Would you pronounce these things evil? All evil comes from man's darkened understanding, from his ignorance, from his false interpretation of life, and from his misuse of his subconscious mind. Uranium, lead, or some other metal could have been used as a medium of exchange. We use paper bills, checks, nickel, and silver, surely, these are not evil. Physicists and chemists know today that the only difference between one metal and another is the number and rate of motion of electrons revolving around a central nucleus. They can now change one metal into another through a bombardment of the atoms in the powerful cyclotron. Gold under certain conditions becomes mercury. I believe that our modern scientists in the near future will be able to make gold, silver, and other metals synthetically in the chemical laboratory. The cost may be prohibitive now, but it can be done. I cannot imagine any intelligent person seeing anything evil in electrons, neutrons, protons, and isotopes.

The piece of paper in your pocket is composed of atoms and molecules with their electrons and protons arranged differently. Their number and rate of motion are different. That is the only way the paper differs from the silver in your pocket.

• How to attract the money you need

Many years ago I met a young boy in Australia who wanted to become a physician and surgeon, but he had no money. I explained to him how a seed deposited in the soil attracts to itself everything necessary for its unfolding, and that all he had to do was to take a lesson from the seed and deposit the required idea in his subconscious mind. For expenses this young, brilliant bc. used to clean out doctors' offices, wash windows, and do odd repair jobs. He told me that every night, as he went to sleep, he used to picture in his mind's eye a medical diploma on a wall with his name on it in big, bold letters. He used to clean and shine the framed diplomas in the medical building where he worked. It was not hard for him to engrave the image of a diploma in his mind and develop it there. Definite results followed as he persisted with his mental picture every night for about four months.

The sequel of this story was very interesting. One of the doctors took a great liking to this young boy and after training him in the art of sterilizing instruments, giving hypodermic injections, and other miscellaneous first-aid work, he employed him as a technical assistant in his office. The doctor later sent him to medical school at his own expense. Today, this young man is a prominent medical doctor in Montreal, Canada. He discovered the law of attraction by using his subconscious mind the right way. He operated an age-old law which says, "Having seen the end, you have willed the means to the realization of the end." The *end* in this case was to become a medical doctor.

This young man was able to imagine, see, and feel the reality of being a doctor. He lived with that idea, sustained it, nourished it, and loved it until through his imagination it penetrated the layers of his subconscious mind and became a conviction, thereby attracting to him everything necessary for the fulfillment of his dream.

• Why some men do not get a raise in pay

If you are working in a large organization and you are silently thinking of and resenting the fact you are underpaid, that you are not appreciated, and that you deserve more money and greater recognition, you are subconsciously severing your ties with that organization. You are setting a law in motion, and the superintendent or manager will say to you, "We have to let you go." Actually, you dismissed yourself. The manager was simply the instrument through which your own negative mental state was confirmed. It was an example of the law of action and reaction. The action was your thought, and the reaction was the response of your subconscious mind.

• Obstacles and impediments on the pathway to riches

I am sure you have heard men say, "That fellow has a racket." "He is a racketeer." "He is getting money dishonestly." "He is a faker." "I knew him when he had nothing." "He is a crook, a thief, and a swindler."

If you analyze the man who talks like that, you discover he is usually in want or suffering from some financial or physical illness. Perhaps his former college friends went up the ladder of success and excelled him. Now he is bitter and envious of their progress. In many instances this is the cause of his downfall. Thinking negatively of these classmates and condemning their wealth causes the wealth and prosperity he is praying for to vanish and flee away. He is condemning the thing he is praying for.

He is praying two ways. On the one hand he is saying, "Wealth is flowing to me now," and in the next breath, silently or audibly, he is saying, "I resent that fellow's wealth." Always make it a special point to rejoice in the wealth of the other person.

• Protect your investments

If you are seeking wisdom regarding investments, or if you are worried about your stocks or bonds, quietly claim, "Infinite intelligence governs and watches over all my financial transactions, and whatsoever I do shall prosper." Do this frequently and you will find that your investments will be wise; moreover, you will be protected from loss, as you will be prompted to sell your securities or holdings before any loss accrues to you.

• You cannot get something for nothing

In large stores the management employs store detectives to prevent people from stealing. They catch a number of people every day trying to get something for nothing. All such people are living in the mental atmosphere of lack and limitation and are stealing from themselves peace, harmony, faith, honesty, integrity, good will, and confidence. Furthermore, they are attracting to themselves all manner of loss, such as, loss of character, prestige, social status, and peace of mind. These people lack faith in the source of supply and the understanding of how their minds work. If they would mentally call on the powers of their subconscious mind and claim that they are guided to their true expression, they would find work and constant supply. Then by honesty, integrity, and perseverance, they would become a credit to themselves and to society at large.

• Your constant supply of money

Recognizing the powers of your subconscious mind and the creative power of your thought or mental image is the way to opulence, freedom, and constant supply. Accept the abundant life in your own mind. Your mental acceptance and expectancy of wealth has its own mathematics and mechanics of expression. As you enter into the mood of opulence, all things necessary for the abundant life will come to pass.

Let this be your daily affirmation; write it in your heart, "I am one with the infinite riches of my subconscious mind. It is my right to be rich, happy, and successful. Money flows to me freely, copiously, and endlessly. I am forever conscious of my true worth. I give of my talents freely, and I am wonderfully blessed financially. It is wonderful!"

• Step up this way to riches

1. Be bold enough to claim that it is your right to be rich and your deeper mind will honor your claim.

2. You don't want just enough to go around. You want all the money you need to do all the things you want to do and when you want to do them. Get acquainted with the riches of your subconscious mind.

3. When money is circulating freely in your life, you are economically healthy. Look at money like the tide and you will always have plenty of it. The ebb and flow of the tide is constant. When the tide is out, you are absolutely sure that it will return.

4. Knowing the laws of your subconscious mind, you will always be supplied regardless of what form money takes.

5. One reason many people simply make ends meet and never have enough money is that they condemn money. What you condemn takes wings and flies away.

6. Do not make a god of money. It is only a symbol. Remember that the real riches are in your mind. You are here to lead a balanced life—this includes acquiring all the money you need.

7. Don't make money your sole aim. Claim wealth, happiness, peace, true expression, and love, and personally radiate love and good will to all. Then your subconscious mind will give you compound interest in all these fields of expression.

8. There is no virtue in poverty. It is a disease of the mind, and you should heal yourself of this mental conflict or malady at once.

9. You are not here to live in a hovel, to dress in rags, or to go hungry. You are here to lead the life more abundant.

10. Never use the terms "filthy lucre" or "I despise money." You lose what you criticize. There is nothing good or bad, but thinking of it in either light makes it so.

11. Repeat frequently, "I like money. I use it wisely, constructively, and judiciously. I release it with joy, and it returns a thousandfold."

12. Money is not evil any more so than copper, lead, tin, or iron which you may find in the ground. All evil is due to ignorance and misuse of the mind's powers.

13. To picture the end result in your mind causes your subconscious to respond and fulfill your mental picture.

14. Stop trying to get something for nothing. There is no such thing as a free lunch. You must give to receive. You must give mental attention to your goals, ideals, and enterprises, and your deeper mind will back you up. The key to wealth is application of the laws of the subconscious mind by impregnating it with the idea of wealth.

11

Your Subconscious Mind as a Partner in Success

Success means successful living. A long period of peace, joy, and happiness on this plane may be termed success. The eternal experience of these qualities is the everlasting life spoken of by Jesus. The real things of life, such as peace, harmony, integrity, security, and happiness are intangible. They come from the Deep Self of man. Meditating on these qualities builds these treasures of heaven in our subconscious. It is where *moth and rust do not consume, and where thieves do not break through and steal.* MATT. 6:20.

• **The three steps to success**

Let us discuss three steps to success: The first step to success is to find out the thing you love to do, then do it. Success is in loving your work. Although, if a man is a psychiatrist, it is not adequate for him to get a diploma and place it on the wall; he must keep up with the times, attend conventions, and continue studying the mind and its workings. The successful psychiatrist visits clinics and reads the latest scientific articles. In other words, he is informed in the most advanced methods of alleviating human suffering. The successful psychiatrist or doctor must have the interest of his patients at heart.

Someone may say, "How can I put the first step into operation? I do not know what I should do." In such a case, pray for guidance as follows: "The infinite intelligence of my subconscious mind reveals to me my true place in life." Repeat this prayer quietly, positively, and lovingly to your deeper mind. As you persist with faith and confidence, the answer will come to you as a feeling, a hunch, or a tendency in a certain direction. It will come to you clearly and in peace, and as an inner silent awareness.

The second step to success is to specialize in some particular branch of work and know more about it than anyone else. For example, if a young man chooses chemistry as his profession, he should concentrate on one of the many branches in this field. He should give all of his time and attention to his chosen specialty. He should become sufficiently enthusiastic to try to know all there is available about his field; if possible, he should know more than anyone else. The young man should become ardently interested in his work and should desire to serve the world.

He that is greatest among you, let him become your servant. There is a great contrast in this attitude of mind in comparison to that of the man who only wants to make a living or just "get by." "Getting by" is not true success. Man's motive must be greater, nobler, and more altruistic. He must serve others, thereby casting his bread upon the waters.

The third step is the most important one. You must be sure that the thing you want to do does not redound to your success only. Your desire must not be selfish; it must benefit humanity. The path of a complete circuit must be formed. In other words, your idea must go forth with the purpose of blessing or serving the world. It will then come back to you pressed down, shaken together, and running over. If it is to benefit yourself exclusively, the circle or complete circuit is not formed, and you may experience a short circuit in your life which may consist of limitation or sickness.

• The measure of true success

Some people may say, "But, Mr. James made a fortune in selling fraudulent oil stock." A man may seem to succeed for a while, but the money he obtained by fraud usually takes wings and flies away. When we rob from another, we rob from ourselves, because we are in a mood of lack and limitation which may manifest itself in our body, home life, and affairs. What we think and feel, we create. We create what we believe. Even though a man may have accumulated a fortune fraudulently, he is not successful. There is no success without peace of mind. What good is man's accumulated wealth if he cannot sleep nights, is sick, or has a guilt complex?

I knew a man in London who told me of his exploits. He had been a professional pickpocket and had amassed a large amount of money. He had a summer home in France and lived in a royal fashion in England. His story was that he was in constant dread of being arrested by Scotland Yard. He had many inner disorders which were undoubtedly caused by his constant fear and deep-seated guilt complex. He knew he had done wrong. This deep sense of guilt attracted all kinds of trouble to him. Subsequently, he voluntarily surrendered to the police and served a prison sentence. After his release from prison, he sought psychological and spiritual counsel and became transformed. He went to work and became an honest, law-abiding citizen. He found what he loved to do and was happy.

A successful person loves his work and expresses himself fully. Success is contingent upon a higher ideal than the mere accumulation of riches. The man of success is the man who possesses great psychological and spiritual understanding. Many of the great industrialists today depend upon the correct use of their subconscious minds for their success.

There was an article published some years ago about Flagler, an oil magnate. He admitted that the secret of his success was his ability to see a project in its completion. For instance, in his case, he closed his eyes, imagined a big oil industry, saw trains running on tracks, heard whistles blowing, and saw smoke. Having seen and felt the fulfillment of his prayer, his subconscious mind brought about its realization. If you imagine an objective clearly, you will be provided with the necessities, in ways you know not of, through the wonder-working power of your subconscious mind.

In considering the three steps to success you must never forget the underlying power of the creative forces of your subconscious mind. This is the energy in back of all steps in any plan of success. Your thought is creative. Thought fused with feeling becomes a subjective faith or belief, *and according to your belief is it done unto you.* MATT. 9:29.

A knowledge of a mighty force in you which is capable of bringing to pass all your desires gives you confidence and a sense of peace. Whatever your field of action may be, you should learn the laws of your subconscious mind. When you know how to apply the powers of your mind, and when you are expressing yourself fully and giving of your talents to others, you are on the sure path to true success. If you are about God's business, or any part of it, God, by His very nature, is for you, so who can be against you? With this understanding there is no power in heaven or on earth to withhold success from you.

• How he made his dream come true

A movie actor told me that he had very little education, but he had a dream as a boy of becoming a successful movie actor. Out in the field mowing hay, driving the cows home, or even when milking them he said, "I would constantly imagine I saw my name in big lights at a large theatre. I kept this up for years until finally I ran away from home. I got extra jobs in the motion-picture field, and the day finally came when I saw my name in great, big lights as I did when I was a boy!" Then he added, "I know the power of sustained imagination to bring success."

• His dream pharmacy became a reality

Thirty years ago I knew a young pharmacist who was receiving forty dollars a week plus commission on sales. "After twenty-five years," he said to me, "I will get a pension and retire."

I said to this young man, "Why don't you own your own store? Get out of this place. Raise your sights! Have a dream for your children. Maybe your son wants to be a doctor; perhaps your daughter desires to be a great musician."

His answer was that he had no money! He began to awaken

to the fact that whatever he could conceive as true, he could give conception.

The first step toward his goal was his awakening to the powers of his subconscious mind, which I briefly elaborated on for his benefit. His second step was his realization that if he could succeed in conveying an idea to his subconscious mind, the latter would somehow bring it to pass.

He began to imagine that he was in his own store. He mentally arranged the bottles, dispensed prescriptions, and imagined several clerks in the store waiting on customers. He also visualized a big bank balance. Mentally he worked in that imaginary store. Like a good actor he lived the role. *Act as though I am, and I will be.* This pharmacist put himself wholeheartedly into the act, living, moving, and acting on the assumption that he owned the store.

The sequel was interesting. He was discharged from his position. He found new employment with a large chain store, became manager, and later on, district manager. He saved enough money in four years to provide a down payment on a drugstore of his own. He called it his "Dream Pharmacy."

"It was," he said, "exactly the store I saw in my imagination." He became a recognized success in his chosen field, and was happy doing what he loved to do.

• Using the subconscious mind in business

Some years ago I gave a lecture to a group of businessmen on the powers of imagination and the subconscious mind. In this lecture I pointed out how Goethe used his imagination wisely when confronted with difficulties and predicaments.

His biographers point out that he was accustomed to fill many hours quietly holding imaginary conversations. It is well known that his custom was to imagine one of his friends before him in a chair answering him in the right way. In other words, if he were concerned over any problems, he imagined his friend giving him the right or appropriate answer, accompanied with the usual gestures and tonal qualities of the voice, and he made the entire imaginary scene as real and as vivid as possible.

One of the men present at this lecture was a young stock-broker. He proceeded to adopt the technique of Goethe. He began to have mental, imaginary conversations with a multi-millionaire banker friend of his who used to congratulate him on his wise and sound judgment, and compliment him on his purchase of the right stocks. He used to dramatize this imaginary conversation until he had psychologically fixed it as a form of belief in his mind.

This broker's inner talking and controlled imagination certainly agreed with his aim which was to make sound investments for his clients. His main purpose in life was to make money for his clients and to see them prosper financially by his wise counsel. He is still using his subconscious mind in his business, and he is a brilliant success in his field of endeavor.

• Boy of sixteen years turns failure into success

A young boy who was attending high school said to me, "I am getting very poor grades. My memory is failing. I do not know what is the matter." I discovered that the only thing wrong with this boy was his attitude which was one of indifference and resentment toward some of his teachers and fellow students. I taught him how to use his subconscious mind, and how to succeed in his studies.

He began to affirm certain truths several times a day particularly at night prior to sleep, and also in the morning after awakening. These are the best times to impregnate the subconscious mind.

He affirmed as follows: "I realize that my subconscious mind is a storehouse of memory. It retains everything I read and hear from my teachers. I have a perfect memory, and the infinite intelligence in my subconscious mind constantly reveals to me everything I need to know at all my examinations, whether written or oral. I radiate love and good will to all my teachers and fellow students. I sincerely wish for them success and all good things."

This young man is now enjoying a greater freedom than he has ever known. He is now receiving all "A's." He   constantly imagines the teachers and his mother congratulating him on his success in his studies.

• How to become successful in buying and selling

In buying and selling, remember that your conscious mind is the starter and your subconscious mind is the motor. You must start the motor to enable it to perform its work. Your conscious mind is the dynamo that awakens the power of your subconscious mind.

The first step in conveying your clarified desire, idea, or image to the deeper mind is to relax, immobilize the attention, get still, and be quiet. This quiet, relaxed, and peaceful attitude of mind prevents extraneous matter and false ideas from interfering with your mental absorption of your ideal. Furthermore, in the quiet, passive, and receptive attitude of mind, effort is reduced to a minimum.

The second step is to begin to imagine the reality of that which you desire. For example, you may wish to buy a home, and in your relaxed state of mind affirm as follows: "The infinite intelligence of my subconscious mind is all-wise. It reveals to me now the ideal home which is central, ideal, is in a lovely environment, meets with all my requirements, and is commensurate with my income. I am now turning this request over to my subconscious mind, and I know it responds according to the nature of my request. I release this request with absolute faith and confidence in the same way that a farmer deposits a seed in the ground, trusting implicitly in the laws of growth."

The answer to your prayer may come through an advertisement in the paper, through a friend, or you may be guided directly to a particular home which is exactly what you are seeking. There are many ways by which your prayer may be answered. The principal knowledge, in which you may place your confidence, is that the answer always comes, provided you trust the working of your deeper mind.

You may wish to sell a home, land, or any kind of property. In private consultation with real estate brokers I have told them of the way I sold my own home on Orlando Avenue in Los

Angeles. Many of them have applied the technique I used with remarkable and speedy results. I placed a sign which read, "For sale by owner" in the garden in front of my home. The day after I said to myself as I was going to sleep, "Supposing you sold your house, what would you do?"

I answered my own question and I said, "I would take that sign down and throw it into the garage." In my imagination I took hold of the sign, pulled it up from the ground, placed it on my shoulder, went to the garage, threw it on the floor, and said jokingly to the sign, "I don't need you any more!" I felt the inner satisfaction of it all, realizing it was finished.

The next day a man gave me a deposit of $1,000 and said to me, "Take your sign down. We will go into escrow now."

Immediately I pulled the sign up and took it to the garage. The outer action conformed to the inner. There is nothing new about this. *As within, so without*, meaning according to the image impressed on your subconscious mind, so it is on the objective screen of your life. The outside mirrors the inside. External action follows internal action.

Here is another very popular method used in selling homes, land, or any kind of property. Affirm slowly, quietly, and feelingly as follows: "Infinite intelligence attracts to me the buyer for this home who wants it and who prospers in it. This buyer is being sent to me by the creative intelligence of my subconscious mind which makes no mistakes. This buyer may look at many other homes, but mine is the only one he wants and will buy, because he is guided by the infinite intelligence within him. I know the buyer is right, the time is right, and the price is right. Everything about it is right. The deeper currents of my subconscious mind are now in operation bringing both of us together in divine order. I know that it is so."

Remember always, that what you are seeking is also seeking you, and whenever you want to sell a home or property of any kind, there is always someone who wants what you have to offer. By using the powers of your subconscious mind correctly, you free your mind of all sense of competition and anxiety in buying and selling.

• How she succeeded in getting what she wanted

There is a young lady who regularly comes to my lectures and classes. She had to change buses three times; it took her one and a half hours each time to come to the lectures. In one lecture I explained how a young man who needed a car in his work received one.

She went home and experimented as outlined in my lecture. Here is her letter in part, narrating her application of my method, and published by her permission:

Dear Dr. Murphy:
This is how I received a Cadillac car—I wanted one to come to the lectures regularly. In my imagination I went through the identical process I would go through if I were actually driving a car. I went to the showroom, and the salesman took me for a ride in one. I also drove it several blocks. I claimed the Cadillac car as my own over and over again.
I kept the mental picture of getting into the car, driving it, feeling the upholstery, etc., consistently for over two weeks. Last week I drove to your lectures in a Cadillac. My uncle in Inglewood passed away, and left me his Cadillac and his entire estate.

• A success technique employed by many outstanding executives and businessmen

There are many prominent businessmen who quietly use the abstract term, "success," over and over many times a day until they reach a conviction that *success* is theirs. They know that the *idea of success* contains all the essential elements of success. Likewise, you can begin now to repeat the word, "success," to yourself with faith and conviction. Your subconscious mind will accept it as true of you, and you will be under a subconscious compulsion to succeed.

You are compelled to express your subjective beliefs, impressions, and convictions. What does success imply to you? You want, undoubtedly, to be successful in your home life and in your relationship with others. You wish to be outstanding in your chosen work or profession. You wish to possess a beautiful home, and all the money you need to live comfortably and happily. You want to be successful in your prayer life and in your contact with the powers of your subconscious mind.

You are a businessman also because you are in the business of living. Become a successful businessman by imagining yourself doing what you long to do, and possessing the things you long to possess. Become imaginative; mentally participate in the reality of the successful state. Make a habit of it. Go to sleep feeling successful every night, and perfectly satisfied, and you will eventually succeed in implanting the idea of success in your subconscious mind. Believe you were born to succeed, and wonders will happen as you pray!

• Profitable pointers

1. Success means successful living. When you are peaceful, happy, joyous, and doing what you love to do, you are successful.

2. Find out what you love to do, then do it. If you don't know your true expression, ask for guidance, and the *lead* will come.

3. Specialize in your particular field and try to know more about it than anyone else.

4. A successful man is not selfish. His main desire in life is to serve humanity.

5. There is no true success without peace of mind.

6. A successful man possesses great psychological and spiritual understanding.

7. If you imagine an objective clearly, you will be provided with the necessities through the wonder-working power of your subconscious mind.

8. Your thought fused with feeling becomes a subjective belief, and *according to your belief is it done unto you.*

9. The power of sustained imagination draws forth the miracle-working powers of your subconscious mind.

10. If you are seeking promotion in your work, imagine your employer, supervisor, or loved one congratulating you on your promotion. Make the picture vivid and real. Hear the voice, see the gestures, and feel the reality of it all. Continue

to do this frequently, and through frequent occupancy of your mind, you will experience the joy of the answered prayer.

11. Your subconscious mind is a storehouse of memory. For a perfect memory, affirm frequently: "The infinite intelligence of my subconscious mind reveals to me everything I need to know at all times, everywhere."

12. If you wish to sell a home or property of any kind, affirm slowly, quietly, and feelingly as follows: "Infinite intelligence attracts to me the buyer for this house or property, who wants it, and who prospers in it." Sustain this awareness, and the deeper currents of your subconscious mind will bring it to pass.

13. The idea of success contains all the elements of success. Repeat the word, "success," to yourself frequently with faith and conviction, and you will be under a subconscious compulsion to succeed.

12

Scientists Use the Subconscious Mind

Many scientists realize the true importance of the subconscious mind. Edison, Marconi, Kettering, Poincaré, Einstein, and many others have used the subconscious mind. It has given them the insight and the "know-how" for all their great achievements in modern science and industry. Research has shown that the ability to bring into action the subconscious power has determined the success of all the great scientific and research workers.

An instance of how a famous chemist, Friedrich von Stradonitz, used his subconscious mind to solve his problem is as follows: He had been working laboriously for a long time trying to rearrange the six carbon and the six hydrogen atoms of the benzine formula, and he was constantly perplexed and unable to solve the matter. Tired and exhausted, he turned the request over completely to his subconscious mind. Shortly afterward, as he was about to board a London bus, his subconscious presented his conscious mind with a sudden flash of a snake biting its own tail and turning around like a pin wheel. This answer, from his subconscious mind, gave him the long-sought answer of the circular rearrangement of the atoms that is known as the benzine ring.

• **How a distinguished scientist brought forth his inventions**

Nikola Tesla was a brilliant electrical scientist who brought forth the most amazing innovations. When an idea for a new invention came into his mind, he would build it up in his imagination, knowing that his subconscious mind would reconstruct and reveal to his conscious mind all the parts needed for its manufacture in concrete form. Through quietly contemplating every possible improvement, he spent no time in correcting defects, and was able to give the technicians the perfect product of his mind.

He said, "Invariably, my device works as I imagined it should. In twenty years there has not been a single exception."

• **How a famous naturalist solved his problem**

Professor Agassiz, a distinguished American naturalist, discovered the indefatigable activities of his subconscious mind while he slept. The following has been reported by his widow in her biography of her famous husband.

"He had been for two weeks striving to decipher the somewhat obscure impression of a fossil fish on the stone slab in which it was preserved. Weary and perplexed, he put his work aside at last, and tried to dismiss it from his mind. Shortly after, he waked one night persuaded that while asleep he had seen his fish with all the missing features perfectly restored. But when he tried to hold and make fast the image it escaped him. Nevertheless, he went early to the Jardin des Plantes, thinking that on looking anew at the impression he should see something which would put him on the track of his vision. In vain—the blurred record was as black as ever. The next night he saw the fish again, but with no more satisfactory result. When he awoke it disappeared from his memory as before. Hoping that the same experience might be repeated, on the third night he placed a pencil and paper beside his bed before going to sleep.

"Accordingly, toward morning the fish reappeared in his dream, confusedly at first, but at last with such distinctness that he had no longer any doubt as to its zoological characters. Still half dreaming, in perfect darkness, he traced these characters on the sheet of paper at the bedside. In the morning he was surprised to see in his nocturnal sketch features which he thought it impossible the fossil itself should reveal. He hastened to the Jardin des Plantes, and, with his drawing as a guide, succeeded in chiselling away the surface of the stone under which portions of the fish proved to be hidden. When wholly exposed it corresponded with his dream and his drawing, and he succeeded in classifying it with ease."

• An outstanding physician solved the problem of diabetes

Some years ago I received a clipping from a magazine describing the origin of the discovery of insulin. This is the essence of the article as I recall it.

About forty years ago or more, Dr. Frederick Banting, a brilliant Canadian physician and surgeon, was concentrating his attention on the ravages of diabetes. At that time medical science offered no effective method of arresting the disease. Dr. Banting spent considerable time experimenting and studying the international literature on the subject. One night he was exhausted and fell asleep. While asleep, his subconscious mind instructed him to extract the residue from the degenerated pancreatic duct of dogs. This was the origin of insulin which has helped millions of people.

You will note that Dr. Banting had been consciously dwelling on the problem for some time seeking a solution, a way out, and his subconscious responded accordingly.

It does not follow that you will always get an answer overnight. The answer may not come for some time. Do not be discouraged. Keep on turning the problem over every night to the subconscious mind prior to sleep, as if you had never done it before.

One of the reasons for the delay may be that you look upon it as a major problem. You may believe it will take a long time to solve it.

Your subconscious mind is timeless and spaceless. Go to sleep believing you have the answer now. Do not postulate the answer in the future. Have an abiding faith in the outcome. Become convinced now as you read this book that there is an answer and a perfect solution for you.

• How a famous scientist and physicist escaped from a Russian concentration camp

Dr. Lothar von Blenk-Schmidt, a member of the Rocket Society and an outstanding research electronic engineer, gives the following condensed summary of how he used his subconscious mind to free himself from certain death at the hands of brutal guards in a Russian prison camp coal mine. He states as follows:

"I was a prisoner of war in a coal mine in Russia, and I saw men dying all around me in that prison compound. We were watched over by brutal guards, arrogant officers, and sharp, fast-thinking commissars. After a short medical checkup, a quota of coal was assigned to each person. My quota was three hundred pounds per day. In case any man did not fill his quota, his small food ration was cut down, and in a short time he was resting in the cemetery.

"I started concentrating on my escape. I knew that my subconscious mind would somehow find a way. My home in Germany was destroyed, my family wiped out; all my friends and former associates were either killed in the war or were in concentration camps.

"I said to my subconscious mind, 'I want to go to Los Angeles, and you will find the way.' I had seen pictures of Los Angeles and I remembered some of the boulevards very well as well as some of the buildings.

"Every day and night I would imagine I was walking down Wilshire Boulevard with an American girl whom I met in Berlin prior to the war (she is now my wife). In my imagination we would visit the stores, ride buses, and eat in the restaurants. Every night I made it a special point to drive my imaginary American automobile up and down the boulevards of Los Angeles. I made all this vivid and real. These pictures in my mind were as real and as natural to me as one of the trees outside the prison camp.

"Every morning the chief guard would count the prisoners as they were lined up. He would call out 'one, two, three,' etc., and when seventeen was called out, which was my number in sequence, I stepped aside. In the meantime, the guard was called away for a minute or so, and on his return he started by mistake on the next man as number seventeen. When the crew returned in the evening, the number of men was the same, and I was not missed, and the discovery would take a long time.

"I walked out of the camp undetected and kept walking for twenty-four hours, resting in a deserted town the next day. I was able to live by fishing and killing some wild life. I found coal trains going to Poland and traveled on them by night, until finally I reached Poland. With the help of friends, I made my way to Lucerne, Switzerland.

"One evening at the Palace Hotel, Lucerne, I had a talk with a man and his wife from the United States of America. This man asked me if I would care to be a guest at his home in Santa Monica, California. I accepted, and when I arrived in Los Angeles, I found that their chauffeur drove me along Wilshire Boulevard and many other boulevards which I had imagined so vividly in the long months in the Russian coal mines. I recognized the buildings which I had seen in my mind so often. It actually seemed as if I had been in Los Angeles before. I had reached my goal.

"I will never cease to marvel at the wonders of the subconscious mind. Truly, it has ways we know not of."

• **How archaeologists and paleontologists reconstruct ancient scenes**

These scientists know that their subconscious mind has a memory of everything that has ever transpired. As they study the ancient ruins and fossils, through their imaginative perception, their subconscious mind aids them in reconstructing the ancient scenes. The dead past becomes alive and audible once more. Looking at these ancient temples and studying the pottery, statuary, tools, and household utensils of these ancient times, the scientist tells us of an age when there was no language. Communication was done by grunts, groans, and signs.

The keen concentration and disciplined imagination of the scientist awakens the latent powers of his subconscious mind enabling him to clothe the ancient temples with roofs, and surround them with gardens, pools, and fountains. The fossil remains are clothed with eyes, sinews, and muscles, and they again walk and talk. The past becomes the living present, and we find that in mind there is no time or space. Through disciplined, controlled, and directed imagination, you can be a companion of the most scientific and inspired thinkers of all time.

• How to receive guidance from your subconscious

When you have what you term "a difficult decision" to make, or when you fail to see the solution to your problem, begin at once to think constructively about it. If you are fearful and worried, you are not really thinking. True thinking is free from fear.

Here is a simple technique you can use to receive guidance on any subject: Quiet the mind and still the body. Tell the body to relax; it has to obey you. It has no volition, initiative, or self-conscious intelligence. Your body is an emotional disk which records your beliefs and impressions. Mobilize your attention; focus your thought on the solution to your problem. Try to solve it with your conscious mind. Think how happy you would be about the perfect solution. Sense the feeling you would have if the perfect answer were yours now. Let your mind play with this mood in a relaxed way; then drop off to sleep. When you awaken, and you do not have the answer, get busy about something else. Probably, when you are preoccupied with something else, the answer will come into your mind like toast pops out of a toaster.

In receiving guidance from the subconscious mind, the simple way is the best. This is an illustration: I once lost a valuable ring which was an heirloom. I looked everywhere for it and could not locate it. At night I talked to the subconscious in the same manner that I would talk to anyone. I said to it prior to dropping off to sleep, "You know all things; you know where that ring is, and you now reveal to me where it is."

In the morning I awoke suddenly with the words ringing in my ear, "Ask Robert!"

I thought it very strange that I should ask Robert, a young boy about nine years of age; however, I followed the inner voice of intuition.

Robert said, "Oh, yes, I picked it up in the yard while I was playing with the boys. I placed it on the desk in my room. I did not think it worth anything, so I did not say anything about it."

The subconscious mind will always answer you if you trust it.

• His subconscious revealed the location of his father's will

A young man who attends my lectures had this experience. His father died and apparently left no will. However, this man's sister told him that their father had confided to her that a will had been executed which was fair to all. Every attempt to locate the will failed.

Prior to sleep he talked to his deeper mind as follows: "I now turn this request over the the subconscious mind. It knows just where that will is, and reveals it to me." Then he condensed his request down to one word, "Answer," repeating it over and over again as a lullaby. He lulled himself to sleep with the word, "Answer."

The next morning this young man had an overpowering hunch to go to a certain bank in Los Angeles where he found a safe deposit vault registered in the name of his father, the contents of which solved all his problems.

Your thought, as you go to sleep, arouses the powerful latency which is within you. For example, let us suppose you are wondering whether to sell your home, buy a certain stock, sever partnership, move to New York or stay in Los Angeles, dissolve the present contract or take a new one. Do this: Sit quietly in your armchair or at the desk in your office. Remember that there is a universal law of action and reaction. The action is your thought. The reaction is the response from your subconscious mind. The subconscious mind is reactive and reflexive; this is its nature. It rebounds, rewards, and repays. It is the law of correspondence. It responds by corresponding. As you contemplate right action, you will automatically experience a reaction or response in yourself which represents the guidance or answer of your subconscious mind.

In seeking guidance, you simply think quietly about right action which means that you are using the infinite intelligence resident in the subconscious mind to the point where it begins to use you. From there on, your course of action is directed and controlled by the subjective wisdom within you which is all-wise and omnipotent. Your decision will be right. There will only be right action because you are under a subjective compulsion to do the right thing. I use the word *compulsion* because the law of the subconscious is compulsion.

• The secret of guidance

The secret of guidance or right action is to mentally devote yourself to the right answer, until you find its response in you. The response is a feeling, an inner awareness, an overpowering hunch whereby you know that you know. You have used the power to the point where it begins to use you. You cannot possibly fail or make one false step while operating under the subjective wisdom within you. You will find that all your ways are pleasantness and all your paths are peace.

• Highlights to recall

1. Remember that the subconscious mind has determined the success and wonderful achievements of all great scientific workers.

2. By giving your conscious attention and devotion to the solution of a perplexing problem, your subconscious mind

gathers all the necessary information and presents it full-blown to the conscious mind.

3 If you are wondering about the answer to a problem, try to solve it objectively. Get all the information you can from research and also from others. If no answer comes, turn it over to your subconscious mind prior to sleep, and the answer always comes. It never fails.

4. You do not always get the answer overnight. Keep on turning your request over to your subconscious until the day breaks and the shadows flee away.

5. You delay the answer by thinking it will take a long time or that it is a major problem. Your subconscious has no problem, it knows only the answer.

6. Believe that you have the answer now. Feel the joy of the answer and the way you would feel if you had the perfect answer. Your subconscious will respond to your feeling.

7. Any mental picture, backed by faith and perseverance, will come to pass through the miracle-working power of your subconscious. Trust it, believe in its power, and wonders will happen as you pray.

8. Your subconscious is the storehouse of memory, and within your subconscious are recorded all your experiences since childhood.

9. Scientists meditating on ancient scrolls, temples, fossils, etc., are able to reconstruct scenes of the past and make them alive today. Their subconscious mind comes to their aid.

10. Turn over your request for a solution to your subconscious prior to sleep. Trust it and believe in it, and the answer will come. It knows all and sees all, but you must not doubt or question its powers.

11. The action is your thought, and the reaction is the response of your subconscious mind. If your thoughts are wise, your actions and decisions will be wise.

12. Guidance comes as a feeling, an inner awareness, an overpowering hunch whereby you know that you know. It is an inner sense of touch. Follow it.

13

Your Subconscious
and the Wonders of Sleep

You spend about eight out of every twenty-four hours, or one-third of your entire life, in sleep. This is an inexorable law of life. This also applies to the animal and vegetable kingdoms. Sleep is a divine law, and many answers to our problems come to us when we are sound asleep upon the bed.

. Many people have advocated the theory that you get tired during the day, that you go to sleep to rest the body, and that a reparative process takes place while you sleep. Nothing rests in sleep. Your heart, lungs, and all your vital organs function while you are asleep. If you eat prior to sleep, the food is digested and assimilated; also, your skin secretes perspiration, and your nails and hair continue to grow.

Your subconscious mind never rests or sleeps. It is always active, controlling all your vital forces. The healing process takes place more rapidly while you are asleep as there is no interference from your conscious mind. Remarkable answers are given to you while you are asleep.

• Why we sleep

Dr. John Bigelow, a famous research authority on sleep,* demonstrated that at night while asleep you receive impressions showing that the nerves of the eyes, ears, nose, and taste buds are active during sleep, and also that the nerves of your brain are quite active. He says that the main reason we sleep is be-

---

* Dr. John Bigelow, *The Mystery of Sleep* (New York and London: Harper Brothers, 1903).

cause "the nobler part of the soul is united by abstraction to our higher nature and becomes a participant in the wisdom and foreknowledge of the gods."

Dr. Bigelow states also, "The results of my studies have not only strengthened my convictions that the supposed exemption from customary toils and activities was not the final purpose of sleep, but have also made clearer to my mind the conviction that no part of a man's life deserves to be considered more indispensable to its symmetrical and perfect spiritual development than the while he is separated from the phenomenal world in sleep."

• Prayer, a form of sleep

Your conscious mind gets involved with vexations, strife, and contentions of the day, and it is very necessary to withdraw periodically from sense evidence and the objective world, and commune silently with the inner wisdom of your subconscious mind. By claiming guidance, strength, and greater intelligence in all phases of your life, you will be enabled to overcome all difficulties and solve your daily problems.

This regular withdrawal from sense evidence and the noise and confusion of everyday living is also a form of sleep, i.e., you become asleep to the world of the senses and alive to the wisdom and power of your subconscious mind.

• Startling effects of sleep deprivation

Lack of sleep can cause you to become irritable, moody, and depressed. Dr. George Stevenson of the National Association for Mental Health says, "I believe it can safely be said that all human beings need a minimum of six hours' sleep to be healthy. Most people need more. Those who think they can get along on less are fooling themselves."

Medical research scholars, investigating sleep processes and deprivation of sleep, point out that severe insomnia has preceded psychotic breakdown in some instances. Remember, you are spiritually recharged during sleep, and adequate sleep is essential to produce joy and vitality in life.

• You need more sleep

Robert O'Brien, in an article, "Maybe You Need More Sleep," in an issue of *The Reader's Digest*, reports the following experiment on sleep:

"For the last three years experiments have been in progress at Walter Reed Army Institute of Research in Washington, D.C. Subjects—more than one hundred military and civilian volunteers have been kept awake for as long as four days. Thousands of tests have measured the effects on their behavior and personality. Results of these tests have given scientists astonishingly new insights into the mysteries of sleep.

"They now know that the tired brain apparently craves sleep so hungrily that it will sacrifice anything to get it. After only a few hours of sleep loss, fleeting stolen naps called 'lapses,' or micro-sleep, occurred at the rate of three or four an hour. As in real sleep, eyelids drooped, heartbeat slowed. Each lapse lasted just a fraction of a second. Sometimes the lapses were periods of blankness; sometimes they were filled with images, wisps of dreams. As hours of sleep loss mounted, the lapses took place more often and lasted longer, perhaps two or three seconds. Even if the subjects had been piloting an airliner in a thunderstorm, they still couldn't have resisted micro-sleeps for those few priceless seconds. And it can happen to you, as many who have fallen asleep at the wheel of a car can testify.

"Another startling effect of sleep deprivation was its attack on human memory and perception. Many sleep-deprived subjects were unable to retain information long enough to relate it to the task they were supposed to perform. They were totally befuddled in situations requiring them to hold several factors in mind and act on them, as a pilot must when he skillfully integrates wind direction, air speed, altitude, and glide path to make a safe landing."

• Sleep brings counsel

A young lady in Los Angeles who listens to my morning radio talks told me that she had been offered a lucrative position in New York City at twice her present salary. She was wondering whether to accept or not and prayed prior to sleep as follows: "The creative intelligence of my subconscious mind knows what is best for me. Its tendency is always lifeward, and it reveals to me the right decision which blesses me and all concerned. I give thanks for the answer which I know will come to me."

She repeated this simple prayer over and over again as a lullaby prior to sleep, and in the morning she had a persistent feeling that she should not accept the offer. She rejected the offer and subsequent events verified her inward sense of knowing, because the company went bankrupt in a few months following their offer of employment to her.

The conscious mind may be correct on the facts objectively known, but the intuitive faculty of her subconscious mind saw the failure of the concern in question, and prompted her accordingly.

• Saved from certain disaster

I will illustrate how the wisdom of your subconscious mind can instruct you and protect you relative to your request for right action as you go to sleep.

Many years ago, before the Second World War, I was offered a very lucrative assignment in the Orient, and I prayed for guidance and the right decision as follows: "Infinite intelligence within me knows all things, and the right decision is revealed to me in divine order. I will recognize the answer when it comes."

I repeated this simple prayer over and over again as a lullaby prior to sleep, and in a dream came the vivid realization of things to come three years hence. An old friend appeared in the dream and said, "Read these headlines—do not go!" The headlines of the newspaper which appeared in the dream related to war and the attack on Pearl Harbor.

Occasionally, the writer dreams literally. The aforementioned dream was undoubtedly a dramatization of the subconscious mind which projected a person whom I trusted and respected. To some a warning may come in the form of a mother who appears in a dream. She tells the person not to go here or there, and the reason for the warning. Your subconscious mind is all-wise. It knows all things. Oftentimes it will speak to you only in a voice that your conscious mind will immediately accept as true. Sometimes your subconscious will warn you in a voice which sounds like that of your mother or some loved one which may cause you to stop on the street, and you find, if you had gone another foot, a falling object from a window might have struck you on the head.

My subconscious mind is one with the universal subconscious, and it knew the Japanese were planning a war, and it also knew when the war would start.

Dr. Rhine, director of the Department of Psychology at Duke University, has gathered together a vast amount of evidence showing that a great number of people all over the world see events before they happen, and in many instances are, therefore, able to avoid the tragic event which was foreseen vividly in a dream.

The dream which I had showed clearly the headlines in *The New York Times* about three years prior to the tragedy of Pearl Harbor. In consequence of this dream, I immediately cancelled the trip as I felt a subconscious compulsion to do so. Three years later the Second World War proved the truth of the inner voice of intuition.

• Your future is in your subconscious mind

Remember that the future, the result of your habitual thinking, is already in your mind except when you change it through prayer. The future of a country, likewise, is in the collective subconscious of the people of that nation. There is nothing strange in the dream I had wherein I saw the headlines of the New York newspapers long before the war began. The war had already taken place in mind, and all the plans of attack were already engraved on that great recording instrument, the subconscious mind or collective unconscious of the universal mind. Tomorrow's events are in your subconscious mind, so are next week's and next month's, and they may be seen by a highly psychic or clairvoyant person.

No disaster or tragedy can happen to you if you decide to pray. Nothing is predetermined or foreordained. Your mental attitude, i.e., the way you think, feel, and believe determines your destiny. You can, through scientific prayer, which is explained in a previous chapter, mold, fashion, and create your own future. *Whatsoever a man soweth, that shall he also reap.*

• A cat nap nets him $15,000

One of my students mailed me a newspaper clipping three or four years ago about a man called Ray Hammerstrom, a roller at the steel works in Pittsburgh operated by Jones and Laughlin Steel Corporation. He received $15,000 for his dream.

According to the article, the engineers could not fix a faulty switch in a newly installed bar mill which controlled the delivery of straight bars to the cooling beds. The engineers worked on the switch about eleven or twelve times to no avail.

Hammerstrom thought a lot about the problem and tried to figure out a new design which might work. Nothing worked. One afternoon he lay down for a nap, and prior to sleep he began to think about the answer to the switch problem. He had a dream in which a perfect design for the switch was portrayed. When he awoke, he sketched his new design according to the outline of his dream.

This visionary cat nap won Hammerstrom a check for $15,000, the largest award the firm ever gave an employee for a new idea.

• How a famous professor solved his problem in sleep

Dr. H. V. Helprecht, Professor of Assyrian at the University of Pennsylvania, wrote as follows: "One Saturday evening . . . I had been wearying myself, in the vain attempt to decipher two small fragments of agate which were supposed to belong to the finger rings of some Babylonians.

"About midnight, weary and exhausted, I went to bed and dreamed the following remarkable dream: A tall, thin priest of Nippur, about forty years of age, led me to the treasure chamber of the temple . . . a small, low-ceilinged room without windows, while scraps of agate and lapis-lazuli lay scattered on the floor. Here he addressed me as follows: 'The two fragments which you have published separately on pages 22 and 26 belong together, are not finger rings. . . . The first two rings served as earrings for the statue of the god; the two fragments (you have) . . . are the portions of them. If you will put them together you will have confirmation of my words.' . . . I awoke at once . . . I examined the fragments . . . and to my astonishment found the dream verified. The problem was then at last solved."

This demonstrates clearly the creative manifestation of his subconscious mind which knew the answer to all his problems.

• How the subconscious worked for a famous writer while he slept

Robert Louis Stevenson in one of his books, *Across the Plains*, devotes a whole chapter to dreams. He was a vivid dreamer and had the persistent habit of giving specific instructions to his subconscious every night prior to sleep. He would request his subconscious to evolve stories for him while he slept. For example, if Stevenson's funds were at a low ebb, his command to his subconscious would be something like this: "Give me a good thrilling novel which will be marketable and profitable." His subconscious responded magnificently.

Stevenson says, "These little brownies [the intelligences and powers of his subconscious] can tell me a story piece by piece, like a serial, and keep me, its supposed creator, all the while in total ignorance of where they aim." And he added: "That part of my work which is done when I am up and about [while he is consciously aware and awake] is by no means necessarily mine, since all goes to show that the *brownies* have a hand in it even then."

• Sleep in peace and wake in joy

To those who suffer from insomnia, you will find the following prayer very effective. Repeat it slowly, quietly, and lovingly prior to sleep: "My toes are relaxed, my ankles are relaxed, my abdominal muscles are relaxed, my heart and lungs are relaxed, my hands and arms are relaxed, my neck is relaxed, my brain is relaxed, my face is relaxed, my eyes are relaxed, my whole mind and body are relaxed. I fully and freely forgive everyone, and I sincerely wish for them harmony, health, peace, and all the blessings of life. I am at peace, I am poised, serene, and calm. I rest in security and in peace. A great stillness steals over me, and a great calm quiets my whole being as I realize the Divine Presence within me. I know that the realization of life and love heals me. I wrap myself in the mantle of love and fall asleep filled with good will for all. Throughout the night peace remains with me, and in the morning I shall be filled with life and love. A circle of love is drawn around me. *I will fear no evil, for Thou art with me.* I sleep in peace, I wake in joy, and *in Him I live, move, and have my being.*"

• Summary of your aids to the wonders of sleep

1. If you are worried that you will not wake up on time, suggest to your subconscious mind prior to sleep the exact time you wish to arise, and it will awaken you. It needs no clock. Do the same thing with all problems. There is nothing too hard for your subconscious.

2. Your subconscious never sleeps. It is always on the job. It controls all your vital functions. Forgive yourself and everyone else before you go to sleep, and healing will take place much more rapidly.

3. Guidance is given you while you are asleep, sometimes in a dream. The healing currents are also released, and in the morning you feel refreshed and rejuvenated.

4. When troubled by the vexations and strife of the day, still the wheels of your mind and think about the wisdom and intelligence lodged in your subconscious mind which is ready to respond to you. This will give you peace, strength, and confidence.

5. Sleep is essential for peace of mind and health of body.

Lack of sleep can cause irritation, depression, and mental disorders. You need eight hours' sleep.

6. Medical research scholars point out that insomnia precedes psychotic breakdowns.

7. You are spiritually recharged during sleep. Adequate sleep is essential for joy and vitality in life.

8. Your tired brain craves sleep so hungrily that it will sacrifice anything to get it. Many who have fallen asleep at the wheel of an automobile can testify to this.

9. Many sleep-deprived people have poor memories and lack proper co-ordination. They become befuddled, confused, and disorientated.

10. Sleep brings counsel. Prior to sleep, claim that the infinite intelligence of your subconscious mind is guiding and directing you. Then, watch for the *lead* which comes, perhaps on awakening.

11. Trust your subconscious completely. Know that its tendency is always lifeward. Occasionally, your subconscious answers you in a very vivid dream and a vision in the night. You can be forewarned in a dream in the same way as the author of this book was warned.

12. Your future is in your mind now, based on your habitual thinking and beliefs. Claim infinite intelligence leads and guides you and that all good is yours, and your future will be wonderful. Believe it and accept it. Expect the best, and invariably the best will come to you.

13. If you are writing a novel, play, or book, or are working on an invention, speak to your subconscious mind at night and claim boldly that its wisdom, intelligence, and power are guiding, directing, and revealing to you the ideal play, novel, book, or revealing the perfect solution whatever it may be. Wonders will happen as you pray this way.

14

Your Subconscious Mind and Marital Problems

Ignorance of the functions and powers of the mind is the cause of all marital trouble. Friction between husband and wife can be solved by each using the law of mind correctly. By praying together they stay together. The contemplation of divine ideals, the study of the laws of life, the mutual agreement on a common purpose and plan, and the enjoyment of personal freedom bring about that harmonious marriage, that wedded bliss, that sense of oneness where the two become one.

The best time to prevent divorce is before marriage. It is not wrong to try to get out of a very bad situation. But, why get into the bad situation in the first place? Would it not be better to give attention to the real cause of marital problems, in other words, to really get at the root of the matter involved?

As with all other problems of men and women, the problems of divorce, separation, annulment, and endless litigation are directly traceable to lack of knowledge of the working and interrelationship of the conscious and subconscious mind.

• The meaning of marriage

Marriage to be real must first be on a spiritual basis. It must be of the heart, and the heart is the chalice of love. Honesty, sincerity, kindness, and integrity are also forms of love. Each partner should be perfectly honest and sincere with the other. It is not a true marriage when a man marries a woman for her money, social position, or to lift his ego, because this indicates a lack of sincerity, honesty, and true love. Such a marriage is a farce, a sham, and a masquerade.

When a woman says, "I am tired working; I want to get married because I want security," her premise is false. She is not using the laws of mind correctly. Her security depends upon her knowledge of the interaction of the conscious and subconscious mind and its application.

For example, a woman will never lack for wealth or health if she applies the techniques outlined in the respective chapters of this book. Her wealth can come to her independent of her husband, father, or anyone else. A woman is not dependent on her husband for health, peace, joy, inspiration, guidance, love, wealth, security, happiness, or anything in the world. Her security and peace of mind come from her knowledge of the inner powers within her and from the constant use of the laws of her own mind in a constructive fashion.

• How to attract the ideal husband

You are now acquainted with the way your subconscious mind works. You know that whatever you impress upon it will be experienced in your world. Begin now to impress your subconscious mind with the qualities and characteristics you desire in a man.

The following is an excellent technique: Sit down at night in your armchair, close your eyes, let go, relax the body, become very quiet, passive, and receptive. Talk to your subconscious mind and say to it, "I am now attracting a man into my experience who is honest, sincere, loyal, faithful, peaceful, happy, and prosperous. These qualities which I admire are sinking down into my subconscious mind now. As I dwell upon these characteristics, they become a part of me and are embodied subconsciously.

"I know there is an irresistible law of attraction and that I attract to me a man according to my subconscious belief. I attract that which I feel to be true in my subconscious mind.

"I know I can contribute to his peace and happiness. He loves my ideals, and I love his ideals. He does not want to make me over; neither do I want to make him over. There is mutual love, freedom, and respect."

Practice this process of impregnating your subconscious mind. Then, you will have the joy of attracting to you a man possessing the qualities and characteristics you mentally dwelt upon. Your subconscious intelligence will open up a pathway, whereby both of you will meet, according to the irresistible and changeless flow of your own subconscious mind. Have a keen desire to give the best that is in you of love, devotion, and co-operation. Be receptive to this gift of love which you have given to your subconscious mind.

• How to attract the ideal wife

Affirm as follows: "I now attract the right woman who is in complete accord with me. This is a spiritual union because it is divine love functioning through the personality of someone with whom I blend perfectly. I know I can give to this woman love, light, peace, and joy. I feel and believe I can make this woman's life full, complete, and wonderful.

"I now decree that she possesses the following qualities and attributes: She is spiritual, loyal, faithful, and true. She is harmonious, peaceful, and happy. We are irresistibly attracted to each other. Only that which belongs to love, truth, and beauty can enter my experience. I accept my ideal companion now."

As you think quietly and with interest on the qualities and attributes which you admire in the companion you seek, you will build the mental equivalent into your mentality. Then, the deeper currents of your subconscious mind will bring both of you together in divine order.

• No need for third mistake

Recently a teacher said to me, "I have had three husbands and all three have been passive, submissive, and dependent on me to make all decisions and govern everything. Why do I attract such type men?"

I asked her whether she had known that her second husband was the effeminate type, and she replied, "Of course not.

Had I known, I would not have married him." Apparently she had not learned anything from the first mistake. The trouble was with her own personality make-up. She was very masculine, domineering, and unconsciously wanted someone who would be submissive and passive so that she could play the dominant role. All this was unconscious motivation, and her subconscious picture attracted to her what she subjectively wanted. She had to learn to *break the pattern by adopting the right prayer process.*

• How she broke the negative pattern

The above-mentioned woman learned a simple truth. When you believe you can have the type of man you idealize, it is done unto you as you believe. The following is the specific prayer she used to break the old subconscious pattern and attract to her the ideal mate: "I am building into my mentality the type of man I deeply desire. The man I attract for a husband is strong, powerful, loving, very masculine, successful, honest, loyal, and faithful. He finds love and happiness with me. I love to follow where he leads.

"I know he wants me, and I want him. I am honest, sincere, loving, and kind. I have wonderful gifts to offer him. They are good will, a joyous heart, and a healthy body. He offers me the same. It is mutual. I give and I receive. Divine intelligence knows where this man is, and the deeper wisdom of my subconscious mind is now bringing both of us together in its own way, and we recognize each other immediately. I release this request to my subconscious mind which knows how to bring my request to pass. I give thanks for the perfect answer."

She prayed in the above manner night and morning, affirming these truths and knowing that through frequent occupation of the mind she would reach the mental equivalent of that which she sought.

• The answer to her prayer

Several months went by. She had a great number of dates and social engagements, none of which was agreeable to her. When she was about to question, waiver, doubt, and vacillate, she reminded herself that the infinite intelligence was bringing it to pass in its own way and that there was nothing to be concerned about. Her final decree in her divorce proceedings was granted which brought her a great sense of release and mental freedom.

Shortly afterward she went to work as a receptionist in a doctor's office. She told me that the minute she saw the physician she knew he was the man she was praying about. Apparently he knew it, too, because he proposed to her the first week she was in the office, and their subsequent marriage was ideally happy. This physician was not the passive or submissive type, but was a real man, a former football player, an outstanding athlete, and was a deeply spiritual man though he was completely devoid of any sectarian or denominational affiliation.

She got what she prayed for because she claimed it mentally until she reached the point of saturation. In other words, she mentally and emotionally united with her idea, and it became a part of her in the same way that an apple becomes a part of her blood stream.

• Should I get a divorce?

Divorce is an individual problem. It cannot be generalized. In some cases, of course, there never should have been a marriage. In some cases, divorce is not the solution, no more so than marriage is the solution for a lonely man. Divorce may be right for one person and wrong for another. A divorced woman may be far more sincere and noble than many of her married sisters who perhaps are living a lie.

For example, I once talked with a woman whose husband was a dope fiend, an ex-convict, a wife-beater, and a nonprovider. She had been told it was wrong to get a divorce. I explained to her that marriage is of the heart. If two hearts blend harmoniously, lovingly, and sincerely, that is the ideal marriage. The pure action of the heart is love.

Following this explanation she knew what to do. She knew in her heart that there is no divine law which compelled her to be browbeaten, intimidated, and beaten because someone said, "I pronounce you man and wife."

If you are in doubt as to what to do, ask for guidance, knowing that there is always an answer, and you will receive it. Follow the *lead* that comes to you in the silence of your soul. It speaks to you in peace.

• Drifting into divorce

Recently a young couple, married for only a few months, were seeking a divorce. I discovered that the young man had a constant fear that his wife would leave him. He expected rejection, and he believed that she would be unfaithful. These thoughts haunted his mind, and became an obsession with him. His mental attitude was one of separation and suspicion. She felt unresponsive to him; it was his own feeling or atmosphere of loss and separation operating through them. This brought about a condition or action in accordance with the mental pattern behind it. There is a law of action and reaction, or cause and effect. The thought is the action, and the response of the subconscious mind is the reaction.

His wife left home and asked for a divorce which is what he feared and believed she would do.

• Divorce begins in the mind

Divorce takes place first in the mind; the legal proceedings follow after. These two young people were full of resentment, fear, suspicion, and anger. These attitudes weaken, exhaust, and debilitate the whole being. They learned that hate divides and that love unites. They began to realize what they had been doing with their minds. Neither one of them knew the law of mental action, and they were misusing their minds and bringing on chaos and misery. These two people went back together at my suggestion and experimented with prayer therapy.

They began to radiate love, peace, and good will to each other. Each one practiced radiating harmony, health, peace, and love to the other, and they alternated in the reading of the

Psalms every night. Their marriage is growing more beautiful every day.

• The nagging wife

Many times the reason the wife nags is because she gets no attention. Oftentimes, it is a craving for love and affection. Give your wife attention, and show your appreciation. Praise and exalt all her many good points. There is also the nagging type of woman who wants to make the man conform to her particular pattern. This is about the quickest way in the world to get rid of a man.

The wife and the husband must cease being scavengers—always looking at the petty faults or errors in each other. Let each give attention and praise for the constructive and wonderful qualities in the other.

• The brooding husband

If a man begins to brood, grows morbid against his wife because of the things she said or did, he is, psychologically speaking, committing adultery. One of the meanings of adultery is idolatry, i.e., giving attention to or uniting mentally with that which is negative and destructive. When a man is silently resenting his wife and is full of hostility toward her, he is unfaithful. He is not faithful to his marriage vows, which are to love, cherish, and honor her all the days of his life.

The man who is brooding, bitter, and resentful can swallow his sharp remarks, abate his anger, and he can go to great lengths to be considerate, kind, and courteous. He can deftly skirt the differences. Through praise and mental effort, he can get out of the habit of antagonism. Then, he will be able to get along better, not only with his wife, but with business associates also. Assume the harmonious state, and eventually you will find peace and harmony.

• The great mistake

A great mistake is to discuss your marital problems or difficulties with neighbors and relatives. Suppose, for example, a wife says to the neighbor, "John never gives me any money. He treats my mother abominably, drinks to excess, and is constantly abusive and insulting."

Now, this wife is degrading and belittling her husband in the eyes of all the neighbors and relatives. He no longer appears as the ideal husband to them. Never discuss your marital problems with anyone except a trained counselor. Why cause numerous people to think negatively of your marriage? Moreover, as you discuss and dwell upon these shortcomings of your husband, you are actually creating these states within yourself. Who is thinking and feeling it? You are! As you think and feel, so are you.

Relatives will usually give you the wrong advice. It is usually biased and prejudiced because it is not given in an impersonal way. Any advice you receive which violates the golden rule, which is a cosmic law, is not good or sound.

It is well to remember that no two human beings ever lived beneath the same roof without clashes of temperament, periods of hurts and strain. Never display the unhappy side of your marriage to your friends. Keep your quarrels to yourself. Refrain from criticism and condemnation of your partner.

• Don't try to make your wife over

A husband must not try to make his wife over into a second edition of himself. The tactless attempt to change her in many ways is foreign to her nature. These attempts are always foolish, and many times result in a dissolution of the marriage. These attempts to alter her destroy her pride and self-esteem, and arouse a spirit of contrariness and resentment that proves fatal to the marriage bond.

Adjustments are needed, of course, but if you have a good look inside your own mind, and study your character and behavior, you will find so many shortcomings, they will keep you busy the rest of your life. If you say, "I will make him over into what I want," you are looking for trouble and the divorce court. You are asking for misery. You will have to learn the hard way that there is no one to change but yourself.

- **Pray together and stay together through steps in prayer**

   The first step: Never carry over from one day to another accumulated irritations arising from little disappoinments. Be sure to forgive each other for any sharpness before you retire at night. The moment you awaken in the morning, claim infinite intelligence is guiding you in all your ways. Send out loving thoughts of peace, harmony, and love to your marriage partner, to all members of the family, and to the whole world.

   The second step: Say grace at breakfast. Give thanks for the wonderful food, for your abundance, and for all your blessings. Make sure that no problems, worries, or arguments shall enter into the table conversation; the same applies at dinner time. Say to your wife or husband, "I appreciate all you are doing, and I radiate love and good will to you all day long."

   The third step: The husband and wife should alternate in praying each night. Do not take your marriage partner for granted. Show your appreciation and love. Think appreciation and good will, rather than condemnation, criticism, and nagging. The way to build a peaceful home and a happy marriage is to use a foundation of love, beauty, harmony, mutual respect, faith in God, and all things good. Read the 23rd, 27th, and 91st Psalms, the 11th chapter of Hebrews, the 13th chapter of I Corinthians, and other great texts of the Bible before going to sleep. As you practice these truths, your marriage will grow more and more blessed through the years.

- **Review your actions**

   1. Ignorance of mental and spiritual laws is the cause of all marital unhappiness. By praying scientifically together, you stay together.
   2. The best time to prevent divorce is before marriage. If you learn how to pray in the right way, you will attract the right mate for you.
   3. Marriage is the union of a man and woman who are bound

together by love. Their hearts beat as one, and they move onward, upward, and Godward.

4. Marriage does not bequeath happiness. People find happiness by dwelling on the eternal truths of God and the spiritual values of life. Then, the man and woman can contribute to each other's happiness and joy.

5. You attract the right mate by dwelling on the qualities and characteristics you admire in a woman or a man, and then your subconscious mind will bring you together in divine order.

6. You must build into your mentality the mental equivalent of what you want in a marriage partner. If you want to attract an honest, sincere, and loving partner in life, you must be honest, sincere, and loving yourself.

7. You do not have to repeat mistakes in marriage. When you really believe you can have the type man or woman you idealize, it is done unto you as you believe. To believe is to accept something as true. Accept your ideal companion now mentally.

8. Do not wonder how, why, or where you will meet the mate you are praying for. Trust implicitly the wisdom of your subconscious mind. It has the "know-how," and you don't have to assist it.

9. You are mentally divorced when you indulge in peeves, grudges, ill will, and hostility toward your marriage partner. You are mentally dwelling with error in the bed of your mind. Adhere to your marriage vows, "I promise to cherish, love, and honor him (or her) all the days of my life."

10. Cease projecting fear patterns to your marriage partner. Project love, peace, harmony, and good will, and your marriage will grow more beautiful and more wonderful through the years.

11. Radiate love, peace, and good will to each other. These vibrations are picked up by the subconscious mind resulting in mutual trust, affection, and respect.

12. A nagging wife is usually seeking attention and appreciation. She is craving for love and affection. Praise and exalt

her many good points. Show her that you love her and appreciate her.

13. A man who loves his wife does not do anything unloving or unkind in word, manner, or action. Love is what love does.

14. In marital problems, always seek expert advice. You would not go to a carpenter to pull a tooth; neither should you discuss your marriage problems with relatives or friends. You should go to a trained person for counsel.

15. Never try to make your wife or husband over. These attempts are always foolish and tend to destroy the pride and self-esteem of the other. Moreover, it arouses a spirit of resentment that proves fatal to the marriage bond. Cease trying to make the other a second edition of yourself.

16. Pray together and you will stay together. Scientific prayer solves all problems. Mentally picture your wife as she ought to be, joyous, happy, healthy, and beautiful. See your husband as he ought to be, strong, powerful, loving, harmonious, and kind. Maintain this mental picture, and you will experience the marriage made in heaven which is harmony and peace.

15

Your Subconscious Mind and Your Happiness

William James, father of American psychology, said that the greatest discovery of the nineteenth century was not in the realm of physical science. The greatest discovery was the power of the subconscious touched by faith. In every human being is that limitless reservoir of power which can overcome any problem in the world.

True and lasting happiness will come into your life the day you get the clear realization that you can overcome any weakness—the day you realize that your subconscious can solve your problems, heal your body, and prosper you beyond your fondest dream.

You might have felt very happy when your child was born, when you got married, when you graduated from college, or when you won a great victory or a prize. You might have been very happy when you became engaged to the loveliest girl or the most handsome man. You could go on and list innumerable experiences which have made you happy. However, no matter how marvelous these experiences are, they do not give real lasting happiness—they are transitory.

The Book of Proverbs gives the answer: *Whosoever trusteth in the Lord, happy is he.* When you trust in the Lord (the power and wisdom of your subconscious mind) to lead, guide, govern, and direct all your ways, you will become poised, serene, and relaxed. As you radiate love, peace, and good will to all, you are really building a superstructure of happiness for all the days of your life.

• You must choose happiness

Happiness is a state of mind. There is a phrase in the Bible which says, *Choose ye this day whom ye will serve.* You have the freedom to choose happiness. This may seem extraordinarily simple, and it is. Perhaps this is why people stumble over the way to happiness; they do not see the simplicity of the key to happiness. The great things of life are simple, dynamic, and creative. They produce well-being and happiness.

St. Paul reveals to you how you can think your way into a life of dynamic power and happiness in these words: *Finally, brethren, whatsoever things are true, whatsoever things are honest, whatsoever things are just, whatsoever things are pure, whatsoever things are lovely, whatsoever things are of good report; if there be any virtue, and if there be any praise, think on these things.* PHIL. 4:8.

• How to choose happiness

Begin now to choose happiness. This is how you do it: When you open your eyes in the morning, say to yourself, "Divine order takes charge of my life today and every day. All things work together for good for me today. This is a new and wonderful day for me. There will never be another day like this one. I am divinely guided all day long, and whatever I do will prosper. Divine love surrounds me, enfolds me, and enwraps me, and I go forth in peace. Whenever my attention wanders away from that which is good and constructive, I will immediately bring it back to the contemplation of that which is lovely and of good report. I am a spiritual and mental magnet attracting to myself all things which bless and prosper me. I am going to be a wonderful success in all my undertakings today. I am definitely going to be happy all day long."

Start each day in this manner; then you will be choosing happiness, and you will be a radiant joyous person.

• He made it a habit to be happy

A number of years ago, I stayed for about a week in a farmer's house in Connemarra on the west coast of Ireland. He seemed to be always singing and whistling and was full of humor.

I asked him the secret of his happiness, and his reply was: "It is a habit of mine to be happy. Every morning when I awaken and every night before I go to sleep, I bless my family, the crops, the cattle, and I thank God for the wonderful harvest."

This farmer had made a practice of this for over forty years. As you know, thoughts repeated regularly and systematically sink into the subconscious mind and become habitual. He discovered that happiness is a habit.

• You must desire to be happy

There is one very important point about being happy. You must sincerely *desire* to be happy. There are people who have been depressed, dejected, and unhappy so long that were they suddenly made happy by some wonderful, good, joyous news, they would actually be like the woman who said to me, "It is wrong to be so happy!" They have been so accustomed to the old mental patterns that they do not feel at home being happy! They long for the former, depressed, unhappy state.

I knew a woman in England who had rheumatism for many years. She would pat herself on the knee and say, "My rheumatism is bad today. I cannot go out. My rheumatism keeps me miserable."

This dear elderly lady got a lot of attention from her son, daughter, and the neighbors. She really wanted her rheumatism. She enjoyed her "misery" as she called it. This woman did not really want to be happy.

I suggested a curative procedure to her. I wrote down some biblical verses and told her that if she gave attention to these truths, her mental attitude would undoubtedly change and would result in her faith and confidence in being restored to health. She was not interested. There seems to be a peculiar, mental, morbid streak in many people, whereby they seem to enjoy being miserable and sad.

• Why choose unhappiness?

Many people choose unhappiness by entertaining these ideas: "Today is a black day; everything is going to go wrong."

"I am not going to succeed." "Everyone is against me." "Business is bad, and it is going to get worse." "I'm always late." "I never get the breaks." "He can, but I can't." If you have this attitude of mind the first thing in the morning, you will attract all these experiences to you, and you will be very unhappy.

Begin to realize that the world you live in is determined largely by what goes on in your mind. Marcus Aurelius, the great Roman philosopher and sage, said, "A man's life is what his thoughts make of it." Emerson, America's foremost philosopher, said, "A man is what he thinks all day long." The thoughts you habitually entertain in your mind have the tendency to actualize themselves in physical conditions.

Make certain you do not indulge in negative thoughts, defeatist thoughts, or unkind, depressing thoughts. Recall frequently to your mind that you can experience nothing outside your own mentality.

• If I had a million dollars, I would be happy

I have visited many men in mental institutions who were millionaires, but they insisted they were penniless and destitute. They were incarcerated because of psychotic, paranoic, and manic-depressive tendencies. Wealth in and of itself will not make you happy. On the other hand, it is not a deterrent to happiness. Today, there are many people trying to buy happiness through the purchase of radios, television sets, automobiles, a home in the country, a private yacht, and a swimming pool, but happiness cannot be purchased or procured in that way.

The kingdom of happiness is in your thought and feeling. Too many people have the idea that it takes something artificial to produce happiness. Some say, "If I were elected mayor, made president of the organization, promoted to general manager of the corporation, I would be happy."

The truth is that happiness is a mental and spiritual state. None of these positions mentioned will necessarily bequeath happiness. Your strength, joy, and happiness consist in finding out the law of divine order and right action lodged in your subconscious mind and by applying these principles in all phases of your life.

• He found happiness to be the harvest of a quiet mind

Lecturing in San Francisco some years ago, I interviewed a man who was very unhappy and dejected over the way his business was going. He was the general manager. His heart was filled with resentment toward the vice president and the president of the organization. He claimed that they opposed him. Because of this internal strife, business was declining; he was receiving no dividends or stock bonuses.

This is how he solved his business problem: The first thing in the morning he affirmed quietly as follows, "All those working in our corporation are honest, sincere, co-operative, faithful, and full of good will to all. They are mental and spiritual links in the chain of this corporation's growth, welfare, and prosperity. I radiate love, peace, and good will in my thoughts, words, and deeds to my two associates and to all those in the company. The president and the vice president of our company are divinely guided in all their undertakings. The infinite intelligence of my subconscious mind makes all decisions through me. There is only right action in all our business transactions and in our relationship with each other. I send the messengers of peace, love, and good will before me to the office. Peace and harmony reign supreme in the minds and hearts of all those in the company including myself. I now go forth into a new day, full of faith, confidence, and trust."

This business executive repeated the above meditation slowly three times in the morning, feeling the truth of what he affirmed. When fearful or angry thoughts came into his mind during the day, he would say to himself, "Peace, harmony, and poise govern my mind at all times."

As he continued disciplining his mind in this manner, all the harmful thoughts ceased to come, and peace came into his mind. He reaped the harvest.

Subsequently, he wrote me to the effect that at the end of about two weeks of reordering his mind, the president and the vice president called him into the office, praised his operations and his new constructive ideas, and remarked how fortunate they were in having him as general manager. He was very happy in discovering that man finds happiness within himself.

• The block or stump is not really there

I read a newspaper article some years ago which told about a horse who had shied when he came to a stump on the road. Subsequently, every time the horse came to that same stump, he shied. The farmer dug the stump out, burned it, and leveled the old road. Yet, for twenty-five years, every time the horse passed the place where the former stump was, he shied. The horse was shying at the memory of a stump.

There is no block to your happiness save in your own thought life and mental imagery. Are fear or worry holding you back? Fear is a thought in your mind. You can dig it up this very moment by supplanting it with faith in success, achievement, and victory over all problems.

I knew a man who failed in business. He said to me, "I made mistakes. I've learned a lot. I am going back into business, and I will be a tremendous success." He faced up to that stump in his mind. He did not whine or complain, but he tore up the stump of failure, and through believing in his inner powers to back him up, he banished all fear thoughts and old depressions. Believe in yourself, and you will succeed and be happy.

• The happiest people

The happiest man is he who constantly brings forth and practices what is best in him. Happiness and virtue complement each other. The best are not only the happiest, but the happiest are usually the best in the art of living life successfully. God is the highest and best in you. Express more of God's love, light, truth, and beauty, and you will become one of the happiest persons in the world today.

Epictetus, the Greek stoic philosopher, said, "There is but one way to tranquility of mind and happiness; let this, therefore, be always ready at hand with thee, both when thou wakest early in the morning, and all the day long, and when thou goest late to sleep, to account no external things thine own, but commit all these to God."

• Summary of steps to happiness

1. William James said that the greatest discovery of the 19th century was the power of the subconscious mind touched by faith.

2. There is tremendous power within you. Happiness will come to you when you acquire a sublime confidence in this power. Then, you will make your dreams come true.

3. You can rise victorious over any defeat and realize the cherished desires of your heart through the marvelous power of your subconscious mind. This is the meaning of *Whosoever trusteth in the Lord* [spiritual laws of the subconscious mind], *happy is he.*

4. You must choose happiness. Happiness is a habit. It is a good habit to ponder often on *Whatsoever things are true, whatsoever things are honest, whatsoever things are just, whatsoever things are pure, whatsoever things are lovely, whatsoever things are of good report; if there be any virtue, and if there be any praise, think on these things.* PHIL. 4:8.

5. When you open your eyes in the morning, say to yourself, I choose happiness today. I choose success today. I choose right action today. I choose love and good will for all today. I choose peace today. Pour life, love, and interest into this affirmation, and you have chosen happiness.

6. Give thanks for all your blessings several times a day. Furthermore, pray for the peace, happiness, and prosperity of all members of your family, your associates, and all people everywhere.

7. You must sincerely desire to be happy. Nothing is accomplished without desire. Desire is a wish with wings of imagination and faith. Imagine the fulfillment of your desire, and feel its reality, and it will come to pass. Happiness comes in answered prayer.

8. By constantly dwelling on thoughts of fear, worry, anger, hate, and failure, you will become very depressed and unhappy. Remember, your life is what your thoughts make of it.

9. You cannot buy happiness with all the money in the world. Some millionaires are very happy, some are very unhappy. Many people with very little worldly goods are very happy, and some are very unhappy. Some married people are happy, and some very unhappy. Some single people are happy, and some are very unhappy. The kingdom of happiness is in your thought and feeling.

10. Happiness is the harvest of a quiet mind. Anchor your thoughts on peace, poise, security, and divine guidance, and your mind will be productive of happiness.

11. There is no block to your happiness. External things are not causative, these are effects, not cause. Take your cue from the only creative principle within you. Your thought is cause, and a new cause produces a new effect. Choose happiness.

12. The happiest man is he who brings forth the highest and the best in him. God is the highest and the best in him, for the kingdom of God is within.

16

Your Subconscious Mind
and Harmonious Human Relations

In studying this book, you learn that your subconscious mind is a recording machine which faithfully reproduces whatever you impress upon it. This is one of the reasons for the application of the Golden Rule in human relations.

MATT. 7:12 says, *All things whatsoever ye would that men should do unto you, do ye even so to them.* This quotation has outer and inner meanings. You are interested in its inner meaning from the standpoint of your subconscious mind which is: As you would that men should *think* about you, think you about them in like manner. As you would that men should *feel* about you, feel you also about them in like manner. As you would want men to *act* toward you, act you toward them in like manner.

For example, you may be polite and courteous to someone in your office, but when his back is turned, you are very critical and resentful toward him in your mind. Such negative thoughts are highly destructive to you. It is like taking poison. You are actually taking mental poisons which rob you of vitality, enthusiasm, strength, guidance, and good will. These negative thoughts and emotions sink down into your subconscious, and cause all kinds of difficulties and maladies in your life.

• The master key to happy relationships with others

Judge not, that ye be not judged. For with what judgment ye judge, ye shall be judged: and with what measure ye mete, it shall be measured to you again. MATTHEW 7:1-2.

A study of these verses and the application of the inner truths therein contained represent the real key to harmonious relations. To judge is to think, to arrive at a mental verdict or conclusion in your mind. The thought you have about the other person is your thought, because you are thinking it. Your thoughts are creative, therefore, you actually create in your own experience what you think and feel about the other person. It is also true that the suggestion you give to another, you give to yourself because your mind is the creative medium.

This is why it is said, *For with what judgment ye judge, ye shall be judged.* When you know this law and the way your subconscious mind works, you are careful to think, feel, and act right, toward the other. These verses teach you about the emancipation of man and reveal to you the solution to your individual problems.

• And with what measure ye mete, it shall be measured to you again

The good you do for others comes back to you in like measure; and the evil you do returns to you by the law of your own mind. If a man cheats and deceives another, he is actually cheating and deceiving himself. His sense of guilt and mood of loss inevitably will attract loss to him in some way, at some time. His subconscious records his mental act and reacts according to the mental intention or motivation.

Your subconscious mind is impersonal and unchanging, neither considering persons nor respecting religious affiliations or institutions of any kind. It is neither compassionate nor vindictive. The way you think, feel, and act toward others returns at last upon yourself.

• The daily headlines made him sick

Begin now to observe yourself. Observe your reactions to people, conditions, and circumstances. How do you respond to the events and news of the day? It makes no difference if all the other people were wrong and you alone were right. If the news disturbs you, it is your evil because your negative emotions robbed you of peace and harmony.

A woman wrote me about her husband, saying that he goes into a rage when he reads what certain newspaper columnists write in the newspaper. She added that this constant reaction of anger and suppressed rage on his part brought on bleeding ulcers, and his physician recommended an emotional reconditioning.

I invited this man to see me and I explained to him the way his mind functions indicating how emotionally immature it was to get angry when others write articles with which he disapproves or disagrees.

He began to realize that he should give the newspaperman freedom to express himself even though the latter disagreed with him politically, religiously, or in any other way. In the same manner, the newspaperman would give him freedom to write a letter to the newspaper disagreeing with his published statements. He learned that he could disagree without being disagreeable. He awakened to the simple truth that it is never what a person says or does that affects him, it is his reaction to what is said or done that matters.

This explanation was the cure for this man, and he realized that with a little practice he could master his morning tantrums. His wife told me, subsequently, that he laughed at himself and also at what the columnists say. They no longer have power to disturb, annoy, and irritate him. His ulcers have disappeared due to his emotional poise and serenity.

• I hate women, but I like men

A private secretary was very bitter toward some of the girls in her office because they were gossiping about her, and as she said, spreading vicious lies about her. She admitted that she did not like women. She said, "I hate women, but I like men." I discovered also that she spoke to the girls who were under her in the office in a very haughty, imperious, and irritable tone of voice. She pointed out that they took a delight in making things difficult for her. There was a certain pomposity in her way of speaking, and I could see where her tone of voice would affect some people unpleasantly.

If all the people in the office or factory annoy you, isn't it a possibility that the vibration, annoyance, and turmoil may be due to some subconscious pattern or mental projection from you? We know that a dog will react ferociously if you hate or fear dogs. Animals pick up your subconscious vibrations and react accordingly. Many undisciplined human beings are just as sensitive as dogs, cats, and other animals.

I suggested a process of prayer to this private secretary who hated women, explaining to her that when she began to identify herself with spiritual values and commenced to affirm the truths of life, her voice, mannerisms, and hatred of women would completely disappear. She was surprised to know that the emotion of hatred shows up in a person's speech, actions, in his writings, and in all phases of his life. She ceased reacting in the typical, resentful, and angry way. She established a pattern of prayer which she practiced regularly, systematically, and conscientiously in the office.

The prayer was as follows: "I think, speak, and act lovingly, quietly, and peacefully. I now radiate love, peace, tolerance, and kindliness to all the girls who criticized me and gossiped about me. I anchor my thoughts on peace, harmony, and good will to all. Whenever I am about to react negatively, I say firmly to myself, 'I am going to think, speak, and act from the standpoint of the principle of harmony, health, and peace within myself.' Creative intelligence leads, rules, and guides me in all my ways."

The practice of this prayer transformed her life, and she found that all criticism and annoyance ceased. The girls became co-workers and friends along life's journey. She discovered that *there is no one to change but myself.*

• His inner speech held back his promotion

One day a salesman came to see me and described his difficulties in working with the sales manager of his organization. He had been with the company ten years and had received no promotion or recognition of any kind. He showed me his sales figures which were greater proportionately than the other men in the territory. He said that the sales manager did not like him, that he was unjustly treated, and that at conferences the manager was rude to him, and at times ridiculed his suggestions.

I explained that undoubtedly the cause was to a great degree within himself, and that his concept and belief about his superior bore witness to the reaction of this man. *The measure we mete, shall be measured to us again.* His mental measure or concept of the sales manager was that he was mean and cantankerous. He was filled with bitterness and hostility toward the executive. On his way to work he conducted a vigorous conversation with himself filled with criticism, mental arguments, recriminations, and denunciations of his sales manager.

What he gave out mentally, he was inevitably bound to get back. This salesman realized that his inner speech was highly destructive because the intensity and force of his silent thoughts and emotions, and personally conducted mental condemnation and vilification of the sales manager entered into his own subconscious mind. This brought about the negative response from his boss as well as creating many other personal, physical, and emotional disorders.

He began to pray frequently as follows: "I am the only thinker in my universe. I am responsible for what I think about my boss. My sales manager is not responsible for the way I think about him. I refuse to give power to any person, place, or thing to annoy me or disturb me. I wish health, success, peace of mind, and happiness for my boss. I sincerely wish him well, and I know he is divinely guided in all his ways."

He repeated this prayer out loud slowly, quietly, and feelingly, knowing that his mind is like a garden, and that whatever he plants in the garden will come forth like seeds after their kind.

I also taught him to practice mental imagery prior to sleep in this way: He imagined that his sales manager was congratulating him on his fine work, on his zeal and enthusiasm, and on his wonderful response from customers. He felt the reality of all this, felt his handshake, heard the tone of his voice, and saw him smile. He made a real mental movie, dramatizing it to the best of his ability. Night after night he conducted this mental movie, knowing that his subconscious mind was the receptive plate on which his conscious imagery would be impressed.

Gradually by a process of what may be termed mental and spiritual osmosis, the impression was made on his subconscious mind, and the expression automatically came forth. The sales manager subsequently called him up to San Francisco, congratulated him, and gave him a new assignment as Division Sales Manager over one hundred men with a big increase in salary. He changed his concept and estimate of his boss, and the latter responded accordingly.

• Becoming emotionally mature

What the other person says or does cannot really annoy or irritate you except you permit him to disturb you. The only way he can annoy you is through your own thought. For example, if you get angry, you have to go through four stages in your mind: You begin to think about what he said. You decide to get angry and generate an emotion of rage. Then, you decide to act. Perhaps, you talk back and react in kind. You see that the thought, emotion, reaction, and action all take place in your mind.

When you become emotionally mature, you do not respond negatively to the criticism and resentment of others. To do so would mean that you had descended to that state of low mental vibration and become one with the negative atmosphere of the other. Identify yourself with your aim in life, and do not permit any person, place, or thing to deflect you from your inner sense of peace, tranquility, and radiant health.

• The meaning of love in harmonious human relations

Sigmund Freud, the Austrian founder of psychoanalysis, said that unless the personality has love, it sickens and dies. Love includes understanding, good will, and respect for the divinity in the other person. The more love and good will you emanate and exude, the more comes back to you.

If you puncture the other fellow's ego and wound his estimate of himself, you cannot gain his good will. Recognize that every man wants to be loved and appreciated, and made to feel important in the world. Realize that the other man is conscious of his true worth, and that, like yourself, he feels the dignity of being an expression of the One Life-Principle animating all men. As you do this consciously and knowingly, you build the other person up, and he returns your love and good will.

• He hated audiences

An actor told me that the audience booed and hissed him on his first appearance on the stage. He added that the play was badly written and that undoubtedly he did not play a good role. He admitted openly to me that for months afterward he hated audiences. He called them dopes, dummies, stupid, ignorant, gullible, etc. He quit the stage in disgust and went to work in a drugstore for a year.

One day a friend invited him to hear a lecture in Town Hall, New York City, on "How to Get Along With Ourselves." This lecture changed his life. He went back to the stage and began to pray sincerely for the audience and himself. He poured out love and good will every night before appearing on the stage. He made it a habit to claim that the peace of God filled the hearts of all present, and that all present were lifted up and inspired. During each performance he sent out love vibrations to the audience. Today, he is a great actor, and he loves and respects people. His good will and esteem are transmitted to others and are felt by them.

• Handling difficult people

There are difficult people in the world who are twisted and distorted mentally. They are malconditioned. Many are mental delinquents, argumentative, unco-operative, cantankerous, cynical, and sour on life. They are sick psychologically. Many people have deformed and distorted minds, probably warped during childhood. Many have congenital deformities. You would not condemn a person who had tuberculosis, nor should you condemn a person who is mentally ill. No one, for example, hates

or resents a hunchback; there are many mental hunchbacks. You
should have compassion and understanding. *To understand all is
to forgive all.*

• Misery loves company

The hateful, frustrated, distorted, and twisted personality is
out of tune with the Infinite. He resents those who are peaceful,
happy, and joyous. Usually he criticizes, condemns, and vilifies
those who have been very good and kind to him. His attitude is
this: Why should they be so happy when he is so miserable? He
wants to drag them down to his own level. Misery loves company. When you understand this you remain unmoved, calm,
and dispassionate.

• The practice of empathy in human relations

A girl visited me recently stating that she hated another
girl in her office. She gave as her reason that the other girl was
prettier, happier, and wealthier than she, and, in addition, was
engaged to the boss of the company where they worked. One day
after the marriage had taken place, the crippled daughter (by
a former marriage) of the woman whom she hated came into
the office. The child put her arms around her mother and said,
"Mommy, mommy, I love my new daddy! Look what he gave
me!" She showed her mother a wonderful new toy.

She said to me, "My heart went out to that little girl, and
I knew how happy she must feel. I got a vision of how happy
this woman was. All of a sudden I felt love for her, and I went
into the office and wished her all the happiness in the world, and
I meant it."

In psychological circles today, this is called empathy, which
simply means the imaginative projection of your mental attitude
into that of another. She projected her mental mood or the feeling of her heart into that of the other woman, and began to
think and look out through the other woman's brain. She was
actually thinking and feeling as the other woman, and also as
the child, because she likewise had projected herself into the

mind of the child. She was looking out from that vantage point on the child's mother.

If tempted to injure or think ill of another, project yourself mentally into the mind of Moses and think from the standpoint of the Ten Commandments. If you are prone to be envious, jealous, or angry, project yourself into the mind of Jesus and think from that standpoint, and you will feel the truth of the words *Love ye one another.*

• Appeasement never wins

Do not permit people to take advantage of you and gain their point by temper tantrums, crying jags, or so-called heart attacks. These people are dictators who try to enslave you and make you do their bidding. Be firm but kind, and refuse to yield. Appeasement never wins. Refuse to contribute to their delinquency, selfishness, and possessiveness. Remember, do that which is right. You are here to fulfill your ideal and remain true to the eternal verities and spiritual values of life which are eternal.

Give no one in all the world the power to deflect you from your goal, your aim in life, which is to express your hidden talents to the world, to serve humanity, and to reveal more and more of God's wisdom, truth, and beauty to all people in the world. Remain true to your ideal. Know definitely and absolutely that whatever contributes to your peace, happiness, and fulfillment must of necessity bless all men who walk the earth. The harmony of the part is the harmony of the whole, for the whole is in the part, and the part is in the whole. All you owe the other, as Paul says, is love, and love is the fulfilling of the law of health, happiness, and peace of mind.

• Profitable pointers in human relations

1. Your subconscious mind is a recording machine which reproduces your habitual thinking. Think good of the other, and you are actually thinking good about yourself.
2. A hateful or resentful thought is a mental poison. Do not think ill of another for to do so is to think ill of yourself.

You are the only thinker in your universe, and your thoughts are creative.

3. Your mind is a creative medium; therefore, what you think and feel about the other, you are bringing to pass in your own experience. This is the psychological meaning of the Golden Rule. As you would that man should think about you, think you about them in the same manner.

4. To cheat, rob, or defraud another brings lack, loss, and limitation to yourself. Your subconscious mind records your inner motivations, thoughts, and feelings. These being of a negative nature, loss, limitation, and trouble come to you in countless ways. Actually, what you do to the other, you are doing to yourself.

5. The good you do, the kindness proffered, the love and good will you send forth, will all come back to you multiplied in many ways.

6. You are the only thinker in your world. You are responsible for the way you think about the other. Remember, the other person is not responsible for the way you think about him. Your thoughts are reproduced. What are you thinking now about the other fellow?

7. Become emotionally mature and permit other people to differ from you. They have a perfect right to disagree with you, and you have the same freedom to disagree with them. You can disagree without being disagreeable.

8. Animals pick up your fear vibrations and snap at you. If you love animals, they will never attack you. Many undisciplined human beings are just as sensitive as dogs, cats, and other animals.

9. Your inner speech, representing your silent thoughts and feelings, is experienced in the reactions of others toward you.

10. Wish for the other what you wish for yourself. This is the key to harmonious human relations.

11. Change your concept and estimate of your employer. Feel and know he is practicing the Golden Rule and the Law of Love, and he will respond accordingly.

12. The other person cannot annoy you or irritate you except you permit him. Your thought is creative; you can bless him. If someone calls you a skunk, you have the freedom to say to the other, "God's peace fills your soul."

14. Love is the answer to getting along with others. Love is understanding, good will, and respecting the divinity of the other.

15. You would not hate a hunchback or cripple. You would have compassion. Have compassion and understanding for mental hunchbacks who have been conditioned negatively. To understand all is to forgive all.

16. Rejoice in the success, promotion, and good fortune of the other. In doing so, you attract good fortune to yourself.

17. Never yield to emotional scenes and tantrums of others. Appeasement never wins. Do not be a doormat. Adhere to that which is right. Stick to your ideal, knowing that the mental outlook which gives you peace, happiness, and joy is right, good, and true. What blesses you, blesses all.

18. All you owe any person in the world is love, and love is wishing for everyone what you wish for yourself—health, happiness, and all the blessings of life.

17

How to Use Your Subconscious Mind for Forgiveness

Life plays no favorites. God is Life, and this Life-Principle is flowing through you this moment. God loves to express Himself as harmony, peace, beauty, joy, and abundance through you. This is called the will of God or the tendency of Life.

If you set up resistance in your mind to the flow of Life through you, this emotional congestion will get snarled up in your subconscious mind and cause all kinds of negative conditions. God has nothing to do with unhappy or chaotic conditions in the world. All these conditions are brought about by man's negative and destructive thinking. Therefore, it is silly to blame God for your trouble or sickness.

Many persons habitually set up mental resistance to the flow of Life by accusing and reproaching God for the sin, sickness, and suffering of mankind. Others cast the blame on God for their pains, aches, loss of loved ones, personal tragedies, and accidents. They are angry at God, and they believe He is responsible for their misery.

As long as people entertain such negative concepts about God, they will experience the automatic negative reactions from their subconscious minds. Actually, such people do not know that they are punishing themselves. They must see the truth, find release, and give up all condemnation, resentment, and anger against anyone or any power outside themselves. Otherwise, they cannot go forward into a healthy, happy, or creative activity. The minute these people entertain a God of love in their minds and hearts, and when they believe that God is their

Loving Father who watches over them, cares for them, guides them, sustains and strengthens them, this concept and belief about God or the Life-Principle will be accepted by their subconscious mind, and they will find themselves blessed in countless ways.

• Life always forgives you

Life forgives you when you cut your finger. The subconscious intelligence within you sets about immediately to repair it. New cells build bridges over the cut. Should you take some tainted food by error, Life forgives you and causes you to regurgitate it in order to preserve you. If you burn your hand, the Life-Principle reduces the edema and congestion, and gives you new skin, tissue, and cells. Life holds no grudges against you, and it is always forgiving you. Life brings you back to health, vitality, harmony, and peace, if you co-operate by thinking in harmony with nature. Negative, hurtful memories, bitterness, and ill will clutter up and impede the free flow of the Life-Principle in you.

• How he banished that feeling of guilt

I knew a man who worked every night until about one o'clock in the morning. He paid no attention to his two boys or his wife. He was always too busy working hard. He thought people should pat him on the back because he was working so arduously and persistently past midnight every night. He had a blood pressure of over two hundred and was full of guilt. Unconsciously, he proceeded to punish himself by hard work and he completely ignored his children. A normal man does not do that. He is interested in his boys and in their development. He does not shut his wife out of his world.

I explained to him why he was working so arduously, "There is something eating you inside, otherwise, you would not act this way. You are punishing yourself, and you have to learn to forgive yourself." He did have a deep sense of guilt. It was toward a brother.

I explained to him that God was not punishing him, but

that he was punishing himself. For example, if you misuse the laws of life, you will suffer accordingly. If you put your hand on a naked charged wire, you will get burned. The forces of nature are not evil; it is your use of them that determines whether they have a good or evil effect. Electricity is not evil; it depends on how you use it, whether to. burn down a structure or light up a home. The only sin is ignorance of the law, and the only punishment is the automatic reaction of man's misuse of the law.

If you misuse the principle of chemistry, you may blow up the office or the factory. If you strike your hand on a board, you may cause your hand to bleed. The board is not for that purpose. Its purpose may be to lean upon or to support your feet.

This man realized that God does not condemn or punish anyone, and that all his suffering was due to the reaction of his subconscious mind to his own negative and destructive thinking. He had cheated his brother at one time, and the brother had now passed on. Still, he was full of remorse and guilt.

I asked him, "Would you cheat your brother now?"

He said, "No."

"Did you feel you were justified at the time?"

His reply was, "Yes."

"But, you would not do it now?"

He added, "No, I am helping others to know how to live."

I added the following comment, "You have a greater reason and understanding now. Forgiveness is to forgive yourself. Forgiveness is getting your thoughts in line with the divine law of harmony. Self-condemnation is called hell (bondage and restriction); forgiveness is called heaven (harmony and peace)."

The burden of guilt and self-condemnation was lifted from his mind, and he had a complete healing. The doctor tested his blood pressure, and it had become normal. The explanation was the cure.

• A murderer learned to forgive himself

A man who murdered his brother in Europe visited me many years ago. He was suffering from great mental anguish and torture believing that God must punish him. He explained that his brother had been having an affair with his wife, and that he had shot him on the spur of the moment. This had happened about fifteen years previous to his interview with me. In the meantime, this man had married an American girl and had been blessed with three lovely children. He was in a position where he helped many people, and he was a transformed man.

My explanation to him was that physically and psychologically he was not the same man who shot his brother, since scientists inform us that every cell of our bodies changes every eleven months. Moreover, mentally and spiritually he was a new man. He was now full of love and good will for humanity. The "old" man who committed the crime fifteen years before was mentally and spiritually dead. Actually, he was condemning an innocent man!

This explanation had a profound effect upon him, and he said it was as if a great weight had been lifted from his mind. He realized the significance of the following truth in the Bible: *Come now, let us reason together, saith the Lord: though your sins be as scarlet, they shall be as white as snow; though they be red like crimson, they shall be as wool.* ISAIAH 1:18.

• Criticism cannot hurt you without your consent

A schoolteacher told me that one of her associates criticized a speech she had given, saying to her that she spoke too fast, she swallowed some of her words, she couldn't be heard, her diction was poor, and her speech ineffective. This teacher was furious and full of resentment toward her critic.

She admitted to me that the criticisms were just. Her first reaction was really childish, and she agreed that the letter was really a blessing and a marvelous corrective. She proceeded immediately to supplement her deficiencies in her speech by

enrolling in a course in public speaking at City College. She
wrote and thanked the writer of the note for her interest, expressing appreciation for her conclusions and findings which
enabled the teacher to correct the matter at once.

• How to be compassionate

Suppose none of the things mentioned in the letter had
been true of the teacher. The latter would have realized that
her class material had upset the prejudices, superstitions, or
narrow sectarian beliefs of the writer of the note, and that a
psychologically ill person was simply pouring forth her resentment because a psychological boil had been hurt.

To understand this fact is to be compassionate. The next
logical step would be to pray for the other person's peace, harmony, and understanding. You cannot be hurt when you know
that you are master of your thoughts, reactions, and emotions.
Emotions follow thoughts, and you have the power to reject
all thoughts which may disturb or upset you.

• Left at the altar

Some years ago I visited a church to perform a marriage
ceremony. The young man did not appear, and at the end of
two hours, the bride-to-be shed a few tears, and then said to me,
"I prayed for divine guidance. This might be the answer for
He never faileth."

That was her reaction—faith in God and all things good.
She had no bitterness in her heart because as she said, "It must
not have been right action because my prayer was for right
action for both of us." Someone else having a similar experience
would have gone into a tantrum, have had an emotional fit, required sedation, and perhaps needed hospitalization.

Tune in with the infinite intelligence within your subconscious depths, trusting the answer in the same way that you
trusted your mother when she held you in her arms. This is how
you can acquire poise and mental and emotional health.

• It is wrong to marry. Sex is evil and I am evil

Some time ago I talked to a young lady aged twenty-two. She was taught that it was a sin to dance, to play cards, to swim, and to go out with men. She was threatened by her mother who told her she would burn eternally in hell-fire if she disobeyed her will and her religious teachings. This girl wore a black dress and black stockings. She wore no rouge, lipstick, or any form of make-up because her mother said that these things were sinful. Her mother told her that all men were evil, and that sex was of the devil and simply diabolic debauchery.

This girl had to learn how to forgive herself as she was full of guilt. To forgive means to give for. She had to give up all these false beliefs for the truths of life and a new estimate of herself. When she went out with young men in the office where she worked, she had a deep sense of guilt and thought that God would punish her. Several eligible young men proposed to her, but she said to me, "It is wrong to marry. Sex is evil and I am evil." This was her conscience or early conditioning speaking.

She came to me once weekly for about ten weeks, and I taught her the workings of the conscious and subconscious mind as set forth in this book. This young girl gradually came to see that she had been completely brainwashed, mesmerized, and conditioned by an ignorant, superstitious, bigoted, and frustrated mother. She broke away completely from her family and started to live a wonderful life.

At my suggestion she dressed up and had her hair attended to. She took lessons in dancing from a *man*, and she also took driving lessons. She learned to swim, play cards, and had a number of dates. She began to love life. She prayed for a divine companion by claiming that Infinite Spirit would attract to her a man who harmonized with her thoroughly. Eventually this came to pass. As she left my office one evening, there was a man waiting to see me and I casually introduced them. They are now married and harmonize with each other perfectly.

• Forgiveness is necessary for healing

And when ye stand praying, forgive, if ye have ought against any . . . MARK 11:25.

Forgiveness of others is essential to mental peace and radiant health. You must forgive everyone who has ever hurt you if you want perfect health and happiness. Forgive yourself by getting your thoughts in harmony with divine law and order. You cannot really forgive yourself completely until you have forgiven others first. To refuse to forgive yourself is nothing more or less than spiritual pride or ignorance.

In the psychosomatic field of medicine today, it is being constantly stressed that resentment, condemnation of others, remorse, and hostility are behind a host of maladies ranging from arthritis to cardiac disease. They point out that these sick people, who were hurt, mistreated, deceived, or injured, were full of resentment and hatred for those who hurt them. This caused inflamed and festering wounds in their subconscious minds. There is only one remedy. They have to cut out and discard their hurts, and the one and only sure way is by forgiveness.

• Forgiveness is love in action

The essential ingredient in the art of forgiveness is the willingness to forgive. If you sincerely desire to forgive the other, you are fifty-one percent over the hurdle. I feel sure you know that to forgive the other does not necessarily mean that you like him or want to associate with him. You cannot be compelled to like someone, neither can a government legislate good will, love, peace, or tolerance. It is quite impossible to like people because someone in Washington issues an edict to that effect. We can, however, love people without liking them.

The Bible says, *Love ye one another.* This, anyone can do who really wants to do it. Love means that you wish for the other health, happiness, peace, joy, and all the blessings of life. There is only one prerequisite, and that is sincerity. You are not being magnanimous when you forgive, you are really being selfish, because what you wish for the other, you are actually wishing for yourself. The reason is that you are thinking it and you are feeling it. As you think and feel, so are you. Could anything be simpler than that?

• Technique of forgiveness

The following is a simple method which works wonders in your life as you practice it: Quiet your mind, relax, and let go. Think of God and His love for you, and then affirm, "I fully and freely forgive (mention the name of the offender); I release him mentally and spiritually. I completely forgive everything connected with the matter in question. I am free, and he/she is free. It is a marvelous feeling. It is my day of general amnesty. I release anybody and everybody who has ever hurt me, and I wish for each and everyone health, happiness, peace, and all the blessings of life. I do this freely, joyously, and lovingly, and whenever I think of the person or persons who hurt me, I say, 'I have released you, and all the blessings of life are yours.' I am free and you are free. It is wonderful!"

The great secret of true forgiveness is that once you have forgiven the person, it is unnecessary to repeat the prayer. Whenever the person comes to your mind, or the particular hurt happens to enter your mind, wish the delinquent well, and say, "Peace be to you." Do this as often as the thought enters your mind. You will find that after a few days the thought of the person or experience will return less and less often, until it fades into nothingness.

• The acid test for forgiveness

There is an acid test for gold. There is also an acid test for forgiveness. If I should tell you something wonderful about someone who has wronged you, cheated you, or defrauded you, and you sizzled at hearing the good news about this person, the roots of hatred would still be in your subconscious mind, playing havoc with you.

Let us suppose you had a painful abscess on your jaw a year ago, and you told me about it. I would casually ask you if you had any pain now. You would automatically say, "Of course not, I have a memory of it but no pain." That is the whole story. You may have a memory of the incident but no sting or hurt any more. This is the acid test, and you must meet it psychologically and spiritually, otherwise, you are simply deceiving yourself and not practicing the true art of forgiveness.

• To understand all is to forgive all

When man understands the creative law of his own mind, he ceases to blame other people and conditions for making or marring his life. He knows that his own thoughts and feelings create his destiny. Furthermore, he is aware that externals are not the causes and conditioners of his life and his experiences. To think that others can mar your happiness, that you are the football of a cruel fate, that you must oppose and fight others for a living—all these and others like them are untenable when you understand that thoughts are things. The Bible says the same thing. *For as a man thinketh in his heart, so is he.* PROVERBS 23:7.

• Summary of your aids to forgiveness

1. God, or Life, is no respecter of persons. Life plays no favorites. Life, or God, seems to favor you when you align yourself with the principle of harmony, health, joy, and peace.

2. God, or Life, never sends disease, sickness, accident, or suffering. We bring these things on ourselves by our own negative destructive thinking based upon the law *as we sow, so shall we reap.*

3. Your concept of God is the most important thing in your life. If you really believe in a God of love, your subconscious mind will respond in countless blessings to you. Believe in a God of love.

4. Life, or God, holds no grudge against you. Life never condemns you. Life heals a severe cut on your hand. Life forgives you if you burn your finger. It reduces the edema and restores the part to wholeness and perfection.

5. Your guilt complex is a false concept of God and Life.

God, or Life, does not punish or judge you. You do this to yourself by your false beliefs, negative thinking, and self-condemnation.

6. God, or Life, does not condemn or punish you. The forces of nature are not evil. The effect of their use depends on how you use the power within you. You can use electricity to kill someone or to light the house. You can use water to drown a child, or quench his thirst. Good and evil come right back to the thought and purpose in man's own mind.

7. God, or Life, never punishes. Man punishes himself by his false concepts of God, Life, and the Universe. His thoughts are creative, and he creates his own misery.

8. If another criticizes you, and these faults are within you, rejoice, give thanks, and appreciate the comments. This gives you the opportunity to correct the particular fault.

9. You cannot be hurt by criticism when you know that you are master of your thoughts, reactions, and emotions. This gives you the opportunity to pray and bless the other, thereby blessing yourself.

10. When you pray for guidance and right action, take what comes. Realize it is good and very good. Then there is no cause for self-pity, criticism, or hatred.

11. There is nothing good or bad, but thinking makes it so. There is no evil in sex, the desire for food, wealth, or true expression. It depends on how you use these urges, desires, or aspirations. Your desire for food can be met without killing someone for a loaf of bread.

12. Resentment, hatred, ill will, and hostility are behind a host of maladies. Forgive yourself and everybody else by pouring out love, life, joy, and good will to all those who have hurt you. Continue until such time as you meet them in your mind and you are at peace with them.

13. To forgive is to *give something for*. Give love, peace, joy, wisdom, and all the blessings of life to the other, until there is no sting left in your mind. This is really the acid test of forgiveness.

14. Let us suppose you had an abscess in your jaw about a year

ago. It was very painful. Ask yourself if it is painful now.
The answer is in the negative. Likewise, if someone has hurt
you, lied about and vilified you, and said all manner of
evil about you, is your thought of that person negative? Do
you sizzle when he or she comes into your mind? If so, the
roots of hatred are still there, playing havoc with you and
your good. The only way is to wither them with love by
wishing for the person all the blessings of life, until you
can meet the person in your mind, and you can sincerely
react with a benediction of peace and good will. This is
the meaning of *forgive until seventy times seven.*

18

How Your Subconscious
Removes Mental Blocks

The solution lies within the problem. The answer is in every question. If you are presented with a difficult situation and you cannot see your way clear, the best procedure is to assume that infinite intelligence within your subconscious mind knows all and sees all, has the answer, and is revealing it to you now. Your new mental attitude that the creative intelligence is bringing about a happy solution will enable you to find the answer. Rest assured that such an attitude of mind will bring order, peace, and meaning to all your undertakings.

• How to break or build a habit

You are a creature of habit. Habit is the function of your subconscious mind. You learned to swim, ride a bicycle, dance, and drive a car by consciously doing these things over and over again until they established tracks in your subconscious mind. Then, the automatic habit action of your subconscious mind took over. This is sometimes called second nature which is a reaction of your subconscious mind to your thinking and acting.

You are free to choose a good habit or a bad habit. If you repeat a negative thought or act over a period of time, you will be under the compulsion of a habit. The law of your subconscious is compulsion.

• How he broke a bad habit

Mr. Jones said to me, "An uncontrollable urge to drink seizes me, and I remain drunk for two weeks at a time. I can't give up this terrible habit."

Time and time again these experiences had occurred to this unfortunate man. He had grown into the habit of drinking to excess. Although he had started drinking of his own initiative, he also began to realize that he could change the habit and establish a new one. He said that while through his will power he was able to suppress his desires temporarily, his continued efforts to suppress the many urges only made matters worse. His repeated failures convinced him that he was hopeless and powerless to control his urge or obsession. This idea of being powerless operated as a powerful suggestion to his subconscious mind and aggravated his weakness, making his life a succession of failures.

I taught him to harmonize the functions of the conscious and subconscious mind. When these two cooperate, the idea or desire implanted in the subconscious mind is realized. His reasoning mind agreed that if the old habit path or track had carried him into trouble, he could consciously form a new path to freedom, sobriety, and peace of mind. He knew that his destructive habit was automatic, but since it was acquired through his conscious choice, he realized that if he had been conditioned negatively, he also could be conditioned positively. As a result, he ceased thinking of the fact that he was powerless to overcome the habit. Moreover, he understood clearly that there was no obstacle to his healing other than his own thought. Therefore, there was no occasion for great mental effort or mental coercion.

• The power of his mental picture

This man acquired a practice of relaxing his body and getting into a relaxed, drowsy, meditative state. Then he filled his mind with the picture of the desired end, knowing his subconscious mind could bring it about the easiest way. He imagined his daughter congratulating him on his freedom, and saying to him, "Daddy, it's wonderful to have you home!" He had lost his family through drink. He was not allowed to visit them, and his wife would not speak to him.

Regularly, systematically, he used to sit down and meditate in the way outlined. When his attention wandered, he made it a habit to immediately recall the mental picture of his daughter with her smile and the scene of his home enlivened by her cheerful voice. All this brought about a reconditioning of his mind. It was a gradual process. He kept it up. He persevered knowing that sooner or later he would establish a new habit pattern in his subconscious mind.

I told him that he could liken his conscious mind to a camera, that his subconscious mind was the sensitive plate on which he registered and impressed the picture. This made a profound impression on him, and his whole aim was to firmly impress the picture on his mind and develop it there. Films are developed in the dark; likewise, mental pictures are developed in the darkroom of the subconscious mind.

• Focused attention

Realizing that his conscious mind was simply a camera, he used no effort. There was no mental struggle. He quietly adjusted his thoughts and focused his attention on the scene before him until he gradually became identified with the picture. He became absorbed in the mental atmosphere, repeating the mental movie frequently. There was no room for doubt that a healing would follow. When there was any temptation to drink, he would switch his imagination from any roveries of drinking bouts to the feeling of being at home with his family. He was successful because he confidently expected to experience the picture he was developing in his mind. Today he is president of a multimillion-dollar concern and is radiantly happy.

• He said a jinx was following him

Mr. Block said that he had been making an annual income of $20,000, but for the past three months all doors seemed to jam tightly. He brought clients up to the point where they were about to sign on the dotted line, and then at the eleventh hour the door closed. He added that perhaps a jinx was following him.

In discussing the matter with Mr. Block, I discovered that three months previously he had become very irritated, annoyed, and resentful toward a dentist who, after he had promised to sign a contract, had withdrawn at the last moment. He began to live in the unconscious fear that other clients would do the same, thereby setting up a history of frustration, hostility, and obstacles. He gradually built up in his mind a belief in obstruction and last minute cancellations until a vicious circle had been established. *What I fear most has come upon me.* Mr. Block realized that the trouble was in his own mind, and that it was essential to change his mental attitude.

His run of so-called misfortune was broken in the following way: "I realize I am one with the infinite intelligence of my subconscious mind which knows no obstacle, difficulty, or delay. I live in the joyous expectancy of the best. My deeper mind responds to my thoughts. I know that the work of the infinite power of my subconscious cannot be hindered. Infinite intelligence always finishes successfully whatever it begins. Creative wisdom works through me bringing all my plans and purposes to completion. Whatever I start, I bring to a successful conclusion. My aim in life is to give wonderful service, and all those whom I contact are blessed by what I have to offer. All my work comes to full fruition in divine order."

He repeated this prayer every morning before going to call on his customers, and he also prayed each night prior to sleep. In a short time he had established a new habit pattern in his subconscious mind, and he was back in his old accustomed stride as a successful salesman.

• How much do you want what you want?

A young man asked Socrates how he could get wisdom. Socrates replied, "Come with me." He took the lad to a river, pushed the boy's head under the water, held it there until the boy was gasping for air, then relaxed and released his head. When the boy regained his composure, he asked him, "What did you desire most when you were under water?"

"I wanted air," said the boy.

Socrates said to him, "When you want wisdom as much as

you wanted air when you were immersed in the water, you will receive it."

Likewise, when you really have an intense desire to overcome any block in your life, and you come to a clear-cut decision that there is a way out, and that is the course you wish to follow, then victory and triumph are assured.

If you really want peace of mind and inner calm, you will get it. Regardless of how unjustly you have been treated, or how unfair the boss has been, or what a mean scoundrel someone has proved to be, all this makes no difference to you when you awaken to your mental and spiritual powers. You know what you want, and you will definitely refuse to let the thieves (thoughts) of hatred, anger, hostility, and ill will rob you of peace, harmony, health, and happiness. You cease to become upset by people, conditions, news, and events by identifying your thoughts immediately with your aim in life. Your aim is peace, health, inspiration, harmony, and abundance. Feel a river of peace flowing through you now. Your thought is the immaterial and invisible power, and you choose to let it bless, inspire, and give you peace.

• Why he could not be healed

This is a case history of a married man with four children who was supporting and secretly living with another woman during his business trips. He was ill, nervous, irritable, and cantankerous, and he could not sleep without drugs. The doctor's medicine failed to bring down his high blood pressure of over two hundred. He had pains in numerous organs of his body which doctors could not diagnose or relieve. To make matters worse, he was drinking heavily.

The cause of all this was a deep unconscious sense of guilt. He had violated the marriage vows, and this troubled him. The religious creed he was brought up on was deeply lodged in his subconscious mind, and he drank excessively to heal the wound of guilt. Some invalids take morphine and codeine for severe pains; he was taking alcohol for the pain or wound in his mind. It was the old story of adding fuel to the fire.

• The explanation and the cure

He listened to the explanation of how his mind worked. He faced his problem, looked at it, and gave up his dual role. He knew that his drinking was an unconscious attempt to escape. The hidden cause lodged in his subconscious mind had to be eradicated; then the healing would follow.

He began to impress his subconscious mind three or four times a day by using the following prayer: "My mind is full of peace, poise, balance, and equilibrium. The infinite lies stretched in smiling repose within me. I am not afraid of anything in the past, the present, or the future. The infinite intelligence of my subconscious mind leads, guides, and directs me in all ways. I now meet every situation with faith, poise, calmness, and confidence. I am now completely free from the habit. My mind is full of inner peace, freedom, and joy. I forgive myself; then I am forgiven. Peace, sobriety, and confidence reign supreme in my mind."

He repeated this prayer frequently as outlined, being fully aware of what he was doing and why he was doing it. Knowing what he was doing gave him the necessary faith and confidence. I explained to him that as he spoke these statements out loud, slowly, lovingly, and meaningfully, they would gradually sink down into his subconscious mind. Like seeds, they would grow after their kind. These truths, on which he concentrated, went in through his eyes, his ears heard the sound, and the healing vibrations of these words reached his subconscious mind and obliterated all the negative mental patterns which caused all the trouble. Light dispels darkness. The constructive thought destroys the negative thought. He became a transformed man within a month.

• Refusing to admit it

If you are an alcoholic or drug addict, admit it. Do not dodge the issue. Many people remain alcoholics because they refuse to admit it.

Your disease is an instability, an inner fear. You are

refusing to face life, and so you try to escape your responsibilities through the bottle. As an alcoholic you have no free will, although you think you have, and you may even boast about your will power. If you are a habitual drunkard and say bravely, "I will not touch it any more," you have no power to make this assertion come true, because you do not know where to locate the power.

You are living in a psychological prison of your own making, and you are bound by your beliefs, opinions, training, and environmental influences. Like most people, you are a creature of habit. You are conditioned to react the way you do.

• Building in the idea of freedom

You can build the idea of freedom and peace of mind into your mentality so that it reaches your subconscious depths. The latter, being all-powerful, will free you from all desire for alcohol. Then, you will have the new understanding of how your mind works, and you can truly back up your statement and prove the truth to yourself.

• Fifty-one percent healed

If you have a keen desire to free yourself from any destructive habit, you are fifty-one percent healed already. When you have a greater desire to give up the bad habit than to continue it, you will not experience too much difficulty in gaining complete freedom.

Whatever thought you anchor the mind upon, the latter magnifies. If you engage the mind on the concept of freedom (freedom from the habit) and peace of mind, and if you keep it focused on this new direction of attention, you generate feelings and emotions which gradually emotionalize the concept of freedom and peace. Whatever idea you emotionalize is accepted by your subconscious and brought to pass.

• The law of substitution

Realize that something good can come out of your suffering. You have not suffered in vain. However, it is foolish to continue to suffer.

If you continue as an alcoholic, it will bring about mental and physical deterioration and decay. Realize that the power in your subconscious is backing you up. Even though you may be seized with melancholia, you should begin to imagine the joy of freedom that is in store for you. This is the law of substitution. Your imagination took you to the bottle; let it take you now to freedom and peace of mind. You will suffer a little bit, but it is for a constructive purpose. You will bear it like a mother in the pangs of childbirth, and you will, likewise, bring forth a child of the mind. Your subconscious will give birth to sobriety.

• Cause of alcoholism

The real cause of alcoholism is negative and destructive thinking; for as a man thinketh, so is he. The alcoholic has a deep sense of inferiority, inadequacy, defeat, and frustration, usually accompanied by a deep inner hostility. He has countless alibis as to his reason for drinking, but the sole reason is in his *thought life*.

• Three magic steps

The first step: Get still; quiet the wheels of the mind. Enter into a sleepy, drowsy state. In this relaxed, peaceful, receptive state, you are preparing for the second step.

The second step: Take a brief phrase, which can readily be graven on the memory, and repeat it over and over as a lullaby. Use the phrase, "Sobriety and peace of mind are mine now, and I give thanks." To prevent the mind from wandering, repeat it aloud or sketch its pronunciation with the lips and tongue as you say it mentally. This helps its entry into the subconscious mind. Do this for five minutes or more. You will find a deep emotional response.

The third step: Just before going to sleep, practice what Johann von Goethe, German author, used to do. Imagine a friend, a loved one in front of you. Your eyes are closed, you are relaxed and at peace. The loved one or friend is subjectively present, and is saying to you, "Congratulations!" You see the smile; you hear the voice. You mentally touch the hand; it is all real and vivid. The word *congratulations* implies complete freedom. Hear it over and over again until you get the subconscious reaction which satisfies.

• Keep on keeping on

When fear knocks at the door of your mind, or when worry, anxiety, and doubt cross your mind, behold your vision, your goal. Think of the infinite power within your subconscious mind, which you can generate by your thinking and imagining, and this will give you confidence, power, and courage. Keep on, persevere, *until the day breaks, and the shadows flee away.*

• Review your thought power

1. The solution lies within the problem. The answer is in every question. Infinite intelligence responds to you as you call upon it with faith and confidence.

2. Habit is the function of your subconscious mind. There is no greater evidence of the marvelous power of your subconscious than the force and sway habit holds in your life. You are a creature of habit.

3. You form habit patterns in your subconscious mind by repeating a thought and act over and over again until it establishes tracks in the subconscious mind and becomes automatic, such as swimming, dancing, typing, walking, driving your car, etc.

4. You have freedom to choose. You can choose a good habit or a bad habit. Prayer is a good habit.

5. Whatever mental picture, backed by faith, you behold in your conscious mind, your subconscious mind will bring to pass.

6. The only obstacle to your success and achievement is your own thought or mental image.

7. When your attention wanders, bring it back to the contemplation of your good or goal. Make a habit of this. This is called disciplining the mind.

8. Your conscious mind is the camera, and your subconscious mind is the sensitive plate on which you register or impress the picture.

9. The only jinx that follows anyone is a fear thought repeated over and over in the mind. Break the jinx by knowing that whatever you start you will bring to a conclusion in divine order. Picture the happy ending and sustain it with confidence.

10. To form a new habit, you must be convinced that it is desirable. When your desire to give up the bad habit is greater than your desire to continue, you are fifty-one percent healed already.

11. The statements of others cannot hurt you except through your own thoughts and mental participation. Identify yourself with your aim which is peace, harmony, and joy. You are the only thinker in your universe.

12. Excessive drinking is an unconscious desire to escape. The cause of alcoholism is negative and destructive thinking. The cure is to think of freedom, sobriety, and perfection, and to feel the thrill of accomplishment.

13. Many people remain alcoholics because they refuse to admit it.

14. The law of your subconscious mind, which held you in bondage and inhibited your freedom of action, will give you freedom and happiness. It depends on how you use it.

15. Your imagination took you to the bottle; let it take you to freedom by imagining you are free.

16. The real cause of alcoholism is negative and destructive thinking. *As a man thinketh in his heart* [subconscious mind], *so is he.*

17. When fear knocks at the door of your mind, let faith in God and all things good open the door.

19

How to Use Your Subconscious Mind to Remove Fear

One of our students told me that he was invited to speak at a banquet. He said he was panic-stricken at the thought of speaking before a thousand people. He overcame his fear this way: For several nights he sat down in an armchair for about five minutes and said to himself slowly, quietly, and positively, "I am going to master this fear. I am overcoming it now. I speak with poise and confidence. I am relaxed and at ease." He operated a definite law of mind and overcame his fear.

The subconscious mind is amenable to suggestion and is controlled by suggestion. When you still your mind and relax, the thoughts of your conscious mind sink down into the subconscious through a process similar to osmosis, whereby fluids separated by a porous membrane intermingle. As these positive seeds, or thoughts, sink into the subconscious area, they grow after their kind, and you become poised, serene, and calm.

• Man's greatest enemy

It is said that fear is man's greatest enemy. Fear is behind failure, sickness, and poor human relations. Millions of people are afraid of the past, the future, old age, insanity, and death. Fear is a thought in your mind, and you are afraid of your own thoughts.

A little boy can be paralyzed with fear when he is told there is a boogie man under his bed who is going to take him away. When his father turns on the light and shows him there is no boogie man, he is freed from fear. The fear in the mind of the boy was as real as if there really was a boogie man there. He was healed of a false thought in his mind. The thing he feared did not exist. Likewise, most of your fears have no reality. They are merely a conglomeration of sinister shadows, and shadows have no reality.

• Do the thing you fear

Ralph Waldo Emerson, philosopher and poet, said, "Do the thing you are afraid to do, and the death of fear is certain."

There was a time when the writer of this chapter was filled with unutterable fear when standing before an audience. The way I overcame it was to stand before the audience, do the thing I was afraid to do, and the death of fear was certain.

When you affirm positively that you are going to master your fears, and you come to a definite decision in your conscious mind, you release the power of the subconscious, which flows in response to the nature of your thought.

• Banishing stage fright

A young lady was invited to an audition. She had been looking forward to the interview. However, on three previous occasions, she had failed miserably due to stage fright.

She possessed a very good voice, but she was certain that when the time came for her to sing, she would be seized with stage fright. The subconscious mind takes your fears as a request, proceeds to manifest them, and brings them into your experience. On three previous auditions she sang wrong notes, and she finally broke down and cried. The cause, as previously outlined, was an involuntary autosuggestion, i.e., a silent fear thought emotionalized and subjectified.

She overcame it by the following technique: Three times a day she isolated herself in a room. She sat down comfortably in an armchair, relaxed her body, and closed her eyes. She stilled her mind and body to the best of her ability. Physical inertia favors passivity and renders the mind more receptive to suggestion. She counteracted the fear suggestion by its converse, saying to herself, "I sing beautifully. I am poised, serene, confident, and calm."

She repeated the words slowly, quietly, and with feeling from five to ten times at each sitting. She had three such "sittings" every day and one immediately prior to sleep at night. At the end of a week she was completely poised and confident, and gave a definitely outstanding audition. Carry out the above procedure, and the death of fear is certain.

• Fear of failure

Occasionally young men from the local university come to see me, as well as schoolteachers, who often seem to suffer from suggestive amnesia at examinations. The complaint is always the same: "I know the answers after the examination is over, but I can't remember the answers during the examination."

The idea, which realizes itself, is the one to which we invariably give concentrated attention. I find that each one is obsessed with the idea of failure. Fear is behind the temporary amnesia, and it is the cause of the whole experience.

One young medical student was the most brilliant person in his class, yet he found himself failing to answer simple questions at the time of written or oral examinations. I explained to him that the reason was he had been worrying and was fearful for several days previous to the examination. These negative thoughts became charged with fear.

Thoughts enveloped in the powerful emotion of fear are realized in the subconscious mind. In other words, this young man was requesting his subconscious mind to see to it that he failed, and that is exactly what it did. On the day of the examination he found himself stricken with what is called, in psychological circles, suggestive amnesia.

• How he overcame the fear

He learned that his subconscious mind was the storehouse of memory, and that it had a perfect record of all he had heard and read during his medical training. Moreover, he learned that the subconscious mind was responsive and reciprocal. The way to be *en rapport* with it was to be relaxed, peaceful, and confident.

Every night and morning he began to imagine his mother congratulating him on his wonderful record. He would hold an imaginary letter from her in his hand. As he began to contemplate the happy result, he called forth a corresponding or reciprocal response or reaction in himself. The all-wise and omnipotent power of the subconscious took over, dictated, and directed his conscious mind accordingly. He imagined the end, thereby willing the means to the realization of the end. Following this procedure, he had no trouble passing subsequent examinations. In other words, the subjective wisdom took over, compelling him to give an excellent account of himself.

• Fear of water, mountains, closed places, etc.

There are many people who are afraid to go into an elevator, climb mountains, or even swim in the water. It may well be that the individual had unpleasant experiences in the water in his youth, such as having been thrown forcibly into the water without being able to swim. He might have been forcibly detained in an elevator, which failed to function properly, causing resultant fear of closed places.

I had an experience when I was about ten years of age. I accidentally fell into a pool and went down three times. I can still remember the dark water engulfing my head, and my gasping for air until another boy pulled me out at the last moment. This experience sank into my subconscious mind, and for years I feared the water.

An elderly psychologist said to me, "Go down to the swimming pool, look at the water, and say out loud in strong tones, 'I am going to master you. I can dominate you.' Then go into the water, take lessons, and overcome it." This I did, and I mastered the water. Do not permit water to master you. Remember, you are the master of the water.

When I assumed a new attitude of mind, the omnipotent power of the subconscious responded, giving me strength, faith, and confidence, and enabling me to overcome my fear.

• Master technique for overcoming any particular fear

The following is a process and technique for overcoming fear which I teach from the patform. It works like a charm. Try it!

Suppose you are afraid of the water, a mountain, an interview, an audition, or you fear closed places. If you are afraid of swimming, begin now to sit still for five or ten minutes three or four times a day, and imagine you are swimming. Actually, you are swimming in your mind. It is a subjective experience. Mentally you have projected yourself into the water. You feel the chill of the water and the movement of your arms and legs. It is all real, vivid, and a joyous activity of the mind. It is not idle daydreaming, for you know that what you are experiencing in your imagination will be developed in your subconscious mind. Then you will be compelled to express the image and likeness of the picture you impressed on your deeper mind. This is the law of the subconscious.

You could apply the same technique if you are afraid of mountains or high places. Imagine you are climbing the mountain, feel the reality of it all, enjoy the scenery, knowing that as you continue to do this mentally, you will do it physically with ease and comfort.

• He blessed the elevator

I knew an executive of a large corporation who was terrified to ride in an elevator. He would walk up five flights of stairs to his office every morning. He said that he began to bless the elevator every night and several times a day. He finally overcame his fear. This was how he blessed the elevator: "The elevator in our building is a wonderful idea. It came out of the universal mind. It is a boon and a blessing to all our employees. It gives wonderful service. It operates in divine order. I ride in it in peace and joy. I remain silent now while the currents of life, love, and understanding flow through the patterns of my thought. In my imagination I am now in the elevator, and I step out into my office. The elevator is full of our employees. I talk to them, and they are friendly, joyous, and free. It is a wonderful experience of freedom, faith, and confidence. I give thanks."

He continued this prayer for about ten days, and on the eleventh day, he walked into the elevator with other members of the organization and felt completely free.

• Normal and abnormal fear

Man is born only with two fears, the fear of falling and the fear of noise. These are a sort of alarm system given you by nature as a means of self-preservation. Normal fear is good. You hear an automobile coming down the road, and you step aside to survive. The momentary fear of being run over is overcome by your action. All other fears were given to you by parents, relatives, teachers, and all those who influenced your early years.

• Abnormal fear

Abnormal fear takes place when man lets his imagination run riot. I knew a woman who was invited to go on a trip around the world by plane. She began to cut out of the newspapers all reports of airplane catastrophes. She pictured herself going down in the ocean, being drowned, etc. This is abnormal fear. Had she persisted in this, she would undoubtedly have attracted what she feared most.

Another example of abnormal fear is that of a businessman in New York, who was very prosperous and successful. He had his own private mental motion picture of which he was the director. He would run this mental movie of failure, bankruptcy, empty shelves, and no bank balance until he sank into a deep depression. He refused to stop this morbid imagery and kept reminding his wife that "this can't last," "there will be a recession," "I feel sure we will go bankrupt," etc.

His wife told me that he finally did go into bankruptcy, and all the things he imagined and feared came to pass. The things he feared did not exist, but he brought them to pass by constantly fearing, believing, and expecting financial disaster. *Job said, the thing I feared has come upon me.*

There are people who are afraid that something terrible will happen to their children, and that some dread catastrophe will befall them. When they read about an epidemic or rare disease, they live in fear that they will catch it, and some imagine they have the disease already. All this is abnormal fear.

• The answer to abnormal fear

Move mentally to the opposite. To stay at the extreme of fear is stagnation plus mental and physical deterioration. When fear arises, there immediately comes with it a desire for something opposite to the thing feared. Place your attention on the thing immediately desired. Get absorbed and engrossed in your desire, knowing that the subjective always overturns the objective. This attitude will give you confidence and lift your spirits. The infinite power of your subconscious mind is moving on your behalf, and it cannot fail. Therefore, peace and assurance are yours.

• Examine your fears

The president of a large organization told me that when he was a salesman he used to walk around the block five or six times before he called on a customer. The sales manager came along one day and said to him, "Don't be afraid of the boogie man behind the door. There is no boogie man. It is a false belief."

The manager told him that whenever he looked at his own fears he stared them in the face and stood up to them, looking them straight in the eye. Then they faded and shrank into insignificance.

• He landed in the jungle

A chaplain told me of his experiences in the Second World War. He had to parachute from a damaged plane and land in the jungle. He said he was frightened, but he knew there were two kinds of fear, normal and abnormal, which we have previously pointed out.

He decided to do something about the fear immediately,

and began to talk to himself saying, "John, you can't surrender to your fear. Your fear is a desire for safety and security, and a way out."

He began to claim, "Infinite intelligence which guides the planets in their courses is now leading and guiding me out of this jungle."

He kept saying this out loud to himself for ten minutes or more. "Then," he added, "something began to stir inside me. A mood of confidence began to seize me, and I began to walk. After a few days, I miraculously came out of the jungle, and was picked up by a rescue plane."

His changed mental attitude saved him. His confidence and trust in the subjective wisdom and power within him was the solution to his problem.

He said, "Had I begun to bemoan my fate and indulge my fears, I would have succumbed to the monster fear, and probably would have died of fear and starvation."

• He dismissed himself

The general manager of an organization told me that for three years he feared he would lose his position. He was always imagining failure. The thing he feared did not exist, save as a morbid anxious thought in his own mind. His vivid imagination dramatized the loss of his job until he became nervous and neurotic. Finally he was asked to resign.

Actually, he dismissed himself. His constant negative imagery and fear suggestions to his subconscious mind caused the latter to respond and react accordingly. It caused him to make mistakes and foolish decisions, which resulted in his failure as a general manager. His dismissal would never have happened, if he had immediately moved to the opposite in his mind.

• They plotted against him

During a recent world lecture tour, I had a two-hour conversation with a prominent government official. He had a deep sense of inner peace and serenity. He said that all the abuse he receives politically from newspapers and the opposition party never disturb him. His practice is to sit still for fifteen minutes in the morning and realize that in the center of himself is a deep still ocean of peace. Meditating in this way, he generates tremendous power which overcomes all manner of difficulties and fears.

Some time previously, a colleague called him at midnight and told him a group of people were plotting against him. This is what he said to his colleague, "I am going to sleep now in perfect peace. You can discuss it with me at 10:00 A.M. tomorrow."

He said to me, "I know that no negative thought can ever manifest except I emotionalize the thought and accept it mentally. I refuse to entertain their suggestion of fear. Therefore, no harm can come to me."

Notice how calm he was, how cool, how peaceful! He did not start getting excited, tearing his hair, or wringing his hands. At his center he found the still water, an inner peace, and there was a great calm.

• Deliver yourself from all your fears

Use this perfect formula for casting out fear. *I sought the Lord, and He heard me, and delivered me from all my fears.* PSALM 34:4. The *Lord* is an ancient word meaning *law*—the power of your subconscious mind.

Learn the wonders of your subconscious, and how it works and functions. Master the techniques given to you in this chapter. Put them into practice now, today! Your subconscious will respond, and you will be free of all fears. *I sought the Lord, and He heard me, and delivered me from all my fears.*

• Step this way to freedom from fear

1. Do the thing you are afraid to do, and the death of fear is certain. Say to yourself and mean it, "I am going to master this fear," and you will.
2. Fear is a negative thought in your mind. Supplant it with a constructive thought. Fear has killed millions. Confidence

is greater than fear. Nothing is more powerful than faith in God and the good.

3. Fear is man's greatest enemy. It is behind failure, sickness, and bad human relations. Love casts out fear. Love is an emotional attachment to the good things of life. Fall in love with honesty, integrity, justice, good will, and success. Live in the joyous expectancy of the best, and invariably the best will come to you.

4. Counteract the fear suggestions with the opposite, such as "I sing beautifully; I am poised, serene, and calm." It will pay fabulous dividends.

5. Fear is behind amnesia at oral and written examination time. You can overcome this by affirming frequently, "I have a perfect memory for everything I need to know," or you can imagine a friend congratulating you on your brilliant success on the examination. Persevere and you will win.

6. If you are afraid to cross water, swim. In your imagination swim freely, joyously. Project yourself into the water mentally. Feel the chill and thrill of swimming across the pool. Make it vivid. As you do this subjectively, you will be compelled to go into the water and conquer it. This is the law of your mind.

7. If you are afraid of closed places, such as elevators, lecture halls, etc., mentally ride in an elevator blessing all its parts and functions. You will be amazed how quickly the fear will be dissipated.

8. You were born with only two fears, the fear of falling and the fear of noise. All your other fears were acquired. Get rid of them.

9. Normal fear is good. Abnormal fear is very bad and destructive. To constantly indulge in fear thoughts results in abnormal fear, obsessions, and complexes. To fear something persistently causes a sense of panic and terror.

10. You can overcome abnormal fear when you know the power of your subconscious mind can change conditions and bring to pass the cherished desires of your heart. Give

your immediate attention and devotion to your desire which is the opposite of your fear. This is the love that casts out fear.

11. If you are afraid of failure, give attention to success. If you are afraid of sickness, dwell on your perfect health. If you are afraid of an accident, dwell on the guidance and protection of God. If you are afraid of death, dwell on Eternal Life. God is Life, and that is your life now.

12. The great law of substitution is the answer to fear. Whatever you fear has its solution in the form of your desire. If you are sick, you desire health. If you are in the prison of fear, you desire freedom. Expect the good. Mentally concentrate on the good, and know that your subconscious mind answers you always. It never fails.

13. The things you fear do not really exist except as thoughts in your mind. Thoughts are creative. This why Job said, *The thing I feared has come upon me.* Think good and good follows.

14. Look at your fears; hold them up to the light of reason. Learn to laugh at your fears. That is the best medicine.

15. Nothing can disturb you but your own thought. The suggestions, statements, or threats of other persons have no power. The power is within you, and when your thoughts are focused on that which is good, then God's power is with your thoughts of good. There is only one Creative Power, and It moves as harmony. There are no divisions of quarrels in it. Its source is Love. This is why God's power is with your thoughts of good.

20

How to Stay Young in Spirit Forever

Your subconscious mind never grows old. It is timeless, ageless, and endless. It is a part of the universal mind of God which was never born, and it will never die.

Fatigue or old age cannot be predicated on any spiritual quality or power. Patience, kindness, veracity, humility, good will, peace, harmony, and brotherly love are attributes and qualities which never grow old. If you continue to generate these qualities here on this plane of life, you will always remain young in spirit.

I remember reading an article in one of our magazines some years ago which stated that a group of eminent medical men at the De Courcy Clinic, in Cincinnati, Ohio, reported that years alone are not responsible for bringing about degenerative disorders. These same physicians stated that it is the fear of time, not time itself, that has a harmful aging effect on our minds and bodies, and that the neurotic fear of the effects of time may well be the cause of premature aging.

During the many years of my public life, I have had occasion to study the biographies of the famous men and women who have continued their productive activities into the years well beyond the normal span of life. Some of them achieve their greatness in old age. At the same time, it has been my privilege to meet and to know countless individuals of no prominence who, in their lesser sphere, belonged to those hardy mortals who have proved that old age of itself does not destroy the creative powers of the mind and body.

• He had grown old in his thought life

A few years ago I called on an old friend in London, England. He was over 80 years of age, very ill, and obviously was yielding to his advancing years. Our conversation revealed his physical weakness, his sense of frustration, and a general deterioration almost approaching lifelessness. His cry was that he was useless and that no one wanted him. With an expression of hopelessness he betrayed his false philosophy, "We are born, grow up, become old, good for nothing, and that's the end."

This mental attitude of futility and worthlessness was the chief reason for his sickness. He was looking forward only to senescence, and after that—nothing. Indeed, he had grown old in his thought life, and his subconscious mind brought about all the evidence of his habitual thinking.

• Age is the dawn of wisdom

Unfortunately, many people have the same attitude as this unhappy man. They are afraid of what they term "old age," the end, and extinction, which really means that they are afraid of life. Yet, life is endless. Age is not the flight of years, but the dawn of wisdom.

Wisdom is an awareness of the tremendous spiritual powers in your subconscious mind and the knowledge of how to apply these powers to lead a full and happy life. Get it out of your head once and for all that 65, 75, or 85 years of age is synonymous with the end for you or anybody else. It can be the beginning of a glorious, fruitful, active, and most productive life pattern, better than you have ever experienced. Believe this, expect it, and your subconscious will bring it to pass.

• Welcome the change

Old age is not a tragic occurrence. What we call the aging process is really change. It is to be welcomed joyfully and gladly as each phase of human life is a step forward on the path which has no end. Man has powers which transcend his bodily powers. He has senses which transcend his five physical senses.

Scientists today are finding positive indisputable evidence that something conscious in man can leave his present body and travel thousands of miles to see, hear, touch, and speak to people even though his physical body never leaves the couch on which it reclines.

Man's life is spiritual and eternal. He need never grow old for Life, or God, cannot grow old. The Bible says that God is Life. Life is self-renewing, eternal, indestructible, and is the reality of all men.

• Evidence for survival

The evidence gathered by the psychical research societies both in Great Britain and America is overwhelming. You may go into any large metropolitan library and get volumes on *The Proceedings of the Psychical Research Society* based on findings of distinguished scientists on survival following so-called death. You will find a startling report on scientific experiments establishing the reality of life after death in *The Case for Psychic Survival* by Hereward Carrington, Director of the American Psychical Institute.

• Life is

A woman asked Thomas Edison, the electrical wizard, "Mr. Edison, what is electricity?"

He replied, "Madame, electricity is. Use it."

Electricity is a name we give an invisible power which we do not fully comprehend, but we learn all we can about the principle of electricity and its uses. We use it in countless ways.

The scientist cannot see an electron with his eyes, yet he accepts it as a scientific fact, because it is the only valid conclusion which coincides with his other experimental evidence. We cannot see life. However, we know we are alive. Life is, and we are here to express it in all its beauty and glory.

• Mind and spirit do not grow old

The Bible says, *And this is life eternal, that they might know thee the only true God.* JOHN 17:3.

The man who thinks or believes that the earthly cycle of birth, adolescence, youth, maturity, and old age is all there is to life, is indeed to be pitied. Such a man has no anchor, no hope, no vision, and to him life has no meaning.

This type of belief brings frustration, stagnation, cynicism, and a sense of hopelessness resulting in neurosis and mental aberrations of all kinds. If you cannot play a fast game of tennis, or swim as fast as your son, or if your body has slowed down, or you walk with a slow step, remember life is always clothing itself anew. What men call death is but a journey to a new city in another dimension of Life.

I say to men and women in my lectures that they should accept what we call old age gracefully. Age has its own glory, beauty, and wisdom which belong to it. Peace, love, joy, beauty, happiness, wisdom, good will, and understanding are qualities which never grow old or die.

Ralph Waldo Emerson, poet and philosopher, said, "We do not count a man's years until he has nothing else to count."

Your character, the quality of your mind, your faith, and your convictions are not subject to decay.

• You are as young as you think you are

I give public lectures in Caxton Hall, London, England, every few years, and following one of these lectures, a surgeon said to me, "I am 84 years of age. I operate every morning, visit patients in the afternoons, and I write for medical and other scientific journals in the evening."

His attitude was that he was as useful as he believed himself to be, and that he was as young as his thoughts. He said to me, "It's true what you said, 'Man is as strong as he thinks he is, and as valuable as he thinks he is.'"

This surgeon has not surrendered to advancing years. He knows that he is immortal. His final comment to me was, "If I should pass on tomorrow, I would be operating on people in the next dimension, not with a surgeon's scalpel, but with mental and spiritual surgery."

- **Your gray hairs are an asset**

Don't ever quit a job and say, "I am retired; I am old; I am finished." That would be stagnation, death, and you would be finished. Some men are old at 30, while others are young at 80. The mind is the master weaver, the architect, the designer, and the sculptor. George Bernard Shaw was active at 90, and the artistic quality of his mind had not relaxed from active duty.

I meet men and women who tell me that some employers almost slam the door in their faces when they say they are over 40. This attitude on the part of the employers is to be considered cold, callous, evil, and completely void of compassion and understanding. The total emphasis seems to be on youth, i.e., you must be under 35 years of age to receive consideration. The reasoning behind this is certainly very shallow. If the employer would stop and think, he would realize that the man or woman was not selling his age or gray hair, rather, he was willing to give of his talents, his experience, and his wisdom gathered through years of experience in the market place of life.

- **Age is an asset**

Your age should be a distinct asset to any organization, because of your practice and application through the years of the principles of the Golden Rule and the law of love and good will. Your gray hair, if you have any, should stand for greater wisdom, skill, and understanding. Your emotional and spiritual maturity should be a tremendous blessing to any organization.

A man should not be asked to resign when he is 65 years of age. That is the time of life when he could be most useful in handling personnel problems, making plans for the future, making decisions, and guiding others in the realm of creative ideas based on his experience and insight into the nature of the business.

- **Be your age**

A motion-picture writer in Hollywood told me that he had to write scripts which would cater to the twelve-year-old mind.

This is a tragic state of affairs if the great masses of people are expected to become emotionally and spiritually mature. It means that the emphasis is placed on youth in spite of the fact that youth stands for inexperience, lack of discernment, and hasty judgment.

• I can keep up with the best of them

I am now thinking of a man 65 years of age who is trying frantically to keep young. He swims with young men every Sunday, goes on long hikes, plays tennis, and boasts of his prowess and physical powers, saying, "Look, I can keep up with the best of them!"

He should remember the great truth: *As a man thinketh in his heart, so is he.* PROV. 23:7.

Diets, exercises, and games of all kinds will not keep this man young. It is necessary for him to observe that he grows old or remains young in accordance with his processes of thinking. Your subconscious mind is conditioned by your thoughts. If your thoughts are constantly on the beautiful, the noble, and the good, you will remain young regardless of the chronological years.

• Fear of old age

Job said, *The thing which I greatly feared is come upon me.* There are many people who fear old age and are uncertain about the future, because they anticipate mental and physical deterioration as the years advance. What they think and feel comes to pass.

You grow old when you lose interest in life, when you cease to dream, to hunger after new truths, and to search for new worlds to conquer. When your mind is open to new ideas, new interests, and when you raise the curtain and let in the sunshine and inspiration of new truths of life and the universe, you will be young and vital.

- ## You have much to give

If you are 65 or 95 years of age, realize you have much to give. You can help stabilize, advise, and direct the younger generation. You can give the benefit of your knowledge, your experience, and your wisdom. You can always look ahead for at all times you are gazing into infinite life. You will find that you can never cease to unveil the glories and wonders of life. Try to learn something new every moment of the day, and you will find your mind will always be young.

- ## One hundred and ten years old

Some years ago while lecturing in Bombay, India, I was introduced to a man who said he was 110 years old. He had the most beautiful face I have ever seen. He seemed transfigured by the radiance of an inner light. There was a rare beauty in his eyes indicating he had grown old in years with gladness and with no indication that his mind had dimmed its lights.

- ## Retirement—a new venture

Be sure that your mind never retires. It must be like a parachute which is no good unless it opens up. Be open and receptive to new ideas. I have seen men of 65 and 70 retire. They seemed to rot away, and in a few months passed on. They obviously felt that life was at an end.

Retirement can be a new venture, a new challenge, a new path, the beginning of the fulfillment of a long dream. It is inexpressibly depressing to hear a man say, "What shall I do now that I am retired?" He is saying in effect, "I am mentally and physically dead. My mind is bankrupt of ideas."

All this is a false picture. The real truth is that you can accomplish more at 90 than you did at 60, because each day you are growing in wisdom and understanding of life and the universe through your new studies and interest.

- ## He graduated to a better job

An executive, who lives near me, was forced to retire a few months ago because he had reached the age of 65. He said to me, "I look upon my retirement as promotion from kinder-garten to the first grade." He philosophized in this manner: He said that when he left high school, he went up the ladder by going to college. He realized this was a step forward in his education and understanding of life in general. Likewise, he added, now he could do the things he had always wanted to do, and therefore, his retirement was still another step forward on the ladder of life and wisdom.

He came to the wise conclusion that he was no longer going to concentrate on making a living. Now he was going to give all his attention to living life. He is an amateur photographer, and he took additional courses on the subject. He took a trip around the world and took movies of famous places. He now lectures before various groups, lodges, and clubs, and is in popular demand.

There are countless ways of taking an interest in something worth while outside yourself. Become enthusiastic over new creative ideas, make spiritual progress, and continue to learn and to grow. In this manner you remain young in heart, because you are hungering and thirsting after new truths, and your body will reflect your thinking at all times.

• You must be a producer and not a prisoner of society

The newspapers are taking cognizance of the fact that the voting population of the elderly in California elections is increasing by leaps and bounds. This means that their voices will be heard in the legislature of the state and also in the halls of Congress. I believe there will be enacted a federal law prohibiting employers from discrimination against men and women because of age.

A man of 65 years may be younger mentally, physically, and physiologically than many men at 30. It is stupid and ridiculous to tell a man he cannot be hired because he is over 40. It is like saying to him that he is ready for the scrap heap or the junk pile.

What is a man of 40 or over to do? Must he bury his talents and hide his light under a bushel? Men, who are deprived and prevented from working because of age must be sustained by government treasuries at county, state, and federal levels. The many organizations who refuse to hire them and benefit from their wisdom and experience will be taxed to support them. This is a form of financial suicide.

Man is here to enjoy the fruit of his labor, and he is here to be a producer and not a prisoner of society which compels him to idleness.

Man's body slows down gradually as he advances through the years, but his conscious mind can be made much more active, alert, alive, and quickened by the inspiration from his subconscious mind. His mind, in reality, never grows old. Job said, *Oh that I were as in months past, as in the days when God preserved me; When his candle shined upon my head, and when by his light I walked through darkness; As I was in the days of my youth, when the secret of God was upon my tabernacle.* JOB 29:2-4.

• Secret of youth

To recapture the days of your youth, feel the miraculous, healing, self-renewing power of your subconscious mind moving through your whole being. Know and feel that you are inspired, lifted up, rejuvenated, revitalized, and recharged spiritually. You can bubble over with enthusiasm and joy, as in the days of your youth, for the simple reason that you can always mentally and emotionally recapture the joyous state.

The candle which shines upon your head is divine intelligence, and reveals to you everything you need to know; it enables you to affirm the presence of your good, regardless of appearances. You walk by the guidance of your subconscious mind, because you know that the dawn appears and the shadows flee away.

• Get a vision

Instead of saying, "I am old," say, "I am wise in the way of the Divine Life." Don't let the corporation, newspapers, or statistics hold a picture before you of old age, declining years, decrepitude, senility, and uselessness. Reject it, for it is a lie. Refuse to be hypnotized by such propaganda. Affirm life—not death. Get a vision of yourself as happy, radiant, successful, serene, and powerful.

• Your mind does not grow old

Former President Herbert Hoover, now 88 years old, is very active and is performing monumental work. I interviewed him a few years ago in his suite at the Waldorf-Astoria, New York City. I found him healthy, happy, vigorous, and full of life and enthusiasm. He was keeping several secretaries busy handling his correspondence and was himself writing books of a political and historical nature. Like all great men, I found him affable, genial, amiable, loving, and most understanding.

His mental acumen and sagacity gave me the thrill of a lifetime. He is a deeply religious man, and is full of faith in God and in the triumph of the eternal truth of life. He was subjected to a barrage of criticism and condemnation in the years of the great depression, but he weathered the storm and did not grow old in hatred, resentment, ill will, and bitterness. On the contrary, he went into the silence of his soul, and communing with the Divine Presence within him, he found the peace which is the power at the heart of God.

• His mind active at ninety-nine

My father learned the French language at 65 years of age, and became an authority on it at 70. He made a study of Gaelic when he was over 60, and became an acknowledged and famous teacher of the subject. He assisted my sister in a school of higher learning and continued to do so until he passed away at 99. His mind was as clear at 99 as it was when he was 20. Moreover, his handwriting and his reasoning powers had improved with age. Truly, you are as old as you think and feel.

• We need our senior citizens

Marcus Porcius Cato, the Roman patriot, learned Greek at 80. Madame Ernestine Schumann-Heink, the great German-

American contralto, reached the pinnacle of her musical success after she became a grandmother. It is wonderful to behold the accomplishments of the oldsters. General Douglas MacArthur, Harry S. Truman, General Dwight David Eisenhower, and American financier Bernard Baruch are interesting, active, and contributing their talents and wisdom to the world.

The Greek philosopher, Socrates, learned to play musical instruments when he was 80 years old. Michelangelo was painting his greatest canvases at 80. At 80, Cios Simonides won the prize for poetry, Johann von Goethe finished *Faust*, and Leopold von Ranke commenced his *History of the World*, which he finished at 92.

Alfred Tennyson wrote a magnificent poem, "Crossing the Bar," at 83. Isaac Newton was hard at work close to 85. At 88 John Wesley was directing, preaching, and guiding Methodism. We have several men of 95 years who come to my lectures, and they tell me they are in better health now than they were at 20.

Let us place our senior citizens in high places and give them every opportunity to bring forth the flowers of Paradise.

If you are retired, get interested in the laws of life and the wonders of your subconscious mind. Do something you have always wanted to do. Study new subjects, and investigate new ideas.

Pray as follows: *As the hart panteth after the water brooks, so panteth my soul after thee, O God.* PSALM 42:1.

• The fruits of old age

His flesh shall be fresher than a child's: he shall return to the days of his youth. JOB 33:25.

Old age really means the contemplation of the truths of God from the highest standpoint. Realize that you are on an endless journey, a series of important steps in the ceaseless, tireless, endless ocean of life. Then, with the Psalmist you will say, *They shall still bring forth fruit in old age; they shall be fat and flourishing.* PSALM 92:14.

But the fruit of the Spirit is love, joy, peace, patience, gentleness, goodness, faith, meekness, temperance: against such there is no law. GALATIANS 5:22-23.

You are a son of Infinite Life which knows no end, and you are a child of Eternity.

• Profitable pointers

1. Patience, kindness, love, good will, joy, happiness, wisdom, and understanding are qualities which never grow old. Cultivate them and express them, and remain young in mind and body.

2. Some research physicians say that the neurotic fear of the effects of time may well be the cause of premature aging.

3. Age is not the flight of years; it is the dawn of wisdom in the mind of man.

4. The most productive years of your life can be from 65 to 95.

5. Welcome the advancing years. It means you are moving higher on the path of life which has no end.

6. God is Life, and that is your life now. Life is self-renewing, eternal, and indestructible, and is the reality of all men. You live forever, because your life is God's life.

7. Evidence of survival after death is overwhelming. Study *Proceedings of Psychical Research Society of Great Britain and America* in your library. The work is based on the scientific research by outstanding scientists for over 75 years.

8. You cannot see your mind, but you know you have a mind. You cannot see spirit, but you know that the spirit of the game, the spirit of the artist, the spirit of the musician, and the spirit of the speaker is real. Likewise, the spirit of goodness, truth, and beauty moving in your mind and heart are real. You cannot see life, but you know you are alive.

9. Old age may be called the contemplation of the truths of God from the highest standpoint. The joys of old age are greater than those of youth. Your mind is engaged in spirit-

ual and mental athletics. Nature slows down your body so that you may have the opportunity to meditate on things divine.

10. We do not count a man's years until he has nothing else to count. Your faith and convictions are not subject to decay.

11. You are as young as you think you are. You are as strong as you think you are. You are as useful as you think you are. You are as young as your thoughts.

12. Your gray hairs are an asset. You are not selling your gray hairs. You are selling your talent, abilities, and wisdom which you have garnered through the years.

13. Diets and exercises won't keep you young. *As a man thinketh, so is he.*

14. Fear of old age can bring about physical and mental deterioration. *The thing I greatly feared has come upon me.*

15. You grow old when you cease to dream, and when you lose interest in life. You grow old if you are irritable, crotchety, petulant, and cantankerous. Fill your mind with the truths of God and radiate the sunshine of His love—this is youth.

16. Look ahead, for at all times you are gazing into infinite life.

17. Your retirement is a new venture. Take up new studies and new interests. You can now do the things you always wanted to do when you were so busy making a living. Give your attention to living life.

18. Become a producer and not a prisoner of society. Don't hide your light under a bushel.

19. The secret of youth is love, joy, inner peace, and laughter. *In Him there is fullness of joy. In Him there is no darkness at all.*

20. You are needed. Some of the great philosophers, artists, scientists, writers, and others accomplished their greatest work after they were 80 years old.

21. The fruits of old age are love, joy, peace, patience, gentleness, goodness, faith, meekness, and temperance.

22. You are a son of Infinite Life which knows no end. You are a child of Eternity. You are wonderful!

The press acclaims
THE LYMOND CHRONICLE

"Rich, juicy, tasty... It gallops for breathless pages . . . gallant ladies, lusty outlaws, scheming and noble soldiers. It is expert entertainment."
—Orville Prescott, *New York Times*

"A rich tapestry . . . should be enjoyed by readers of historical and adventure novels . . . Recommended." —*Library Journal*

"A spirited pastiche of history and melodrama which has... elegance." —*Kirkus Reviews*

"For those who yearn for adventure-romance... intrigue... mystery... exotic settings... Lots of excitement." —*Publishers Weekly*

"A stunning achievement...an extravagant era lives... the characters are both real and convincing... villains have their towering moments and the good are not without their frailties... it will keep you reading late into the night."
—*Daytona News-Journal*

Books in Dorothy Dunnett's
THE LYMOND CHRONICLE

The Game of Kings

Queens' Play

The Disorderly Knights

Pawn in Frankincense

The Ringed Castle

Checkmate

Published by
WARNER BOOKS

CHECKMATE

DOROTHY DUNNETT

Le grand tapis plié ne monstrera
For qu'à demy la pluspart de l'histoire
Chassez du regne loin aspre apparoistra
Qu'au fait bellique chacun le viendra croire.

WARNER BOOKS

A Warner Communications Company

WARNER BOOKS EDITION

This Warner Books Edition is published by arrangement with G. P. Putnam's
Sons, Inc., 200 Madison Avenue, New York, N.Y.

Warner Books, Inc.
666 Fifth Avenue
New York, N.Y. 10103

 A Warner Communications Company

Printed in the United States of America

First Warner Books Printing: September, 1984

10   9   8   7   6   5   4   3   2   1

In the end, as in the beginning,
for Alastair,
who was the inspiration of the
legend of Francis Crawford,
and whose love of Scotland,
in word and deed,
has done more for her
than Lymond ever could.

Northern France and the Low Countries 1557-8

Non-French towns—Arlon

THE LOW COUNTRIES

Calais
Gravelines
Dunkirk
Ostend
Boulogne
St Omer
Brussels
Lille
Montreuil
FLANDERS
Douai
ARTOIS
Arras
Doulens
Abbeville
Péronne
Amiens
Corbie
St Catelet
Calais
R. St Quentin
Albert
Liesse
Pierrepont
DICY
Noyon
Laon
Compiègne
R. Rhine
Arlon
Luxembourg
Thionville
Reims
Verdun
Metz
St Germain
la Ferté Milon
Châlons
Paris
BRIE
Thoul
LORRAINE
CHAMPAGNE
R. Seine
Fontainebleau
Orléans
EANS
BASSIGNY
FRANCHE-COMTÉ
NIVERNAIS
R. Loire
BURGUNDY
R. Saône
Besançon
ERRY
Lake of Neuchâtel
BOURBONNAIS
Lake of Geneva
CHE
Bourg-en-Bresse
AUVERGNE
Lyon
R. Rhône
SAVOY

AUTHOR'S NOTE

In 1961 the initial manuscript in the Lymond chronicle, *The Game of Kings*, was first launched in the United States of America. It had the great good fortune to be received and handled by a lady whose name is known and respected throughout the publishing world, Lois Dwight Cole.

To Lois, for her unfailing support and interest throughout the series, my warmest thanks are due.

I should also like to pay tribute to the Librarian and staff of The London Library, who have aided me so courteously over the years to assemble fact as well as fantasy.

The verse quoted at the head of each chapter is taken from the prophecies of Michel Nostradamus.

Part I

*Liepard laisse au ciel extend son oeil
Un aigle autour du soleil voyt s'esbatre.*

CHAPTER 1

Quand ceux du pole arctiq unis ensemble
Et Orient grand effrayeur et crainte.

What the celebration at the castle had been, Austin Grey never discovered. He rode in to his tryst at the *Tournai* and found the inn ankle-deep in drunk burghers, thronging the common room and spilling out into the courtyard where inoffensive travellers like himself were attempting to sup their bread and mutton and chicory salad in the airless July dusk of Douai.

He avoided using his title. Money, and a steady, effective insistence, procured a room for him. There he removed the dust of his two days' journey through French-speaking Flanders from Calais.

He had meant to dine indoors, but the heat and the smells forced him down to the yard where he cut food as best he could, between the elbows of a wheezing book-pedlar and a talkative merchant from Antwerp, playfully intent on the bodice-strings of the serving-maids. A group of students somewhere under the gallery were hymning cuckoldry *(co co co co dae)* with an artistry worthy of a Magnificat; and a pair of fishmongers, locked in liquescent brotherhood, reeled up and sent his cup rolling. A black-eyed Piedmontese slid past, limping, with a dubbed duckwing cock churring under his elbow.

There was no sign so far of the man he had come to Flanders to rescue. Austin Grey sat, seemingly quite at his ease, expertly deflecting the attention aroused by his uncommon good looks and reviewed, without pleasure, the mission he owed to his uncle, of the English fortress at Guînes, beside Calais.

'If Francis Crawford wishes to leave Western Europe,' irritably had said Lord Grey of Wilton, 'then it is England's duty to help him. Do you want him to lead the French armies into battle against us? Do you want him to go home to Scotland

11

and encourage his countrymen to cross the Border and march into England? If he intends to go back to Russia, I for one will be happy to send him. You have his message. There is no doubt that it is authentic. Go to Douai and fetch him. You won't be in any danger. He's already thirty miles on the wrong side of the French frontier if he's got there. He'll be skulking, not you.'

And seeing the sleek, grey-bearded head turning to other business already—'You have considered,' had said Austin Grey gently, 'that this may be a French trap?'

And his uncle, an irascible but by no means unjust man, had laid down his pen. 'This I can tell you. If anyone else here were able to recognize Crawford of Lymond or be recognized by him, I should send him in your place. But I really cannot see any man laying an ambush for you at Douai, with Pembroke and the whole English army to one side of him and King Philip at Valenciennes on the other.

'We are invading France, Austin; and this man, if he stayed in France, could be a danger to us. It is enough to know that the French will not lightly release him, and that he has turned to us for help.

'You dislike him,' had said Lord Grey, folding his hands and raising the combed grey beard at his nephew. 'You cannot possibly dislike him as much as I have reason to do. But you will go to Douai. You will tell no one your mission; and you will take the most excellent care that no one discovers that Crawford has crossed into Flanders. For much as I esteem our lady Queen's husband, I should prefer King Philip of Spain to win this war and those after it with the distinguished commanders he has, and without the services of your much-sought-after gentleman at Douai.'

But the man best known briefly as Lymond had not come to Douai, and now the torches were lit and full night had fallen. Also, as the tavern trestles were cleared and pushed together to form a square-walled platform, the presence of the duckwing was abruptly accounted for.

The fatherless only son of a despot and the last of a long line of soldiers, Austin Grey, Marquis of Allendale, had been compelled as a boy to witness altogether too many cockfights. He rose, intent on leaving the courtyard, and halted.

In front of him, blocking his way, stood the Italian he had already observed in the Piedmontese bonnet. In either hand this time the man held a linen bag within which something live struggled and grumbled. He smiled, displaying a swollen, broken-toothed mouth and reaching across, hooked both bags into place on the wall behind Austin's shoulders and stood back, arms akimbo, regarding him. 'You wish to lay a wager, monsieur?'

He was a travelling cock-master, and there would be others with him. Austin said, also in French, 'Later. Just now I wish to hear the singers.'

'Les Amis de Rabelais? We had them last year. They perform at the castle. Four students from Montpellier, monsieur.'

He knew that already, having been struck half-way through his meal by the quality of the singing, close as a toothcomb. All Calais spoke of them. The cocker said, 'But being English, monsieur, the words maybe escape you?'

His French was good but not good enough, apparently, to pass off as native. They were singing *Je fille quant Dieu* with the Swiss counter-tenor, silk in the weave, in the girl's part. Austin said, 'Thank you. I know both meanings of *quenouille*,' and made smiling to pass.

The cocker stood aside. 'Saucy, yes? And the Battle of Marignon? Ah!' And raising a mellifluous tenor he warbled:

> *'Soyez hardis, en joye mis,*
> *Chascun s'asaisonne,*
> *La fleur de lys,*
> *Fleur de hault pris*
> *Y est en personne.*
> *Suivez Francoys . . .'*

He broke off, grinning, to a chorus of drunken hissing and catcalls.

Follow Francis. Austin Grey stared at the Italian cocker and the cocker, grinning, addressed him in perfect English. 'Go and hear the singers, Lord Allendale. That is where you will find him.'

*

He went and heard the singers: four young men in breech hose and buff jerkins led by solid Hunno, the bass: Andreas, the lank, pale-headed Saxon tenor, Oswald of Basle, baritone, brown, energetic and cheerful; and auburn-haired Hilary from the eastern cantons whose ragged moustache and bleeding cheek told of the violent and continuing battle to defend his virility. From behind the moustache emerged the delicious head-voice of a eunuch, while the three others chanted, with the force and precision of wire-weavers:

> *La plus belle de l aville, c'est moy*
> *La plus belle de la ville, c'est moy*
> *Non est*
> *Sy est*
> *Non est*
> *Sy est*
> *Non est, non est, je vous jure ma foy*
> *Non est, non est, je vous jure ma foy . . .*

Then someone shouted a pleasantry and the next moment Hilary had leaped straight into the thick of the crowd, followed protesting by his three colleagues striving to restrain him. Deafened and buffeted, Austin was standing, searching in vain for his quarry, when Francis Crawford made himself known, as a quick, amused voice in the mêlée. 'Faith has a fair name, but *falsheid faris bettir*. In your room, after the cockfight.'

But when Grey twisted around, there was no one behind him that he recognized.

*

He would have gone to his room then and there, but the Piedmontese cocker waylaid him. 'You heard him? Till then, you're to stay in the courtyard.'

'Who are you?' said Austin Grey.

He had wound a filthy scarf round the torn mouth, but you could tell the dark face was grinning. 'A friend. Did you not see who he was?'

'He spoke from behind. No,' said Austin.

'The counter-tenor. There he is, at the cock platform. Go and watch. But do not speak to him,' said the cocker; and grinning, made off through the crowd.

Austin gazed at his back. Then he forced his way with extreme firmness to the mat-covered platform of trestles.

Le Amis de Rabelais were there, vociferously proclaiming their bets from the opposite side of the platform. And there, visibly battered, his fists full of livres and sols and deniers, was Hilary of the tousled red hair, bouncing with glee like a clown on a clock spring.

It couldn't be. This half-fledged, ebullient Graindor could never be the man who controlled armies in Russia; whose skill in war was so celebrated that Lord Grey was prepared to take any risk to help him leave France; and even to keep him out of the hands of his allies.

And yet ... Take away the moustache, and the hair, and you had a man nearer thirty than twenty; whose eyes had seen more than the frets of a lute and the inside of a medical college, and who had learned lessons other than his praxi and chirurgiâ and theoriâ.

It was Francis Crawford of Lymond. He drummed his fists on the ledge, and talked and quarrelled and shrieked with his friends, casting no single glance in Austin's direction. But Austin, all through the fight, watched him silently.

It was not, he thought, acting. Most men of war delighted in cock fighting. Socrates had drawn from it an example of valour; the sons of the Emperor Severus had been brought to watch it daily before being sent to reduce England. And Themistocles had braced his army to vanquish the Persians with the same analogy: *Behold: these do not fight for their household gods, for the monuments of their ancestors, for glory, for liberty or the safety of their children; but only because the one will not give way to the other.* In Christian lands, to give one's cocks strength, one fed them filched bread from the altar-table.

Austin continued to watch. The docked birds dashed to each other and remained beak to beak, each shaved serpent neck straining upwards. Then came the familiar, blustering rattle of a masterless sail in a whirlwind. Beating, gnawing and striking the cocks sprang from the mat, wrung together, and the red-haired student screeched and shot his arms over his head, half concussing a dyer and knocking a barber's hat over his face like a chafing dish.

Then the birds dropped, in a fury of warm, gouting blood and black feathers, and Austin saw that the birchen grey, a big eight-pound fowl, had a spur sunk up to the hilt in its enemy's neck, and the fight was already over.

He would have gone then to his room, but the crowd behind held him stapled fast to his place. They took the dead bird out for the pot, and the owner, his beaming face red in the torchlight, lifted the victor tenderly in his thick hands and with his tongue began searching its injuries.

Soon, stinking with curative urine, it would take a pat of sweet rosemary butter and be put to stove in the straw of its sweating basket. It had been fortunate. He had seen a fight between two wounded cocks last a couple of hours, even though the spurs were cut smooth and sharp with a penknife. As the ancients had said: in their raging pride, indifferent to pain and injury, they would fight to the end of their powers.

Looking through the eyes of the man opposite you could, he supposed, see a barbaric magnificence in it. You could admire the quick, graceful movements of the bird they now put on the mat, with its tight glossy plumage and muscular thighs; brilliant yellow on shoulder and saddle. Or the sprightly strut of its black and red adversary, the polled head darting and glinting; the spurs growing low and wicked and curved on the white and sinewy legs.

They liked to fight, it was said. It was their instinct. They would seek battle regardless of the presence of man, and would pine if denied it. And here, in the darting bodies, the sparring, the dodging, the high, rustling flirts when with beak, foot and spur, bird grappled with bird, there was strength and fire and most unflinching valour for men to admire and emulate.

Half an hour went by of the struggle. By the end of it the golden fowl, slashed and impaled, was sorely beaten, but continued steadily to attack its superb and untouched antagonist.

Then it weakened. In silence among the screaming spectators Austin Grey watched the tired legs beginning to tremble; the beak to open; the tongue to palpitate. One barred yellow wing trailed on the mat and when, in the flurries, it sought to grip with its beak, the rich red wings of its foe beat it down, and the other's strong spurs struck again and again, at its head, its throat or its neck, or the place in its back where, sinking through, the sharpened point would spear through its vitals.

Austin had laid no wagers. But when, in one such bustle, the golden cock struck to the head and against all expectation, the bigger bird disengaged and dropped aside, staggering, he was glad; as if he and not the duckwing had been suffering. Then he saw what the chance blow had done. The black-breasted red had lost the use of its eyes.

Silence fell. The yellow bird, its abdomen slit, was almost

vanquished. It moved as if drunk, toppling first on its breast and then on its ragged docked tail and you could see sweat, like citrines, on the torn feathers. It lay, red eyes glaring its challenge.

And the red, strong still, trod forward groping in the darkness and found and gripped the fallen bird with its beak. Then, beating down its cut wings, it attacked and went on attacking its enemy's body.

It should have been the end. The yellow bird twitched and raised its stained head. It lifted itself, shivering. It stood, and might have fallen. Instead, in a single magic explosion of courage and anger, it hurled forward the naked head and caught the blinded red foe by the throat. Then springing high in the air, the yellow cock brought down its spurs in a stroke no living bird could have fended.

The black-breasted red toppled and lay, in the jumping, glistening stream of its blood. And the yellow stepped on its back, and moved its one wing, and throwing back its gored head, crowed in triumph.

Courage, of a noble and humbling order. Courage of the brute, subject to neither reason nor discipline. Courage which could inspire emulation or greed, or brutality. What were they celebrating now, these bellowing figures about him, but a win against odds, and the making or losing of money?

Opposite him, the red-haired student had won his wager. The others had thrown him in the air and he descended upside down, in a rain of silver, attempting through hiccoughing laughter to semaphore to himself a serving of Auxois.

It was easy now to get away from the mat. Austin Grey turned, his face unsmiling, and ran up the gallery stairs to his chamber.

Inside was the Piedmontese cock-master and two other men, one of whom closed the door behind him and locked it. The other, as Austin snatched at his scabbard, pricked with a blade the wadded back of his doublet. They took his sword from him.

'Ah, Lord Allendale,' said the Piedmontese, indolent thumbs in his sword-belt. 'A fine, small head; a muscular pair of shanks and a bold, smart demeanour for a game foul. But all the same, as you will note, we have our spurs in you and you will shortly (bind the gag tightly, Demetrio) also be made, as you see, safely voiceless.

'What are you trying to say? Where are we taking you?

17

To France, of course. It will be a pleasant captivity, and short-lived, unless your uncle is foolish. But then, I don't imagine Lord Grey could ever be foolish. And you are, are you not, as a son to him?'

They had to shift the knife in order to bind him and he fought then with considerable success, because he had been well trained and did not care, in that moment, what they did to him. But against three, he had little chance; and soon enough his limbs were tightly corded and he had been heaved, wrapped in his cloak, into a smaller room where they dropped him on a pallet and left him.

Bound, gagged and thrown in a corner with less accommodation than any trussed fowl in its cock bag, there was nothing Austin Grey could do but give way, breathing hard, to bitter anger.

If Francis Crawford wishes to leave Western Europe, his uncle had said, *then it is England's duty to help him.*

And what if it is a French trap? he had answered. For of course, a man who revered bloody courage and was stirred to wildness and laughter by its apotheosis was not of his kind, and did not hold to his rules. But his uncle had trusted the fellow.

He could not move. Through the shuttered window he could hear from the noise, surging and checking, that another cock fight had started. Perhaps the 'Piedmontese' had been forced to take part in it, since this was his alibi. And of course, as a travelling cocker, he would have horses and carts and a perfect excuse for leaving late at night for his next station. No one would look in his feeding sacks, or under the straw. No one would suspect he was a French spy taking back captive an Englishman.

Of course, the cock-master was not a Frenchman. He had spoken fluent Italian, and his English, though accurate, was inflected with the same accent. Naturally, since the Queen was a Florentine, the French court was full of Italians.

A Florentine . . .

What was it Lord Grey had said, testily, only last week? *The devil has a charmed life. He got a hackbut ball full in the mouth in Italy, and all it did was shatter his dog-teeth.*

The dark and masterful man with the broken mouth was not a Piedmontese or a cocker. He was Marshal of France Piero Strozzi, one of King Henri's most able generals. And a friend, long since in Scotland, of Francis Crawford.

The bragging red game-cock—two of them—against the tormented yellow, indeed. And since he had a high pride of his own, although he would have denied it, Austin Grey sought about him for a weapon . . . a baton he could wrench out with his fingertips, a sliver of glass . . . anything with which to free himself, or inflict injury at least on his captors.

What he found, lost in the straw, was an eating-knife. He felt, disbelieving, the sting of its blade, and ignoring the blood on his hand, did not rest until he had disentangled it. Then, hacking and sawing, he cut through the cords on his feet and then, in a gory mess, those on his wrists, and freeing himself from the gag, strode to the door of his prison.

It was locked and would not give way, although he charged it again and again. Nor, because of the noise, could he make his voice carry.

There remained the casement. He ripped open the shutters. It did indeed give on to the courtyard. Noise and torchlight streamed in, but he could not get out. The window was barred.

He could not get out, but it wouldn't matter, if he could attract someone's attention. Outside were his enemies, but there were only three of them, and Francis Crawford. In this room, even armed with a knife, he might have little chance against four resolute men. But what chance had four men in French pay in a tavern in Douai, once the burghers knew of their presence?

So Austin Grey snatched up his cloak, and thrusting it between the bars of his window shouted at the fullest pitch of his voice, 'Treachery! Treachery! There are French spies among you! The cock-master with the broken mouth is Piero Strozzi!'

Faces turned. He waved his cloak and shouted again. With careful clarity he was still calling when he heard a key grate in the lock behind him. He wedged his cloak in the bars and whipped round, knife in hand, to defend himself.

In the doorway stood Hilary of the red hair, with steel in his hand and neither laughter nor civility in his voice. He said, 'Come with me.'

Behind him, the door rested invitingly open. An eating knife versus a sword made long odds again, but it was worth a leap and a stab, which the other man countered quickly. In the moment's fighting that followed, both weapons clashed to

19

the ground; and Austin fell with a grim and heady satisfaction on the man who had so coolly betrayed him.

But although brave and obstinate, he had not the iron will that subdues armies. He saw coming the blow which would fell him, but unlike the gold cock, by that time had no means to parry it. It hit him cleanly, and he knew nothing more.

❋

He had thought, in his innocence, that a Marshal of France would enter Douai with only two men to accompany him. Had Austin Grey been conscious and still at his window, he would have seen the courtyard doors swung suddenly shut and, plucked from the crowd, a circle of thirty men range themselves, sword in hand, enclosing the cockfight and all its spectators. Men oddly attired: here a tinsmith, there a clerk or a book-pedlar. But none of the three remaining Amis de Rabelais who stood where they were, staring about them.

Staring perhaps at the fourth of their number, who had stopped in midflight, sword in hand; with two of Strozzi's men behind him at the top of the staircase and two below, their hands ready to grasp him. The fourth student Hilary, divested at last of red moustache and wig, who stood, looking down at Piero Strozzi, with the famous Crawford hair gilt in the torchlight.

Strozzi said, grinning, *'La plus belle de la ville.* I was not sure which you were, until you spoke to the beautiful marquis. You will have discovered. All the exits are guarded.'

'Who betrayed me?' said Francis Crawford. The voice, very different from that of Hilary, was light and level and empty and he held his sword, its point on the stairs, like an extension of his own flexible body.

"Your own men,' said Strozzi. 'Guthrie and Blacklock and Hoddim and Hislop. They have no mind, *mon fils,* to go back to Russia. They want you, as all of us do, to remain with kind Mother France. You will give up your sword.'

'Hardly,' said Francis Crawford.

'Then we shall have to take it,' said Strozzi reprovingly. 'As you see, we are clearing the courtyard. Soon all will be locked in the tavern. Then you will be one man against thirty. What can you do?'

'I can kill,' said the man on the stairs known as Lymond.

'You cannot kill thirty men. Even you,' said Strozzi, grinning again. He turned. 'Citizens of Douai, do not be alarmed.

I have not come to harm you, but to take back to France this gentleman who thought so little of King Henri's hospitality that he decided to spurn it. In a little, we shall be——'

Lymond hurled himself down. Someone screamed. Under Francis Crawford's swung steel the man at the foot of the staircase perished. Still running, Lymond killed the next who opposed him, and a third rolled under his feet as a dozen more, racing, converged on him. He staggered as first one and then another crashed into him but the sword still stabbed and glittered and Strozzi, his brows drawn under the Piedmontese cap, saw a fourth stuck and collapse, choking. For a moment, it made the rest falter. Then they swarmed after, ducking, dodging, clutching at that damnable, that diabolical sword-arm.

On that, furious, Strozzi shouted an order and the fools drew off at last and deployed, cutting off the way to the gates, so that Lymond was forced back against the doorless wall with a half circle of men crouched before him, out of reach of that swift clotted sword-blade.

Piero Strozzi snapped his fingers and, with a fresh-lit torch in his hand, walked forward and joined the gasping group of his men.

Crawford and Lymond watched him come, his breathing fast, his knuckle bones white on the sword hilt. He said, 'The Kyng of Fraunce spared none ... But sent for hem everychone. What have you promised them?'

And Strozzi, holding the illuminating torch just out of reach, said calmly, 'That the man who harms you will die. As you see, their swords are still in their scabbards. You have killed four. You may kill four more before they take your sword from you, But you cannot escape. Is Russia worth eight loyal men's lives?'

'Yes,' said Francis Crawford. 'You will have to watch me take them.'

'Including mine?' said Marshal Strozzi.

'If you insist,' said the other man pleasantly. He had recovered his breath. 'My dear Piero, I abide and abide and better abide. How can I be made to take a command in your army? The bribe does not exist that would interest me.'

'There is one, they say,' said Piero Strozzi. 'You had wealth in Russia, and power. You may have both in France. You may also have something they tell me Russia could not offer you'.

21

'A loyal Florentine friend?' Lymond suggested.

'No, although you will thank me for this yet,' said Strozzi with equanimity. 'You cannot obtain an annulment, they say, for your marriage.'

Distantly from the inn came the sound of voices and hammering. In the darkness someone groaned, and the dying torches, spluttering, lit the long grotesque rows of the game bags, each with its occupant. A cock chuckled and another, savagely, gave tongue in answer. Lymond said, 'I hear gossip too. I do not always repeat it.'

'This gossip,' said Strozzi, 'says that there is nothing you will not pay to be freed of this contract. I am to tell you that unless you come back to France you will never secure this divorce. I am to tell you that it will be granted to you when you have served the King of France for a year, freely and to the best of your powers in any theatre where he may need you. And, in case you may doubt what I say, I have the promise in writing, with the Cardinal Legate's own signature.'

Lymond took the thrown packet and opened and read it, without relaxing his guard, in the light of the fresh burning cresset.

Strozzi watched him.

This time, there was no trick and Lymond would know it. The Pope, the friend of France, could withhold or grant this annulment as France requested. All that mattered now was whether gossip spoke truly. Whether, to obtain his divorce, Francis Crawford would conceivably undertake the year's service demanded.

He stood for a long time, considering. Then the point of his sword moved slowly downwards, and Strozzi knew, amazed, that he had surrendered.

'I have one condition,' said Francis Crawford. 'Les Amis de Rabelais should not suffer. They had no idea who I was.'

Strozzi doubted it. But there was no need to quibble. 'Am I a clod,' he said, 'deaf to the call of the Muses? They may return on St Luke's Day for their doctorates. Their punishment, *mon fils*, must be the loss of their tenorino. So you are coming?'

'I find your arguments irresistible,' said Francis Crawford. 'You didn't think to introduce them before? You might have saved four soldiers' dead pay.'

'Christ,' said Piero Strozzi, relieving him prudently of his sword, 'I didn't think, to tell you the truth, that marriage weighed so heavily on you. You surprise me. Does she bore you, or have you met a rich heiress?'

'I am abandoning,' said Lymond, 'the foul yoke of sensual bondage. You'd better hurry. I sent Austin Grey for the eswardeurs.'

They did not know whether, on the last point, to believe him, but it encouraged Marshal Strozzi to vacate the *Tournai* quickly. And certainly Austin Grey, hurriedly searched for, was nowhere to be found on the premises.

It hardly mattered. Of the two men he had hoped to appropriate, Piero Strozzi was bringing the jewel.

He whistled, leaving the tavern, and on his way to the gates blithely slit, one by one, all the hooked row of hanging white cock bags.

Before he had stepped on to the quay the serpent necks, stretching and twisting, were out of the canvas.

Before he had sculled up the small river or the rest had reached, in their various ways, the Porte d'Arras, the Porte d'Equerchin, the Porte d'Ocre, the fighting-cocks had flounced to the earth two by two in the wide, empty yard of the *Tournai*; and tearing, gouging and stabbing, with dogged courage were killing each other.

❧

Like the Duke of Arschot, Austin Grey made his escape in the pipe of a privy. How he got there he did not remember, but he awoke to find he was free and that his enemies, thwarted, had left Douai without him.

Lord Grey's fury over the matter, when he reported it, exceeded even his own, but seemed to derive less from the deceit than from the consequent waste of Lord Grey's time and energy. When, some weeks later, the English army in France received notice of other consequences rather more telling, he made a point of informing his nephew.

'Your man Crawford of Lymond has left Court to go south to Lyon,' said the Governor of the English fortress at Guînes. 'On a French mission, naturally. It really is damned inconvenient that you didn't kill him at Douai. It was a trap. They were out to catch you. You were quite entitled to.'

With Lord Grey, one did not make excuses. 'I'm sorry, sir,' said Austin woodenly.

'He's gone to Lyon,' said his uncle, irritably repeating himself. 'Ostensibly to raise money, but it won't be. The last

23

place I want a senior French command to interest itself in. Those Spanish tacticians want their great donkey mouths pasted shut for them. First, the French find out we're using Lyon as a mail-box. Next, they'll hear about the German levies at Ferette. They've probably heard of them already. Two thousand horse and ten thousand cavalry preparing to attack Lyon once we've taken Saint-Quentin. And with Lyon and Paris in our hands, the war'll be over.'

'Paris, sir?' said Austin Grey, his eyes on his uncle. Obstinate, old-fashioned, over-meticulous to a degree, Lord Grey was a figure of melancholy fun to his valet, his secretary and all those between wars who served him.

In battle, it was a different matter. He had a flair for it: a military instinct revered by the English high command and also by their allies the Spaniards, to whom he was now seconded.

'Naturally, Paris,' said Lord Grey of Wilton. 'After Picardy is overrun, who is there to stop us? The Constable, in his dotage? The princes of the blood, St André and the rest of their decadent chivalry? Who is there? Even Piero Strozzi is on his way back to Italy.'

'And Mr Crawford to Lyon,' said Austin. 'Is that such a bad thing for us, sir? It must have weakened the Constable's forces.'

'It might have,' said Lord Grey testily, 'if he had taken any troops to Lyon with him. All he has are some officers of the Bureau of Finance and a group of his own captains. They'll be mustering Switzers on the spot, I shouldn't wonder, and withdrawing Piedmont troops into the bargain. He's no fool. It's what I should do. And it'll leave the Constable a full army here in the north to attack us with. As you know,' said Lord Grey of Wilton, 'I can't stand the fellow. But I wish to God he were fighting for us instead of against us. Or that he wasn't fighting at all.'

He glared at his nephew, who had failed to kill Francis Crawford of Lymond, and Austin Grey sustained his gaze without moving.

At Lymond's hands he had risked the loss of more than his time and his patience. He had enjoyed a grim satisfaction in attempting to repay him, painfully, in that brief moment of fighting at Douai.

But he had not sought to kill him.

One could not say that to Lord Grey. One could not say

24

that in honour one could not bring oneself to slay Francis Crawford, then or at any time in the future, no matter how much one disliked him.

One could not say that one deeply loved, and wished to marry, Francis Crawford's exquisite wife.

CHAPTER 2

Dedans Lyon ving cinq d'une balaine
Cinq citoyens, Germains, Bressans, Latins
Par dessous nobles conduiront longue traine
Et descouvers par abbois de mastins.

That a Royal deputation was coming was known to every burgher in Lyon by the last week in July, but only the doughty Scottish merchant called Jerott Blyth knew who was to lead it, for Francis Crawford sent him a letter.

Once, Jerott had fought under Lymond, when his band of mercenaries had first made their mark throughout Europe. He still exchanged news and heard from his former colleagues occasionally. He knew, for example, from Adam Blacklock what Lymond had done and said on his return from Douai, when his captains had succeeded, with Strozzi's help, in preventing him from leaving France.

Jerott Blyth was a tough and even a foolhardy man, but he was glad he had not been there. He was content to receive his instructions by letter and to carry them out in the pleasant place where he had chosen to settle, in the Presqu'île, the flat pendant of land on the breast of the south-flowing Rhône which was the heart of commercial Lyon.

To his north lay the streams of the Saône and the Rhône, the cords of the pendant here united. From Marseille up the Rhône to the Presqu'île there came the wine, the crystal, the oil, the vats of silk and the ostrich feathers, the gold, the carpets, the almonds, the sugar, the balms and the spices of Venice, Africa and the Orient. Through the river-passes to the north and the west, trade and conquering peoples flowed over the Alps and into Italy as well as into Germany, Flanders and Paris. Long after the Romans had founded it, Lyon remained the crossroads of the world: the springboard of every Transalpine campaign; the station in every traveller's journey from the Mediterranean to the Court in the north.

And so Lyon was larger than Paris, and, fed by the rich blood of its immigrants, grew richer and still more brilliant. It gave to the world silks and poetry, the finest banking system Europe possessed, and the most distinguished collection of printing houses. And from its wealth, it came in time to pay the penalty. Four French Kings, coated in silver-etched armour, had hurled themselves into warfare on the bankers' orders loyally proffered by Lyon, and the burghers were in no doubt at this moment as to why a Russian general with French and Scottish titles should be riding from Compiègne to address them. But none the less, on this Sunday 15 August they gathered outside the Hôtel de Ville on the Presqu'île and waited for the welcoming party to appear on the bridge with their visitors.

And Jerott Blyth, standing with them in his expensive high-collared cloak and paned pourpoint wondered why, successfully settled in this handsome city, he troubled to further the career of someone who was, after all, no longer his commander. And why, gazing over the river to the tree-cloudy hill of la Fourvière palisaded with the tall, crowded homes of the bankers, the administrators, the clergy, he should find his gloved fingers clenched, his pulse hurrying.

He had nothing to fear. He was beyond the age, now, of being hectored. He was even now, in a sense, part of the family.

To his left, darkly curving, was the rue Mercière, the richest street in the city, in which stood his great house of Gaultier, which had come to him with his wife.

There were some, he knew, who believed he had married Marthe for the house, or for her inheritance from the two people, now dead, who had lived in it. She had never troubled to conceal her illegitimacy. It still angered him that, set against her looks, her quick wits, her business acumen, it should be held to matter.

The connection with Lymond she had never publicized. Until last week, when the letter to Jerott from Francis himself had referred to it. 'Your former service with me is no doubt common knowledge. Since the resemblance between Marthe and myself will cause comment, you might refer to her now as my step-sister. Any antecedents you care to invent on this score, I shall be happy to substantiate.'

It had, in fact, been difficult to persuade Marthe to agree to this, but he had succeeded and the reaction among their

27

neighbours had varied, as he had expected, from austere disbelief to jocularity.

There was no doubt that Lymond would never have dreamed of advertising the link except from necessity. The resemblance between himself and Jerott's wife could have been no greater if they had been of one birth, brother and sister.

As it chanced, neither Lymond nor Marthe knew the reason, and neither cared. One assumed that Lymond's late father, a foot-loose nobleman, had sired Marthe and left her in France, where four years ago, Francis had come across her, on his way to Turkey.

At the end of that voyage he, Jerott, had married her. But Francis had not seen her since, nor had he corresponded with her. Whatever its antecedents the link, so lately formed, had proved a tenuous one. Once, to be sure, he had got the impression they hated one another.

Then the man on his left said, 'There they are!' and Jerott saw the flashing of halberds and morions and the flutter of flags between the tall houses on either side of the bridge. The Delegation had spent the previous night outside the walls of Saint-Just and had come fresh this morning down the steep path of the Gourguillon, where a Pope had since lost his tiara, and along the crowded right bank of the Saône.

Escorting it would be the twelve members of Lyon's Consulat but not the Governor, the Marshal de St André. The Marshal was on campaign in Picardy. The Governor's lodging, in an elegant square on the other side of this bridge, was where Lymond would henceforth be staying.

Jerott Blyth had been relieved to hear it. Any visit Lymond paid to the Hôtel Gaultier would consequently be a brief one. A young priest standing beside him said, 'I'm told you fought, sir, under his lordship of Sevigny. In Scotland, is he of good family?'

The usual question. 'He is the second son of a very old Scottish house,' Jerott said, watching the bridge. 'He has a Scottish property at Lymond and a French estate at Sevigny, on the Loire. His brother, Crawford of Culter, has the title.'

'Ah!' said the monk. He looked impressed. 'I have heard of Lord Crawford of Culter.'

And the usual answer. 'You will have heard of the first baron,' Jerott said. 'This is three generations away. This Mr

Crawford has only fought occasionally in France and has just spent two years in Russia.'

Which in some degree, he supposed, must have altered him. On that point, Adam's letters had not been informative. The mounted procession, feathered caps bobbing, was coming closer. He had not far off a hundred men at arms with him, Jerott calculated; and God knew how many servants, as well as a jogging group in black skirts: the finance officers. Then the Consulat and the chief burghers. Then Adam Blacklock, lean and unexpectedly scarred, riding next to a small, fresh-faced person unknown to him. Then . . .

Then Francis Crawford of Lymond, comte de Sevigny. At Douai, before he killed Strozzi's men, he had played the part, Adam said, of a red-headed student counter-tenor.

Now he was not playing a rôle. Jerott wondered what the Douaisiens would have made of this fair, slender man with the sculptured face and wide, watchful eyes, and the lyre marks of satire and also of arrogance about the long mouth. Lymond rode under the personal banner of his house, and wore for his entry a high-throated doublet and surcoat of floating Persian tissue whose stuff drew comment like the chatter of looms from all the watching weavers, and whose jewel, luminous in the sunlight, cast their bloom as through a wine glass, citrine and azure and amethyst; to gratify bankers and make merchants fall silent, appraising them.

Then the Captain-General dismounted and Jerott found himself, all too soon, summoned to his place in the introductions. Face to face: 'My God,' said Francis Crawford in English, smiling cordially and shaking his hand. 'Caffa and purled lace and pinking, and a butt on him like one of Shah Mahmút the Ghaznérides' elephants. How is Marthe?' To his escort he added blandly, in French, 'Forgive me. Mr Blyth and I are old acquaintances.'

'Don't apologize. M. le Prévôt speaks English,' said Jerott coldly.

'So he does,' said Lymond thoughtfully. 'Remind me to tell him that the Shah Mahmút the Ghaznérides kept very small elephants. And Marthe, you that in love find lucke and habundance? May I call on her?'

'If you wish. That is, we shall be honoured,' said Jerott quickly. Francis could always tie him in knots.

Lymond, his mouth twitching, moved on. His two captains, Adam Blacklock and Daniel Hislop watched him go and turned their gaze with one accord upon Jerott Blyth, left staring after him.

'This man Jerott,' said Danny Hislop accusingly. 'You said he was middle-aged.' Jerott turned.

'I didn't,' said Adam Blacklock indignantly. 'I said he was stinking rich and cut his old allies dead in the street. I did not say he was middle-aged.'

Vivid, black-haired and muscular, with passions far from middle-aged lodged between the flat belly and lean hips on which he had just been insulted, Jerott Blyth looked at the two men and, for the first time, his face lost its apprehension.

Then Adam put his hand on his arm, and laughed, and introduced the short, sandy-haired man called Danny Hislop, and together they went into the Hôtel de Ville after Lymond.

*

Jerott's golden-haired wife watched them go. Unknown to him, Marthe had stood for an hour in the crowd facing the church of Saint-Nizier to obtain a sight, her first for three years, of the Scotsman who so resembled her.

Conscious of her own singular beauty she had wondered if he had lost his own looks, but this was not so. Indeed, he had come into them in an odd way; the pastel colours subtly enlivened by the snows of Muscovy; or what he had found there.

The thought did not please her. She watched him dismount and, her lips tightening, saw him speak to her husband and Jerott, flushed, answer him. Then Jerott was joined by two other men and the three followed her brother to the entrance of the Hôtel de Ville.

In the archway, Francis Crawford paused and turned. The crowd, readily sycophantic, raised some applause for him. He smiled, acknowledging it and, turning his gaze unerringly to where Marthe stood, performed for her lightly a complete Court salutation, his hand on his heart. Then, amusement on his face, he continued on his way leaving behind him Jerott, red with embarrassment, and the smaller of the two captains staring in her direction, his roomy mouth fallen open.

Other heads, craning, had recognized the woman dealer from the Hôtel Gaultier. Marthe turned and, without hurrying, strolled through the dispersing crowd to the rue de la Platière behind her.

So, riding by without a glance, Lymond had still noticed her. And telling her so, delivered a warning. *You must do better than this*, that charming greeting conveyed, *if you wish, my dear Marthe, to study me*. It was useful to be reminded that she, too, had tended always to underrate Francis Crawford.

It was not a mistake she intended to repeat. In a few moments, walking north, she had reached her meeting place.

The road was full, as usual, of carts coming through the Porte de la Lanterne, and a clutter of stalls, and knots of gossiping people on their way to and from market. Sitting on the steps of the Cross was a small, weather-worn person with a broken nose, working with a knife at a piece of wood. A group of children surrounded him.

And she approached, he stood up and said something in idiomatic French with a strong Scottish accent, handing the piece of wood as he did so to one of the children. It seemed to be a puppet of some sort. They ran off, laughing and shouting, and the man turned and came towards her.

Close to, his face was not prepossessing: the grizzled beard more grey than black, and the skin seamed with scars and stiffened with suns hotter than those in Scotland or France. Marthe said, 'You keep your words, Mr Abernethy. Is Mr Crawford's wife coming to Lyon?'

Archie Abernethy, a veteran of more skirmishes than Marthe could have imagined, stopped, cocked his mahogany cranium and said, 'Aye so, Mistress Blyth; and good day to ye. But ye didna tell me Mr Crawford would be here at the same time, now. Or is that a coincidence?'

The long-lashed blue eyes held his, peacefully. 'Does it matter? I told your mistress that a visit would be rewarding. When she died, the Dame de Doubtance left many papers. Mr Crawford may have no interest in his family history, but his wife, I am told, is a tireless investigator. She shall have free access to all the documents. Whether Mr Crawford is here or not, surely, will make no difference.'

Through a gate in the wall was the small churchyard of Saint-Pierre, with shade under the trees, and some white marble benches. Jerott Blyth's wife, turning, entered and seated herself. 'Unless, of course, Mistress Philippa is still afraid of him?'

Arms folded, the little man stood and considered her. 'You

could say she doesna relish the notion of meeting him. He would be in Russia now but for his wife handing him over to the French ship that captured him.'

'Why? I didn't know that!' said Marthe sharply.

In a liquid gesture, Mr Abernethy expressed helpless ignorance. 'She didna want him to go back to Russia.'

'I wonder why?' Marthe said. 'She hasn't changed her mind about the divorce?'

'Fegs, no,' said Archie. 'Ye havena seen her since the English court got hold of her. She's had suitors like a pierhead has wulks ever since she left home, and since she came here we're fair palsified with them.'

'So Philippa is already in Lyon?' said Marthe softly.

He stared back at her owlishly. 'Aye. At Mr Crawford's bankers, the Schiatti,' he said. 'We had lodgings, but they took a fancy to her, and invited us to stay. We came properly escorted, with a safe conduct.'

'The Schiatti,' said Marthe thoughtfully. There were two middle-aged brothers, both with sons.

'Aye,' said Archie Abernethy. He cleared his throat. 'You have no objection, then, to this hunt through the Doubtance papers?'

'I?' said Jerott's wife, and raised her arched eyebrows at him in a stare which recalled, unpleasantly, her masculine counterpart. 'The facts of my birth are beyond either redemption or further embarrassment, Mr Abernethy. If Mistress Philippa finds satisfaction in laying bare the truth about her husband's origins, it is not for me to dissuade her. . . . Do you know, I wonder, his purpose in coming here?'

'To raise a loan for the King. So the bankers say.'

'The bankers know more than they say,' Marthe said. 'And Mr Crawford—or should we call him the comte de Sevigny?—knows more than most of them. The greater the general, the greater his grasp of the manifold uses of espionage. Through all his months in Russia and after, he required my husband to write to him. And obviously, he has other correspondents.'

'In Lyon?' said the man Abernethy. He was listening intently.

'Some of them,' Marthe said. 'One can guess perhaps where. For a long time, M. le comte has had cronies among printers. He has been a paid soldier, a courtier, a galley-slave.

He knows his Paris, his Algiers, his Geneva. He must have a friend in every whore-house in Germany. And men who write him from Scotland.'

'Not me,' said Abernethy, agreeably. 'My writing's terrible. But he has his wife followed frae London to Dieppe. It made her nervous.'

'And after Dieppe?' said Marthe; and had her answer in the sudden gleam in the man's eyes.

'No one followed us,' said Archie Abernethy with simplicity. 'So unless you tell him, Mr Crawford—M. le comte—need never know that she's here.'

'Except,' said Marthe dryly, 'that the whole male Schiatti family are at this moment in the Hôtel de Ville with him.'

'Sworn to silence,' said Archie. 'I told ye. She's dead set on avoiding her husband. Only she needs his signature to look at the papers. We were hoping you could get it.'

It was what she had counted on. 'Yes,' said Marthe. 'If you bring her to my house in the rue Mercière at six o'clock tomorrow. Do you want to swear me to secrecy also?'

'No,' said the little man slowly. He added suddenly, 'Does Mr Blyth know all about this?'

The truth, one supposed, was often the best. 'He knows,' said Marthe, 'that there are family papers. He doesn't know that Mistress Philippa has come south to look at them. And if he did, he would discourage a meeting between her and Mr Crawford. Jerott believes Mr Crawford should be encouraged to dissolve his marriage and set out for Moscow. He likes the idea of Mr Crawford in Moscow. The French monarchy, as you may know, does not. If M. le comte wants his freedom from Philippa, he has to stay in France for a twelvemonth.'

'So I heard. Marshal Strozzi, they say, put the proposition to him in Flanders. It couldn't be right,' said the little man gently, 'but they say that Marshal Strozzi got the idea from Mr Blyth, your husband?'

'Do they?' said Marthe, and rising, smoothed her gown and began walking slowly over the grass to the gateway. 'Then I suppose there is nothing to be gained by contradicting it. But you may tell your mistress that Jerott played no part in baulking my brother.

'Philippa may have sent him to France. But I, dear Mr Abernethy, devised the ultimatum that will keep him here.'

*

She was at home when the Hôtel de Ville emptied; nor did she see fit to mention her rendezvous. But in fact, Jerott Blyth had no thought of her. Like the other burghers of Lyon exposed to that stinging forty minutes' exposition by the new Captain-General from Compiègne, he came down the steps silent, sober and thoughtful.

So often, in the past, had he heard Lymond use this technique. The graceful exordium with its poetic and classical allusions: in this instance to Colonia Copia Lugdunum, sometime shelter of Popes and of Kings; home of wisdom, of poetry, of beauty; birthplace of Delorme and foster-parent of Rabelais; fount of learned men—M. Grolier; M. Gueraud the Receveur; M. Aneau the Rector beside him.

And, of course, the distinguished daughters of Lyon ... Madame Labé; Madame de Bourges whose words, with those of Scève and Dolet and Marot, might be recorded for posterity in more than four hundred printing-shops.

The silk ... the merchants ... the bankers; the Gondi, the Spini, the Gadagne, the Arrighi, the Schiatti who, for two hundred years had married the wisdom of Italy to French acumen.

Those who created annually her four magnificent fairs. All those who had made a city fit for Marot's description: *ce Lyon qui ne mord point; Lyon plus doux que cent pucelles.*

'... And from these loyal burghers of Lyon,' had continued the agreeable voice of the King's new commander, 'from among these 50,000 fine souls in the wealthiest jewel of our crown, come the eight rotting heads you see on the Bridge of Saône gateway this morning.'

The well-placed knife, which takes a moment to declare itself. With an interest almost clinical, Jerott waited for the rumbling stir, and the ensuing silence, and then for the voice, less melodious, taking up the brief, nasty story of treachery.

He watched Lymond, since he hardly needed to listen. He himself had provided the report on which much of it was based. Letters had been found, under cover of packets to merchants in Lyon and Besançon, and a plot uncovered to admit troops at the next fair, dressed as traders. He, Jerott, had taken no direct part in the arrests. The orders for that, he now realized, must have come direct to the city from Lymond.

On one side of him, Adam Blacklock sat quietly; long and brown and tougher in some ways than Jerott remembered

34

him. And on the other, the short man with the hazel eyes and snub nose and drift of thin, sandy hair whom they had called Danny Hislop. A man more recently in Lymond's employment, Jerott guessed, and still with an edge that could cut. And enjoying, of course, the expertise of it all.

'Every family, I need not tell you,' Lymond said, 'has its wastrels. Those of yours have been extirpated. A great city, steadfast and loyal, can withstand that which would annihilate a divided one, and draws to herself, by her greatness, the succour of others. . . .'

The Captain-General from Russia stopped, and let his eyes travel over his audience from wall to wall. He had spoken without notes; his bearing relaxed, his hands still, his easy French conveying all the emphasis he required. He waited, and then said gravely, 'Burghers of Lyon, you are standing upon a new battlefield. Philip of Spain has decided to capture this city. The Baron Nicolas de Polvilliers, a lieutenant of the Duke of Savoy and a disciple of the Bishop of Arras, has mustered two armies and is preparing to march with both to Bourg-en Bresse, ten leagues from this spot. While King Philip's army engages his Excellency, the Constable's forces in the north, Polvilliers will advance upon Lyon.'

He paused. 'Will you, as these eight traitors wanted, open your gates to him?'

Not the knife a second time, but the bludgeon. Stunned by the unexpectedness of it, Jerott heard the repercussion begin; the noise increase; the sharp voices of inquiry, of denial, of anxious disbelief.

Lymond held up his hand. 'You ask how I know. I tell you, the monarch knows everything. You ask why I am here, and I will tell you. To seek out and punish the merchants who invited Polvilliers . . . You need not look at one another. It is done. The men were invited to Saint-Just last night and persuaded to confess. You may think it should not be long before they join their fellow traitors, there on the bridgehead. I shall read you their names.'

It was new to Jerott, but he believed it. Two of the arrested men were neighbours of his. He listened, absorbed, to the details. The enemy, it seemed, was on the march through the Franche-Comté.

Jerott said aloud, 'But we have an agreement. The Franche-Comté has promised not to allow hostile troops through its territory.'

'It's being looked after,' said Adam Blacklock. 'The Swiss Cantons are to be reminded of their treaty also. We're holding a Diet of Switzers to levy 8,000 and we'll place them as soon as possible at Mâcon and Bourg as well as round Lyon. Part of the Piedmont force is on its way already. You'll hear if you listen.'

Jerott heard. He listened to Lymond read out the formidable tally of the armies being brought to save Lyon. Discussions about the defence of the town had taken place already with their Consulat. Instructions would be posted: every citizen would be told how he or she could assist them. They, the responsible burghers of Lyon, had been informed first because on their resolution depended the safety of the city.

'There will be no panic,' said the King's commander quietly. 'There will be no evacuation of the city; and any man attempting to leave, or to send his goods or his money to safety, will, I assure you, be hanged. The King is not abandoning his city of Lyon to King Philip. If the enemy comes, he will find a defensible fortress, with about it an army which will die for you. For this, your King will strip himself of all but honour. He asks for your help, and trust. What more you can do, you may think of.'

'How much?' said Danny Hislop as they came down the steps with Blyth presently.

'Imagination boggles,' said Adam dreamily. 'Two hundred thousand. At least. They'll pour up to Saint-Just tomorrow with their money-bags.'

Danny smiled at the splendid, unsmiling face of Jerott Blyth. 'They know very well, you see, what happens when Switzers don't get paid. And none knows better than a banker that the King hasn't an écu to pay them with. Added to which, if they don't contribute——'

'The King's representatives might just conclude that they are in sympathy with the enemy. He hasn't changed,' Jerott said.

'Lymond? I think he has,' said Adam shortly. 'I have to make an arrangement on his behalf, Jerott. He would like to visit you later.'

'Tomorrow?' said Jerott. He remembered what Marthe had suggested. 'About six of the clock would suit best, if he can manage it. I expect you are all busy this evening.'

The nostalgia, for a moment, must have shown. 'Danny is

busy,' said Adam cheerfully, 'but I'm not as it happens. And I must say, I've a thirst that a Cossack would envy.'

*

Which was how, when my lord of Lymond and Sevigny came to recross the bridge to his lodging, Adam Blacklock was not in the procession; nor were Jerott Blyth or his wife this time anywhere in the vicinity. On the other hand, the Captain-General was receiving the fullest attention of his banker, a heavily built gentleman gowned in black who, riding by his side, had become gently insistent that Mr Crawford should visit the Hôtel Schiatti with him.

Riding within earshot, behind the hundred men at arms, the servants and the finance officials, Danny Hislop deduced that Lymond was not interested in his bank balance, or in the papers which M. Schiatti apparently thought it his duty to look at.

Nor, it became further clear, did he wish to discuss his future plans with M. Schiatti, or even to enlarge on his curious situation vis-à-vis his wife. Danny sympathized with M. Schiatti, who appeared to be sitting on a sizeable fortune belonging to somebody whose sole ambition was to remove himself and it from the country as soon as its rulers would let him. For a moment Danny wondered why Lymond didn't arrest the conversation more sharply, and then realized, with admiration, what reassurance the burghers would draw from it. The King's commander had money in Lyon; and was leaving it there.

They were crossing the bridge. Bracketed by the sunlit river, the low green hill before them rose from a confection of tender bisque buildings, deeply lit by the afternoon glow. They lined the river like marquetry and sank melting into the china-blue water in a gloss of towers and gables and galleries. Upriver a handful of skiffs floated, newly painted, at the steps of Saint-Eloi.

On the bridge a horse plunged, a little ahead of Danny Hislop. He thought, but did not say so, that perhaps the rotting heads had upset it. There were people here too, watching them pass from the parapets: shopkeepers, clergy, housewives, children. A scattered cheer rose as the main party, with himself in it, rode by. He could not discover in it anything particularly ironical.

Another horse reared far ahead, and there was a clatter of

hooves, a flash of morions and some controlled explosions of
the human voice among the orderly percussion of trotting
horses as the near-by riders were inconvenienced by it. Without interrupting M. Schiatti's discourse Lymond turned his
head and, meeting the look, Danny Hislop moved unobtrusively away and spoke to the captain of arquebusiers, who broke
rank and rode quickly forwards. It was not a wide bridge.
One did not, at this point in a campaign, want an accident
among the proletariat.

Danny returned to his position just behind Lymond. He
had just got there when his saddle dropped from his buttocks.
His horse was bucking. Shaken loose, Danny whacked at it,
hurtling forward. He was still going forward when it reared,
smashing his nose against its neck and tearing the reins from
his fingers. He was half off, swearing in Russian with tears
and blood pouring down his face, when someone gripped the
bridle and the animals on either side converged on him.

One of the riders was Lymond, his gloved hand running
along the horse's belly. He pulled, and Danny exclaimed
again, his glove palming his face, as his horse bucked and
whinnied. Then he saw the steel dart in Lymond's fingers.

'Blown through a metal tube. An old stephanois custom,'
said Lymond, and turned to the men at arms nearest him.
'You two, to that parapet. You two, to this. Round up all
those boys and girls under twelve and tell them they are
being taken back to the Hôtel de Ville for sucketts. Have we
a priest? . . . Yes? Perhaps, monseigneur, you would go for
reassurance with them. M. le capitaine, I wish the march to
proceed slowly until the children are taken away, and then
halted until the Grand' Rue is also made safe ahead.'

Danny got out his handkerchief. When the orders ceased
he said, 'Children?'

Lymond glanced at him. 'It seems so, from the angle of
trajectory. An adult on his knees with a blowpipe would be
apt to astonish his neighbours. In any case, I saw one of
them.'

'How?' said Danny. 'You weren't looking towards me.'

'I beg your pardon. My attention wandered,' said Lymond.
In his palm lay now not one steel barb, but two. 'Death with
a dart in his hand. It struck the brooch in my cap. Whoever
paid those children,' said Lymond, 'was hoping for more than
a stampede, a number of unnecessary deaths and a storm of
animosity towards this delegation and its purposes. . . . I sup-

pose, M. le Prévôt, that arrangements can be made to entertain these little ones when they arrive at the Mairie?'

The master merchant, bewildered, stared at him. 'Assuredly. I imagine so. That is, I shall give instructions. . . . You wish to question these children?' asked the Prévôt.

'And antagonize the parents? There would be no evidence,' said Lymond. 'All the blowpipes would long since have been thrown in the river. It is for you, messieurs, to hunt not children, but those among you who still wish to shame your city and kill its defenders. I shall not report this to His Majesty, in case he should conclude that the premier town in this kingdom is a dunghill upon which the blood of loyal men should not be squandered.'

Behind his gore-drenched handkerchief, Danny Hislop dispatched a thought, hopefully, to wherever Adam Blacklock might be. 'One hundred thousand more, interest-free, my boy. And if someone actually kills M. de Sevigny, they'll make an outright gift of their wives into the bargain.'

On the way along the Grand' Rue he had a second thought, and delivered it aloud, to his commander. 'I thought you said you saw one of the children.'

'He shall,' said Lymond, 'ben lyk the lytel bee That seketh the blosme on the tre And souketh on the primerole. You want me to look for him?'

'It would seem obvious,' Danny said. From experience, this kind of talk made him wary.

'It would seem obvious,' Lymond agreed peaceably, 'if I ever expected to know him again. Can you dispose of your swaddling band, or do I have to introduce the top of your head and your chin to the wife of the Governor?'

They had arrived. Danny, inhaling, removed his handkerchief. The idea had been conveyed to him, he noticed, that M. de Sevigny had observed one of the murdering brats, but not closely enough to identify him.

He distrusted, for some reason, that implication.

He went further. He was perfectly sure that his lordship had lied to him.

CHAPTER 3

Et Ferdinand blond sera descorte
Quitter la fleur, suyvre le Macedon
Au grand Besoing defaillira sa routte
Et marchera contre le myrmidon.

Danny Hislop had been warned about the Governor's wife, and when he saw her waiting with her staff and her ladies in the upper courtyard of the Hôtel de Gouvernement he believed every word of it.

The Governor, rich, gallant and lifelong friend of the monarch, was in Picardy, fighting Lord Grey and King Philip with the Constable's army. His wife, Madame la Maréchale de St André, was a woman of the Court and unlikely therefore to repine over or even notice the absence of her brilliant husband; particularly if the stories Adam told about her were true.

That the other stories were also true was more than borne out by her manner. Madame la Maréchale resented the presence of Mr Crawford of Lymond and Sevigny as a guest under her roof. A magnificent tolerance invested the painted face within the black-tinted hair. The rest of her statuesque presence appeared covered with jewels. Her gable headdress, her honeycomb sleeves, her glistening skirts were stitched with aiglets and cabuchons, and a medallion the size of a plate reposed on the gathered cambric of her bosom.

Then Lymond walked up the stairs from the street and Danny, following behind, saw Madame's eyes rest on the Persian coat, and the size and quite matchless splendour of his lordship's jewels and lastly, on his face, which was as urbane as her own. And to himself: *Blessed shall ye be when men shall hate you*, said Danny Hislop; and delighted, settled to witness a conflict.

It did not come. It appeared that, if driven to it, M. de Sevigny could conduct and sustain a soothing conversation which comprised not only an exchange of news but also some skilful anecdotes and even, entrancingly, a little fresh scandal now and then.

Madame la Maréchale, listening, allowed her defences to dwindle. After dinner she dismissed her women, her clerk and her chaplain, and appeared prepared to sit alone in her visitors' company without digging trenches beforehand. The names of Condé and d'Enghien and the Vidame of Chartres which had appeared with mysterious frequency in her previous discourse tended to disappear, to the disappointment of Danny, who was hoping for further details of his commander's disgusting past.

Of his peccadilloes in Russia, Danny had made a complete study in person. But even Adam had not been with Lymond during that stay six years since at the French court. Rumour agreed on some aspects: that he had been drunk most of the time; that he had performed some service for the Crown and had been taken up by the courtiers as a result.

Adam had reminded him that the French court was notorious for licence, and had hinted that Lymond's offences in Madame la Maréchale's eyes were partly to do with her husband. Her husband, Danny gathered, had not been offended: rather the contrary. The same appeared to be true of Messrs the Vidame, the Marquis d'Enghien and the Prince of Condé.

Added to what Danny knew for a certainty of Lymond's more orthodox conquests, it made an impressive tally. He stared into space, his nose in a handkerchief, thinking of a Tartar girl he had promised himself to stop thinking of.

Marguerite de St André had forgotten he was there at all. The golden-haired commander whose drunken wildness had once so attracted Jacques had learned manners. He was quite charming and also, clearly, of inordinate wealth. She smiled at him: the particular smile, for the first time, that made the most of her eyes and hid her bad teeth and said, 'And when is your next deputation? In half an hour? I cannot believe that, sitting here, you are conducting our defence against invading armies.'

'You will believe it when the couriers start arriving,' said Lymond pleasantly and stood up. 'All my orders were given before I came here. Then, when your leading burghers have had a chance to confess, I hope they will look for military guidance to Mr Hislop. . . .'

He made a small, unexpected turn towards Danny who sat up, radiating alertness.

'. . . whose nature, unlike the mastiff, is to be tenderly nosed,' Lymond finished. A little fan had been shaken from table to floor by his movement. The Governor's wife saw his eyes become aware of it. He paused, and then sinking to one knee collected it between his ringed hands and rose, with infinite slowness, admiring it. Then he looked up and smiled at the Maréchale.

His eyes were a brilliant blue; the disliked chameleon face illuminated with sweetness and warmth and vivid intelligence. His hands, enclosing the fan, were classical in their purity. The Maréchale returned the look, her lips parting.

Lymond said, 'I wish it were not so, but I fear my deputation is arriving.'

She had hoped that the confusion of sound in the street had escaped his attention. Carrying his eyes with her she rose, and passing Danny Hislop walked to the window, where she unlatched and drew inwards one of the five slender casements. Danny got up and stood, grinning sourly, beside her.

A handcart perched in the street guarded by a group of armed men wearing sleeve badges. On the cobbles beside it, newly unloaded, were lodged half a dozen deep wooden boxes and a group of arguing servants. Some of them, Danny saw, wore the Governor's livery. The rest showed the same badge as the men at arms: a badge he could not place, although he had seen it quite recently. Madame la Maréchale, looking over her shoulder, said, 'M. de Sevigny. You bank with the House of Schiatti. Are you expecting document boxes?'

Lymond came and stood beside her. Then, drawing open the neighbouring window, he watched without speaking as the skirmishing voices below came clearly upwards. 'They seem to be indicating,' said Madame de St André after a moment, 'that the coffers are to be delivered to you personally. My staff, naturally, are not accustomed to allow other servants into the house.'

'I am causing you trouble,' Lymond said. 'I apologize. I did ask M. Schiatti to send me some papers. There are rather more of them than I anticipated. Perhaps it would suffice if one of the carriers was allowed to enter and speak to me personally. The child, perhaps. Don't you think he is charming?'

Danny looked at the child. He was not particularly

charming, being bent double with a cloth and a leather harness wrapped around his head, complaining viciously about the size of the box two others were lowering on to his back. But he was certainly the youngest of all the Schiatti servants and the filthy hands were agile enough, and the language sufficiently foul, to suggest why Lymond wanted to see him.

Marguerite de St André's thoughts were in another direction. She said, 'He is dirty.'

Francis Crawford closed the window and turned, so near that they shared breath between them. Then he smiled, and lifting his hands, took hers lightly in them. 'But mine are clean, and it pleases me to keep them so,' said the King's Captain-General. 'You will have him sent up for a moment?'

And as she smiled and inclined her head, he dropped one hand and led her with the other to the door.

Danny watched it close, awestruck, behind her. He said. 'A wool seller kens a wool buyer. You do know what in hell you are doing?'

With some trouble, Lymond stopped laughing. 'I suppose so,' he said. He sank into a chair and still smiling, gazed at the flower-painted beams of the ceiling. 'If they force me to stay in France they will have to put up, won't they, with the consequences? In any case, you're the one who likes mature gentlewomen. L'échange de deux fantasies et le contact de deux épidermes. When I've trained her, you may put in a bid if you want to.'

'Was that the boy?' Danny said, switching subjects. With Lymond in this mood, it was useless. 'The boy on the bridge?'

The door opened. 'I told you,' Lymond said, and rose, taking his time, while the Governor's wife entered the chamber behind him. 'I shouldn't recognize him again.' And he turned, as the child from the street shot in and halted. Lymond said, 'You were right. He is really appallingly dirty.' His voice had not quite recovered.

Danny Hislop stalked to the door, shut it, and held a chair for the Maréchale de St André, well out of blowpipe collimation. The child scowled under its thicket of wadding. Its breeches and sleeveless green livery jacket were several sizes too large for it, but the grimy arms were muscular enough under the rolled-up sleeves and its hands, gripped behind its back, were quite capable of wielding a weapon. He might well have one concealed in the turban-like headdress. He most certainly, thought Danny, had lice. The boy, red-faced under the triple scrutiny, said thinly, 'De la part de M. Schiatti, huit coffres-forts pour M. de Sevigny,' and facing Danny, unclasped his hands, bowed sketchily, and gripped his hands once more, defensively.

In tranquil French, Lymond intervened. 'Unlikely though it may seem, I am François comte de Sevigny. What is your name?'

The urchin turned quickly and eyed him. 'Je m'appelle Annibal, monseigneur.'

'Ah,' said Lymond, 'I must introduce you to an elephant-keeper I know. And how long have you been in M. Schiatti's employment?'

The child's brown eyes shot round the room and, disarming in his smudged visage, returned to the Persian doublet. 'Three years, monseigneur. My mother is one of his sauce cooks.'

'I see,' said Lymond, and lifting Madame la Maréchale's fan chose a chair and sat down on it, spreading the delicate leaves in his fingers. 'So you came with M. Schiatti from the Hôtel Schiatti in Amboise?'

'You are correct, monseigneur,' said the boy Annibal. A thread of impudence for the first time reached Danny's critical ears through the nervousness in the child's answers.

'But,' said Lymond looking up, 'M. Schiatti has no château in Amboise.'

Danny winced. He wondered why his lordship had claimed to be unable to identify the boy on the bridge. Then he recalled something he had heard rumoured. Once, Lymond had questioned a child and lived to regret it. This time, knave that he was, the child had a fraction of Danny's sympathy.

The boy stared at his tormentor and said shrilly and with confidence, 'You are mistaken, monseigneur. M. Schiatti possesses a château at Amboise.'

Double bluff. Danny Hislop glanced at Madame la Maréchale and hurriedly away again. Her forbearance, her polite expression declared, was not without boundaries. 'Indeed,' said Lymond. 'I should like to hear where, and of what quality.'

Feet apart, the boy thrust his turbanned head forth like a turkey-cock. 'If you do not know, monseigneur, I must tell you that I do not believe you to be M. Crawford of Lymond and Sevigny. If you know, then I wish you to tell me by what right you question one of M. Schiatti's loyal servants? I am the son of a poor kitchen woman, delivering boxes. It does a great gentleman no credit to tease me.'

'Were you on the bridge this afternoon?' said Danny Hislop.

The boy turned quickly. 'No, Monsieur le Bec. I did not make you fall off your horse. Perhaps you should question your harness-maker.'

'Be quiet!' Madame la Maréchale had realized what was afoot. She sat up. 'Were you among those murdering children? Then we shall soon have the truth out of you. Mr Hislop, ring for my steward. Then I should be glad if you would remove the child to the window embrasure. He offends the nostrils.'

The child's mouth opened. 'He does, rather,' said Lymond; and closing the pretty fan, tossed it to the boy before Danny could shift him. 'Annibal,' said Francis Crawford. 'You have made Madame unwell. You will oblige me by fanning her.'

The fan was worth a great deal of money. Annibal allowed it to fall within six inches of the floor before he condescended to catch it, watched with well-bred impassivity by Marguerite de St André. Then, one-handed, he flicked the fragile fan open and stood holding it. 'To me,' he said, 'she does not look faint.'

'Then you may close the fan,' said Lymond, 'as skilfully as you have opened it.'

Below the dirt, the young skin of the boy Annibal went scarlet. He pursed his lips, his eyes on the speaker, and then smiling with a flash of small teeth, he lifted his hand and caused the leaves of the fan to pour shut in a brief courtly gesture. 'Attrapé,' he said apologetically.

'Attrapé indeed,' agreed Lymond. 'With a double *e* and no proper shame that I can discover. Pull his headgear off, Hislop.'

'What?' said Danny; and Madame la Maréchale, rising, made sharply to stop him. But since an order was an order, Danny Hislop did put out one fastidious hand, and grasp the end of the soiled, greasy linen and unseat, with a single rough gesture, the whole of the brazen child's headgear.

A quantity of matted brown hair, thus released, tumbled down the child's back and over its jacket where it lay, damp and nastily odoriferous.

45

'Attrapée. With two *e*'s,' said Danny. His eyes were unfocused.

'It's a girl!' exclaimed Madame la Maréchale.

The boy Annibal and Francis Crawford stood, silently regarding one another. Then Lymond walked softly forward and taking the child's grimy hand, raised it to his lips in formal salutation. 'It is a gentlewoman,' he said, 'of the title of Philippa Crawford of Lymond, comtesse de Sevigny. Madame la Maréchale de St André, may I beg leave to present to you the lady I am divorcing?'

Danny choked. Madame la Maréchale, to do credit to her breeding and initiative, walked forwards, not back, and stood gazing at the long-haired child in the green jacket two sizes too big for it whose liquid brown eyes, one now saw, bore wiped-off traces of fine cosmetics, and whose straggling hair still held a pin with a diamond in it.

The Governor's wife drew a breath, but how she meant to deal with an unprecedented situation was never to be recorded. Francis Crawford's lady removed her hand, wiped it, and said to him bluntly, 'And what do you expect Madame la Maréchale to say to that? There's no occasion for both of us to be childish.'

When he could speak: 'I beg your pardon,' said Lymond. 'I had some idea it would spare you a flogging. Madame la Maréchale——'

'I think,' said his wife, interrupting him, 'I had better make my own apology. Mr Hislop, how are you?'

Danny jumped. 'Excessively happy to see you,' he said, with truth. He altered rapidly the nature of his expression.

The Governor's wife said, 'I see, of course, that you have been playing some sort of game with M. de Sevigny. There is no need for an apology. Why don't we all seat ourselves, and I shall ring for refreshments?'

'You see?' said Lymond to his wife. 'There is no difficulty. You may even sit down, if Mr Hislop will spread his cleaner handkerchief over that chair. I do not think you want any refreshments.'

'You are so kind, Madame la Maréchale,' said Philippa gratefully. 'But of course, we must not impose on you. I didn't mean to intrude. I had no idea my husband would recognize me. Mr. Crawford didn't even know I was in Lyon.' She paused, and adding, 'My breeches are quite clean,' sat down with a great deal of aplomb on a coffer-seat.

After a moment, Madame la Maréchale followed her example. Only Lymond remained standing, looking down on her, and Danny, watching rapt from the door. Lymond said, 'No. I didn't know you were here. Not after you gave the slip at Dieppe to my man who was following you.'

Dirty hands folded primly in her breeches lap, his wife gazed serenely up at him. 'I didn't know it was your man,' she said. 'Archie said we had better get rid of him.'

Lymond said, 'I called him off in any case when I heard Archie was with you.' He looked down at the fan, which he had taken from her fingers, and Danny thought, he doesn't want an audience. On the other hand, he isn't going to dislodge the Maréchale. He wondered why in heaven's name Philippa had come to Lyon in the first place.

Lymond looked up and said, 'Did you want to speak to me? Or merely have a look at the papers from the Hôtel Gaultier?'

His wife gazed winsomely at him. 'I thought perhaps I could slip in with the boxes and then sit and go through them at leisure. While M. Schiatti had them, he wouldn't unlock them for me.'

'And you didn't want to risk asking me for permission?' Lymond said. 'After what happened in London, you were extremely wise.'

She looked up, found him watching her, and looked away again, smiling nervously for the Maréchale's benefit. She said, 'You don't need to remind me. I stopped you from going to Russia.'

'Temporarily,' Lymond said. 'However, so did Guthrie and Hoddim and Blacklock and Hislop here. Danny will confirm. They survived the experience.'

'Just,' said Danny. He didn't see why he should have to connive at a falsehood. Philippa looked at him. 'Mr Crawford has dispensed with our services,' said Danny. 'Alec and Fergie are fighting for the Constable. Adam and I are with him only until we can be found posts in other companies.' He could feel, in front of him, Lymond's unspoken rancour.

The bedraggled child on the coffer turned slowly to look at her husband. Then she said, 'I wouldn't call that a very balanced reaction. What will you do to me? I interfered with your freedom of movement a good deal more than that.'

47

Mesmerized, the Governor's wife gazed at M. le comte de Sevigny, who was gazing in turn at the speaker. He stirred, laid the fan on a table, and then addressed his wife concisely. 'They were under my orders, and they disobeyed my orders. For what you do I have no redress, nor do I require any. If any circumstance of my life displeases me, I am more than capable of setting it right without outside interference. In the meantime, you wish to look at the papers bequeathed me. You may do so. I have no objection.'

Danny, who had been holding his breath, promptly released it. Madame la Maréchale, who had felt little but contempt for the creature's escapade, experienced for the first time a shadow of pity. She stood up and so, tardily, did the comtesse de Sevigny.

Philippa said, 'The trouble is, you would say all that anyway.' She gazed at her husband, her grimy brow wrinkled sadly. '*If only* we could get Güzel here for you!'

Danny made a loud, painful noise with his nose. Lymond, who had not been prepared for it either, just avoided vocalizing his reaction. He said, his skin flushed to the roots of his hair, 'She might not be prepared to emigrate.'

'No,' said Philippa. She paused. 'It has *all* been rather ... adolescent. I hope you will overlook it. You do mean I may see the papers? There are more, you know, at Marthe's house. She was going to help me. I was to call on her at six tomorrow.'

Moving to the door, he stood, arrested in the moment of opening it. 'What a coincidence. So was I, at Jerott's insistence.'

They looked at one another. Then Lymond added, 'Suppose we share the Kittasoles of State and go together? Where are you staying? Or wait. I should be able to guess. As a guest of the Hôtel Schiatti, with the family sworn not to tell me?'

She nodded, and Lymond's grim mouth relaxed. 'Don't brood over it,' he said. 'Madame Marguerite knows the English are crazy. I shall call for you at half-past five.' And with Danny saluted her briefly as, escorted by the Governor's wife, the girl in servant's livery descended the stairs to the courtyard.

They did not hear Philippa repeat, handsomely, her apologies to her hostess. Or hear her add, cheerfully, that she had met the Maréchale's daughter in Paris.

Madame, smiling, was not forthcoming. 'She enjoys her work. Catherine, you will know, is one of the Queen's demoiselles of honour.'

'Well, she's on her way to Lyon,' said Philippa cheerfully. 'At Queen Catherine's warm insistence. I think there's a very good chance that M. le comte will take to her. Next after dark night, the mirthful morrow, you know.'

Not for the first time that evening, Madame la Maréchale de St André gazed at the wife of her guest with an astonishment edging on horor. Within her desk upstairs at this moment was a letter. In it her husband the Marshal begged her to humour this whim of the Queen's: to bind the comte de Sevigny closer to the French crown by the gift of the richest heiress in France, their only daughter.

Marguerite de St André had been less than beguiled by the prospect. Knowing what she now knew of the Count's style and his person, she was reluctant for other reasons altogether. But at no time had she expected the man's wife to know of the plan, far less support it.

She said, 'My daughter, Madame de Sevigny, has a sizeable fortune. Do you imagine that your husband is a suitable spouse for her?'

Philippa pondered. 'I haven't heard of any complaints,' she said with honesty.

Complaints . . . !

'More than most men,' said the Governor's wife carefully, 'my lord of Sevigny seems to have led a life of some . . . irregularity. You do not resent this?'

'Well: not, of course, the Rosc-tree of the Garden of Fidelity,' said the comtesse de Sevigny, 'but there would be very little point, I should say, in resenting it. You know. *Zyf you know or you knyt, you mayst you Abate: And yf you knyt er you knowe, Than yt ys to late.* He has a wonderful——'

'What?' said Madame la Maréchale. She was beginning to feel the faintest fondness for Philippa Crawford.

'. . . mistress,' said Philippa apologetically. 'That's why he wants to get back to Russia. None of us would mind his having Güzel with him, but we do think he ought to stay in France. Perhaps Catherine is the very person to keep him.'

'Perhaps she is,' said the Governor's wife, and saw, with

some disappointment, that her footmen had arrived to take the young lady home to her lodging.

'Catherine, or someone else suitable.'

*

Lymond was still up when Adam returned, very late, from his evening's freedom. He saw the light under the door, and, after flinging his cloak on the bed beside Danny, returned to the master suite to tap for admission.

From the curtness of the reply, he guessed Lymond was working; and on entering, the first thing he saw was a candle-lit table loaded with papers, with more in boxes stacked on the floor. The campaign had been relegated, he observed, to a side desk, whose neat piles of maps and plans and papers and folders bore witness to the rest of the evening's work. Half undressed under a sleeveless over-robe, Lymond was standing over one of the heavy boxes, sealing it. He said, 'How was Jerott?'

'Unhappy,' said Adam. 'I've just paid two tavern servants to come with me and see him home safely.'

Lymond blew out the taper and, lifting a ring, pressed the cartouche into the soft wax and held it there. 'Thirst, the devil of the desert. He didn't invite you into his house?'

'He was unconscious,' said Adam shortly. 'No. He chose to take me in the first place to an inn. We had supper and wine there.'

Lymond slid the ring on to his fourth finger and lifting the box by its handles, placed it with the rest on the floor. Then he straightened, and walked to a cupboard. 'Sit down,' he said. 'I am going to have a cup of Charnico. What will you have?'

Adam shuddered. 'Nothing,' he said. 'Thank you.'

'I am still going to have a cup of Charnico,' Lymond said. He showed no fatigue. The demands of his profession seldom seemed to weigh on him, Adam knew from the past. Even after that long address to the burghers he had been perfectly fresh; and since Douai, noticeably, he had deferred not at all to the weaker flesh on his captains.

Now he poured his wine and sat down in the chair next to Adam's, the silver goblet held poised on his fingertips. He said, '*Aut nulla Ebrietas, aut tanta sit ut sibi curat*. Under stress, Jerott always took refuge in drink.'

Adam said quietly, 'Not only Jerott. But this is a habit of very long standing.'

There was a little silence. Then Lymond said, 'Is it affecting his commerce?'

'No,' said Adam. 'The company is flourishing: he has a good business head and is well thought of. His wife deals in antiques. They trade from the house Marthe was brought up in. The old couple died.'

Lymond savoured his wine. The pounced gem-cut seal on his ring flashed as he let the cup rest on his chair-arm. It was incised, Adam saw, not with this coat of arms, but with Russian characters. Lymond said, 'Marthe is a bastard. The couple who lived in that house were a usurer-dealer called Gaultier, who called himself uncle. And his patron, an elderly woman who dabbled in mysticism. When they died, the house and fortune were both left to me.'

Adam was silent. Jerott had told him that, ramblingly loquacious before the weeping had started. The Dame de Doubtance, the old woman who had made mad prophecies for Francis Crawford, and dying had left him everything, no one knew why. Unless it was because Marthe, brought up nameless and parentless, was sufficiently like him to be his twin sister.

Lymond said, 'Naturally, I offered both to Jerott's wife, since the Dame de Doubtance had virtually reared her. But though as you may have observed we are as twoo buddes of the same tre, we do not always see eye to eye with one another. She refused.'

'But accepted the house?' Adam said.

'Jointly with Jerott,' said Lymond. 'The Dame de Doubtance's own rooms she kept intact for me. If the marriage founders, one or other will have to give up his tenancy.'

Naturally, he had guessed. He knew Jerott. And presumably, in the four years since he had discovered her existence, he had come to know Marthe as thoroughly. Adam said, 'He adores her.'

'And yet he takes his friends to a tavern. His own marriage is in trouble. What then,' said Francis Crawford, 'does he think of mine to Philippa? You know my wife is a virgin?'

Adam thought of leaving the room, and then decided, blearily, to go through with it.

He said, 'Jerott asked if she was. He says you married her three years ago in Turkey and parted immediately. He says it

51

was a wedding of convenience, to be annulled when you got back to England. He says you've been back for five months, and if it hasn't been dissolved yet, it must be for your own private reasons.' Adam paused. 'He has some tall stories, even for Jerott, about what happened on that journey to Stamboul.'

Francis Crawford raised his eyebrows. 'You are hoping I am going to tell you it was all due to Jerott's vivid imagination, but of course, it was perfectly true.'

He lifted his cup, smiling and twisted it, admiring the entwined lizards and winged duck-head ornament. 'The little attack of blood-frenzy in Algiers; the fat Turk I was good to, on Djerba. The whores . . . the opium . . . the bastard I propagated on an Irish kern's mistress . . . Jerott knows it all. And Jerott would have me boiled in hell and strained through a cloth if I behaved to Philippa as my dear Marthe is no doubt behaving to him. . . . You know she is in Lyon?'

Adam sat up. 'You're talking of Philippa?'

'Staying with the Schiatti. She has been invited to call on Marthe at six tomorrow afternoon. So have I, in a message from Jerott. If what you say is true, why should Jerott chose to throw Philippa and myself together?'

'He didn't know,' Adam said. 'I swear he didn't know Philippa was in Lyon.'

'But Marthe did. So Marthe isn't afraid for Philippa's virtue. Marthe wants us to meet there tomorrow. I wonder,' said Lymond, 'why?'

Adam shook his head. A scar, thready in the flickering candles, marred the thin, distinguished lines on his face, and his hands lay open on his lap, their sketching days over now that there was no great band of fighting men on whom to exercise daily his talents. Lymond rose with eloquent ease and said, looking down at the other, 'You should have stayed with the Muscovy Company.'

'I know,' said Adam. He got up.

There must have been something over-critical or oversearching in his expression. Francis Crawford lifted his open hand and arming the other man with sudden force, walked him to his threshold and released him beyond it. The slam with which the door closed reverberated through all the stout floors of the Hôtel de Gouvernement.

Madame la Maréchale recognized it, as perhaps he intended. Lymond was clearing away the last of his papers when

52

he heard her door open. He waited, listening, but there was no further movement. He finished therefore what he was doing and then, pouring himself another cup of wine, walked to his own door and opened it.

Candlelight spilled from the double carved door of her room, defining the tall shadow of her robed figure, standing there. Her black hair, unconfined, fell straying over the silk of her night-shift. Her face, freshly painted, was young in the kind, golden light and her scent, invading the corridor, reached him where he stood in turn, the cup in his fingers. She said softly, 'Have you finished your wine? I can offer you some.' And waited as, seasoned, desirable, he came to her through the quiet passageway.

CHAPTER 4

Le capitaine conduira la grande proye
Sur la montagne des ennemis plus proche.

The next morning the pots of war boiled, and the merchants of Lyon discovered, as Danny Hislop remarked, what they were paying for.

At dawn the first messengers began to come in: from Berne and Metz; Marseille, Mâcon and Turin. A little later, the chief officers of the Consulat arrived to report and confer, followed by the members of the new safety committee and the captain of the guard. Danny Hislop left shortly with a book of orders, to accompany them. Adam stayed behind with Lymond's secretariat, correlating the reports as they came in and transmitting the resulting instructions as the comte de Sevigny issued them.

He had been up at dawn. Adam knew. Depressed and faintly liverish, he resented Lymond's unclouded acumon; his competence; his unflagging versatility. He had heard, last night, the door of Madame la Maréchale's room open. He had heard it open again, some time later, and another door quietly close.

They said that whatever Lymond might elect to do in a woman's bedchamber, he never slept there. Irritated, Adam lifted the list he had just been given and began stabbing pins into maps. Lymond had been quite right. He should have stayed with the Muscovy Company.

Marguerite de Lustrac, Maréchale de St André, came downstairs a little late; superbly corseted; a little ponderous; her aura heady as peaches, sun-ripened and perfumed in a silversmith's workshop. She brought them spiced wine and almonds with her own hands and Adam, sharp-set by then, was glad of them. But she was charmingly dismissed after ten minutes: she had hardly withdrawn, smiling, before Lymond had the table cleared for the next item on his agenda.

It was an appallingly hard morning's work.

54

Outside, the sun blazed, close to its zenith. At eleven, the travails in the Hôtel de Gouvernement came to a brief halt for dinner. Just before twelve, the small, broken-nosed man called Archie Abernethy left the Hôtel Schiatti where he served and looked after his young mistress Philippa, and proceeded to walk downhill through the town to the river.

The last street to cross his path was the Grand'Rue, and on the opposite side of that was the cobbled square round which the Petit Palais and the Hôtel de Gouvernement were built. It was cool where he stood, under the arch spanning the rue de Garillan. Archie Abernethy folded his arms, and disposed himself inconspicuously in a corner, and waited.

A monk came out of a side door in the square, wearing the habit of the noble order of the Chapter of St John, which demanded of its chanoine comtes a minimum of sixteen quarterings on the escutcheon. The man called Archie Abernethy, detaching himself silently from the shadowy neck of the rue de Garillan, moved out into the busy Grand'Rue and, mingling with the passers-by, followed him.

As might be expected, the monk turned to his left and walked south, towards the Cathedral. Almost immediately, however, he changed direction and took the right-hand road into the rue Berthet, and then turned left and right again up the steep slope of the rue Tirecul to reach the highest lateral street on the hillsde, the Montée St Barthélemy.

This he followed, climbing up to the left he came to one of the small ports in the town wall. Passing through a good deal behind his quarry, Archie Abernethy found himself among green trees, on the heights of the Fourvière hill. Noiseless on the deep grass the little man climbed the hill until, just below the chapel, the monk found an outcrop of rock by a clearing and turning, halted to enjoy the view. His pursuer stopped also.

Below them, the mottled, dun-coloured roofs of the city descended the hill to the water. Across the river the Presqu'île lay in sunshine, the painted ships crowding its quays and fringing the window-brocaded frontage, and the vista of roofs and tall chimneys above it. Behind that stretched the Rhône, and the rolling country beyond its one bridge. And furthest of all, glimmering in the sun-hazy sky, the Alpine snows of the gateway to Italy.

The hubbub of the city lapped them, low and muted as

sea-surf, rising and falling; bearing a cry, or the sound of a bell on its wrack. On the hill, there was birdsong and silence and the smell of warm herbage and myrrh from the chapel.

There was a shrine tangled with ivy overlooking the outcrop and beside it a spring, and a small statue, decently carved. The monk, turning, dipped both his hands in the water and then, shaking free of the stifling hood, cupped his face in its sweet, mossy coolness. His hair, burnished gold in the sunshine, was innocent of any tonsure. And the supple fingers, laced over his eyelids, identified him to Archie Abernethy as clearly as the rich fabric glimpsed under the habit.

With a crack, a rotten bough broke in the wood and fell from branch to branch with a hiccoughing swish. The little man with the broken nose turned, startled, to watch it.

He removed his gaze from the monk for only a moment, but it was enough.

He heard no one moving. Only a hand gripped his thigh and another his arm and grunting, he found himself jerked from his niche and forced hurtling through the air, somersaulting to the edge of the outcrop. His knife was wrenched from its sheath. He hit the ground with his shoulders and roared as his feet plunged and stamped into vacancy. He began to fall just as Lymond's voice said *'Archie!'* and Lymond's hands, still wet from the spring, gripped him with all their sinewy strength and drew him back up to safety.

Archie Abernethy lay on his back gasping, and his mistress's domineering spouse stood over him, eyeing him coldly.

'And what the bloody hell,' said Francis Crawford, 'do you think you are doing? Trying to prove to somebody that I can't protect myself?'

The small, sun-tanned man with the grey beard sat up and rubbed himself where it hurt most. 'Ye didna ken it was me,' he retorted.

'No. I thought it was that pot-bellied oaf from Midculter who was watching the house all this morning. Why?'

'I wanted a word wi' ye,' said Archie placatingly. 'I would have nudged ye in the street, but I fell to wondering if anyone else was following ye. I couldna approve of the heid of an army wandering about the like o' yon with all the work still to do. What do I call ye . . . milord Count?'

'Mr Crawford will do,' said Lymond tersely. They had

known each other, if fitfully, for seven years. He returned to the spring, rinsed the dust from his hands and picking up Archie's knife, threw it to him. 'With all the work still to do, as you say, I have to go down soon. You don't seem to have lost any of your native effrontery.'

'I do well enough,' said Archie. 'I stayed in Scotland while ye were blowing your tucket in Russia. When Mistress Philippa came to tell us she was going to France, your leddy mother tellt me to go with her.' His black eyes, sharp in the seamed face, scanned every change in the other man's countenance.

'Philippa called at Midculter?' said Lymond. He had drawn out a handkerchief and was drying his fingers one by one on it, slowly. 'And how is the third baron Crawford of Culter?'

'Your brother is well,' said Archie shortly. 'And all the bairns, and his wife. They consider your place is in Scotland.'

'So I hear,' said Lymond agreeably. 'Unfortunately for almost everyone, I have no intension of going. Do I gather Mistress Philippa is in France to fetch me?'

'You ken better than that,' said Archie tartly. 'If we'd known ye were in Lyon, she'd never have come here. She was going to Blois to track down some bluidy papers, but Mistress Marthe answered her letter first, and told her to come here to begin with.' His black eyes rested on Lymond's downcast blue ones. 'She means you and Mistress Philippa to meet in her house.'

'By shifty means and crooked ways. I have realized that,' said Lymond. 'Ah, and who is he apart, marked out with sprays of olive and offering sacrifice? Perhaps she is anxious to have nieces and nephews.'

'She also says,' pursued Archie, who was used to this, 'that she suggested the ultimatum that kept ye from Russia. If that makes mair sense to you nor it sounds like.'

Lymond lifted his eyes. 'So you've seen her?' he said. 'Yes, it makes sense. Someone told Piero Strozzi on his way north to Court that this divorce was proving troublesome, and that the way to keep me was to defer it. I was informed Mr Blyth was responsible.'

'No,' said Archie. 'He wants you to go back to Russia.'

'And take Marthe with me, I suspect,' said Lymond. He studied Archie. 'You know what these papers are, that Philippa is looking for?'

'I guessed,' said Archie. Under the tanned hide, his neck had reddened.

'You needn't let it disturb you,' said Lymond calmly. 'I am not the only man whose wife has diligently attempted to prove him a bastard. The novelty lies in the fact that my lady mother apparently allowed her to come here and do it. And, of course, Mistress Marthe, whose share in the family tree no one can deny, even if no one can begin to explain it. . . . You came here, therefore, to warn me about Marthe?'

'Yes,' said Archie. 'And Mistress Philippa says, can you talk with her privately before this afternoon's meeting?'

'No,' said Lymond. 'I have no intention of meeting Mistress Philippa privately, either before or after this afternoon's meeting. What she does is of no possible interest to me: my reputation doesn't rest on my parentage. The quicker she finds what she is looking for, the sooner presumably she will get out of France and cease troubling us.'

'I'll tell her,' said Archie grimly. His neck was still red. He said suddenly, 'Why did you come to the hill?'

Lymond looked at him, and for a moment perhaps, might have answered. Then he said crisply, 'To look at the view. You have seen Marthe. You have seen me. You are staying with Philippa. You can only be loyal to one of us.'

There was a little silence. 'Do you say?' said Archie Abernethy. 'Then I suppose I must be Mistress Philippa's man.'

He bowed neatly and, refraining from limping, stepped off the ledge and moved downhill through the undergrowth.

Francis Crawford, standing still, watched him vanish. Faint upon the air, the treble voices of boys floated behind him in plainsong: a recorder, uncertainly played, picked up a counterpoint and accompanied them. Birdsong veiled it in notes of dazzling sound as he moved downhill, his habit drifting through ferny shadow. Above his head, corridors of luminous green rose up to the sunlight, leaded like a rose window with wrought twigs and delicate filaments. Cascades of green light fell on his path and damasked all the tall tree trunks descending below him; arresting him with blinding dazzlements.

Between the bright particular leaves he looked down for the last time on the city: the misty tesserae, grey and beige and brown of the tall, garden-hung buildings; the four square towers, ochre and grey of the abbatiale; the copper-verdigris patina of the smooth river; the pure, cold snows like a lamp in the distance which, as he watched, dimmed over with mists, leaving nothingness.

Then, walking briskly, he stepped from the hillside.

✳

Returned presently to his cabinet in the Hôtel de Gouvernement, M. de Sevigny isolated with clinical exactitude all the errors of execution which had occurred during the past hour and corrected them, with an acid ruthlessness which reduced one man to tears and Adam to silent, blind fury.

At the end of the afternoon, having worked for a further five hours, the Captain-General dismissed his staff and left to call on his wife at the Hôtel Schiatti. He took four men at arms with him.

He arrived exactly as planned at five-thirty and Adam Blacklock, had he been there and not thankfully slumbering, would have noted that by this time he looked tired, and with reason. Philippa, on the other hand, was charged with bountiful vigour, even if her greeting had in it still something guarded. Three of the Schiatti cousins, well-built young men with padded breeches and earrings, surrounded her longingly.

With the skill born of long experience, Lymond lent himself to all the introductions, circumnavigated the subsequent questions with steely courtesy, and mounting his bride on the little chestnut they brought out for her, rode beside her down the precipitous slopes of the rue de Garillan, past the Round House, and up to the approaches of the bridge, his escort docilely following.

Philippa began talking immediately. 'Your hostess Madame de St André called on me this morning. She thinks, as a maiden lady, I should wear my hair down. Bow. To your right. Someone is bowing to you.'

Lymond said repressively, 'As a maiden lady, you would wear anyone down, including Madame la Maréchale de St André, particularly if you were looking like that.' He bowed to his right. 'Were you?'

Philippa gazed down consideringly. Her pointed bodice, outrageously stiffened, was latticed with large pearls in gold-foil, and her pearled girdle had a tassel of bullion that would have felled an ox at twelve paces. Her hair, indubitably clean, was braided under a high-crowned velvet hat with a number of trembling jewels arranged under the brim, and an ostrich feather. 'I can't remember,' said Philippa. 'I think I may have put on something more elaborate.'

The contemplative brown eyes inspected him. 'What about you? I don't notice you going about in crewel garters and wadmoll mittens, that I can recall.'

His profile remained undisturbed. 'I do,' he said. 'I wear them at night. Whereby presumption and arrogancy shall be withstanded, malice and contention expelled and carnal liberty refrained and tempered. The Tsar used to get very fussed.' He returned the salutes of another group of gratified merchants and obtained, with a glassy stare, Philippa's approval.

Philippa said, 'Madame only wanted to satisfy herself that it was really family papers that brought me here. She thinks I'm following you about because I have a youthful passion for you.'

'But you were able to reassure her?' said Lymond. A market wagon, driven too fast, jolted past them on to the bridge and he let his horse feel the bit, leaning gracefully away from her.

Philippa said tartly, 'I am extremely tempted to say "no" and make you fall off your horse. I said you were a friend of my mother's and I was a friend of your mother's.'

'I should think that about sums it up,' Lymond said. His voice was a trifle unsteady. 'It doesn't do my self-esteem much good though, does it?'

'Your self-esteem has had a lifetime of steady attention,' said Philippa abstractedly. She studied him a little, soberly. 'Archie reported that I could look for these records? You have no really deep objection?'

He did not answer at once. But when they had descended the other side of the bridge and, crossing the square of the Lannerie, were preparing to turn right into the long, shadowy canyon of the rue Mercière, he said, 'Lest of an evil chick comes an evil bird? The time is long past, Philippa, when it mattered to me. I have a campaign to conduct. I should like, candidly to see you out of Lyon. That is why I am making this visit. I have also, I hope, shortened your investigation in other ways. I have studied the papers held by the house of Schiatti, and they contain nothing of interest.'

He paused, to let his horse pick its way past some unloading carts in the sharp shadows of the busy street. The clatter of six sets of hooves, reverberating between the almost unbroken line of tall, crooked houses, stitched its way through the general heat and the stinks and the clamour, and even the blue and silver pennant and the livery meant little, it was plain, to a street full of Lyonnais intent on making a profit.

The rue Mercière, running across the crowded Presqu'île like the crossbar of a gate, was the main trading thoroughfare between the Saône and the Rhône; which was why the horologist and dealer and usurer who had called himself Marthe's uncle had chosen to tenant it.

The name *Gaultier* still appeared, freshly repainted, among the signboards ticketing the long block of buildings ahead on their right. It seemed typical of Marthe that the house she shared with her husband should not bear his name or her own, but that of the defunct and unpleasant man whose business she still continued.

Trotting behind, Philippa found that her eminent escort was making better speed than she was; opened her mouth; closed it, and touched up her horse as soon as she could, to jog alongside him. She said peevishly, 'Do you consider I'm old enough to stop calling you Mr Crawford?'

'No,' said Mr Crawford shortly. 'What alternatives would you suggest? Master? Uncle?'

'That would certainly unsettle the Maréchale, for one,' said Philippa more cheerfully. 'I shall call you "mon compère", as the King does the Constable. You haven't enough artillery, have you?'

'Against you or the Germans?' said Lymond. He had relaxed again.

'If M. Polvilliers's troops are well armed and have cannon, you are going to be in a little difficulty until the Piedmont troops arrive, or M. de Guise from Italy, aren't you? That's why you want me out of Lyon,' said Philippa. 'Among other reasons.'

'Among other reasons,' Lymon agreed. That she had a nose for illicit information was known to him. He added, 'You must surely miss the court at London?'

'They wouldn't have me back after I sent you to France,' said Philippa briefly. She thought, and remarked, 'I miss Austin Grey.'

'Tristram Trusty?' The opening of the rue Tupin appeared sunlit ahead on their left. On their right, the sign of the Hôtel Gaultier swung from the second of its five irregular storeys. Below, an ornate door with a wrought-iron fanlight gave on

61

to a spiral staircase which went down as well as up. Next to it was a stone arch with a clock and crowned turban sculptured in stone set above it. Lymond drew his horse to a halt and dismounted, taking the bridle. 'You heard he came to meet me at Douai?'

'Everyone was very anxious to tell me,' said Philippa. 'You know what I think about this obsession with Russia. But you were right to trust him, and I'm glad he escaped. Kate always said he was too sensitive for a Somerville, but I think I could do something with him. Don't you?'

At a glance from Lymond, one of the men at arms came to help her dismount. There was a general vacating of saddles, attended by a number of grooms who emerged from the Gaultier archway. The archway door, opened wide, revealed a cobbled tunnel lit by indifferent wall torches. Leaving the horses, Lymond raised his eyebrows at Philippa and walked towards it. He said, 'Everyone is too sensitive for the Somervilles: I shouldn't let that deter you. He's as nice as a nun's hen, but you're right, I think. There is good stuff there. And he's a chivalrous child.'

'That's the trouble,' said Philippa doubtfully. 'Do you think my friends will corrupt him?'

'I don't know about your friends,' said Lymond, 'but you can rest assured that your husband's behaviour will be impeccable. If you're going to marry the youth, I shan't touch him.'

'But you will be nasty to him,' said Philippa gloomily. 'You know you can't help it.'

'I shall probably be nasty to him,' Lymond agreed firmly. 'But I shan't touch him. . . . You were here four years ago, when the Dame de Doubtance was alive?'

'Yes,' said Philippa dimly. She remembered then, as now, this dark vault with the cressets flickering, and the grotesques peering down at them from the arched caissons over their heads. She said, 'You were here too, with Jerott. When she prophesied that your father's two sons would never meet in this world again.'

'A depressing encounter,' Lymond assented. 'Do you suppose that Marthe too has discovered that revelation is a participation of the Eternal Divinity? I take it that marriage to Jerott has made her a Christian. What it has made Jerott, of course, is another matter entirely.'

He *had* met his brother again: Philippa knew that. Passing through Scotland on his way home from Russia Lymond had

had an encounter with Richard, third baron Crawford of Culter, which had ended in blows because, again, Francis Crawford would have nothing to do with his own bastard son, or his family. Summoning her considerable moral fibre from the wilting reed-beds of apprehension, Philippa Somerville forbore either to twitch or to apply to Lymond's arm for reassurance. Lymond did not like to be touched: she had found that out a good while ago.

He was, however, reasonably prescient in other directions. He stopped and looked at her, just at that moment. 'Wrestling with ghosts, after the manner of the Antabatae? It's a merchant's house now, not a temple of high Gothic fantasy. All that is going to be required of you, I fancy, is a great deal of social ingenuity for which, as everyone knows, you have a certificate.'

Philippa looked at him, her qualms replaced by another kind of misgiving. 'If you are going to be malicious, I shall walk out. Jerott and Marthe once saved your wits for you.'

'Lethaeo perfusa papavera somno. Now you mention it,' said Lymond, 'I seem to remember. Nevertheless, I have a feeling that someone is going to be malicious, and we may as well set them a standard. Shall we go in, lewd and rude, and provoke them?'

It was, Philippa supposed with a groan, her punishment for involving him in her private obsessions. She refrained, with no difficulty, from grasping his sleek, grogram arm and marched forward instead, out of the tunnel and into the Gaultier courtyard.

*

So Jerott Blyth, waiting for Lymond, saw a young woman emerge just ahead of him, preceded by a puff of chypre and an aura of extreme self-possession. He priced her gown automatically and then shifted his attention to the tinted face under the ostrich feather. The brown eyes, the decided nose, the curled lips belonged to no one whose parents he knew.

She was smiling at him, and he answered the smile because, indeed, she was exquisite, while at the same time he was aware, his anger rising, of Francis Crawford standing behind her, sardonically watching. He had invited Lymond alone to his home, out of bitter pride, for one purpose. If Lymond then chose to bring with him some empty-headed young nobleman's daughter, it was quite deliberate, and in tune with his conduct outside the Hôtel de Ville the previous morning.

Lymond had stopped by the orange trees at the entrance. Jerott made no attempt to walk forward. But the girl came straight towards him and, taking his hand, leaned up and kissed his cheek, smiling. Behind him, his wife Marthe's voice said, 'Don't you recognize her? It's Philippa Somerville.'

And of course, if you looked into those enlarged, reassuring dark eyes, it was the undersized bride of sixteen you had last seen dispatched home from Volos. So how in God's name did the girl come to be in Lyon?

Marthe knew. The edge on her voice told him that, and her lack of surprise. And there was more to it than that. Martha knew, and had invited Philippa to come at the same time as Lymond.

Jerott's right hand jerked and then remained still, trapped under Philippa's tranquil fingers. She leaned up and kissed him on the other cheek. 'We've been working on this for days. Did we succeed in surprising you?'

'You've certainly frightened him silly,' said Lymond. 'If you open your fingers, he'll drop like an egg to the paving.' He came forward, and as Philippa retreated, took Jerott lightly by the shoulders. 'You will have to suffer the same from me,' he said. 'It is a forfeit we exact from all bridegrooms.'

It had never happened before. Jerott received the swift, insubstantial embrace and then found that Lymond, stepping back, was looking at him with amiable satisfaction. Marthe said, 'If you will all do it again, the servants will give you a round of applause. The practice is to kiss the bride, Francis. You may come, if you wish, and shake hands with the bridegroom.'

Lymond turned to the woman he now called his step-sister and Philippa, her skin chilled to goose-flesh, watched them together.

They were so alike: pretty as jonquils with their white skin and blue eyes and pale perfumed heads, gilding the gloom of the courtyard. From the archaic stone lips of a wall-fountain a ceaseless jet fell to its basin. The trill of water braided the silence. Then Lymond, his eyes on the other identical eyes, turned out the palms of his hands, yielding and empty. 'I have no more than you have,' he said to his sister.

Marthe said, 'My dear, you have all the Dame de Doubtance's fortune,' and Jerott turned on her sharply.

'He offered you it all, and you refused it.'

Marthe laughed, and Philippa's hands curled inside their elaborate gloves. Whatever Lymond and his sibling were talking about, it was not money. Perhaps Marthe had saved him once from the degradation of his own addiction, but there was something different in her eyes now: contempt; defensiveness. And what Lymond had just divined: a subtle envy. Philippa said, looking round her, 'The house hasn't changed.'

It was bigger, indeed, then she remembered it. Gabled buildings with strange angled roofs totally enclosed the courtyard in which they were standing. Above Marthe rose four tiers of open arched galleries upheld on red columns with writhing forms, half beast and half human, carved on the capitals, and there were more figures on the painted beams roofing each gallery. Across the courtyard, a tower enclosed a second spiralling staircase and a roofed bridge, held on wrought brackets, joined one wall to its neighbour above it.

Two of the wide arches giving on to the yard led to stables and their horses had already been led there. On the side opposing the entrance, there stood yet another dark archway, still more handsome, with a spire and some sort of entablature. Jerott, who had been watching her, said, 'It leads to the quay. You know about the traboules?'

The Schiatti had told her about the traboules. With rare intersections, the houses of Lyon ran in unbroken ranks parallel, as a rule, to the river. To give access from one street to the other, public passageways or traboules passed through the tall houses. Since the habit began, gardens and yards had been filled with more buildings and now such a tunnel might lead you through three or more different homes and across as many courtyards before you emerged in the road at the end of it.

'Anyone who has visited Edinburgh knows about traboules. Don't be parochial, Jerott,' said Lymond. 'So you trade from the quayside block? Puissant, proud, mighty, cruel and bloody; the natural savour, taste and quality corrupted by th' infection of the pomp and other filthiness of your ships? What merchandise do you handle?'

'Sad irons,' said Marthe, before Jerott could answer. 'Ribbons, fringes, and little drums for bairns. He will show you them, I am sure, presently. My rooms are here.'

'And what do you trade in, Marthe?' Lymond asked, as she turned to lead them up the wide turning stairs. They had neither embraced nor touched hands, Philippa was aware.

'Bodily and ghostly comfort. And objects of antiquity,' Marthe said. And added, before he could speak, 'You appear to have profited by the first two. And of course, I have been well rewarded. Shall we see now what service we can perform for your wife? There are papers below she will wish to investigate. And after that, you may search the Dame de Doubtance's chambers.'

'Philippa can do both,' Lymond said. 'It is her self-appointed vocation.'

'Have you remembered nothing of the terms of your inheritance? None of these papers was to be read without your consent and your presence. And the first to enter her rooms after her death on pain of cursing had to be Francis Crawford.'

They had resumed climbing again. On the first gallery, looking down between the pillars at the heads of Philippa and Jerott, ascending below: 'You invoked all this research?' Lymond said. 'It doesn't trouble you?'

'I have nothing to lose,' Marthe said. 'So nothing can harm me.'

Below, Philippa had asked a question and Jerott had paused to detail an answer. Lymond said, 'Why did you want me to stay in France? You know that Prince Vishnevetsky has taken my place in Vorobievo?'

With slow charm, Marthe gave him a smile. 'And I have Jerott,' she said. 'How cheaply you rate me. You will not go to Russia because your fate is here. Or do you not know it?'

❋

In the event, Philippa plodded alone through the papers, which were in the vaulted basement room once employed by the man Gaultier as his store room and workshop, which had once contained a horological spinet of some small notoriety. Lymond, having fulfilled his obligations to the extent of entering the room and wincing at the dust and the dampness, had retreated upstairs again to the modified conviviality of Marthe's chamber.

Panelled in handsome oak and clad in paintings and fine pieces of plate and stonework and statuary it bore, as did all Gaultier's rooms they had seen, the lustreless chill of a complex house maintained by masterless servants. Each of the objects Philippa had asked to handle, exclaiming over its beauty, had left its trace of dust on her fingers. Even the Venetian goblets from which they drank were clouded, although the wine itself was clearly Jerott's best: crimson, mellow and potent.

Predictably, Jerott himself had consumed most of it. Returning after the installation of Philippa. Lymond saw that the flask was empty, and that Marthe also had gone, after lighting the heavy candelabra on the long sideboard. Outside, the engulfing darkness had risen almost to the sun-red gables of the opposite houses: the rue Mercière had quietened as the day's commerce came to its end and the pigeons under the wooden eaves shook their broad grey wings and planed down into the darkness to nod among the split meal and horse-dung. Jerott Blyth, his dark head against the paned window said, 'You still don't drink.'

'My excesses are other,' Lymond said. He picked up his half-full glass. 'But I don't refuse wine like this. You have heard what the merchants' loan to the King is to be? Six hundred thousand crowns, 100,000 of it without interest. On touche toujours sur le cheval qui tire. Or, whom God loves, his bitch brings forth pigs. Your reports were invaluable.'

'Is Polvilliers coming?' Jerott asked. Against the window, his face was hard to read, although the candlelight glimmered on the figured silk which clothed his finely built body; and on the powerful legs, and the rings on the strong, swordsman's hands.

Lymond said, 'Hell, Jerott: you gave me half the information yourself. It's true enough. The prospects are as fair as they can be. The cantons have promised to help us raise eight thousand Ku'milchers, and I'm clearing the ground round them and putting 2,000 Germans into that fortress as soon as I can. Mâcon will have 3,000 Switzers. I have someone working on one of Polvilliers's captains as well. He might desert. He was well treated once as a prisoner. You know the sort of thing that has to be looked after. It all requires money.'

'I wondered what you were doing, that was all,' Jerott said. He left the window, looked vaguely round for the wine and finding none, rang a bell and waited. 'It's hard to get well-trained servants. Marthe has to travel a good deal to buy stock. She's as well known as Gaultier was. You can see. She makes more money than I do.' The door opened, and he turned his head. 'God's bones, you took your time coming. . . . Oh.'

It was Marthe, with another flask of wine in her hands. She said, 'We find it a little hard to keep servants. They don't always work on the same time-adjustment as Jerott. I should have had a second flask ready: I'm sorry.' She met Jerott's dark eyes and said to Lymond, 'I think you might sit down, even if no one has asked you. Have you been questioned yet on your triumphs in Russia? Jerott is longing to ask you.'

'He has been talking about you, and your successes,' Lymond said. 'And thank you, but I have enough wine. How is Philippa progressing?'

The lint-blue gaze lingered on him, caressingly. Marthe placed the flask at Jerott's side and subsided in a sigh of wide, harebell skirts on a foot-stool. 'Forgive! and never will I aft trespass. She is half-way through: the acme of speed and efficiency. Why don't you settle for marriage with her, my Francis? A little house well filled, a little land well tilled, a little wife well willed. . . ?'

'After *Russia?*' he said with amusement.

The schooled face accepted everything, smiling. 'Don't you think Philippa worthy of you? Or is she finding you a little too experienced for her? What effected the transformation?'

'She was trained at the English court,' said Lymond pleasantly. 'Mary Tudor on top of the ministrations of Güzel would alter anyone's habits.'

'I had forgotten,' said Marthe. Whimsically, the disarming blue gaze scanned her step-brother. 'Of course, she was taught by Güzel. Then you must certainly forget your divorce and do your duty by her, my gallant Francis. Think of the continuity!'

For a moment no one spoke. Then Lymond got to his feet. 'I have a better idea. *You* marry her,' he suggested.

Neither the words nor the sense had filtered to Jerott, who was staring from sister to brother, his black hair faintly dishevelled. He said, 'You don't mean it. You can't mean it, either of you. Philippa went into this marriage, assured that it was only a paper one. I was there. I remember how it happened. My God, Francis . . . She's Kate Somerville's daughter, an innocent hardly more than a schoolgirl. If she's turned out a prize, it still gives you no damned right to talk about bedding her.'

'That was Marthe's share in the discussion,' Lymond said.

'I merely sat displaying passive resistance. If I may put it so crudely: should I wish satisfaction, I hardly need to resort to my wife.'

'Then why are you still here?' demanded Jerott. He sat, his face blurred with claret, peering at Francis Crawford in the dusk. 'Devil take it, you were overlord of a country. You had the Tsar and his minions running pecking like poultry, so Adam says. Why don't you go back? Or are you waiting to force that girl back with you?'

Wildly, Lymond stared at him. Then he turned, and in an explosion of breath slapped his hands on the sideboard and rested his weight over them. Crusts of wax, jarred from the candles, lay about him. He said softly, unlocking each separate syllable, 'I am trying to go back. I thought, believe it or not, that nothing could stop me from going back. I was wrong. Marthe has stopped me. She suggested to the French that my divorce should be withheld unless I fight for them.'

He looked at Marthe as did her husband, his mouth a little open. '*Mother of God,*' said Jerott Blyth stormily.

'I beg your pardon,' said a firm voice from the doorway. A wash of light brought clarity suddenly into the darkening room and bestowed a robust chestnut gloss on the bare head of Philippa Somerville entering with another candlestick in one hand. She advanced, aiming the flame at her husband and said, 'I'm sorry, but I couldn't help overhearing. Do I gather you stayed in France because of a bargain?'

Lymond turned round and laid his hands on the edge of the sideboard. Then he looked at his step-sister.

'Yes,' said Marthe and stayed precisely where she was, sitting on the low stool, staring with curling lip at her husband. 'I suggested it to Piero Strozzi. They say the Tsar is power-mad. By the end of a year, there will be no controlling him, or the Russian army. There is little chance of it now. That is why Adam and his other captains have been trying so hard to prevent Francis from leading them to disaster. And why his wife has conspired to keep him in West Europe also. Is it not allowed,' said Marthe dulcetly, 'for a sister to protect her brother?'

Philippa set down the candlestick with a thump. 'Is that true? You're here only because they won't give you a divorce otherwise?'

'I'm sorry. Are you insulted?' said Lymond.

'Why do you want a divorce?' said Philippa bluntly.

69

Stricken silent, three by no means inarticulate people looked at her. Then Lymond, speaking carefully, said, 'Because, I assume, you would prefer to be free.'

Philippa's clear brow wrinkled, and then smoothed again. 'I suppose I should,' she said. 'But on the other hand, the Pope is old and I'm in no particular hurry. Was that the only reason?'

'No,' said Lymond. The double candlelight underlit his hair and his eyes and his cheekbones, all of them untrustworthy evidence. Philippa, from long experience, watched his hands, long-fingered and resilient, pressed hard on the walnut frieze of the sideboard. He removed them. He said, 'In this far from seemly conversation, I suppose I had better bring in the name of Güzel.'

'Yes. Well, we all know about Güzel,' Philippa said. 'But you told me once you didn't intend her to have any children. So why after all this time feel bound to marry her? Wouldn't she have you without it?'

'Yes. Do tell us,' said Marthe with interest. 'Wouldn't she have you without it?'

There was a brief silence. Francis Crawford said to his wife, 'I am not sure if I follow you. Am I to assume that you are willing to dispense with a divorce if I wish to escape from France and find my way after all to Russia? I am, of course, delighted. Only the change of policy is, may I say, a little tardy?'

Philippa Somerville stood with her hands clasped and viewed, a little pale, the spectacle of Lymond losing his temper. She said, 'Don't be silly, it would be stupid to go back there now, unless you had to. That's what I wondered. I wondered whether it might suit you instead to stay in Europe and marry someone important. Or whether it would do if you simply went on sleeping with people like Madame la Maréchale.'

'Where the spirite is, where it is always sommer,' said Francis Crawford semi-automatically. He was gazing at her. 'Go on. There must be other options. Sum fra the bordell wald nocht byde Quhill that thai gatt the Spanyie Pockis?'

Philippa said patiently, 'All I am trying to point out is that you may please yourself. With or without a divorce, I am quite capable of making my own arrangements.'

'What? Who with?' Jerott had jumped to his feet. 'Damn you, Francis,' he said.

Lymond paid no attention. He relinquished the edge of the table and moved gently forward until he stood over Philippa, his hands clasping one another behind his straight back. He said, 'I hit you once, on the jaw. Do you remember?'

'Yes,' said Philippa. She added, 'You hit me another time, on the arm.'

'Oh? I had forgotten that,' said Francis Crawford. 'Why?'

'It happens all the time,' Philippa said courteously. 'I was where someone didn't want me. If they place the sun in my right hand and the moon in my left and ask me to give up my mission, I will not give it up until the truth prevails or I myself perish in the attempt. Are you going to strike me?'

'I am considering it,' said Lymond. 'Jerott is now convinced I am corrupting you. Fortunately I know, if Jerott does not, when you are speaking from conviction and when you are being deliberately and spitefully obstreperous. You have never made any arrangements outside marriage and you have no intention of making any, even if I felt constrained to break my agreement and start back to Moscow tomorrow.' He lifted his eyes to Jerott. 'The Somervilles,' he said tartly, 'are adept at sheer, bloody, domineering interference.'

Jerott sat down. He said, 'I don't understand'; and then, after a moment, 'Christ, Francis. Have you got into the Maréchale's bedroom already?'

Lymond began to laugh. Slightly weak with relief, Philippa looked at Marthe and found Lymond's sister already staring at her with an odd look, not entirely friendly, which she failed to interpret. Jerott, receiving no answer, seized the flask of wine, tipped some into all the glasses and pushing Lymond's across the table said, irritably, 'Well, come and sit down and tell us. Have you——?'

'I heard you,' said Lymond. He dropped into a chair, elbows on knees and tented his hands over his eyes, still laughing silently. After a while, he looked up and said, 'You know how it is. *Au travail, on fait ce qu'on peut, mais à table, on se force.* If time allowed, I should be delighted to discuss my private life in every choice particular with all of you, but it really isn't relevant.

'As soon as I'm released from my obligations, I'm going back to Russia, where there is a place there for me, or whether I have to make it. I should break my pledge and go now, if I didn't know very well the kind of revenge this monarchy would take. Also, if I might make the point, I myself wish to be freed.'

'To marry Güzel?' Marthe said. 'Or take a bed-fellow to Russia with you?'

Lymond smiled, and leaning back in his chair, placed his ringed hands together, master of himself, unpleasantly, once more. 'There was a suggestion,' he said, 'that the Tsar could find a better, younger, wealthier match which would be worthy of me. Güzel would be sent to a nunnery.'

'You said she was with Prince Vishnevetsky,' said Marthe. She was not smiling.

He opened his fingers expressively. 'So the Tsar's suggestion may prove very timely. Would it trouble you if I excused myself from the inquisition and asked Philippa what she found in the documents?'

'Nothing,' said Philippa shortly. She sat down and stared at the soiled parquetry floor, her hair falling forward. 'I recited the names of the three witnesses to the only servants still left who belonged to the Dame de Doubtance. Nobody knew the two women. The third witness, the man, was a priest. They remembered him. He died ten years ago in a fire in his house, leaving no records and no relatives.'

'Witnesses to what?' Jerott said; and Philippa looked at Lymond, who glanced at the elaborate German clock on its bracket and got up. 'You aren't old enough to be told yet,' he said. 'Philippa have you finished?'

Philippa gazed up at him. 'I haven't finished,' she said. 'And you haven't started yet. We have the rest of the house to search: remember? The harvest is great, but the labourers are few.'

'Oh, confound you. In the *dark*?' said Francis Crawford. 'Faint, faltering and fearful? Importuned?'

'Unless you would prefer to come back another day?' said Philippa with forgivable acidity; and lifting the torchière, waited politely for Marthe to lead them to where the Dame de Doubtance's inheritance lay, locked and waiting for its reluctant beneficiary.

CHAPTER 5

De feu volant la machination
Viendra troubler au grand chef assiegez.
Sera laisse feu vif mort cache
Dedans les globes, horrible, espouvantable.

Antique, adamantine, rich as Daedalus' honeycomb, the
house of Gaultier did not easily give up its privacies to the
chance-met foreigner to whom, so surprisingly, the Dame de
Doubtance had willed it.

The Lady's own rooms, locked since her death, were the
last to which Marthe led Lymond. Before that, as if constrained to prove her custodianship, she moved ahead of him
with her candle through the strange uneven passages and up
the winding turnpikes of all the great house, from the stone-
flagged kitchens where the servants huddled, staring at them,
to the vaulted warehouses on the quayside where Jerott's
stock-in-trade lay stacked, in bags and barrels and boxes.

In Jerott's stockrooms, his office and his cabinet was the
only order in all the brooding jumble of chambers. Swept,
stacked, spartan in their furnishing they bore the last vestiges
of the sea-going knight-hospitaller he had once been. And to
Philippa, following silently on the heels of her husband, it
was painfully clear that this was so because Jerott cared for
these rooms himself. Shirt-sleeved in the darkness he stood
beside her now, a little heavy footed, as Marthe swept her
candelabra around, and Philippa asked him questions. There
was nothing else of moment to see: only empty rooms, bare
of panels or chests or armoires. Wherever the Dame de
Doubtance had kept her secrets, it was not here.

Then she took them up the winding stairs and along a
high, open gallery to a door so low that she stooped, unlocking it. The key took a long time to turn and the door, when it
swung slowly open, showed them only the foot of a narrow,
worn staircase, stretching up into darkness.

Marthe turned and facing Lymond, proffered the candlestick to him. 'At the top is a curtain and another door, which leads into an anteroom. On the left of that is the Lady's bedchamber. On the right of the antechamber is her study, her oratory, and a suite of other small rooms. There is a locked door at the far end, where her visitors could enter without Gaultier seeing them.'

'And on the left?' Philippa said. 'Beyond the Dame de Doubtance's bedchamber?'

'Nothing,' said Marthe. 'There is no other door from that room, and the windows are sealed with bronze shutters.'

'You aren't coming?' said Lymond. In the airless dark, the pointed flame in his hand drew the eyes of all the tongued gargoyles, and painted the gallery rafters in ribbons of satin and charcoal. A fading of river-mist, sunk from the chimneys, lay waist-high below in the courtyard, bearing the dim lotus-heads of the orange trees.

Marthe said, 'She has not told me to come,' her voice tranquil. The Dame de Doubtance, to hear her, might not have been three years and more dead in her grave.

It disturbed Jerott. He made a sound of exasperation, and his wife turned on him instantly. 'If you are unhappy, go back to my room. There is wine in the flask.'

'Or come with me?' said Philippa. 'If Mr Crawford will let us follow him?'

As she spoke, the gallery darkened: Lymond had passed through the low door already. His voice, in a canon of echoes, came to them hollowly from the steep, thin-leaved stairs. 'I am Hermes, Conductor of Souls. Come if you wish. Come if you dare. All things arise from Space and into Space they return: Space is the beginning and the final end. There isn't much of it here: watch your head on the newel-post. . . . I have found the curtain. Jerott, do you remember the curtain? We came this way, the only time that we called on her. And the doorway. I am opening the door . . .'

Philippa, stepping through from the gallery, was half-way up with her kirtled gown and her candle when Lymond stopped speaking. Jerott, behind her, put his hand on her arm and with a movement unexpectedly lissom swung himself up before her and round the last curve of the staircase.

The curtain Jerott remembered was now pulled fully aside, but the door beyond was only half open. Silhouetted in the light of his own candle, Lymond stood there on the threshold, his hand on the door edge, looking at something unseen on the floor. Jerott said, 'What? What is it?'

'An empty room,' Lymond said. 'And a sacrifice. Where was the Dame de Doubtance buried?'

'By the Roman Amphitheatre,' said Jerott. 'Apparently. She arranged it herself beforehand.'

'Not in hallowed ground? Why?'

'Not because the Chruch stopped it,' said Jerott. 'They never proved that she practised black arts; only that she cast horoscopes and sometimes performed acts of healing. It was because of the way she wanted to be buried. And even that was better than her first choice. She was mad. She wanted them to embalm her enshrined in her baldachine chair.'

Without moving further into the room, Lymond lifted the flame in his hand. The light fell on a small, tapestried room, simply furnished with a coffer, some stools and a plain hooded fireplace in which the ashes of its last fire still lay, overlaid was a shroud of grey dust. On the coffer stood a group of wire cages, empty and open. And on the floor beside it, another tall cage lay on its side, with husks and sawdust and bird droppings strewn about it.

Lymond said, 'She wanted her creatures buried with her? I suppose she would. No one would care for them. Gaultier was dead. Marthe hadn't returned yet, bringing Jerott. They wouldn't resist. Perhaps they sensed she was dead. Only the dog didn't want to die.'

'What?' said Jerott; and Lymond, moving forward at last, let them walk past the door and see what was lying behind it.

Stretched where the free air of thc four seasons over and over had moved past the weight of his muzzle were the delicate ruins of a tall, noble dog, dead so long that the dry smell of his passing had grown part of the other queer smells in the fabric around them: of faded herbs and fine woods and lost incense.

The tail, long and silky and fronded, lay with pride and with elegance on the soiled floor: the pearly coat and the long, slender shafts of the legs were of a breed unknown to both Jerott and Philippa. It was Lymond who said, 'It was an Arabian gazelle-hound. He must have hidden when they came to slaughter him, and they went away, thinking perhaps he had escaped.'

He bent and rose again with a small, dusty dish in his fingertips. 'He might have lived for a few days on what was left in the cages, but the water would spill or evaporate. The house was said to be haunted. No one would come to his barking.'

'Poor beast,' said Jerott. 'We could open the grave, if the Lady set store on having him.'

'Oh, no,' said Philippa. Her throat was painful, but no stupid tears came to disgrace her. She said, 'He led a separate life. He ought to be buried separately. If he was a creature of hers, he would have gone where her body went.'

'Perhaps he wasn't a creature of hers,' Lymond said. The door to the bed-chamber was shut. He laid down the small dish and turning right, touched the door which Marthe had said belonged to the study. It was not even latched but gave at once to his hand and entering, the three of them began the long walk through the Dame de Doubtance's suite.

No one spoke, least of all Philippa. In these rooms, four years ago, had begun that long journey to the Levant in which she and Francis Crawford had become man and wife, and she had rescued a child for her mother to care for. On that journey, Lymond and Marthe had met for the first time and attained the guarded truce, based on mistrust, whose fruits they were seeing that evening. And Jerott, meeting Marthe, had fallen in love with her and made her his wife, to end here, walking silently beside her. On that journey, they had all met again the great courtesan called Güzel, by whose favour they had escaped with their lives from Stamboul, and with whom Lymond had then travelled to Russia.

Had it all been foreseen? Had the Lady known that undreamed-of power was waiting for Lymond in Russia: that he and Güzel, by the side of the unstable Tsar, might hold the future of a nation in their hands? Or that, sent on embassy back to London, Lymond would find himself overmastered by his friends and conveyed for his own safety to France and now to this house in Lyon where, although she was dead, the Dame de Doubtance lived in every corner?

A woman whose grotesque appearance and dominating habit had induced people to think her a witch, in spite of her bond with the usurer Gaultier, her wealth, her two houses, the importance of her customers.

What was her true name? No one knew. No one knew how long she had lived in Blois before the presence of the child Marthe was discovered but never elucidated.

The Lady whom Francis Crawford had met only twice,

76

and yet who, dying, had left him all she and Gaultier had owned. Call it an old woman's whim, Philippa thought, but you still had to explain the similarity between Lymond and Marthe. And once you admitted the possibility of a relationship, you had to believe that somewhere in this queer house there must be a record of it, which would dispose once and for all of the ignorance which had now severed every tie between Lymond and his mother and brother in Scotland. And not, of course, for Francis Crawford's sake, but for theirs.

So Philippa, her head up, her rigid hand gripping her candlestick, walked through the study which was not a study, but was hung with charts and long, pleated record-rolls, and whose carved desk and heavy tables were laden with papers held down with brass instruments beside a litter of broken quills and crayons and rules, pounce-box and abacus, hourglass and oil lamp.

There was a torchière with half-melted candles still standing cold in the sockets. Under its still light Lymond went through the papers quickly and neatly, and then ran his fingers, grimy with dust, over the scrolls and the tall, leatherbound books on the wall-shelves, singing under his breath as he did so.

> *Atant la gent Camile apele*
> *Il fist les pucelles venir,*
> *Lor Dame lor fist descovrir.*
> *Ele estoit tote ansanglante . . .*

'That's odd,' said Lymond. 'Where's Jerott?'

'Gone into the next room. He couldn't stand the Tomb of Camille,' Philippa said. 'What's odd?'

'Shouldn't there be more books? The armoires under there are mostly empty. And look at the gaps on the shelves. I can think of half a dozen works which should be standard for anyone making a living from medicine and the casting of horoscopes, yet none of them is here. Wouldn't you expect some mysterious papyri, for example, from Memphis and Busiris and Hermopolis? Think of Jíwaka, who gave an aperient to the great Buddha himself in the smell of a lotus flower.'

'I think of him constantly,' said Philippa shortly. She tried, and failed, to lift a bronze inkstand, two feet high, in the shape of Mithras surrounded by bulls with gilt garlands.

'It wasn't theft,' said Lymond absently. 'There's a Cîteaux Bible over there among other things.' He resumed singing:

> *'D'eve rosade l'ont lavee,*
> *Sa bele crine l'ont trenchiee,*
> *Et puis l'ont aromatiziee;*
> *Et basme e mirre i ot plente,*
> *Le cors an unt bien conree . . .'*

'Talking,' said Jerott, 'of embalming: you should come and see the Oratory.'

In the candlelight he stood in the doorway like a piece of good, sturdy carving, hand-tinted in white lead and flesh colour. Lymond wandered towards him, his soiled hands curled limp at his sides. 'To dispel doubt and error, one must exercise the light of supreme wisdom. You didn't imagine it *would* be an Oratory?'

And of course, it wasn't, although a tinge of aloes and myrrh still lingered in the dead air and a bronze font, flanked with marble, stood where perhaps once an altar had been. Now, there were shelves laden with jars, their mouths stopped with parchment; with retorts and horn flagons; with mortars, crucibles and alembics. And funnels, beakers and ladles lay on tables below the dried herbs—hellebore, plantain, club-moss, centaury, camomile—which hung in faggots from the low rafters.

The stand of candles Jerott had lit glimmered on ovens; on a tall figured ewer of blackened silver and a situla, banded with jewels and peopled with patient religions. There was a lead casket, inscribed, on a prie-Dieu. Lymond lifted it.

Inside, pink as a nude human body, was a plant root. 'A female ginseng,' said Lymond. 'Guaranteed to bring back youth and beauty ... She had something, didn't she, for every contingency? Foxglove, laudanum, strychnine; roots of hemlock, dry pepper, valerian ... Unicorn's horn.' He took down a glass jar and opened it. 'Ivory dust? Or narwhal, more likely. The Lord created the medicines of the earth, and he that is wise will not abhor them. There should be a cauldron.'

'Here it is. The font.' Philippa pointed.

'But of course!' said Lymond cheerfully. He leaned on the rim and breathed into it. 'Wings of a screech-owl, entrails of a wolf ...'

'Medea,' said Philippa. 'I thought you were occupied with Camilla the Volscian.'

'I was. I can't think why,' said Lymond. 'Or I can. It was the painting of Amazon arms in the afternoon. The myrtle shaft, the golden bow, the darts, the sling, the javelin. Oh, God, there's nothing here; and call him that doubts it a gull. I am not entering another astrologer's workshop. *Ne sui pas abandonè A chascun qui dit "Vien ça".*'

But the other rooms were only bedchambers, hung with ancient fabrics, their painted friezes lurking over the candlelight in an applied procession of furred haunch and scaly shoulder; their tarnished treasures crowded on tables draped with time-stiffened embroideries, their mirrors blind, their blackened coffers striated already with virgin clefts of sprung wood.

Only one room was in any way different, and there, the funeral obsequies of Camille suffered another interruption.

> *'D'un drap de soie d'Almarie*
> *Fu la meschine ansevelie,*
> *Et puis l'ont mise an une biere*
> *Qui molt fu riche et molt fu chiere.*
> *. . . Li liz fu de coton anpliz*
> *Et desus fu mis uns tapiz,*
> *Qui covri tote la litiere . . .'*

Philippa, following on Lymond's heels into the bedchamber, stopped when he stopped, and then bit back an immature hiss of pure panic. The blockish shape of a naked man stood erect just inside, facing them. It was made of worn wood with a head of blackened silver: the jutting lips were crudely gilded.

And behind, the weaves on the wall were from a world more ancient than that of the Lady, and the vessels and goblets, the statues and ikons, the winged chair and the golden-pawed leopards which upheld the tall ebony bed stirred a memory in Philippa of things she had put behind her: a memory she was just, with pain, bringing to light when Jerott saw the statue and exclaimed, 'Christ, Francis. What in God's name is that?'

Lymond walked into the room without answering. There was a swan-necked oil flagon of tinselled glass on one table: he unstoppered it, and filling a silver lamp, set it alight. Not until he had finished, did he turn to them both. 'It is a statue of Perun,' he said. 'A Slavic pre-Christian idol. The door was a little open. The dog must have come from this room.'

Philippa said, 'You knew there was oil in that flagon!' and Lymond answered from where he was searching, quickly, discreetly, knowledgeably as in all the rooms they had entered.

'I have another like it in my house at Vorobiovo.'

Philippa felt Jerott stir. She said quickly, 'I told you I met Güzel here once. The Dame called her cousin. Did you ever ask Güzel about the connection?'

'The occasion never arose,' Lymond said. 'Güzel was Dragut's mistress, and Dragut on occasion sent expensive gifts to King Henri, as the Sultan himself did. That would be how Güzel's visits were made, and how the dog came here. I fancy "cousin" was a courtesy title.'

'Will Güzel come back?' Jerott said.

'No. I rather think, in this Jeu de Prophètes, her part has been played,' Lymond said. 'I told you I thought there were some books missing. I have another mystery for you to ponder. Where are the horoscopes?'

They stared at him. 'With her clients?' said Jerott. 'We've seen the charts and the room where she worked on them. If she kept any back, they'd be stored there.'

'The commissioned ones, of course, with her clients,' said Francis Crawford. 'But she was a mischievous, meddling woman. The interesting horoscopes in this house would be the uncommissioned ones. The horoscope of the King; the Queen; the Constable; the Duchess de Valentinois ... Of all of us, since she took such an interfering interest in our lives. We have one room to search yet. Will you do something for me? Will you let me search it myself?'

His sleeves blackened; his wine-ruddy face smeared with dust, Jerott viewed his former commander. 'I was going downstairs anyway,' he said with hauteur. 'If you don't need my help any longer. Philippa?'

'I'll come in a moment,' said Philippa quietly. And as Jerott took his candle and left, she added, 'I should like, as a safeguard, to wait in the anteroom. Would that worry you?'

Jerott's footsteps receded. Philippa heard the stair door open carefully, and then firmly close. The tread, still truculent, diminished in sound and then vanished. Lymond said, '. . . For it is full of serpents, of dragons and of cockodrills, that no man dare dwell there. For whose safety? Mine? And from what?'

'The beastly snare,' said Philippa tartly, 'of over-confidence. A certificate for social ingenuity isn't going to carry much weight in that bedchamber.'

Lymond beat the dust off his hands and quenching the flame in the lamp, lifted the triple candlestick which had lit his part of their journey and led the way, undisturbed, past the rooms they had just explored. 'You forget. I am in such high favour, the Lady left me all her fortune. And here I am—All sall de done, fair lucky Dame—to obey her. I think you should go downstairs.'

They had reached the antechamber, closing the last door behind them. In the stilled flame of the candles, she turned and faced him. Behind the well-mannered authority she wondered if there was a thread of tension: an echo of the tightness she felt in the air, in her head, in the quality of the silence about them. The windowless room wavered in shadow; the dog, its long head laid where it had last breathed, seemed to stir as if the woven princes had called it. Philippa said, 'I smell what you smell. I smell danger.'

Surprisingly, he gave her his attention. He said, 'Shall I seal the last chamber, and leave it?'

There was a long pause. Then Philippa shook her head slowly. 'I brought you here; but the knowledge of what you must do should come to you, not to me,' she said. 'Go in, if you must. I shall wait for you.'

'Yes, I must,' Lymond said. 'If I run out barking, you may commit me with her other familiars. There is the candlestick. I shall light another to carry. Do you know the rest of the poem?'

'What? No!' said Philippa, taken aback.

'It's very beautiful,' Lymond said.

> 'Camile vestent de chemise,
> De fin blialt de balcasin;
> Corone ot an son chief d'or fin,
> La cepre tint an sa main destre,
> En son piz tint la senestre.
> Enmi la volte fu asise
> La tumbe ou Camile fu mise . . .'

'Why are you charming?' said Philippa. 'To warn off the spirits, or to bring them?'

Lymond picked up his fresh-lighted candlestick. 'Because it seems appropriate,' he said. 'Or I have been made to think so.

> 'Une liste ot d'or el tonbel,
> Letres i ot fait a neel,
> Son epitafe i fu escrit.
> La letre sone, li vers dit:
> "Ci gist Camile la pucelle,
> Qui molt fu poz et molt fu belle
> Et molt ama chevalerie
> Et maintint la tote sa vie...." '

The door to the bedchamber was bronze, hung between twisted stone posts, and the handle was a grinning horned head with a shining bronze ring in its mouth. Philippa watched Lymond's hand closing on it; saw him press; saw the heavy door stir on its hinges.

It began to open, on darkness. When it was wide enough to admit him and no wider, Francis Crawford released the ring and walked past it into the chamber.

*

Because he had been here before, he knew what to expect: the windowless cathedral with its silent worshippers of wood and marble and metal; the falling black gauzes of mouldering colours; the dead precipitation of incense; of damp; of decay. The statues, culled from every age and every civilization, still glimmered within the weak measure of the candleflame: the hawk-head of Menthu; the axe of Rama; the bow of Eros; the four stone mouths of Svantovit from their niches above the pale sarcophagi, the tables of bronze and of marble, the chests with their labyrinthine friezes of clutching hand and smooth eye.

Flanked by seraphim, the four golden pillars of the bed, shrouded in membrane, glimmered far to the right. Ahead, drowned in tapestried shadows, the tall chair of state stood empty now on its dais. The canopied chair with its crocketed spires where the Dame de Doubtance had sat, austere as a worn silver monstrance within the Saxon gown and the gross yellow plaits, saying, 'You don't ask the date of your death? I can tell you.'

Holding high the candlestick, Francis Crawford made his way through the room, his tread quiet on the figured tiles; his attention on the empty chair. He approached, as if he had measured the place, to a spot at the foot of the dais and then, resting the candelabrum on a low column, stood in silence, his hands lightly clasped before it.

Gryphon, pegasus and hippocamp stared unmoving back at him. Nothing had changed. On the right of the chair stood a papal candlestick ten feet high, mitred and peopled with penitents. On the left, on a low Roman table lay a chessboard. The pieces of rock crystal and silver digested the candlelight translucent and bulbous as lenses. A gilded ring-dove, fixed high in one cornice, bore in its beak a silver gilt chain from which a jacinth lamp hung next to the canopy.

In the candlelight it flared like a poppy. Lymond glanced up, drawn by it. At the same time, a breath of air, light as a chimaera, moved against his skin and extinguished the whole of his candelabrum.

Lymond stood perfectly still, his hands at his sides; his eyes open on darkness. Nothing moved. Weighted and waxen, the old fabrics were silent; the closed and untenanted chests had no voices left: the gods in their alcoves were beyond reach of a whispered awakening. He waited for what, even to himself, seemed a very long time, and then, moving softly, drew out tinder and relit the candles.

Beyond them, on a table, stood an oil flagon, the third of its kind; identical with the one he had just opened in the room which had once been Güzel's. As he noticed it, the candleflame again wavered.

Before the draught could strengthen, he had lifted and unstoppered the oil flask. Then, drawing the lamp chain gently down on its light pulley, he filled and lit the lamp and raised it once more, so that its mellow glow touched the tarnished fringe of the heavy canopy and burnished the breast of the ring-dove. Then, taking up the candlestick, he turned his back on the chair and began, with infinite pains, the task of searching the bedchamber.

A task from which an imaginative man might have excused himself from superstitious fear, or from revulsion. An exercise which a sensitive man would have abandoned at the outset, attuned to the pagan spirits within the chamber: the sense of dim, faded anger; of resistance, even, as the coffers were persuaded open and the gowns, the hangings, the linens, the caskets of contorted rings and filigree necklaces and turned wooden girdles were deftly investigated.

Francis Crawford embarked on his search and completed it, neglecting nothing; and if he had any natural feeling, none was visible. Even when, as he was finishing, the candles finally expired he showed no surprise, but closed the last drawers in a marquetry desk without hurry, and turned in the shadows to look at the long crowded room and the high chair at its end, still illumined by the small fiery star of the oil lamp. Across the dark spaces the monumental candlestick shone dusty gold, and the chessmen glimmered like moonstones.

Less bright than either were the folds of brocade which charged the seat of the chair and fell from it. Tarnished brocade, which stiffly coped the still kneecaps it covered, and lay in stony scrolls about the slippered foot on the dais. The half-open hand on the bliaud held no sceptre, and there was no crown on the regal head which stared from the canopied blackness; only a hennin set on two coarse golden plaits which lay within the red veil of the lamplight.

The Dame de Doubtance's chair was once more occupied. And the cold, running drenching through all the room, told of anger as the lightless eyes, without movement, stared straight into Lymond's.

His hands closed. Then, his back very straight he walked slowly forward until he stood, as before, in front of the dais.

There he halted. In the dim ruby light his hair glowed like silk seen through a wine glass. A breath came from the chair, bearing speech with it.

'*Aucassins . . .*'

'I am here,' Francis Crawford said softly.

'*And not afraid?*' The whisper was harsh.

'Of many things. But not of the grave.'

Within the cavity of the chair nothing moved but sound, and that barely. '*Li beaus, li blonz . . . Of what are you afraid?*' came the whisper.

'Search my mind,' Lymond said calmly. 'It is open to you.'

The chair was silent. Below the threshold of hearing the other dead forms in the room, touched by air and by warmth seemed to stir faintly, waking. The man, unmoving, gave no appearance of heeding them.

So it seemed untoward that presently he should flinch without warning, and that his chin should lift and his face

84

harden, like that of a man threatened by enemies. From the chair, loud and harsh and not in a whisper at all came a long, contemptuous cackle of laughter. Then the whisper said, as if nothing had happened, '*You are foresworn. You should fear me.*'

This time he did not answer at once, and when he did, it was carefully. He said, 'I am here because you willed it.'

'*I willed,*' said the seated figure, '*that all I owned should be yours. You have wronged me.*'

He said gently, 'Had I done otherwise, I should have wronged Marthe. Who is Marthe?'

Like a powerful snake coiled and striking within the chair, the voice hissed and cried, loud as a street-call: '*Sottel Putain! Trafiqueuse! Have I died for this?*'

He did not speak. The lamp burned. Then softly the voice said, in the old threadbare whisper, '*Marthe is a vagabond. You have learned pity. You have met evil. What, Aucassins . . . What of love?*'

This time his voice of its own accord was quite steady. 'I have learned love as well. For a nation,' said Francis Crawford.

'*For no person?*' said the voice from the shadows.

'For no person,' said Lymond, assenting. 'If Marthe is a vagabond, who is Güzel?'

A snigger came from the chair. Then the whisper said, sharply, '*The mistress of Dmitri Ivanovich Vishnevetsky.*'

'And what,' said Lymond softly, 'is your name?'

The room all about him stopped breathing. Then from the chair rose a singing vibration, like the note of a tuning fork, or a voice humming in madness, or pleasure. When it came, it was the loud voice that spoke, coyly muted. '*You know . . . You know. You see, you cannot quite keep me out. You know. Ah! . . . that it is Camille the Volscian.*'

He said abruptly, 'I know. You will harm her.'

And the voice, threadbare again, said, '*You speak in riddles. What would you ask me?*' And then, loudly, '*He will not ask. He is afraid.*'

'I will ask,' Lymond said, 'who is my sister?'

The faint voice, sighing, answered him. '*You wish to know who you are? Many men go to the grave without that favour. You are the husband of Philippa Somerville and under cursing, will remain so. Do you hear me? Do you hear me, both of you?*'

'She is outside,' Lymond said.

'*She is at your elbow*,' said the whisper from the canopy. A voice laughed harshly. His face blanched, Francis Crawford swung round from the dais.

Behind him, Philippa stepped from the murmuring darkness. The distant light textured the floating brown hair and drew glints from the absurd fluted stomacher. Her face, high-browed and burnished, looked up at his without fear.

'I am of the loyal cranes,' she said, 'that stand round the King at night holding stones in their feet. Love, fear and reverence: write these upon the three stones of the cranes.'

She smiled at him gravely and, turning to the tall chair under the ruby lamp, spoke to it. 'Accident joined us. Why should any such marriage be binding?'

The young, fresh, practical voice rang through the room. Round the chair, the air became dead. When the next words came, they were slow and faint, and addressed to Lymond. '*I have promised your grandfather.*'

Lymond said, 'My grandfather is dead. And what did you promise concerning the marriage of Marthe and Jerott?'

The voice was cold. '*Did the woman Marthe promise love?*'

'She promised kindness,' said Lymond. Behind him the room spoke, in a sound as fine as the stretch of a ligament.

'*Jerott Blyth has had kindness*,' said the still, sexless voice; and chilled them with the breath of its disdain. It deepened. '*Have you learned nothing? You should have died with the dog. . . . The bond will endure. Swear to it! The marriage will stand. Swear to it! Speak my name?*'

'Camille,' said Lymond. Behind him there came again, far away, the small sound of movement.

The voice rang. '*Keep me with you.*'

'I am with you,' said Lymond. The sound came again, louder. Philippa looked at him.

'*Then swear!*' The voice altered and rolled, rebutted from corner to corner. '*The marriage will stand. I have your mind in my palm. I will crush it.*'

'Then do so,' said Francis Crawford. 'I renounce the bond and the marriage. I defy you, Camille. Do us harm if you dare.'

'No!' said Philippa suddenly. A wand of pale light, dropping through the powdery air, fell slanting beside her and accepted the contours of cabinet and ewer and ciborium. Her hands on her skirts, she swept round and saw what had caused it.

Jarred by a monstrous and uneven thrust, the bronze door behind her had begun to swing out on its hinges. It opened slowly, shuddering, and the boom of it rose and fell like a mustering wave in a sea cavern, gathering resonance with its momentum.

Philippa heard Lymond shout, pitching his words through the clamour; but she did not hear what he said.

Nor did the man on the threshold. Wide-shouldered and powerful, silhouetted against the flickering light of the candlesticks Jerott Blyth found the resonance, in his wrath, of Assurbanipal. But fiercer even than that was the shrieking voice from the chair, overpowering it. *'Swear! Swear! The marriage stands, or I curse you! Francis Crawford!'*

Then the swinging bronze door reached its terminus. It thundered into the wall; and the shock of it rolled through the room like the hoofbeats of the Volscian's squadrons, splendid with brass; and clashed in the skull like its bucklers.

'Francis Crawford!' said the powerful voice. *'In fire is your friend; in flood is your foe; in powder is your release. Remember me!'*

Then Jerott set foot in the chamber.

Philippa faced him. Francis Crawford ran like a deer in the other direction. Before Jerott was well inside the room Lymond was half-way to the dais. As the echoes diminished, he reached it. The flame from the jacinth lamp streamed in the draught, plunging the mouth of the chair into darkness. The light from the doorway, rimming Jerott's striding legs and broad shoulders, played on other limbs that were also moving: golden limbs, sweetly poised below the pure childish face and outspread wings of the Eros.

Jerott stopped. Philippa cried out. Only Lymond, unheeding, pitched himself headlong at the dais as the singing silence was marred by a rattle.

The bolt had sprung from the bow of the statue. Bright as fire it swam through the air to where, rosy-breasted, there swayed the golden ring-dove with the silver-gilt chain in its keeping.

The bolt struck. The dove hung on the air, a tinselled cloud of white powder. And the chain, whipping back through its pulley, sent the carmine lamp flying downwards, streaming flame and hot oil, to the canopy.

Before it reached it, Lymond had rammed the tall chair with all the force of his shoulder. The canopy broke in a spray of webbed dirt and splinters. The chair heeled and lingered under his pressure. Then it toppled, almost dragging him with it, and the blazing lamp dropped where it had rested.

There was a table carpet near Philippa, its surface burdened with treasures. She wrenched the mat from beneath them and fled with it. Lymond, jumping down, had already done the same with an altar cloth, and disregarding the complaining angels, had flung the thing on the spreading flames and was trampling on it. Side by side they twisted: thrashing, stamping, stifling the seeded fires sprung up all around them.

The head of Kuan Yin, her fingertips streaming fire, lay on Philippa's shoulder as she swaddled her, and Lymond beat out the last of the flames and addressed her.

'Et chi est la fins dou Roumanch. It pays to study one's Gothic romances,' said Francis Crawford. 'Perhaps you will allow me to handle this. As you say, we are going to need more than a certificate.' And turning, he made his way through the smoke and the debris to where the felled chair still lay motionless.

Caught up in the crisis, Philippa had almost forgotten what led to it. But Jerott had not. Unmoved by the flames as if they had no true existence, he had occupied himself with bringing in light. The candelabra from the antechamber were now inside the room, and beside it Lymond's candles, all burning. He had found and touched off others too, and it was with his hands full of light that he strode now to where the splintered throne lay on its side, in a tawdry tangle of spangles and buckram.

Beside the rucked cloth lay a slipper, of a fashion long since disappeared; the velvet toe narrow and pointed, and the laces tied with a jewel. And woven into the tumble of fabric was something else: a long plait of coarse yellow fibre tossed with a sheet of pale silk which divided, moving, into shining ribbons of young, living hair, combed back from a face which, recumbent and dust-smeared, still contrived for her husband a stare, looking up, of contempt and anger and bitterness.

The moment of surprise for Jerott was long over, but he

still spoke her name, looking down, the candles bright in his hands. 'Marthe.'

And Francis Crawford, walking over, said gently. 'Touch not mine anointed, and do my prophets no harm. She could have died, Jerott.'

'Who would have mourned?' Jerott said. He was breathing heavily. He said, 'You know her. To get what she wants, she'll do anything, hurt anyone. Even . . .' He stopped and then said, 'Most of all, me.'

'Was this to hurt you?' Lymond said. 'I don't think so. For some reason she wants me to hold by my marriage. I don't know why. Perhaps, if you ask her, you'll find the old woman wanted it. At any rate, Marthe had nothing to gain by it. And she took the greatest risk, knowingly. Anyone aware of that poem would guess what was going to happen. The Dame de Doubtance was mad. But she tried to ensure that if anyone usurped her shadow, it would be one of her own kind, who knew the danger and was prepared to withstand it.'

Marthe moved. With the golden light bright on her hair she began, slowly and smoothly, to free herself from the broken chair and its canopy, saying nothing and ignoring the hand Lymond held, kneeling, to her.

Jerott, standing, made no move to help her at all. Instead, he said, 'She had something to gain. By maintaining your marriage, she keeps you beside her.'

Martha stood upright. 'For carnal pleasure?' she said, and laughed wildly. 'Like unto Uranus and Gaea? It hadn't occurred to me. On the other hand, it is a gift of Francis's to fill his house with sons bred in incest.'

Jerott lifted his hand. Lymond caught the powerful wrist in his fingers. Philippa choked, and Francis Crawford spoke softly to the lovely woman he had called his step-sister. 'He who strips the wall bare, on him will it fall.

'You knew of the trap. Why not dismantle it?'

'Because,' said Marthe, 'that was the instruction the Dame de Doubtance left for me. I am cursed enough, I sometimes fancy, without incurring her further displeasure. The trap was to be sprung only by you.'

'Why?' said Lymond. At his side he gripped Jerott's wrist still.

'Is this why?' said Philippa, her voice reaching remote over the chamber. And the three others turned.

With eyes of copper, of stone, of crystal, the images in the room gave back unchanged the stare of its invaders. Only, the painted leather panels of the wainscotting had all, as in a galliard, changed places. Where they had been was a chequer of pigeon holes: neat recesses in black from which, here and there, gleamed a scroll-end of slender, rolled paper.

'The horoscopes?' said Lymond. He let Jerott go.

'And other things,' said Philippa, a trifle austerely. Her legs were trembling. 'If she didn't actually use a broomstick, there were one or two things she preferred to keep out of the way of the Consulat. They're filled by Zodiac symbols. What sign were you produced under?'

'I haven't the slightest idea,' said Lymond shortly. 'But I'm sure, whatever it is, you will find the chart before anyone. Jerott, come with me. Marthe, your stock in trade is lying all over the floor. I suggest you begin to pick it up and leave the genealogy to Labour here, with a vine in her hand. Did you reach the chair through a door in the panelling?'

'Yes,' said Marthe. Her bearing was still one of contemptuous amusement but she also had begun, if you looked very closely, to tremble. She said, 'Are you going to tell me that you guessed who I was from the beginning?'

He looked at her. 'Not from your appearance.'

'How, then?' Where another woman might have been tearful, she was angry.

'You spoke . . . in words,' he said.

'So did she!'

'So did she,' he assented. After a moment he said, 'What did you mean, In fire is my friend?'

Marthe said, 'What?' She looked both upset and defensive.

'In flood is my foe? In powder is my release?'

But Marthe's fair face remained blank. 'It doesn't matter,' said Lymond. 'I suggest you stay here until I come back, and that you govern your tongue. You are unlikely to drive either Philippa or myself to the wineflask.' He turned away without looking at Philippa.

Jerott did not want to leave the room. It was a commentary on his lack of trim that Lymond was able to compel him, and quickly, leaving Philippa and his step-sister together.

Philippa was pleased to see them go. Disregarding instructions without hesitation she crossed to where Marthe stood, her ruffled head bent, studying a chipped Isnik dish without seeing it. Philippa said, 'There's blood on your arm. Are you hurt anywhere else?'

90

'No,' said Marthe. She watched as Philippa tore a neat strip from her shift and then folded it. She allowed her arm to be taken. 'A flank attack? Your tactics are a little more subtle, at least, than your husband's.'

Philippa, baring the gashed forearm, began deftly to bind it, a smear of dust on one tinted cheek. She said, 'Do you know you spoke in two voices?'

She was so close, she saw Marthe stop breathing and start again. Lymond's step-sister said, 'I tried to sound as she might.'

'You succeeded,' Philippa said. 'I think you need to be careful. In any case, he doesn't give anything away, whoever he thinks he is speaking to. You ought to know that. It only upset Jerott and made him fling out those accusations. Anyone with any sense can see that you have no more romantic interest in Lymond than I have.' She completed her task and glanced upwards.

Even to Marthe, born of guile, the honesty of that severe, painted brown gaze must have been palpable. She said, 'It's true? You have no interest in him? But everyone either abominates Francis Crawford or longs to possess him. I wonder why you alone should be immune. And if you are ... Why are you wasting your life in this tedious search for our parentage?'

Philippa released the bandaged arm. 'Madame la Maréchale also diagnosed it,' she said, 'as a case of Irene and the Emperor Leo. But it's very much simpler and duller. Mr Crawford's family think his proper place is at home in Scotland. I agree with them. And while his birth is in doubt, he won't go there.'

'I didn't suspect him,' said Marthe, 'of such childishness.' She no longer looked contemptuous; only thoughtful. 'Then for yourself, you do want to remarry?'

'Well, I should prefer not to remain a lifelong spinster,' said Philippa tartly. 'But as I said before, I am in no great hurry. Mr Crawford is. There is literally nothing he will not do to have his marriage dissolved, as you notice.'

'It seems a pity,' said Lymond's step-sister. 'So far as I can see, this marriage should be as convenient for him as any other. Why break it? He can find elsewhere all the pleasures he wants: I take it you wouldn't grudge them to him? Or does lack of love not exclude jealousy?'

Cornered, Philippa considered her answer. One could remain silent. One could claim, without truth, to be jealous. One did not say, to Marthe or anybody, that since one was a schoolgirl of ten, one had watched the deepening bond between Francis Crawford and one's mother.

'Would you have married M. Gaultier?' said Philippa shortly.

*

By the time Lymond came back, alone, she had completed her search of the panelling and had spread her chief discoveries on a long coffer cleared for her by Marthe, her self-possession once more in evidence. It was, appropriately, a wedding chest, chastely painted with garlands, cupids and large-nosed persons engaged in prenuptial activities of unlikely but harmless intention.

Lymond heeled the door shut and stood watching her.

Marthe straightened, her arms full of silver. 'Where is Jerott?'

'Where hast thou hung the carlish knight? And where bestow'd his head? Drunk as a wheelbarrow,' said Lymond. 'I thought you would approve. And it's ever so much kinder than handcuffs. What have you discovered?'

Before Philippa could answer: 'You will find him on your doorstep tomorrow,' Marthe said. 'Begging to be re-admitted to the great corps of St Mary's.'

'As the gentleman said, *Though you were not roasted, madam, it was a pity you had not been a little scorched,*' Lymond remarked. 'He has asked me already. I have told him that he may join me, on condition that he brings you along with him. I see no reason why your inconvenient responsibilities should fall on my shoulders. What have you found?'

With regret, 'Almost nothing,' Philippa said. 'Again. Some of the books you might expect. A few drug pots and nasty packages. Some horoscopes of well-known nonentities. All the signs of the Zodiac. If you're 1st November, you're Scorpio. *A large reporter of his owne Acts. Prudent of behaviour in owne affairs. A lover of Quarrels and theevery, a promoter of frayes and commotions. As wavery as the wind; neither fearing God or caring for Men.*'

'Better,' said Lymond coldly, 'to be stung by a nettle than pricked by a rose. What does *your* panegyric say?'

'I'm not going to tell you,' said Philippa. 'But although the

92

horoscopes are mostly missing, she kept a ledger of subjects and birth dates. You and Marthe are both in it.'

'Well?' said Lymond. 'New gripes of dread then pierce our trembling breasts. Tares or wheat?'

'No information at all except birth dates. You and Marthe aren't twins. She was born in '24, two years before you. But there's no sign of a surname for her.'

It was obvious that he did not care. But he said, 'And no clue therefore to Marthe's parents, or the Dame de Doubtance's family?'

'None,' said Philippa. 'There was a nephew of the Lady's called Cholet, but the branch seems to have died out. She doesn't seem to have thought it worth including their horoscopes.'

'Whereas,' said Marthe, 'she thought it worth while including the Crawfords. Don't force him to ask. Read the dates out.'

But Philippa had given the book already to Lymond. 'Look. There are seven names under Crawford, but you and Richard and your mother are the only ones living. The splendid first baron, of course, born in '75 and his wife, born 1477, Honoria Bailey. Then in 1495 his son, the nasty Gavin, second baron Crawford of Culter, who married Sybilla Semple, born in '88. And then Sybilla's three children, of which you are one. That, at least, we are sure of.'

'Are we?' said Marthe with interest.

Lymond, running his hands through the ledger, left Philippa to answer. 'We talked downstairs about trying to trace three witnesses. We heard of these people in England. What they witnessed . . .' She stopped, glancing at Lymond.

'Go on,' he said, without looking up. 'I am unlikely, under the circumstances, to be discomfited.'

'. . . what they witnessed was a pair of deeds by Sybilla, declaring that Mr Crawford and his young sister were hers, but not born to her husband.'

'Bastards?' said Marthe. Her eyes were shining. 'But brought up as if they were Gavin's?'

'You have it,' said Lymond. 'At the end of the day, look what divine bounty we bring you.'

'And the true father?'

'No one knows. But look, there are the entries,' said Philippa. 'Richard, the eldest son, born in 1516 and legitimate.

Then in '26, Mr Crawford. Then, three years afterwards, Eloise, the young sister who died.'

'You should make a Jesse window of it,' Marthe murmured. 'So that is what you are looking for? The names of Sybilla's lover? Then I wonder perhaps if I have found it?'

She had, at last, Lymond's fullest attention as well as Philippa's.

'Where?' Lymond said. He laid the ledger aside.

'Inside the dais,' Marthe said. 'Come and see.'

There on its side lay the baldachine chair. Beside it the blackened carpet, felted with dust, had been lifted.

Below were the boards of the dais. And cut through the boards a deep cavity, within which something lay, wrapped in bandaging.

Marthe said, 'The moving chair tripped some sort of lever. I saw the carpet had sagged and investigated. I haven't taken anything out.'

She hadn't taken anything out, Philippa thought, because she hadn't yet resolved to reveal it. Until just now. Until she had the pleasure of knowing that Francis Crawford, too, had no lineage.

She watched Marthe lift the package, and Lymond receive and unwrap it.

It was small, and inside were only two objects. One of them was a key. The other was a folded sheet of thick yellow paper, with the name *Francis Crawford* in an unknown hand above the deep-printed wax of the signet.

The key, large enough to fit a main lock, was finely made: for a house, one would say, of no mean size or quality. 'It doesn't belong here,' Marthe said. 'It might suggest the house of Doubtance at Blois. Or perhaps Sevigny. Or of course, some house here in Lyon, for that matter. I could take it, if you like, to a locksmith.'

'Thank you,' said Philippa sourly. She ought, she knew, to be grateful that they had a large door to find, instead of a box or a drawer or a casket. What could possibly be behind it defied her jaded powers of conjecture. She said to Lymond, 'And the epistle?'

He lifted the letter.

She gave him a paper-knife but he did not use it. He broke the seal with a single impatient movement which tore the sheet and sent the splintered wax flying. Philippa swallowed a

94

cry and sat like a dog as he read it. And Marthe, without speech, did likewise.

He was, of course a volatile spirit. And no doubt, in their overt concern, they looked ludicrous. His eyes lifted, and switched from the brown to the blue gaze devouring him. Then he said, his voice hoarse, in a whisper:

> 'His children let be fatherles
> Hys wife a wydow make
> Let his offspring be vagabondes
> To beg and seke their bread:
> Wandring out of the wasted place
> Where erst they have bene fed.
> And so let hys posteritie
> For ever be destroyde
> Theyr name outblotted in the age
> That after shall succede . . .'

They relaxed. 'What is it?' said Marthe impatiently.

'A record of death,' said Francis Crawford. 'The death of an unbaptized male child in Lyon: parents unspecified; date of death 20 November 1526. Signed by a physician with an unreadable signature. Witnessed by the same priest who attended my mother and who, as we know, is dead also.'

There was a pause. Then Philippa said, 'Did the child have a name?' He was smiling.

'Yes,' he said; and tossed the torn sheet in her lap. 'Can't you guess? It was called Francis Crawford.

'I do not exist. What you have in your hand is my death certificate.'

CHAPTER 6

La splendeur claire à pucelle joyeuse
Ne luira plus, longtemps sera sans sel
Avec marchands, ruffiens, loups odieuse
Tous pesle-mesle monstre universel.

When they left the Hôtel Gaultier it was after midnight, and there was heavy mist like a sleeve through the courtyard.

The fog altered their plans. Instead of returning as they had come, Lymond dismissed the four men at arms and, shrouded in hooded cloaks lent them by Marthe, he and Philippa set out on foot, the quiet way.

Jerott had been asleep. Marthe, half-heartedly, had suggested they stay until morning. Stupid with overstrain, Philippa had listened gratefully to Lymond pointing out with acerbity that some minor affairs might require his attention.

The war was his business and this, for him, had been an interlude. She admired his detachment, and also his hardihood. Untrained by the Russian steppes, she was lured by self-interest only out into that dank sticky blackness. She wanted her bed. And she could not face the prospect of the cold ashes, the wrinkled mattress, the wounding brilliance of any haven Marthe might offer her.

The appalling news of those last moments in the Dame de Doubtance's room showed no signs of weighing on her companion. She wished she could feel the same, with all her plans cut from under her feet. How did one discover who Lymond was, if he was not Francis Crawford? Whom had Sybilla substituted for the dead son she had borne, whose father was not Gavin, her husband? An unknown infant, whose full sister happened to be Marthe? Or was the other tale one had heard partly true: had Gavin, in turn, fathered children on some woman in France, and had he compelled Sybilla to ac~pt one of these, and pass him off as her own?

Grasping Lymond's cloak, she negotiated the cobbles, still thinking. They were not to speak, he had told her.

He had also given her, handsomely cased in jewelled leather, his own poniard to strap at her girdle.

The fog was so thick that the darkness had curdled to lead-colour, smudged here and there by a whorl of vapour with a seed of shrunk light in its middle. But for that, and the emanations of fish and cooking, of oil and urine and horses, they might have been ranging an unsanded tiltyard instead of this long, narrow street of tall houses. There seemed to be no one about, but she knew, without being told, that Lymond's right hand rested on the hilt of his sword, while his left kept it still in the scabbard. Their spurs removed, his soft boots made no more sound on the cobbles than her slippers, through which every dropped nail and wood-shard and rope-end forced its impression.

The mouth of the rue Chalamon appeared suddenly ahead on her left, defined by the three rows of lit windows which bridged it; and then faded in a freakish swirl of the fog. They were half-way to the bridge. Then they had to cross it, and climb up the network of streets to the Hôtel Schiatti. Philippa wished she had protested more vigorously against this odd idea that the horses should go back without them. Because Lymond was the Voevoda of all Russia and a friend of her mother's, it did not mean that he had more common sense than a Somerville of Flaw Valleys.

She wondered, plodding along, how far she was right in trusting Marthe with the key as she had done. There were several likely locksmiths in Lyon. And if nothing came of that, she herself would follow the other faint trails: she would visit Sevigny, Lymond's home in the Loire valley, and from there try the locks in the Dame de Doubtance's other house in the district.

It was empty, Marthe said, with all the money transferred to the Schiatti, and all the treasures to her rooms here in Lyon.

That might well be so, but she wanted to see for herself. There was something else also she wished to do, of which she had said nothing to Marthe. Jerott had found for her, unsurprised by her interest, the name of the convent where Marthe had been reared. It was near Coulanges, and close to both Blois and Sevigny. And now that she knew Marthe's age, she could ask to search through their records.

She still found it hard to believe Marthe's true age with all those fine-skinned blonde looks to refute it. But then, the Schiatti had been disinclined, for other reasons, to accept what she had told them of Lymond. The Constable was 64; Piero Strozzi 57; the Marshal de St André 52. The leaders of nations did not appoint young men to have overlordship of their armies. It took many years to establish a famous squadron of mercenaries. It required a man of exceptional power and maturity to attain, as M. le comte had done, the principal post in all Muscovy.

But whatever else he was not, Lymond was the infant a few weeks old whom Sybilla had brought home to Scotland that winter of 1526. Powerful he certainly was and mature, heaven knew, he had shown himself over and over to be. But he was also, however much he might wish to disguise it, only thirty years old in reality.

Which was, however, old enough to compel instant obedience when he said, as he did now, in a murmur, 'Stand there and keep quiet a moment.'

He had drawn her to the side of the road, and up the steep kerb to a doorway. She waited, eyeing her husband as he stepped back, fading, into the atmosphere. It seemed, on the whole, a fatuous idea to remain there when she could guard his back, at least, with the dagger. Just before he vanished totally, Philippa stepped down from her doorway and followed him.

In fact, he walked back twenty yards and then halted. Philippa halted behind him. Months of esoteric training in the Sultan Suleiman's virgin seraglio had taught her, if nothing else, how to move silently. She had used her skill in the Hôtel Gaultier, to insinuate herself after Lymond. In point of fact, it came to her, she had really spent a large proportion of her young life following Lymond. Madame la Maréchale might be forgiven for imagining it was with an ulterior motive.

Marthe had thought the same. It was tedious, and a little undignified. Standing there, just within sight of the blurred shape of her husband, Philippa thought crossly that the formal nature of their relationship ought really to be self-evident. Quite literally, Lymond never touched her. A few times, in the past, he had struck her. But his threat tonight, needless to say, had not been serious.

He had a temper, but it would hardly drive him to injure her. Now his response was merely to detach himself from personal contact. Looking back, she could not remember a conversation veering on the intimate from which he had not withdrawn immediately. He had had of course, in the past, more than enough of being devoured alive by the consuming interest of his admirers. A boy called Will Scott, back in Scotland. An Archer, they said, called Robin Stewart. Jerott, perhaps, long ago. Small wonder that Francis Crawford today took routine precautions to repel invaders.

And of course, that was it. Standing there, her eyes blank in the fog, Philippa saw plainly so much which had escaped her. The dismissals she had suffered; the exchanges he had broken off; the measures he took, when he remembered, to dampen the ardour of any impressionable fool who might dream of clinging to him.

Such as herself. She remembered the ringed, picturesque hands on which she had fixed her eyes, and their abrupt withdrawal. It was not only in the eyes of the world that her pursuit of Lymond was being put down to a blossoming schoolgirl devotion. Warily, Lymond himself had considered it time to start taking precautions.

Shame and anger ran tingling over her skin and sank into her stomach, twisting all her tired organs. Like beads on a rosary, small encounters turned and winked in her memory. Occasions where he had seemed grateful, or pleased, or approving and where the moment of rapport had vanished. Before, clearly, the underlings could become over-excited. Reasonably, he had had enough of torrid devotion. All he wanted now were experienced people to go to bed with, like Madame la Maréchale and Güzel and Oonagh O'Dwyer, who had borne his son and then perished.

She understood all that perfectly. The wounding thing was that he should not think her capable of simple goodwill with no overtones of childish infatuation. She remembered, chilled, his nervousness, and Marthe's, when she had questioned his reasons for requiring a divorce in the first place. The possibility that she would hold him to this marriage must have haunted him since the day it was contracted. She needn't fear, after all, that he would be nasty to Austin Grey, or to anyone else who came courting her. He was more likely, she thought sourly, to encourage them warmly to compromise her.

Transmitted by some freak of the fog, Lymond's voice said, apparently in her ear, 'If you call out, I shall kill you, my child. Did you imagine I should not know you another time?'

Where there had been one person, there were now two; and no longer in the dark but hazily lit in the swimming glow from the rue de Chalamon archway. And it was a child Lymond had caught: a muscular ten-year-old in bare feet and tunic who kicked and twisted and bit in the expert, impervious grasp as Lymond drew him into the tunnel, and darkness.

Following hurriedly, Philippa cannoned into them before she could stop herself. The child wrenched himself free. He was two paces away when Lymond's hand, sweeping round, caught him a blow on the jaw that jarred him back to the wall again, staggering. He began to slide down, his tousled head lolling.

Before he reached sitting-position, Lymond had unbuckled his belt and turning him round, had lashed the boy's arms hard together. Then he rose, the weight of his foot on his captive, and pulling a thin package from the child's tunic, tossed it over to Philippa.

The fog lapped and coiled in the indirect light from the archway. She opened the package.

In it were some steel darts and a blow-pipe. 'I recognized him in Marthe's kitchen,' he said. 'He tried to kill me on the bridge yesterday. If you had attended to a simple request to stay in a doorway, I should not have needed to hit him.'

'I thought,' said Philippa curtly, 'that you might need your poniard. Was this why you sent the horses first as a decoy? You knew that the boy would send word when you were leaving?'

'It seemed likely,' said Lymond. 'Then I asked Jerott to lock the kitchen door so that the child couldn't betray the change of plan to whoever is paying him. One hopes that it isn't Jerott who is paying him. Or Marthe, of course.'

'You don't mean that,' said Philippa.

'You overrate me,' said Lymond. 'So does Danny Hislop. He thought I didn't like manhandling children as a matter of conscience. You! What are you called, you?' He had switched to French again.

The boy had recovered. He sat, his bound hands against the bridge wall, and blasphemed. Lymond picked up his sword from where he had laid it and poised it, with great care, across the tendons of the child's ankle. 'There is a lady here,' he said. 'Do you understand? We do not wish to know why Abaddon in the bottommost pit will be receiving you. We wish to know who paid you to try and kill us.'

'You will find out,' said the child. He was sitting very still under the blade. Even so, a hairline of blood showed on the bare flesh and then was concealed by the fog-wreaths, drifting pallidly into the darkness.

'Do you think so?' said Lymond. 'My horsemen were expecting an attack. Perhaps your friends are all dead. Who will pay you then?'

'The same,' said the boy hardily. But he was watching the sword. 'But there will be more for me, then.'

'You say?' said Lymond. 'But these men know what they ask of you. To kill a royal commissioner, and not only at night. In broad daylight, where you may be recognized and caught, as I have caught you. For the risks you run, the reward must be riches undreamed of. What is it worth, to go through life footless? What do they pay you?'

There was a short silence. Then, 'My name is Paul. They pay me three écus,' said the boy thinly.

'I see,' said Lymond. 'And what would you do, if you were paid with such an object as this lady's girdle?'

Tears, stinging Philippa's eyes, obscured her sight as she scrabbled to unhook her girdle. She held it out by the light of the archway, so that the skeined pearls all dimly glimmered, and the bullion tassel swung like a pendulum. Lymond said, 'What are their names?'

The boy Paul said, 'They would kill me.' His eyes, shifting back and forth, followed the swing of the bullion.

'I shall kill you,' said Lymond, very softly.

There was silence. Then the boy turned his head and spat. 'I will tell you.'

The names were those of merchants, three in number. From Lymond's face, Philippa could not tell if the answer surprised him. He listened, thoughtfully, and when the boy had finished he neither removed the sword nor asked Philippa to hand over the girdle. Instead he said, 'What you say may be true. Now I require proof of it.'

The boy Paul started up, and then shrank back under the cut of the sword. He cried, 'You said——'

'I made a bargain,' said Lymond coolly. 'It remains to be seen whether you have kept your share of it. You will come back now to the Hôtel de Gouvernement, and you will remain there until my men have taken these merchants and

101

searched them. So soon as your story is proved, you will be set free, along with the girdle. Until then, you are my prisoner . . . footless or dead, as you will.'

It was common sense: the simplest of precautions. Philippa, slowly reclasping her girdle, made no comment as Lymond withdrew the sword; as the boy crying and protesting was dragged to his feet and then, propelled in front, was made to stumble before them, along the rue Mercière towards the bridgehead. Only she said, gripping his cloak as they set off, 'Who freed the boy? If the kitchen was locked, then who freed him? Jerott was sleeping.'

'Marthe, of course,' Lymond said. 'The servants' door is thick, but they would make quite a noise with their banging. By then, it was too late for the boy to find and warn his friends that we weren't with our escort. He was bound to try and follow us, and probably try to kill us himself, if he could. After all, he had three écus to gain by it.' He shook the boy. 'Was that so?'

The boy Paul agreed. He had become very much quieter. Hazily, Philippa wondered, again, why Lymond had not admitted Marthe to his confidence. Why risk death for them both, when surely all he had to do was interview the boy there, in the kitchen? Unless, of course, he didn't wish to embroil Marthe or Jerott. Or unless he didn't trust them, which she didn't want to believe. Or unless . . .

She had only got so far when Lymond's cloak, with a tearing wrench, was ripped from her hand. The boy, she saw, had flung himself on the ground, breaking the grip on his collar. Then he sprang to his feet and set off, panting, into the darkness.

It was a slim hope, with Francis Crawford behind him. Lymond did not use his sword. But he used, without hesitation, all the other skills which permit an armed man to bring down an unarmed boy, flying; and then having knocked him to the ground, stood over and partly on him, another precaution undoubtedly wise. Philippa said, 'He was lying?'

'I don't think so,' said Lymond. 'I think he just doesn't want to cross the bridge with us.'

There was a small silence. The boy Paul breathed heavily, exposing gapped teeth. His nose running. Lymond said, 'You were not the only paid assassin in the Hôtel Gaultier?'

They stared at one another. Then Paul shook his head.

102

'There was another boy? Someone who was not in the kitchen?'

'Another man,' said the boy sullenly. 'The groom in the stables.'

'I see. So the decoy party will have reached home quite unmolested, and the welcoming party will be looking out, not for them, but for this lady and myself on foot? What is the groom's name, and who is he paid by?'

'His name is Jérôme. He is paid by the same three. There are some of us in the employment of many merchants. The couple Blyth know nothing,' the boy said. 'Let me go. Let me go! They will kill me.'

'I'm afraid they will,' said Lymond thoughtfully. 'How many of them are there?'

'Many. Very many,' the boy said. He was gasping.

'Where?'

'Hereabouts,' said the boy Paul desperately. 'Let me go! I don't want the girdle.'

'On the other hand,' said Lymond, 'you're going to need it, my friend, to escape with.' He lifted his sword, and laying the edge against the child's bond, quickly severed it. Then, gripping Paul's arm, he spoke in English. 'Give him the pearls. He won't want to share those with anyone.'

Philippa gave Paul the pearls. He snatched them, his eyes veering to Lymond's hard hand on his shoulder. Lymond lifted it, and the child bolted.

'A total vindication for Danny Hislop,' Philippa said shakily.

'Undoubtedly, if you expected me to kill him,' said Lymond. 'Are you as tired as you look?'

'Don't tell me,' Philippa said, with a venom sluggish with weariness. 'You want us to traboule through to the quayside and swim the Saône to the Côte de la Baleine, from which we clamber over the Petit Palais roof to your lodging.'

'You've been listening to Jerott,' said Lymond absently. Philippa followed his gaze into the smoky vapour at the neck of the street. Through it, black against the faint incandescence of invisible lamplight, appeared the spoked carcass of an overturned wagon. Within its pattern something moved, and sharpened in outline. Two men, advancing.

Philippa turned, her hood sweeping back. Fog swirled at the mouth of the rue de Chalamon, blemished with random shadows. The shadows turned from ashen to charcoal and

103

then, moving and shouting, to black. She said, 'There are two men behind us as well.'

The arched mouth of a traboule lay just beside them. Lymond looked at her then, his sword drawn, his eyes smiling, his hood also fallen back from his hair, since there was no longer any point in concealment. 'Trust me,' he said. 'Do what I tell you. No one is going to harm you.'

With four men rushing upon them and another, no doubt, at the other end of the tunnel, the carefree voice might have seemed ludicrous. But Philippa's heart, oddly, lifted; her tiredness vanished and she returned his smile, unshadowed and fleeting as his hand closed on her arm and he drew her, in a single, silent rush, into the arched passage under the building.

The fog streamed in with them: past closed doors and shuttered windows to the foot of a narrow staircase; a grille and a plangent statue of St Peter, his key-holding hand lit by an oil lamp. Behind that, another lightening of the darkness suggested a courtyard to one side with a lanthorn in it. And beyond that, unrelieved darkness again.

A little whistle from pursed lips sounded suddenly from the traboule arch they had just left behind them. And almost immediately an identical whistle answered, from the darkness at the other end of the tunnel.

'Damn!' said Lymond cheerfully, and released her. In one liquid series of movements, he removed and draped his cloak on the statue. In another, he rehung the lamp swiftly behind it, and retrieving his poniard placed it among the stony keys. Point outwards, it glimmered there dully.

'I'm going to delay them,' he said, 'while you explore the courtyard.

> *'The man in the moon drinks claret*
> *The huntsmen whoop and hallowe*
> *Ringwood, Royster, Bowman, Jowler,*
> *All the chase now follow.'*

Philippa said, 'I used to be rather good with a peashooter. There's Ringwood.'

A shadowy figure appeared at the mouth of the traboule. 'And Royster,' said Lymond. He had vanished into an alcove opposite the dim silhouette of St Peter. The fog swam round the hood of the statue and the knife in its châtelaine fingers.

A second pursuer, less distinct than the first, gesticulated in the entrance. Philippa, withdrawn deep into the darkness, watched them as she unpacked the boy's parcel and drew from it the sarbacane and a handful of blow-darts. One of the men at the traboule entrance repeated his whistle.

Lymond was whispering. His voice, agreeably eerie, echoed through the foggy stone vaulting.

> 'O God breake thou theyr teeth at once
> Within theyr mouth throughout
> The tuskes that in their great chaw bones
> Like Lions whelpes hang out.'

The two figures hesitated. Philippa fitted a dart to her blowpipe. Lymond's voice, a little louder this time, said hollowly, 'May Gibil devour you! May Gibil catch you! May Gibil kill you! May Gibil consume . . . !'

The words rose to a shout. The clash of steel on stone drowned it. The man nicknamed Ringwood had rushed into the traboule. With a roar and a sweep of his sword he slashed the hooded figure which loomed in the darkness. The head of St Peter, immovably benign, jumped from its shoulders. With equal precision Lymond stepped from the shadows and forced his sword through the hide, flesh and bone of Ringwood's broad leather back.

Ringwood fell. The statue tottered. Lymond pulled out his sword. Philippa, vouchsafed at last a perfect view of Royster plunging in to the rescue, aimed her sarbacane, took a deep breath and spat.

Royster screamed. Two other shapes, rushing precipitately in from the roadway, hesitated, stopped, and remained suspended, like washed-out dye, in the entrance. Lymond kneeling said, 'Christ. . . . My dear girl, you've killed him.'

'I meant to,' said Philippa irritably. 'To devise is the work of the master: to execute, the act of the servant. There's a courtyard there with a couple of workshops, a turnpike tower and a stable.' She spat again, and a yell came from the mouth of the traboule. One of the shadows, clutching its shoulder, was cursing. She said, 'You could try banging on a few doors, but they'll be mad if they answer,' and realized that she was talking to herself: Lymond had passed her like a wraith and was already in the courtyard banging on doors. The two men at the entrance of the traboule stayed where

105

they were, debating. The man or men at the opposite end had made no further sign either. It seemed to argue that they were pretty certain there was no escape possible. She thought they were probably waiting for reinforcements.

Philippa put the pipe in her teeth like a flautist, and kicking off her shoes, began unhooking her bodice. The men in the entrance arch faded and vanished. She called, 'They're gone! Mr Crawford!' and hopped to her feet, kicking aside her discarded gown and petticoat as Lymond, reconstituted, became again visible.

He examined the traboule entrance and with equal interest the knee-length chemise of his companion. 'As least we'll let them think we think so,' he said. 'What in God's name are you doing?'

'Looking for a piece of string,' said Philippa. 'Since someone gave away my pearl cincture.'

Lymond pulled undone the knot of his shirt and tossed her the silk cord with its aiglets. 'Kirtle your chemise up with that, and keep your cloak on. I've managed to break a few locks. There's a house, a knife-grinder's and a shoemaker's workshop. Hurry. They're bound to try and come in from the quayside.'

She took St Peter's lamp with her. He had the courtyard lanthorn already inside the stable. The cobbler's workshop produced thirty left-footed shoes on a spar, a greasy felt helmet and a tunic apron, the last two of which covered her hair and her chemise respectively. She chose two identical shoes and jammed them on, hopping, prior to making one or two fast dispositions. A horse's feet, trampling excitedly inside the stable, told that Lymond was occupied also. She returned from the traboule in time to see him race over the courtyard and up the first flight of a turnpike.

He came down again almost immediately. 'There's a group of men on the quay at our entrance. When I send the horse through the traboule, take that awl and run like hell after it. Jab it if it stops. Jab it when it gets to the entrance so that it turns left and makes off downriver. Then sprint across the quay to the Chalamon jetty. I'll join you there.' He listened. 'They're coming. Now!' And he opened the doors of the stable.

'I only accept it,' said Philippa, 'to avoid cavillation.' A large, portly horse cantered out with, affixed to his back, the six-foot sweep of the shoemaker's other spar, containing thirty right-footed shoes. Pinked by the awl he neighed, bucked, and pranced his way into the traboule's low-ceilinged corridor. Then head down, he charged along its black length to the entrance.

On each side of him the spar, sweeping the walls, hissed and whipped and let fly smartly from time to time with a boot or a patten. Within six paces it had hooked a yelling man under the chin and carried him a fair way, his teeth sunk in his tongue, before dropping him. At the same moment it fired off the companion of Philippa's footgear, which she had been hopefully watching. She caught it, galloping. A man somewhere ahead shouted, ducking, and then was sprawled on the ground by a chopine. The entrance burst upon her, a vaporous dazzle of yellow. She aimed for the horse's right haunch and jabbed the awl in it.

With a squeal and a snort, the horse hurtled out through the entrance and turning left, thundered off up the quay, with the sound of running men's steps dwindling after it. Two shadows on her right became a pair of men advancing on her brandishing axes. While she looked, they lay down; chiefly because someone had cut and let fall a fishing net on them. Philippa said 'Ha!' and set off, scampering, across the Chalamon quay to the riverside.

Below her was a short wooden jetty whose steps led to a cluster of rowing-boats. She stood on one leg, momentarily, to put on her new hard-won foot-gear and then slid down the steps and into one. The quay lamps showed her Francis Crawford, his sword in its scabbard, arrived on the jetty and laughing at her. 'In Moab I will washe my feete, Over Edom throw my shoo ... Meditate, O Bhikshu, and be not heedless. There aren't any oars! Your place and mine is *under* the jetty. Your cloak, my child. Quickly!'

He took it, but didn't follow her. Clambering out of the rocking shallop and along the rotted cradle of timbers that upheld the jetty, Philippa heard him shouting behind her. 'To the boats! Quickly! Quickly!' There was a thud; then another, and a splash as the boat she had just left was cast off. From her refuge under the planks she saw him thrust the tenantless boat until it was caught by the current. It swung a moment and then turned twisting into the flow of the river. There were two huddled sacks in it, one of them draped in her mantle. He was busy a moment longer and then, ducking, be-

107

gan making his way along the dark scaffold towards her. Then reaching her, he signalled for silence.

Armed with knives, their pursuers had not taken long to slash through the fishing nets. And with their whistles they had summoned all those who could move within earshot. The thud of footsteps sounded over Philippa's head as she clung to the timbers, accompanied by a good deal of shouting and swearing and a series of dull thumping noises, followed by a splintering as if someone was forcing a doorway. There was, she remembered, a ferryman's hut by the quayside. Bowman and Jowler were going to have oars therefore. Then followed a trampling, and voices, and the creak of laden boats settling, and the splash of loosed ropes, followed by the rattle and groan as the oars made their first sweep in the water. The sounds faded away, and silence descended.

The fog, it seemed to her, had become rather thinner. The lamplight, striking down through the joints in the planks, showed her Francis Crawford's ruffled fair hair and open shirt and the filthy brocade of his pourpoint. He was doubled up, laughing. Philippa poked him. He unfolded, still laughing, and scrambling out from under the jetty, gave her his hand to emerge on the steps in the lamplight. There was no sign of the boats: only, quite far downriver, a faded outburst of hysterical shouting.

> *'With Emeroides in the hinder parts*
> *He strake his enmies all*
> *And put them then unto a shame*
> *That was perpetuall ...*

'I took the bungs out of the shallops,' said Lymond.

*

He pulled himself together before she did, dropping her hand and running his fingers through his tangled hair, restoring it to something like normal orderliness. Then he surveyed her, seeing, one supposed, the dirty chemise and long cobbler's apron, and the greasy felt cap, with the hair leaked from under its ear-flaps.

The familiar blandness returned to his face, smoothing out all the wild elation. 'Well,' said Francis Crawford. 'Make my compliments to the boys of Flaw Valleys, or whoever trained you in the use of a peashooter. You did very well. I shall now return you to the Schiatti, Hathor's temple; home of in-toxication and place of enjoyment. They won't know whether to lock up their sons or their daughters.'

Philippa Somerville shoved her hair under her cap, stuck her hands on her hips, and without budging a step, stood and glared at him. 'Do I appear,' she inquired, 'crazed with lust?'

His eyes flicked wide open, Lymond considered her. Then he bent his head, and she could not tell if he was smiling. 'Very seldom,' he said.

'Or artless? Or addled? Or excitable?' She was getting an-grier. 'Is that why you keep recoiling as if I was a line of armed cavalry?'

He was not smiling. He looked up slowly and met her gaze, his own level. He said, 'I beg your pardon. I didn't know I was giving quite such an insufferable impression. I think I forget sometimes ...' He hesitated, choosing his lan-guage.

Philippa finished it for him. '... that I am aged twenty, and Kate Somerville's daughter; and sensible? For Sybilla, I am willing to involve you in any kind of genealogical embar-rassment. But you really needn't have fears of the other kind.'

'I don't. I know that perfectly well,' Lymond said. 'I am trying, I believe, to avoid offering you the kind of attentions which would be expected by Madame la Maréchale.'

He did not cite Güzel, she noticed. Who had the same training she had. Touched with remorse, Philippa said so-berly. 'Since we're being frank ... Wasn't that foolish? The Queen is going to offer you the Maréchale's daughter in mar-riage. It might well be what you need.'

'What I *need*?' said Lymond. Then he said, 'Oh, I see. But you haven't seen Madame la Maréchale in *her* chemise.'

With commendable patience, Philippa made no rejoinder. By mutual consent, they had begun walking rather swiftly towards the gate to the bridge-head. After a moment he went on. 'I knew Catherine d'Albon was being sent south to meet me. I don't want her. That is why I did what I did with her mother.' He hesitated again, and then said, 'What I told Marthe tonight was not strictly true. I am already pledged, and not only to the nation of Russia.'

Behind the cobbler's apron unpleasant changes took place in Philippa's abdomen. She ignored them. 'To Güzel?' she said steadily.

He shook his head. She saw that, looking ahead in the fog,

109

his profile contained a curious and suspended calm, the smiling mask of some state far from peaceful. 'Not to Güzel,' he said. 'But for my lifetime.' And walking still he offered her, smiling again, four lines of verse, lightly spoken.

> 'Tant que je vive, mon cueur ne changera
> Pour nulle vivante, tant soit elle bonne ou sage
> Forte et puissante, riche de hault lignaige
> Mon chois est fait, aulter ne se fera.'

'I didn't know,' Philippa said. It was a half-truth. Subconsciously, she supposed she had always known, since she was a schoolgirl. She said, 'It's my turn to beg your pardon. I only wanted to assure you that I have nothing to tender but friendship. But if you want it, there is a great deal of that, going cheaply.'

He slowed, with the intension perhaps of confronting her. But on second thoughts he said only, 'Then the cost should not be beyond me. The pledge, without Latreia or Douleia, is simple friendship?' He had begun once again to walk briskly.

Rousing herself: 'The pledge,' said Philippa, tartly, 'is friendship. Simplicity is not, you will agree, one of your prominent attributes.' They had passed through the gateway and turning left, mounted the rise of the long eight-arched bridge crossing the Saône. The fog was still thick on the bridge, concealing all but the first pair of flambeaux, but a current of air, winding through it, revealed the Fourvière heights for a moment, black against a starlit sky with the chapel lights bright on its summit, and the roofs of lamplit houses with their feet in the fog at its foot.

Dancing red in the haze, one of the bridge torches swayed in its socket. Gazing at it, Philippa was aware that she had been ungracious. She said, 'But if you've no objection to fish scales, I'll shake on it.' And Lymond, to her gratification, accepted the hand that she offered him.

He did not shake it. He took it in a grinding and sinewy grip and dragged her sideways until she was running. Then he released her, spinning, to sprawl on the cobbles. His sword hissed from its scabbard. And gasping, she sat up and stared at him.

What she had seen was not the bridge flambeau swaying. It was a torch in the grip of a burly man with a fierce, swollen face and a patch of raw flesh two inches wide running down brow, cheek and jawbone. A man who strode out of the fog on the crown of the bridge, axe in hand and stood, holding the torch high and grinning. 'Well met, M. de Sevigny: I might have been in the boat if your little bitch hadn't blocked the traboule with Renaud's knife-grinding wheel, and left it running. You may put up your sword. There is a line of men awaiting you at the other end of the bridge, and another line closing the bridgehead behind you. You would have met them if you had come out of the rue Mercière. As it is, you came by the quay gate, and this makes me very happy, and also my friend Octavien beside you. Only, where is the little bitch?'

He never did hear the answer, for Philippa stabbed him from behind with her husband's poniard. She dragged it out as he fell and stabbed him again, gritting her teeth, in the area delineated in white paint by the black eunuch who instructed the princes' class in the seraglio. A staccato hack of steel, interspersed with an outbreak of retching, told that the man Octavien had flung himself on Lymond. She caught up the fallen man's torch and lifted it.

In a flare of yellow, the blade of an axe parted from the haft and whistled out of their sight in the darkness. The owner, the stock still in his hand, was in Lymond's grip and Lymond's hand was over his mouth, stifling his cries and forcing his head back with an expertise which Philippa saw was swift, impersonal and utterly final. As Lymond lowered the dead man to the ground she uttered neither comment nor commendation. It could hardly have been otherwise, man to man; or Octavien had flung himself on Lymond. She caught up the fallen man's rate paid assassin.

But from this point onwards it was not man to man, but Francis Crawford and herself against an unknown number of men at each end of this bridge. And although she had joked about swimming, there was no escape that way. Below the bridge was swift current and a tumble of rocks that would kill them. Lymond's voice very quietly said, 'Christ, Philippa: I won't ask where you learned that. Now prop up the torch and come and give me a hand. *Si leonina pellis non satis est, assuenda vulpina.*'

'Or, *Si Dieu ne me veut ayder, le diable ne me peut manquer,*' said Philippa valiantly. 'I am listening, mon compère. As a drunkard believes a drunkard, and a madman a madman.'

Very soon after that, the chain of five men at the Fourvière end of the bridge heard break out again, and closer, the clash of sword blades in the vapour. This time they could also hear voices, including the screams of a woman.

Their orders were to remain where they were. But it was galling to stand by and listen, when it was clear that the King's emissary and his lady had been quite overthrown by the ambush. Presently, the girl's screeching voice rose to a shriek: there was a shout, and a thud and a splash from the river bed. A moment later, the foreigner's cries were cut off also. Then, speaking their own patois, an indignant voice, presumably Octavien's said, 'Don't be a fool! Get the rings at least before he goes over!'

After that, it would have been foolish to stay. One of the five men began to stroll forward, and was overtaken by another. In a moment, all five were running headlong for the parapet, where the smoky light of a torch flared on the jewelled points and rich doublet of M. le comte de Sevigny, encasing a very dead body already dangling half over the handrail. Boots and laces and buttons were already torn off in ten grasping handfuls before the first of the five men realized that the body was not that of M. de Sevigny. And when, whirling round, they thought to dash back the way they had come, the two people they sought were already running, softly and fast for the bridgend.

Because Lymond was steering his wife by the arm, they both saw the obstacle in their path just before they cannoned into it. It was large and lukewarm and soft. Fending herself off, Philippa's hand pressed against buckles and leather and then, stumbling, she recognized something else—the unyielding steel of plate armour.

A horse and rider, both dead. With others, she suspected, lying beyond them. Lymond's voice said, 'Run to the end of the bridge, turn right, and hide yourself in the porch of the Customars' house.'

As a madman obeys a madman, and a drunkard a drunkward. Asking no questions, she did as he told her.

So their escort had been waylaid after all. No quartet of men at arms had arrived back at the Hôtel Schiatti or at Lymond's lodging: no one even knew that she and Lymond had left Jerott and Marthe. Instead, their attackers were more numerous and better organized than anyone had expected. They could cordon off the bridge on the chance that the Captain-

General had escaped from the quayside. It was equally possible that the roads to Lymond's destination and her own on this side of the river were watched.

Hence her instructions. Instead of running on she turned right, along the rue de la Pescherie as far as the church of St Eloi. Then facing uphill and away from the river, she turned round the back of the church and into the tall, jutting porch of the Custom-house. Inside, the studded door with its wrought iron hinges was firmly locked, and the windows were dark.

Lymond had not told her to knock. And indeed, the noise would bring their assailants sooner, in all likelihood, than the customars. She waited therefore, breathing hard, with sweat drops, erratic as mice, straying over her neck and her temples, and listened for the footsteps which meant Lymond was coming.

She never did hear them. Instead there struck on her eardrums a sonorous sound, hardly deadened by fog, of another calibre altogether. The alarm bell on the bridge had been set swinging.

For perhaps eight strokes it rang deeply and loudly. Then, shaking lightly, it came to a halt, revealing a ground-bass of excited men shouting.

Lymond, in his shirt-sleeves, shot into her hiding-place breathlessly. 'They've cut him down. Hell.' He listened. 'I was afraid they'd seen us. The fog is going. This way. Traboules, my knife-grinding Philippa. With your invention and mine, it will really go hard if we can't lose them. . . . *Wake up, you bastards!*'

She could hear running feet now, as he had done. But even so, he stopped in his stride and scooping up first one stone and then another hurled them with a vicious crash straight through the Customars' windows. Then, catching up, he caught Philippa under the arm and plunged through and under the first of the rows of tall houses which climbed the steep hillside in front of them.

Fear had gone. He had touched her. He had admitted her to the sexless friendship she had asked of him. She had been treated at last as a partner and adult. She was free, as he had said, to join her invention to his; to expect and give co-operation without fear or favour, as might be done by Adam or Jerott or Danny.

A heady experience, for an only child accustomed to

113

single-thread happiness, and not to the moment of creation that occurs when the warp is interlocked with the weft. When the singer is matched with the sounding-board; the dancer partnered; the dream with the poet. When the sun and the fountain first meet one another.

Side by side they were evading, she and Francis Crawford, a pack of men who intended to kill them. To escape them would be a miracle. To try to escape them with wit and grace and all that civilization could add to an occasion essentially barbarous was her care, her delight, and her intention. And the outcome he had foreseen touched her in its terrible proximity not at all.

So they fled into the night-black traboules: up the steps, between the pillars, over the courtyards and again into the twisting broken-backed tunnels, with the thudding of feet always tracking the darkness behind them.

Since the flight from Greece when he had been sick with opium, she had never seen unleashed, for such a span of time, his strength, his gaiety and his physical charm.

Every circumstance conspired, like a merchant, to display them to her. Swooping like birds from space to space of the tall houses scaling the hillside, they used what fortune suggested to defend themselves with. Baulked by a locked door, they took to a high, sprawling staircase whose galleries overlooked a nest of different courtyards: as their pursuers swarmed after them he bombarded them blithely with geranium pots, chanting: 'Ding ye the tane and I the uther' as she helped him, so that children screamed and dogs barked and a man in his night shirt, opening shutters, discharged an arquebus into the night air and dislodged an entire family group of Jupiter, Ganymede and the eagle from a cornice. 'A sangre! A fuego! A sacco!' sang out Francis Crawford; and seizing her hand, set off running again.

He talked, indeed, all the time, breathlessly, with snatches of verse and of laughter and a flow of frequently ribald comment which only ceased, now and then, in the cause of evasion. To begin with, also, he guided her, until she showed him there was no need for it. Philippa Somerville had spent a childhood competing with schoolboys among the woods and streams of north Tyneside, and in her cap and apron and sensible shoes was as agile as he was and, she wished to prove, not without invention.

They clambered over the cold nested clay of the pantiled

roofs and crossed a narrow street on a ladder, because Philippa insisted on it. They sprang from niche to balcony and swung between pillars. They arrived at ground level and freed a mastiff and unshackled the door of a pig sty: at first floor, and found looms and a great roll of silk which streamed and bounded, calendaring all their assailants; at second and third and fourth floors and found sacks of flour to upset, or a bucket of slops or a wallsconce to send flying downwards, first from her hands and then from his, watched by the winged lions and griphons on the ceiling bosses, the angels guarding the windows; the fanged faces grinning from corbels or spewing open-throated from gutters above them. Decoration Gothic and classical heaped its profusion around them: shell and pilaster, acanthus and ballflower, bas relief and statuary in niche and fountain and rooftop as they crossed the road on a plank and began again, in the next house above them.

It gave them, also, a profusion of openings. Hanging gardens contained jets of water which could be diverted and pools into which the unwary could be enticed in the darkness. Fruit hurtled down (*Pesches de Corbeil! les pesches!*) and Tyndale's snake, in a glorious mélange of colour (*Tussssssh! Ye shall not dye . . .*) burst from the vats of a dyeshop.

Walls handsome with stone frieze and tracery were not hard to climb, any more than garden ramparts with vine and trellis and niche, whose cage or pot or plaque or classical amphora might suggest a ponderous helmeting. And there was alway something to use, a row of melting grey plates from a kiln shelf: a slither of fish; a bag of pepper, left by a spicer, which touched off a sneezing and barking that spiralled up all the wide turnpike and flew trouncing back from the roof vaults.

Philippa had carried the pepper. Francis Crawford had a flask of neat spirits, filched from an apothecary's windowledge. He broke the neck at the top of the staircase and splashed it into the channelled stone handrail below him. Then he snatched down a sconce and set fire to it.

They fled hand in hand to the rooftops, and flung shut the hatch on the fire and the shouting. 'It won't spread,' said Lymond swiftly. 'It will hold them a little.' And stood for a moment on the dizziest edge of the roof-peak, bright and breathless and smiling.

His eyes were on the south; his hands held two flaming

brands which streamed in a soft flowing air that had melted the fog to scraves and streamers wreathing the chimney tops. Fed by flame and by moonlight his hands and hair and shirt contained their own glow, like the globe of a sorcerer.

But he was not a figment of daydream or of fantasy. He was the quick-witted man who had raced with her; the man whose strong wrists had pulled her from trouble; whose laughter recognized, more than his own, her buffoonery; whose voice had whispered, sung, exclaimed or cursed, with equal felicity, carefree as birdsong on top of their striving.

Whose essence, stripped by necessity was, it now seemed, warm and joyous and of great generosity.

He stood, his eyes on the plunging rue de la Orfeverie below him, and intoned, gravely and musically.

'By the grace and ineffable Providence of God, the only Unoriginated, and Infinite, Invisible, Inexpressible, Terrible and Inaccessible, Abiding above the Heavens, Dwelling in Unapproachable Light, and with a Vigilant Eye inspecting the Earth at suitable intervals . . .

'Adam Blacklock has got off his backside and done something about the bloody uproar eventually.'

Philippa dragged off her cap and pushing back her drenched hair, looked below them. He was right. At last the alarm had been raised; the troops mobilized. It seemed that all the streets from the river were flowing with pebbled silver, rising higher and higher and flooding now to the roots of their building as Lymond, shouting, caught their gaze with his voice and his fire-brands. Then he dropped them and spoke to the night air. "Well, it's impressive, you know, but there's a thing in't, as the fellow said drinking the dish-clout. The bastards might dodge out the back way.'

'The side way,' said Philippa, peering. 'They're forcing open a door to the ruelle.'

'Are they, dammit?' he said. 'Then let's stop them!'

To stop them they had to arrive first at the head of the ruelle. There should be, said Lymond, a tavern there.

To reach it, Philippa fled with him round and round spiral stairs, across landings, along balconies, into arches and doorways and courtyards. There was a tavern there. They went through it like gimlets through butter and gained the top of the ruelle, up which all that was left of their enemies was painfully staggering.

The ruelle Punaise was less a street than a near-vertical

drain between houses, roughly stepped and little more than the width of one person. Because they were tired, their former pursuers found speed beyond them. Because, below in the street, the first of the troops were arriving, the climbing men slipped and staggered and fell in their fear but kept running, for at the top of the ruelle lay the steep road to the wall, and the hill of Fourvière, and freedom.

Until the last moment, indeed, they hoped to reach it. They saw the mouth of the ruelle above them, open, empty of people. If they discerned, through the sweat, a certain unevenness on the horizon, it seemed no more, very likely, than a profile of the stone and pebble and mud of the vennel. They were not to know that the outline was that of eight four-gallon blackjacks, arrived there by a neat piece of leverage.

By dint of the same leverage, they released themselves, one by one, as the group of men neared the top of the ruelle. Eight full barrels, naturally, would have occasioned a profound maceration. Eight empty barrels were not very pleasant: they knocked every man off his feet and then kicked him belabouring down all the stairs and into the arms of the soldiers.

Lymond watched them judicially, calling out strikes and setting off each barrel at the required angle. Towards the end he found some boules and bounced them down as well: they hailed upon barrels and footpads and trilled, with ringing reproach, on the rising helmets of the pikemen beyond them.

> 'As Snailes do wast within the shel
> And unto slime do run
> As one before his tyme that fel
> And never saw the sunne . . .

'Whoops! That was Adam,' said Francis Crawford, watching open-eyed the progress of his latest invention. 'Serve him bloody well right. Syne Sweirness, at the secound bidding, Came lyk a sow out of a midding. Am I running about; are you running about so that the fat officers of the Christian Crown of France can lie in the Hôtel de Gouvernement, taking advantage of the wife of the Maréchal? Mind you,' and he chose a spot at the top of the steps and sat down, surveying the scene with continuing interest, 'no one could say that we hadn't brought ourselves now to the attention of this majestic metropolis.'

Philippa sat down as well rather weakly, and watched. The barrels, trundling down, had done their worst with the miscreants and were now cutting swathes through the rescue team. The boules, flashing in the new torchlight, ricocheted still from step to wall to other less fortunate targets. She saw Adam, getting up, fend off another just before it capsized him and Danny Hislop, behind, caper hurriedly. She further realized that what she was seeing was not the effect of miscalculation.

Perched beside her, a clutch of gaming balls in his lap, Francis Crawford was making his own strictures felt with all the artistry of a practising juggler. Danny, sweetly struck on a fine point of balance, disappeared as she made her discovery and the sergeant, a man of some presence, flung his arms up and tumbled back, shouting. Restored at a stroke, Philippa cheered and jumped to her feet, seizing a boule as she did so. She aimed, and shied.

Melodiously, Lymond supported her: 'And eek the buttokes of hem faren as it were the hyndre part of a she-ape in the full of the moone.' His voice was husky with laughter. 'Go on. The one with the beard. He's an Anglophobe if ever I saw one.'

The one with the beard disappeared. Behind him, in slow succession disappeared also the Prévôt des Marchands and the column of officials and magistrates who had been mounting the ruelle behind him.

Whooping, Lymond sprang to his feet and in his face was child and man; Kuzúm and Francis Crawford; triumph and mischief and a ridiculous, thoughtless delight that made her seize his hands and fling them apart and say, 'Francis! Francis, you fool. *This* is what you should be!'

A cock crew, far away, disturbed by the uproar.

And as in that grotesque shrouded room, the air deadened. The noise below her sank into dumbness; the colours faded; the brightness dwindled and perished in ashes.

'What a very uncomfortable remark,' Lymond said. His face, from wholly blank, became blankly benignant. He said, 'Perhaps I should. I'm afraid I am more like Abraham. A godly man, you remember, but the denial of his wife ... was such a fact as no godly man ought to imitate.'

He stopped. His fingers, courteous prisoners, remained suspended inside her grasp, clearly desiring freedom but unwilling to impose it.

Philippa opened her hands and released him; and as if she had once more restored him his tongue he went on, with gentle apology. 'But I am no godly man. I'm only a commander of some experience, who knows how to ask a tired army to throw its heart into a citadel and follow it. Forgive me.'

He straightened. 'Here is Archie. And, good God, the Schiatti cousins, a bouquet in one hand and a bell in the other. They will see you safely home.' He smiled at her. 'Clever child. Even for a Somerville, my dear, it was an irresistible performance.'

He smiled again, turning to leave her. Assured, experienced, equal to any minor contretemps, however embarrassing, he had saved her from blundering further. Sitting motionless on the steps she watched him stroll down to address Adam and Danny and give them their orders; to dispose of the men they had caught; to seek out the injured; to visit and arrest the three merchants whose names the boy Paul had given them. His voice carried to her, propounding, instructing; replying. Despite his rough hair and clothes his authority, his command of himself and of others had never been more in evidence. She had been a fool, of the kind she and Kate had no patience with.

She had been artless, and addled, and excitable. She had demanded his friendship, and at his instance had lightly abjured what might follow: Latreia, the superior worship of adoration, and Douleia, the inferior worship of honour or reverence. He had given her friendship and hoped perhaps against hope to receive in return nothing more.

But the wine had been too strong for her, as it had for the others; and like the others she had stepped from the safe shores of friendship. She stood now in another country, whose sun burned and whose air was too rare for her breathing. And she stood there alone, with the words of a warning for company:

Tant que je vive . . .

Long as I live, my heart will never vary
For no one else, however fair or good

119

Brave, resolute or rich, of gentle blood.
My choice is made, and I will have no other.

❊

Four hours after that, at six o'clock in the morning of Tuesday, 17 August, a royal courier swept with his train down the Gourguillon and hammered at the Hôtel de Gouvernement portals. He was admitted at once, and after a long delay, was brought to speak to the King's chief envoy, M. de Sevigny.

At eight o'clock the Consulat were notified that their presence was required by M. Crawford of Lymond and Sevigny. By nine, the Crown officials were with him. By that time he had also seen the captain of the city guard, and had given orders to his own officers, his men at arms and his servants. And before anyone, had spoken to Madame la Maréchale de St André, going with measured pace about her dispositions, a little more erect, a little less superbly groomed than was usual.

At noon, in his first free five minutes that morning, Adam Blacklock dropped exhausted into a settle and heard tolling round him the bronze bells of Lyon, mourning the news which had laid low the city. The news of a defeat in the north such as no French army had suffered since Agincourt.

On St Lawrence's Day, with 24,000 men and the chivalry of his country behind him, the Constable of France had set out for Saint-Quentin, besieged by the troops of King Philip.

Old-fashioned and cross-grained and headstrong, the Constable had compounded, it seemed, blunder on blunder. He had tried to send a relief force through the marshes. The saga that followed was painful: a tale of sunk boats and labouring marches, of mistaken paths and faulty spy-work and a childish stubbornness beyond anyone's crediting. The results, spreading outwards in shock through the nation, were such as to reduce men to silence.

Only four hundred and fifty men had managed to enter Saint-Quentin. The rest had been cut to pieces by Count Egmont, the lieutenant-general of the King of Spain's cavalry.

They said 12,000 had been killed, and in one day the manhood of the best houses in France either dead or wounded or prisoner. Among the missing were Guthrie and Hoddim, the two Scottish captains turned off by M. de Sevigny. Among the dead were the Counts of Villars and Enghien. Among the wounded and captured, the Constable himself and his son; the Dukes of Montpensier and Longueville, François de La Rouchefoucauld and Jean d'Albon, Maréchal de St André, Governor of the King's city of Lyon.

Two French leaders had escaped. The Duke of Nevers and the Prince of Condé remained near Saint-Quentin to reform and make fresh levies. But the thousand men in Saint-Quentin, under Admiral Coligny and his brother d'Andelot, must give way beneath the combined assault of the entire Spanish army. And when they did, the road was open to Paris.

What had to be done now was obvious, even if the King had not sent to command it. Until help came, Lyon must rely on its present small force under Adam himself backed by Hislop. And Lymond must go to Paris, where the court, fled from Compiègne, was to entrench itself.

For in the absence of captains and Constable, of de Guise and Strozzi in Italy, of de Thermes and Brissac in Piedmont, there was no one left to save France, if the King of Spain marched upon Paris.

Adam thought, his face sombre, of Fergie Hoddim and Alec Guthrie. And of the contrivance which had sent Lymond away from the King's eye in the first place, and which now looked like bringing him the rôle of saviour of France which the Constable and the Duke de Guise had both coveted. To stand at the side of this monarch as he had stood by the Tsar. And to face, in the oddest upshot of all, an English army under Lord Grey of Wilton.

Five minutes' rest was all Adam could afford, and he was already on his feet when yet another summons came from de Sevigny, brought this time by Danny, curtly efficient, with none of his usual ebullience. He did not know what Lymond wanted, or who was with him on this occasion. Adam shut the windows against the beat of the bells, and went off soberly.

In the event there was no one there at all but Lymond himself, seated as he had been all morning at his desk in front of the tall latticed windows, the motionless heart of the hurricane. Round him, the scattered benches and stools were now vacant. And against the wall, neatly stacked, were the leather bags, the boxes, the coffers ready strapped for the journey to Paris. His desk was empty, and the extra candles extinguished. Embedded, flinty and pure as a cameo against

121

the dark boards of his chair-back Lymond said, 'Shut the door. I have four questions to ask you.'

Three of them concerned recent orders and, thank God, he had excellent answers. The fourth stemmed from the impending visit of Catherine, heiress of the captured St André, who would require to return north with her mother.

Five minutes sufficed to dispose of it all. Adam rose. There was nothing more to be said. It was moment of crisis, and war their métier. He was half-way to the door when Lymond spoke again. 'By the way. Who brought me home early this morning?'

So there was something more to be said. His voice neutral: 'Archie,' he answered. 'Helped by your friend Macé Bonhomme the printer. There were no spectators. Archie sent a message ahead and Danny and I opened the door to the three of you.'

'Thank you. Where is Archie?' said Lymond.

'He called back ten minutes ago. Do you want to see him?' asked Adam.

From the square below came all the clatter and cursing and stamping of a body of men saddling up for an expedition. The tolling bells, near and far, slipped through the hubbub. Two of Lymond's household, tapping, were permitted to enter and began, without wasting time, to carry out all the baggage. Lymond looked at the hour glass. He said, 'I can give him five minutes.'

Adam went out. By the time he found Archie Abernethy and pushed his way back through the turmoil, the last of Lymond's luggage was out and Adam saw that the hour glass was empty. In civil warning: 'Watch out,' he observed to his colleague, and closing the door, left Archie to Lymond's cold mercy.

Had he stayed, he would have heard Lymond say nothing. Instead it was Archie who stood inside the door, lips tight and naked head glaring and said, *'Ye senseless bluidy tupheidit madman!'* with venom.

Seated still at his desk his hands loose on the smooth oak before him, Francis Crawford did not answer; nor did he interrupt the long tirade that followed. Only when it was finished did he say, without lifting his eyes, 'You make your point. Who else was at Macé Bonhomme's?'

Archie Abernethy, without looking, sat down on the stool just beside him. 'Of course. Ye were blind . . .'

122

'Of course. You know how much I drank better than I do. Who else was at Macé Bonhomme's?'

'A barber-surgeon,' said Archie. 'A short, brosy chiel' with grey whiskers staying wi' Macé. They cried him Michel. And Macé himself, that was all. Twa men of by-ordnar' discretion. If ye expect to ride post to Paris, I expect to ride with ye.'

There was a very long pause. 'Hence the cuirass and spurs,' remarked Lymond. 'I wondered. And what about Mistress Philippa?'

'I thought you knew,' said Archie Abernethy. 'She left Lyon early this morning. To go to Sevigny, I rather fancy. She didna need me, so the Schiatti sent her off with a nice puckle of pikemen, and twa of their weel-pitten-on nephews.'

In the shadow, the Captain-General's eyes were inimical. He said, 'You told me you were her man.'

'I am,' said Archie Abernethy shortly and got up. He walked to the desk. 'There's your riding jacket. And there, if you have some water, is a physic I got for the headache. And that'—and removing a crumpled paper from his pouch, he tossed it between Francis Crawford's unoccupied hands—'is what you had in your fist when we found you. I took it away. It's not what you want every burgher to gab about.'

He did not need to read it again but he did, stretching the blood-stiffened folds, until the writing of thirty years since was quite legible.

The record of death of a human being called Francis Crawford.

123

Part II

Sur le milieu du grand monde la rose
Pour nouveaux faits sang public épandu
A dire vray on aura bouche close
Lore au besoin viendra tard l'attendu.

CHAPTER 1

La cité obsesse aux murs hommes et femmes
Ennemis hors le chef prestz á soy rendres
Vent sera fort encontre les gen-darmes:
Chassés seront par chaux, poussiere et cendre.

'I told you,' said the Queen of Scotland, her head bowed, her hands clasped in worship. 'The carpet is muddy. And Catherine d'Albon does *not* have her feet bare.'

Her voice, although not shrill for her age, was quite distinct enough to vanquish the organs. Catherine d'Albon glanced round. Black sackcloth, there was no doubt, set off brunette hair. It was best of all, naturally, with auburn.

'Your grace, she has a dispensation from Monseigneur your uncle,' Mary Fleming said in an undertone. 'Because of her hurried journey to and from Lyon, and grief for her father.' The other maids of honour prayed with assiduity.

'Her father?' said Mary Queen of Scotland. 'The Marshal de St André is only a prisoner. He was taken when the Constable was taken. Monseigneur my uncle says that but for the mistakes of the Constable, Saint-Quentin would never have fallen. The King says that those who failed to execute his orders have brought the army low, and in future he will act alone as God inspires him. Until, of course, Monseigneur my other uncle returns from Italy.'

She scowled forbiddingly at the members of her little suite, wrinkling the white skin and picking out particularly the four Scottish maidens called Mary. 'You are not afraid that the King of Spain will march into Paris? He would never dare. The Queen Regent my mother will send such armies into England that no English troops can be spared to fight for a foreigner. And God is on our side. He looks down on us today. The noblest blood in France walks barefoot in penitence from the Sainte Chapelle to the Cathedral of Notre-Dame, bearing the relics of the Passion on their shoulders. How can

127

King Philip, who makes war on the Pope, expect to conquer us?'

No one answered her. A twilight of smoky crimson and violet enclosed them. The tented glass, sixty feet high, soared above them, densely diapered in blue and cramoisy, exotic as tissues from India. The King, the Cardinal, the Bishop had completed their business high in the shining gold tribune and the Reliquary was raised to its place on men's shoulders. Jewels glowed; silver-gilt sparkled; incense thickened. In a series of angular movements, the noblesse of France dropped to its stiff knees in reverence.

Mary Fleming noted that Madame de Brêne had corns. Her cousin the Queen of Scotland's narrow arched feet, on the other hand, merely displayed two arcs of dirt, as did the thirteen-year-old feet of her affianced lord the Dauphin, eldest son and heir of King Henri.

If the King of Spain marched from Saint-Quentin to Paris, there were few with as much to lose as Mary of Scotland. Then the wedding, so long planned by messeigneurs her uncles between herself and the Dauphin, would never take place. She would never be Queen of France. Nor would she be sent back to Scotland, to make trouble for Spain. More likely she would be taken to Spain, Mary thought, and married to King Philip's idiot child. Or to King Philip himself, if his English Queen died. And thus in one stroke he would join Scotland, England and Spain in one monarchy.

Small wonder she would not believe that Paris could be in danger. Mary Fleming looked at the thin, auburn-haired imperious mistress before her and drawing on the lessons of nine years of service realized that, as usual, she had mistaken her courage. Cousin Mary knew of the danger. Cousin Mary was sick with fears for the future. But to display it, or allow her entourage to display it, would be less than royal.

The shrine passed, containing the Crown of Thorns, the Sponge and the Lancehead. The courtiers stood, in a crackle of stretched bones and sackcloth. The procession formed, with the cross borne before it. The twelve stone Apostles watched it pass with blank eyes, smooth and calm in their beauty. Against the tall smoking fires of the stained glass the empty tribune was now hardly tangible. Ultramarine and bistre and veridian, the rose-window hung over the interlaced carvings, the painted pillars and fine fretted arches running with angels; and shone bright and jade green and wholesome as the apple trees of Compiègne.

Compiègne. Where once before, Mary had displayed a passing fretfulness, and for the same reason. Mary Fleming carried her thought down the forty-four steps of the staircase and through the cemetery and out of the Palais and along the narrow streets to the Parvis of Notre-Dame, where no one could talk because all Paris was watching, and even the mills on the bridge stilled their throbbing and clattering.

Because of the weight of the shrine, they moved slowly. The priests sang, and the censer-smells lingered. There on the left was the rue des Marmousets, and the cleared space of the house of the pâtissier, who had made pies from the flesh of those barbered to death by his neighbour. Next door, imagine, to Notre-Dame, rising foursquare, sprigged and buttoned above her, with its band of crowned and gaily conversing stone monarchs.

Which brought her back to Queen Mary at Compiègne, saying, 'I believe my Scotsman Mr Crawford will show some of these princes how we wage war. How long must it be since last he saw me?'

They had gone into the matter. It had been six years previously, when Mr Crawford of Lymond had served her with some effectiveness, and had accepted her glove as his guerdon.

'Then I must have been eight. One changes in six years,' had said Mary complacently, and had waited. But he had not come to pay his duty. And next, he had been sent to Lyon, and recalled almost immediately.

He had arrived five days ago, and had been lodged in the Hôtel de Rochepôt, a house of the imprisoned Constable's. The King had brought him out of there. The King had sent him yesterday to the Hôtel St André in the rue d'Orleans, where the Maréchale and her daughter, just back from Lyon, had welcomed him. Mary Fleming waited until they were established inside the Cathedral and the vicissitudes of the Corpus Christi were under way, and then said, testing her theory, 'Your grace, I don't see Mr Crawford?'

At the time, a rebuking glance was her answer. But a little later, pacing together: 'Mr Crawford apparently could not spare the time to be present,' said Mary of Scotland to Mary Fleming negligently. She paused. 'I am not wholly in favour

129

of this scheme to unite him to Mademoiselle d'Albon. It mocks the Church. He is married already, to a bright, well-favoured girl. I met her on her way south of Lyon.'

'They say he wants a divorce,' Mary Fleming said. 'They say his wife will leave for England soon, and won't oppose it.'

The Queen turned. 'Do you think he will want to marry Catherine d'Albon?' said Mary.

'I think it would be politic to hope for it,' said Fleming cautiously. 'If he is so fine a commander, the King will wish to keep him beside him.'

'I see you think he should marry her,' said her mistress. 'I do not. I think it unsuitable. She has manners, breeding, education I grant you, but he will marry her not for these but her fortune. His present wife has no flaw. I say that the situation may quite equally be met by Mr Crawford remaining attached to his wife, and resident here, where he may continue to serve His Majesty. These things are not hard to arrange.'

There was a guarded silence. Then, 'Your grace . . .' began Fleming warningly.

Queen Mary smiled: an illuminating, mischievous smile which dispatched, for the moment the strain and discontent from her features. 'You need have no fear. These matters can be brought about with perfect discretion.

'What are you afraid of? He will enjoy our favour, his wife can surely have no objection, and he will be married, and therefore free of the intrigue which surrounds a divorced man. Nothing could be more suitable.'

So she had thought of that. There were some people at court, notably of the Constable's party, who would be happy to see the Queen of Scotland tied to one of her own noblemen, instead of to the Dauphin of France, Mary Fleming looked up. Ahead, Queen Catherine, sackcloth raised, was stepping with care into her litter. Holding back her black curtain was Catherine, the Maréchale's daughter, who was not auburn-haired but who had, none the less, a great many fine gifts to offer.

Mary Fleming said, 'They say that he has not . . . That the charms of his wife do not interest him.'

'Respect,' said Mary of Scotland, 'is all one requires, surely, in wedlock. Do you suggest that he might find a fondness for Catherine d'Albon?'

130

It was the question which had launched the discussion, and was harder to sidestep a second time. From the wisdom of fourteen years old: "Perhaps,' said Mary Fleming saunctimoniously, 'he is married to his profession?'

'Then,' said Queen Mary of Scotland, 'it is time he was shown better ways of spending his leisure. After, that is, our city of Paris has been made safe for our people. Remind me to send for him.'

Mary Fleming, with gravity, dropped a curtsey.

*

Five days after that, on a Saturday at the start of September, Jerott Blyth and his wife entered Paris. They were met by Archie Abernethy, and led to the Porte Montmartre where part of the old Séjour du Roi had been made habitable for them. Then, briefly refreshed, the one-time merchant of Lyon set out, together with Archie to find Francis Crawford and report to him.

It was a week now since Saint-Quentin had surrendered, and as yet no combined army from England and Spain threatened Paris.

One understood their hesitation. Even as far south as Orléans, word had filtered through of the reception the King's new commander had prepared for the enemy. Of the 70,000 armed troops who had entered the city; the cannon brought in by river; the new fortifications; the stores of food and weapons and powder; the novel traps and ingenious devices built for him.

Of course, further help would be coming. Eight thousand workmen, Jerott had been told, had dug the trenches outside the walls to hold the 22,000 new German and Swiss levies. The Duke de Guise and his Italian troops were approaching; M. de Thermes was expected daily from Piedmont. He listened, and wondered indeed why more help was needed. In ten days, it seemed to him, Paris had become a defensible city.

It had never been that before. To Marthe, new to the town, he had talked of it, as it might be a honey-bee straddling the river, its body an island, with the Cathedral of Notre-Dame at its tail and as its head the Sainte Chapelle and the old Palais and gardens.

Outspread on either bank, you would say, were the wings, outlined with walls and with river-filled fosses. On the left,

131

the University quarter flowed over its confines and into the Pré aux Clercs, where the religious houses lay in their vineyards, and students wandered, the cows plodded out to their grazing. And on the right stood the Town, with its streets of artisans, its quays, its markets, its churches, its mansions. With its tiltyards and Town House and prisons and palaces: the Louvre, rebuilding; the royal Hôtel des Tourelles and the other great houses in the St Anthony quarter belonging to the Constable, to the King's mistress en titre, to the de Guise family with whom the Scottish Queen their niece was living.

The unpaved streets which were drains, and the lanes, fenced at either end, which had become refuse-dumps. The plaques, the shrines, the fountains. The holy statues, Huguenot-broken, encased in iron grilles with flowers wilting before them. The gardens, with vine-arbours and pear trees and strawberries; the taverns and the private houses with their bright painted sign-boards; the bridges over the Seine, three joining the right wing and two joining the left with their mills and tradesmen and houses. Beneath which, they said, few men dared to look after dark, for under the piles lived all the evil women and cut-throats in Paris.

Marthe had not been interested. Without her, Lymond would not accept Jerott back as an officer. That she knew; and freely used as a weapon to taunt him with. But she had left Lyon, to Jerott's guarded astonishment. She had come to Paris, and he did not believe this time, after that foul masquerade, that it could be to follow her step-brother. Her business was trading, and the finest sight for a man-at-arms or a dealer has always been a city abandoned.

Everyone was ready to tell them where Lymond was. They found him in the end at the Arsenal, between the Bastille and the river. He came out of the Tour de Billy with the Master of the Artillery and two échevins and, it turned out, was on his way to a converted wine store in the rue de la Vannerie, and thence to a stable-yard near the Tournelles, to supervise some unpredictable experiment.

No one explained. Archie, it seemed of intent, had told Jerott nothing.

There was about it all an air of orderly, intensive creation which was acutely familiar. He received no kind of boisterous welcome: the exchange, and the introductions, resembled those due to a captain just back from furlough. Then the

132

King's commander in Paris continued with his round of appointments with Jerott and Archie striding after.

In due course, they shed the Master of the Artillery and one of the échevins; picked up first the Maître des Arlbalétriers and then the Prévôt Général des Monnaies et Maréchaussées and finally dropped them all to have supper at the home of the Prévôt of Paris, who had to leave halfway through to deal with rumours of an impending clash in the University quarter.

From there, surprisingly, they called at the lodging of the Venetian Ambassador, where Jerott was ceremonially introduced and offered a glass of very good Candian wine, which he accepted with silent gratitude. He had been travelling since soon after daybreak. He gathered from Archie that Francis, exchanging pleasantries with Signor Soranzo, had been up and about even earlier. He thought Archie, whose seamed and sun-darkened face rarely altered, was for the first time showing all the weight of his years. But it was better, said Abernethy philosophically, than the first three or four days back in Paris, when they worked day and night like a coo-clink.

The chair was comfortable and he was sorry they had to leave, which they did shortly, exchanging greetings on the way with various sergeants, Cinquanteniers and Dixeniers who seemed to know Francis by sight. It struck Jerott that, rare in blue-blooded campaigns, Francis was taking particular trouble to involve the City. Men and money the burghers had already agreed to provide: he knew the Queen had gone herself to the Parliament of Paris and had obtained from them 300,000 francs for King Henri, and a promise to pay 25,000 infantry for two months, and raise a defence garrison of 74,-000. Since then, nursed by Lymond, it seemed that the City had continued to offer co-operation instead of the customary uneasy alliance, soon perverted, withdrawn or transformed, on three rousing speeches, into revolt.

Their last call, in darkness, was to the ramparts. Accompanied this time by a group of officials from the Arsenal, a pair of gunners and an Italian engineer called Batiste, they walked out through the Porte Saint-Denis, and crossing the water by torchlight took up a position by the Priory of Saint-Lazarus.

They were to see an artillery demonstration, Jerott was told, about which the citizens had been warned before couvre-feu. Against the last pale staining of sunset he could see pricks of light in the tall, turreted portals of the gate, Porte de deuil, Porte de joie, and its heroic St George and the dragon. Men, small and black, moved along the ramparts on either side among the angular barrels of the artillery.

Jerott felt unsafe, on the flat ground below. It was an unusual position from which to judge the success of a bombardment. He felt even more unsafe when abruptly, a marigold of bright fire blossomed high in the firmament and was followed by the flat clap of sound from a cannon.

Since no one else ran, he remained where he was, controlling a wince as a second, third and fourth explosion followed almost at once, and then a string of others on either side of him. The night filled with spangled grey smoke, and with whorls of flame which burst in the air, and lay and shuddered below in the ditch-water.

He counted eighty cannon, and then eighty more salvoes as they were recharged and fired almost immediately. Wheeling birds filled the sky, and every child, dog, goose, sheep, goat and chicken in Paris and out of it gave tongue, but unlike the proving of Jean Maugué's bombard, no bloody cloud of arms, legs and heads had risen to heaven: *Priés pour l'âme de Jean Maugué, qui nouvellement est allé de vie à trespas entre le Ciel et la terre, au service du Roi notre Sire.*

Lymond appeared to be pleased. The voices of his companions, thin in the deafening silence, were raised in praise and ejaculation. There was more talk, and people began to disperse. Lymond, appearing, said, 'Having achieved the condition of *una miserla di spernaza piena*, I think we may consider the day's business concluded. Has thow, Foly, ane wyfe at hame? If Archie calls to tell her you are well, will you spare me a moment at the Hôtel St André? I shall entertain you with a gloss on my cannon.'

It was the invitation, seven hours too late, that Jerott had been waiting for. If he sat down now to talk about anything, he would most likely fall asleep. He hesitated. A set of fingers closed on his elbow and a voice he recognized as Archie's said, 'Go and hae your clack. I'll tell Mistress Marthe you'll come later.'

One of Archie's more powerful hints. Removing his arm and rubbing it, Jerott said, 'All right. Thank you. Did you say the Hôtel St André?'

Undisturbed, Lymond answered him. 'The home of the Maréchale and her nubile daughter. It's quite near you, on

134

the other side of the Porte de Montmartre. As in the poem. *C'est du vin de Montmartre Qui en boit pinte, en pisse quarte.'*

They were on their way there already, with the Watch walking beside them. Archie had vanished. Since the atmosphere seemed fairly emancipated Jerott said, 'And the Marshal is still a prisoner? Doesn't that present certain interesting problems?'

'I don't know about problems,' Lymond said. 'It certainly presents certain interesting opportunities: the air is heady with *alacritas*. But recalling our rank, we are behaving ourselves with unimpeachable purity.

'In any case, the d'Albon girl is at odds with her mother. She will court whom she must; she will marry where she has to; but none of the arts taught to young girls by duchesses can conceal the fact that she despises us. You too, Archie mentioned you were coming. She thinks you have broken Catholic faith with your Order, le bouclier de la foy, le fort de la Chrestienté et le fleau des infideles, to serve Mammon in drapery. Here we are.'

'I suppose I have,' Jerott said. They were speaking in English. A pair of oak doors made their appearance in the lamplight whose panels, beneath the coat of arms of the d'Albon family, gave a stirring account of the siege of Troy, at which the Marshal de St André would no doubt have been present, had the event not occurred prematurely. They opened on Lymond's approach.

'Not at all,' said Francis Crawford, leading the way across a magnificent tiled courtyard, past a fountain and up a flight of steps to a door which also opened before he could touch it. 'Your troubles arise from the tenets you insist on adhering to, not the ones you depart from. If we cross to this staircase we should avoid . . . I beg your pardon.'

A tall young woman with unbound black hair who had been standing turning the pages of a book in the room they were traversing turned fully round and remarked in French, 'Please do not apologize. My mother the Maréchale is out, but you may still avoid me should you wish simply to pass through the door. Unless I can offer you and your friend some refreshments?'

She despised him, Francis had said; and that much was clear. What he had not said of Catherine d'Albon was that she was beautiful. Strong-limbed and slender with a clear,

135

high colour, she had slate-grey eyes pure as ice-water under level black brows, and the long, straight fall of her hair on the loose brocade robe she was wearing was hazed like bolled silk in the candlelight.

At the end of such a day's work as Lymond had devised and carried out, he was immune, understandably, to any possible impact from either her looks or her anger. Jerott heard himself being introduced; heard the damning grace with which, giving it just enough attention, Lymond refused the offer of food and asked after the health of the Maréchale.

'She will come back later this evening. She asked me, should you return, to beg you to excuse her. Since it seems M. de Sevigny requires neither food nor entertainment at her hands, the constant presence of his hostess may not be entirely necessary.'

'You see?' said M. de Sevigny, opening his unfortunately metal-soiled hands. 'I am like Time, *Li tens, qui s'en vait nuit et jor, Senz repos prendre, et senz sejor.* How can I expect my friends to forgive me?'

'I shouldn't worry. You haven't got any,' said Jerott, and smiled hazily at Mademoiselle d'Albon who smiled reluctantly back. Lymond made no effort to continue the conversation, but bowed and stood aside to let Jerott mount the circular staircase which led to his apartments.

Their luxury was what one might have expected, given the scale of the rest of the building. Recalling the girl's eyes following them both up the stair Jerott said suddenly, his hands in scented water, 'What did you mean? That she would court whom she must?'

'Don't let's go into all that: it's too tedious,' said Lymond, and dropping his towel on a tray, walked across to where the table of wines glowed by the fireplace. 'I am not going to marry Catherine d'Albon, and that is all that need concern anyone. Are you, do you think, of sober habit on this trying campaign of non-aggression?'

He looked up and Jerott, meeting his inquiry, felt the colour rising under his skin. He said shortly, 'Have you ever known me drunk in the field?'

'Sometimes the bedchamber *is* the field,' Lymond said. 'I am offering you one glass, out of moral parsimony. *As a skin bottel in the smoke So are you parcht and dride. Yet will you not out of your hart Let my commandement slide.* What news of Lyon?' He sat down, a cup of Pedro Ximénès in his palm.

Jerott sat down too, in a tapestry chair with cord fringes, and a lugged back which held his head between the ears like a pillow. He said, 'The troops from Piedmont should be coming into Lyon about now. Danny means to come north as soon as they settle. Adam will wait until the Duke de Guise and Strozzi arrive. By the way ... there seems to be a prevalent idea that the Italian army is about to march in to help Paris any day now. When I was in Lyon, de Guise and Strozzi were in Rome still. They won't be here for a month.'

'I know. The Piedmont troops will take ten days to march here at the minimum: St Laurent's Swiss and Colonel Rekrod's levies will take longer. And the 40,000 loyal French from the provinces will require another four weeks I fancy to muster. So like me, you cannot sally forth yet and avenge Alec and Fergie.'

So he, too, had been thinking of the two missing officers. Who, if he had not turned them off, would be here in Paris now.

It was not a tenable subject. Jerott, catching himself in the act of draining his wineglass, arrested it and said, 'I don't see why you can't march. Why not, Francis? You leave Paris impregnable, surely, behind you. De Nevers is collecting fresh troops at Laon. And the Picardy garrisons, they say, add up to quite an army.'

'Saint-Quentin held out fifteen days,' Lymond said. 'It gave de Nevers time to work on the frontier and garrisons, certainly. Salignac is at Le Catelet; Sancerre at Guise, de Bourdillon at la Fère, d'Humières at Péronne, Chaulnes at Corbie; Sepois in the Castle of Ham, d'Amboise at St Dizier and Montigny at Chaulny. Soissons and Compiègne are empty. The ground round about has been burned, but there is a limit to the value of that: the harvests in the Low Countries are in, and Philip will have all the bread he has need for. The garrisons have been active too, cutting off Spanish supply lines, robbing wagon trains and taking powder and munitions and money. But the rumour is that Philip is sitting in Saint-Quentin with his eye on those fortresses. He can stay and pick them off one by one, in which case he has lost his one chance of Paris. Or he can march on us now. And, I'm afraid, take us.'

Jerott stared at him through bleared eyes. 'With an armed

garrison of 175,000 men, and a battery of eighty guns on the Porte Saint-Denis ramparts?'

'Yes. Well, in some ways France, like the island of Zanzibar, hath a peculiar monarchy,' Lymond said. 'Unsurpassable for culture and courtesans, but somewhat confused about fortifications. They did some work in the scare of '23, and added a few trenches and ditches and bulwarks in '36, but that long curtain wall by the Bastille has been building for four years and the bastions are God's gift to a good squadron of German gunners, working for almost anybody.

'And the University side, of course, is hardly protected at all. The general theme seems to be that it's all much too difficult, and if things are bad, the rabble will rise against you anyway, so you might as well pack your silk coats and your candlesticks and take horse smartly for Orléans at the first sign of trouble. Half female Paris had evacuated already by the time I got here, and the men would have followed if I hadn't tripled the watch on the gates and the river and announced I'd hang anyone I caught leaving illicitly.

'My greatest task has been to prevent the royal family from melting off to the Loire like refined candle wax. They sent the Dauphin away, but after that were persuaded to listen to reason, once they had brought away the Charlemagne Jewel from Saint-Denis and added four hundred archers to the King's bodyguard. Thereby somewhat diminishing the required atmosphere of superior confidence.'

'You let them dress in sackcloth and carry out the relics from the Sainte Chapelle,' Jerott said.

'Candidly, I doubt if I could have stopped them,' Lymond said. 'I should point out, however, that it was not an expression of panic. It was an indication that the Almighty, having observed the bared feet of the entire royal family, must now be on our side. So you think that Paris is strong? I hope King Philip and the Duke of Savoy have that impression too. For apart from digging a few trenches, we haven't put a spoonful of earth on their inadequate fortifications since I came here. There wasn't time for it. We had to convey, instantly, the appearance of a well-armed, well-protected stronghold, and we apparently succeeded, because Philip didn't march on us. He may of course change his mind. In which case, the King will wish he had obeyed his impulse to rush out of Paris. And so, no doubt, shall I.'

Behind Jerott the man, who drank too much and worried

about Marthe and Alex and Fergie, was Jerott the Knight of St John, the officer who had once seemed to be Lymond's tanist. He said, 'Christ, Francis. You can't do that with a city. How much was fake? The guns? Was that why no shot came our way?'

'We have eight pieces of ordnance: that's all,' Lymond said. 'The garrison is almost mostly fantasy. We towed seventy thousand artisans upstream in barges and had them enter the city at night, drums beating and pennants flying. The Venetian Ambassador was most impressed.'

'You're feeding him false reports? Is that why you were telling him tonight about new offers of alliance with Turkey? But living in the city,' said Jerott, 'he must know more than you want him to know.'

'Not much,' said Lymond. 'But in any case, his dispatches are most carefully edited. The version which falls into Spanish hands is not always, shall we say, the version which his secretary wrote out for him. Don't worry. I know that a highly trained set of European statesmen and soldiers isn't going to be deceived in quite the same way as a boatload of Algerian corsairs.

'On the other hand, they have other weaknesses. Double spies, for example, and a willingness to believe any written material they find on dead men or in captured wagon trains. We even managed a few evil portents. You didn't hear of the screaming devils who floated one midnight over Saint-Quentin and Cambrai? King Philip's German mercenaries in particular didn't like them at all, especially as they haven't been paid for some time. They've been pouring in to de Nevers at Laon ever since. I won't risk them in Paris, but for an instant down payment, they can help protect Amiens, for example, and make themselves as much of a nuisance to their old employers as they like.

'You see, at any rate, that we have one or two ticklish weeks still before us. If they do attack, we can do very little about it, and the monarchy will indeed have to escape south, which is one reason why I have been anxious that Polvilliers shouldn't be waiting for them in Lyon with an evil smile and six thousand infantry. That's all. I shouldn't have kept you from Marthe. I only wished to explain why I should like you to stay in Paris meanwhile.'

He stopped and then said, 'I should say, too, since you have been so unnaturally reticent, that everything possible is being done to find out what happened to Guthrie and Hoddim.'

'If I hadn't married Marthe,' Jerott said, 'I should have been there as well, I suppose. Or maybe not. I shouldn't have stopped you from going to Russia.'

The subject hung in the air. Lymond stirred. His wine, on the table beside him, was almost untouched. Then, as Adam had done, he answered an unspoken appeal. 'Why did you marry Marthe?' he said. And then rephrased it. 'I know what you feel about her. Why did you insist on marriage?'

Beneath Jerott's drawn brows, his splendid dark eyes were stark with misery. 'She thinks it was to compensate for her birth. I suppose it was. I loved her. I wanted to give her a position.'

'She has a position,' Lymond said. 'Is it not that of housekeeper, nor of a mother, to you or your children. Marriage has weakened it: she is fighting not to lose it altogether.'

It hurt. 'You mean,' said Jerott, 'she wants to be like Güzel? A raddled courtesan selling her body round Europe for power?'

He had meant to wound. But instead Lymond said, smiling faintly, 'No. Not like Güzel. Kiaya Khátún is above and beyond any man's criticism, whereas Marthe is aware of shortcomings. She requires to be taught, Jerott; not to be worshipped.'

'I understand,' Jerott said. 'I don't think I am the person to do it.'

There was a short silence. Then Lymond said, 'I think you must. There is no one to do it for you.'

Jerott looked at him. Then he said. 'No.' After a while he said, 'I want to take her out of that house. You heard her. You would think the old woman was still alive.'

'I think you should blame me for that, rather than Marthe,' Lymond said. 'The Dame de Doubtance's interest in my parentage seems to have entangled us all. I am sorry if I have been less explicit than I might have been. It involves, as you might imagine, the closest members of my family.'

Jerott said, 'If you believe anything discreditable about the closest members of your family then you're a fool, Francis; and so are Marthe and Philippa for misleading you. Why don't you stop them from tampering?'

Lymond laughed, and lifting his cup, toasted him mockingly. 'Why don't I go to Russia?' he said. 'In fact, Philippa appears dedicated to whitewashing my antecedents and Marthe to carrying out, with some reluctance, the last behests of the Lady. That I imagine, concludes her interest, unless she has received further instructions from the hereafter. The two people who led us into the ambush at Lyon were both from her household.'

Jerott went very red. 'Marthe didn't know that,' he said. 'Neither did I. Marthe heard the hammering and let the boy out. You didn't warn her.' He paused and said shortly, 'At any rate, you and Philippa dodged them. No real damage was done.'

'No,' Lymond agreed, and laid his cup gently down. 'No real damage was done. Come. Finish your wine and I shall take you downstairs and past the sleeping d'Albons.'

'Wait,' said Jerott. 'I had a message from Marthe. She had no success in Lyon in tracing the old woman's key. She's sent it to Philippa to try it at Sevigny. You know Philippa has been staying there, and went to see the Dame de Doubtance's old house in Blois?'

'Yes,' Lymond said. 'Nick Applegarth writes to me.'

'You do keep her under surveillance, don't you?' said Jerott. 'Apparently she has made no world-shaking discoveries. She is going to visit the convent at la Guiche and then leave for England. The Schiatti boys brought back a letter for Marthe. Is Philippa safe to wander about the countryside, Francis? I told Adam she had some Culter grooms with her.'

'I have asked Nicholas to make up her entourage,' Lymond said. He lapsed into thought. Jerott, losing all of his shallow momentum, remained resting and closed his eyes presently. When he opened them the room was quite silent and the fire, burning down, had left the room dim so that all he saw of the King's commander in Paris was a line of admirable, unmoving limb and a hand finer than Marthe's, loosely laid on the chair-arm.

He was not asleep. He was listening, Jerott saw, to the sound of rapid footsteps. A moment later there was a rap on the door and hardly waiting, Archie Abernethy marched in.

Encumbered with sickening torpor, Jerott assembled his guts and made to stand upright. 'I beg your pardon. I fell asleep. Marthe must be worried.'

'She was going to bed when I left her,' said Archie Abernethy. Jerott had never noticed before how the little man studied Francis. The bright black eyes in the lined face covered every inch of his body and face, from his unchanged clothes to his hand by the half-empty wine cup. And Francis, although his words were not addressed to Archie, had his eyes fixed on him in return.

'It's one o'clock, Jerott,' said Lymond softly. 'Marthe will long since have been asleep. Archie?'

'I was sweirt tae interrupt ye,' said Archie. 'And it's a civil mischief forbye, no' an army matter. But the clash has gone round that the Calvinists are holding a coven at the Hôtel Bétourné and sacrificing live bairns on the altar. The Châtelet's sent out 500 foot and archers to block either end of the rue St Jacques, and they've got wagons and armed men in the rue du Foin and the rue Poirée and all the other streets thereabout. They say the Calvinists will leave their meeting-house at two in the morning, and God help them when they skaill. The streets are clear, but the houses are buzzing with Papes like a wasp-bike, all gleg-set tae stone them.'

'Five hundred isn't enough,' said Lymond. He was at his desk, pulling out writing-paper. 'Thank you, Archie. I shall want three messages taken at once to the two Prévôts and the Connétablier Prévôt-Général. Will you warn them below?'

Jerott, on his feet, said, 'You advised the Prévôt at supper to make his troops unobtrusive, or they would stir up the whole quarter?'

'Yes,' said Lymond. As he spoke, he was writing. 'Either they thought better of it, or they found the quarter thoroughly stirred up already when they got there. The latter, I suspect. There's been an Evangelical Church in Paris for two years under this man le Maçon, with psalms and hymns and exhortations and prayers and Bible-readings. They were to administer the Lord's Supper tonight, but they've done that before too, without interference. While both Henri and Philip are fighting their wars with Lutheran mercenaries, neither monarch is going to come down very hard on the sect.'

'So what happened tonight?' Jerott asked.

'A body from the Collège du Plessis reported them for the first time officially. Someone wants trouble,' said Lymond. He had finished the three notes and was sealing them with a wafer of wax and his signet ring. 'In times of national danger, nothing simpler. The devout ladies and gentlemen insist on meeting at night, with their families. Night gatherings are associated with orgies, and the presence of children with hideous sacrifices. A few ominous hints in the right quarters, and all the neighbours are ready to believe that unless they clean God's house, he will transfer his favours to the Imperialists. Martine will have to take these people into protective custody when they begin to emerge from their meeting, and he won't do it with five hundred gens d'armes.'

'You mean,' said Jerott, 'the people will kill them?'

'Like the Knights of St John slaughter Osmanlis.' Three members of his staff arrived, breathing quickly, and received one by one their commissions. The last, departing, collided sharply with someone approaching. The door opened and Catherine d'Albon plunged into the chamber.

The pen was still in Lymond's hand. He laid it down and stood, looking at her. The black hair, once so carefully brushed, was now loose and rough as it had lain on the pillow, and under her open robe she wore her night-rail. Her feet were bare, as they had not been in the Sainte Chapelle on a famous occasion. She said, looking at Lymond, 'Mr Abernethy has told me. He says you want to protect the Calvinists.'

She looked magnificent. His fatigue forgotten, Jerott stared at her. She has a lover, he thought. A lover or an admirer, trapped in the Hôtel Bétourné.

Lymond said calmly, 'This is a matter for the Church and civil authorities. I can't protect anybody. I have a commission under the Crown, and the Crown cannot support Calvinism publicly.'

'But you have sent out orders?' said Catherine d'Albon.

'I have proffered advice,' Lymond said. 'Which the city will listen to. They will need more men to safeguard the congregation when they come out at the end of the service. Neither the Swiss Cantons nor the German princes will be gratified if there is overmuch bloodshed—why are you asking?'

Mademoiselle d'Albon looked at him without speaking. Jerott, studying her, forgotten in his corner, saw her tongue run over her lips, wetting them.

Lymond waited. Then he said, his voice not unkind, 'I think you may trust me. I am not paid to steady the rocking bark of Peter; only to defend Catholics from other Catholics with bigger artillery. Who are you anxious about?'

'My mother. My mother is there,' said the daughter of the Maréchale de St André abruptly. 'In the Hôtel Bétourné with the Calvinists.'

No one spoke. Then Lymond said briefly, 'Alone?'

'With the comtesse de Laval, M. d'Andelot's wife. They have a valet de chambre with them. My mother said ... that quite a number of the Queen's household were also going.'

'We can't save them all,' Lymond said. 'If God wasn't won over by muddy Catholic feet, he's going to be propitiated next by a quantity of Protestant martyrs. All right. I'll do what I can, but not as an officer. You and your staff must be willing to swear that no one left this house tonight. Jerott?'

Jerott Blyth turned his back on the girl. He said rapidly, 'Francis. If you are discovered helping a high-ranking noble-woman to escape from a Protestant orgy, they'll burn you in the Marché aux Porceaux, whatever you've done for them. No one could stop this. Except maybe the Cardinal.'

'The soul of the King, and who has so many brave brothers? Exactly,' said Francis Crawford of Lymond and Sevigny, 'what I was thinking.'

144

CHAPTER 2

De gens d'Église sang sera espanché
Comme de l'eau en si grand abondance
Et d'un long temps ne sera restranché
Ve vë au clerc ruine et doleance.

During the singing of the first table of the Decalogue word reached the pastor in the Hôtel Bétourné that crowds were gathering in the rue St Jacques outside the building. He did not announce it, but allowed the Decalogue to finish, delivered the prayer for forgiveness and during the intoning of the remaining Commandments sent out for the latest report, which was that the road had been cleared by mounted archers and armed men of the City's militia, who had then formed a block at either end. Behind, the Sorbonne had closed the doors leading into its street and men were guarding these too. The chanting finished, leaving in its wake the trailing voices of tired children in the arms or at the knees of the women who formed tonight the greater part of his congregation.

Speaking carefully, M. de Morel proceeded to the reading of the Word of God and to his exposition. Tribulations of mind and body, he informed them, were not a sign of Christ's displeasure. God's Elect did not refuse to do battle for their faith but sought for their Defender and hence for their final deliverance.

He hoped they would take to heart what he was saying. He hoped God the Father was listening also and would send a miracle that, whatever he said, would save his congregation from stampeding outside, to be hunted like geese by their enemies. The windows were crowded, it seemed, with all the men of the quarter. And they had piled wall-stones and paving slabs on their sills to cast down on the heads of the faithful. Whether the archers were there for their arrest or for their protection would hardly matter. He proceeded, his hands trembling, to celebrate the Lord's Supper.

145

Marguerite de St André, standing with the comtesse de Laval at the break of the big, candlelit room, was aware of noise penetrating the thick old walls. Next door was the Church of St Benoît le Bétourné with its twisted High Altar which had once given the whole street its nickname. Opposite was the high, galleried frontage of the double College of Marmoutier and Plessis, and all around, arm in arm with the other tall houses, the rest of the scattered colleges of the University.

One would put down the disturbance perhaps to the students, except that the college streets were mostly barred off at night for this reason. And in any case, the students were allies: they were aware, as no one else, of the abuses of the old order. They realized, as she had not until Claude had explained it to her, and her friend the Prince of Condé, and, discreetly, so many of those who held high positions at Court, that she could place no reliance on confession and a Catholic penance to save her. To obtain salvation, she must be one of the Elect. And, stricken with humility, the Maréchale de St André was from time to time much aware of her need for salvation. Worried, she moved forward to receive the bread and the wine with Claude, murmuring the incantation: *C'est la communication du corps et du sang du Seigneur;* then returned to her place for the psalms, and the prayers for the King and the Church and the prosperity of the kingdom.

The preacher had contrived a few words with his elders. If no help had arrived by the end of the service, he would put a choice to the congregation. Either they could wait for the law and give themselves up to justice; or the more active among them could force a path into the street, and fight their way through the crowd with their weapons.

He hoped, to the conclusion of the Aaronic benediction, that it would not be necessary to do this, but he was disappointed. Against a steady increase in the quantity of sound filtering through from the rue St Jacques, he asked for the attention of his congregation and told them, his voice calm, what was happening. Then he led them in prayers for guidance.

The children wept, and some of the women. The men talked. As he had expected, all those with swords were willing to attempt an escape, and most of the unarmed volunteered also to go with them. There was no possibility of leading out the women, or the old. In the open, no gallantry would protect them.

Shortly after that, the first group of men, swords drawn, dashed from the doors of the meeting-house.

Outside was cool air and a long, empty street, bathed in the flickering light of two bonfires. Certainly, the windows were thronged with calling people. But it must have looked as if a quick man, turning right or left, could run into a pend or a sidestreet, or through a garden, or across to the cemetery or into the cloisters of St Benoît itself.

They reached the road running and scattered. Before they had taken three steps, a curtain of driving rock swept the street, thudding on flesh and knocking on bone or dashing to shards on the causeway. Three men lay in the road. One, his head broken open, staggered from doorway to doorway. A fourth and fifth, slashed and limping, threw themselves into neighbouring gardens where hands grasped and held them.

The next group standing within the doorway of the Hôtel Bétourné saw it all. They waited only a moment, then in their turn ran out into that storm of rubble.

By the third foray, the stones were finished. They threw pikes for a while, which stuck in a man's flesh and quivered, like harpoons in a sharkskin. When these were done, the inhabitants of the rue St Jacques, oblivious to the shouts of the sergeants, seized axes and halberds and swarmed downstairs into the roadway. Tardily, the soldiers at either end of the street began to move round the overturned wains and run towards the seat of the fighting.

There were still between sixty and seventy women and children inside the Hôtel Bétourné including the comtesse de Laval and the Maréchale de St André, when the pastor pulled the doors shut and locked them against the carnage outside. Alight with religious frenzy, with fear, with unreasoning blood-lust, the God-fearing people of Paris set upon the Calvinists trapped in the street, and did not use stones this time to attack them. One man died, kicked to death in the church cloisters. The others, spinning from fist to fist, were lashed with belts and beaten with cart-whips and chopped at with axes. The horses of the Huissiers, plunging amongst them, made little difference, nor did the strong arms of the sergeants and the archers. There were not enough of them. And blocking the light of the bonfires, they rendered Catholic and Calvinist quite indistinguishable.

147

The crowd swayed against the Hôtel Bétourné and commanded, screaming, that the Lutherans should come out. The door panels shuddered to the blows of bodies and fists. A torch, flung through the smashed windows, lay ablaze on the cloth of the altar table. The women, weeping, scrambled to smother it. *'Mon Dieu donne la main à ta servante,'* prayed Madame la Maréchale de St André. *'Je te recommande mon âme.'*

Then quite simply, a miracle happened. The shattered windows blazed and burned with a flickering and unearthly brilliance. The blows on the door ceased. The screaming altered. And there rang out the voice of their deliverer, in a thunder of arquebus shot that made every other noise puny and caused the uproar outside to falter, to stagger and perish.

'I command you,' said that scathing, peremptory voice, 'to cease Satan's work and stand back as you look for redemption. Will God rejoice that we send him blackened souls in place of penitent lambs who have seen their unwisdom? Will the strong arms here, who defend you day and night from the enemy, be given fresh heart from your actions tonight, or will the dawn find them sick at heart and weary, in no case to protect you? Be not led astray, men of Paris, by the dark angels who whisper of revenge, of slaughter, of retribution. The church sees your trouble; the law acts upon it. Give your case to the law, who will take these men and women and deal with them justly. Captain!'

'Your Eminence . . .'

'Enter the meeting place. Take these Calvinists with you. Link them with bands and make your men a living corridor through which they may march to the Petit Châtelet. Save your fellow men from sin, and the souls of these unfortunates for redemption.'

'Your Eminence.'

Then the doors opened, and the Maréchale saw the speaker.

Even in the uncertain darkness, you could not mistake the scarlet robes of the Cardinal of Lorraine, or the coat of arms on the velvet housings of his mule; or the red velvet hoquetons of the twelve men with torches and hackbuts behind him.

No one in Paris had ever been known to ignore Charles de Guise, brother of the Duke, uncle of the child Queen Mary and, next the King—and, some said, before him—the most powerful man in the kingdom.

As he rode forward the crowd withdrew, weapons dropping. At his sweeping signal the soldiers arrived, hurrying, in their place; picking up the injured and dead and ushering the rest, whole or limping, weeping or silent, back into the Hôtel Bétourné. There, with two of the Cardinal's servants to help, they were tied, two by two, in a column of degradation together.

The preacher was last, and with him, Claude de Laval and the Maréchale de St André with their servants. Dry-eyed, Marguerite de St André had no need to ask why the Cardinal had singled them out for this special attention. The husband of Claude Laval was nephew to the captured Constable of France, the Cardinal's most inveterate enemy. The disgrace of Claude was a blow at the Constable, as her disgrace would be the ruin of her husband, also a prisoner. And a triumph for Charles de Guise and his brother.

He had come to gloat. Madame la Maréchale watched him pass through the meeting-house in a sweep of red robes, and caught a glimpse of the fair skin and shallow hat with its long swaying strings. His clothes smelt of incense. He stopped, his very bearing a reprimand, beside her.

'There are two litters outside the door,' said the pleasant voice of Francis Crawford from under the Cardinal's shadowy brim. 'The pastor and Madame la Comtesse will go in the first, and Madame la Maréchale and her chamber valet in the second. If anyone speaks to you, you hold the curtains closed and you do not reply. Geoffrey and Clément will help you.'

Geoffrey and Clément, she realized, were the velvet-clad bodyguard. One of them turned and smiled, wet-eyed into her eyes. It was Catherine, her own daughter.

And then, almost immediately it seemed, she saw Claude's startled face looking at her from between the blazoned curtains of a splendid litter, its poles picked out in gold and the coat of arms of the house of Guise collaring the nodding plumes of its framework.

It moved off, and another took its place, into which she climbed with her servant. Then, drawing the curtains close, she felt it raised on the shoulders of the Cardinal's bodyguard. As it crossed the street she heard the voice so like the Cardinal's behind her, conveying to the murmuring people his blessing. And on top of that, the rumble of many horses' hooves, arriving from the direction of the Petit Pont and the Châtelet. The procureur du roi and his men, to protect the march of the long train of prisoners.

Jolting, the litter continued. The noise retreated. The running feet of a boy or two and the whine of a beggar pursued them still for a while, and then stopped as one of the bodyguards issued sharp orders. Shortly after that, she and her servant were plunged into darkness as the torches outside were extinguished. The motion continued for a little longer. Then abruptly, the palinquin was set down and the curtains drawn back on cool air and darkness.

'If any be afflicted,' said Francis Crawford, 'let hym praye; and if any be mery, let hym syng Psalmes. We've hidden the robes and the doublets at the back door of the Collège du Plessis, and I hope the clyping bursars get hanged for it. Madame, can you walk? Mademoiselle and your man here will help you. Mr Blyth and Archie are looking after the Comtesse and the preacher.'

They were behind the church of St Hilary's, and Catherine, in a tunic and breech hose of her father's, was standing beside M. de Sevigny, dressed in riding clothes, waiting for her. Even as she got out of the litter, it was taken away. The other had already gone, and the rest of the spurious bodyguard. Before she could speak, Lymond said, 'If you please, we must hurry. There's a Dizainier and some troops coming uphill from the rue St Jacques.'

'There is another,' Catherine said; and her mother marvelled at the steadiness of her voice. 'Coming down from the St Geneviève crossroads. They must be looking for escaped Huguenots.'

'No doubt,' said M. de Sevigny. He was standing, his hands on his hips, looking up at an extremely high wall. 'Do you think they have rebuilt that recently? Ah, well. Faith, without Hope and Charitie Avalit nocht, my Sonne, said he.'

God then performed a series of miracles. M. de Sevigny stepped from her valet's back straight into the flank of a vertical wall, climbed it in three moves and disappeared over it. From the other side, almost at once, came the noise of many feet, frenziedly running. The Dizainier and his men climbing the slope from the rue St Jacques heard it also. Someone shouted. There was a rattle of arms, and then the slap of more feet as the whole party set off, pursuing. An instant later the troops from St Geneviève could be heard joining them.

M. de Sevigny reappeared, quietly, through a postern. 'I thought from the smell they still kept goats there,' he said cheerfully. 'Now, mesdames, you must run as fast as the goats did. *Va, va te cacher que le chat ne te voie.*'

One realized, running, that it was not a miracle: that there had been footholds on that wall, and that he had known about them. One further realized, as he led the way through all the twisting alleys about the Clos Bruneau, that he was not merely avoiding pursuit, but was making for one particular building. It was not until they reached it, in the darkness, that she recognized the low arcades on the corner of the rue Jean de Beauvais and knew what it was he had been aiming for.

She was familiar with the main entrance with its arched, studded door and wreathed busts of dead poets. He passed these, however, and stopped instead at a plain wooden gate with a grille, across which he drew the hilt of his poniard, gently, in a muted rattle of sound. He repeated it, at deliberate intervals until, without prior warning, a voice on the other side said, 'This is the Collège de St Barbe, full of those who have stout right arms to protect their Christian sleep on a night such as this. State your business.'

The porter was an elderly man. The Maréchale could see the gleam of white hair on the other side of the grille, and a bony hand clutching a blanket Lymond approached until he, also, was close to the grille. He had pulled his cap off. He said, 'They told me you were still here, mon compère. Have you beaten anyone else for filling your best boots with horse-glue?'

There was a pause. And then the hand left the blanket and gripped the bars of the grille, while an unshaven face peered closer still. 'The Master of Culter!' The peering eyes moved in her direction, and then on to Catherine, her long hair round her shoulders. 'And still my wild young friend, entangled in escapades. Who is after you? The father or the husband?'

'The friends of the Cardinal of Lorraine, Joseph,' said Lymond.

The old eyes opened and then steadied. 'You were at the Calvinist gathering?'

'They are searching the streets,' Lymond said. 'We need

151

refuge until we can reach the river and cross it. But it need not be here.'

'It was always here before,' said the man Joseph. 'Why not now?' And, unlocking the gate, he pulled it open and held it for herself and the three others to pass through.

They were there for an hour only, and she could not speak to her rescuer because he disappeared almost immediately. She could hear his voice occasionally, and other voices raised in protest or laughter. The porter had not used his proper title. It was to be supposed that they did not know his present station.

Catherine, sitting in her incongruous clothes with her arm around her, was also listening: since they sat down she had not spoken to her mother. A stubborn girl, who had been too well bred to disobey, but who had made it plain from the outset that this marriage was not to her liking. One wondered what rumours might have come north from Lyon, but one did not ask why. The Maréchale de St André, shivering, said 'You knew we were in danger? How did M. de Sevigny learn Claude and I were there?'

The dark eyes, so like those of Jacques her father, turned and studied her. 'I told him,' said Catherine d'Albon. 'He could do nothing openly. So he broke into the Hôtel de Cluny and stole the Cardinal's robes, and the livery.'

'Under the nose of Charles de Guise?' It was the act of a madman.

'No,' said her daughter. 'That was the point. He said that it could be taken as certain that this evening the Cardinal would be asleep at his other house over the river. And so he must be. There was only his household, either asleep or out Huguenot-baiting. Mr Blyth said they had to tie up three men. When they are discovered, they will perhaps start searching not only the streets, but the houses.'

'He risks his life,' said the Maréchale de St André, huskily.

There was a small, impatient silence. 'I think,' said Catherine d'Albon, 'that he permits himself an extravagance after the labours of the last weeks. We were told, if we wished, to serve ourselves from the pot by the fire. Would you like some spiced wine? It would warm you.'

It was true: there was a sharpness in the September night air, and she was cold with anxiety. She said, accepting a rough pewter mug of steaming wine, 'They will find Claude. And the preacher.'

'I don't think so,' said Catherine. 'They are with the man he calls Jerott Blyth, and the little man with the broken nose. It seems they have friends all round the district, at the Sign of the Elephant, and the Sign of St Sebastien, and the Sign of La Corne de Cerf.'

'The printers?' said Madame la Maréchale, and subsided into thought. Of course. This was the quarter of the printers, the first to become disaffected, the most advanced in any new tide of thought.

'Yes. They will hide them,' said Catherine, 'and will see them safely home in the morning. M. de Sevigny cannot remain out of touch with his command overnight. He must return, and he seems sure that he can take us with him.'

'With the bridges closed, and the streets being searched?' said her mother. The wine had made her warmer. She rose and refilled her mug from the ladle and then served Catherine and, kindly, her valet. It was not his fault that death by faggot lay before all of them. She thought of it, staring into the red heart of the small fire lit to warm them. She did not think she would be very brave. They said that if they had nothing against you, they were sometimes willing to strangle you before the flames took a proper hold. If one recanted, one would be sure of it. She found, delving with the ladle, that there was at least another cupful in the pot.

She was not, therefore, too severe on M. de Sevigny when he finally returned, his arms full of clothes, and persuaded them all to dress up as peasants. There was no mirror, so she slapped the white gathered cap on her head and pulled at the drawstrings. The valet, whose job it was, helped her out of her silk skirts and into a rough cotton gown with an apron. Catherine, in a gown very like it, soaked a handkerchief and, bringing it to her, helped her to wipe off the careful cosmetics.

The water was refreshing. It was like a masquerade. Madame la Maréchale remembered an occasion when she had dressed up at court as a milkmaid, although her dress was of satin, and she had had little slippers sewn with cabochon rubies instead of these difficult wooden clogs M. de Sevigny had brought her. She stumbled, trying to walk in them, but her valet had a good grasp on her arm, and M. de Sevigny would doubtless come to help him.

She had remembered the milkmaid dress because it had brought her such good fortune. The present King, masked, had commanded her to be his partner that evening, and not only at the dance. She watched for her newest conquest to reappear and smiled at him when he did, dressed in a shapeless felt hat and a frayed shirt and hose with a jacket.

She did not know when she smiled that Catherine was watching her, or that, unconstricted by buckram, her opulent flesh billowed within the cheap garments. Or that her face, yellowed and pitted under its pigments, might yet have retained a kind of lined nobility, except that without its wired superstructure of headgear, the tight skull and big jaw were ludicrous.

Catherine saw her mother, mildly tipsy, produce that assured and brilliant smile; and saw Lymond returned it charmingly, with all the easy deference of which, up to now, she had been so scornful. He took her mother's free hand and spoke to her.

'Will you forgive me? It cannot be comfortable. But we must cross the river, and the College has a boat beside the Augustins. Joseph has found us a guide. We are four humble workers who had leave from our bakehouse to cross the bridge and bait the Huguenots, but the bridge is closed, and we have had a little too much cheap wine, and unless we return to our master before the morning batch is put in the ovens, we shall be beaten and turned out to starve in the gutter. Can you act in such a way, when we meet people?'

The Maréchale was pleased to say that she could and Catherine her daughter thought that with the aid of the spiced wine so thoughtfully provided, she was probably right. Then they were at the postern by which they had entered and the grey-haired porter was unlocking it for them, and grinning, and wishing them good fortune as they passed through. Catherine wondered how much M. de Sevigny had paid him. Then she saw that they had been joined by a big-handed young man in sweaty clothes, also grinning, whose likeness to Joseph told all that was necessary. His name, said M. de Sevigny, was Moses, *cum duplicantur lateres qui venit*.

Whether or not his name was Moses, it described his function exactly. Since they had entered the rue St Jean de Beauvais an hour previously the barriers had been put up, which in college time prevented the carts and wagons of the millers and the vinegar-merchants from rumbling through and spoiling the lessons.

Moses had a key to the barrier. He also knew just where

the corps de garde were working in the roads leading back to the rue St Jacques: with the Maréchale de St André's elbow tucked under his arm he led them from one safe alleyway to another, pausing from time to time to hail groups of home-coming artisans as the crowds, having seen the Calvinists safely in prison, began coming away from the Petit Châtelet.

Everyone seemed in cheerful mood. Justice had been done, which was satisfactory; and a good many personal blows had been struck, which was more satisfactory still. In the main street, the shutters were still open and a tavern had lit its serving-window and was handing out pots of liquor, to the trill of a flute in the background. Half a dozen customers, with drunken gravity, were measuring a dance among the litter of bloodstained paving stones.

They were singing in the rue Coupe-gorge cul de sac and for throughway to the rue des Maçons demanded a way-farer's fee of a ditty. Surprisingly, Madame la Maréchale's valet, opening his mouth for virtually the first time that eve-ning, produced a magnificent tenor and a sentimental vau-de-ville which made a group of ancient filles publiques in a condemned cellar burst into weeping: invitations followed them into the top of the rue de la Harpe where there was an-other party in active sport round the fountain. Someone tried to duck M. de Sevigny who retaliated with the abandon of a man who has been throwing other men into water for the greater part of his life. He then intoned a brief duet with Madame la Maréchale's valet, and catching Madame de St André and Moses round the waist, surged with them down into the rue de la Hachette, where the sign of the hunting-horn blazed in the light of twenty roasting spits turning. There he bought a little capon from Mans fresh off the char-coal, and they tore it to pieces and ate it between them, all five of them quoting Italian: *Veramente, queste Rotisserie sono cosa stupenda!*—while the Corps de Garde moved off down the rue du Chat qui Pesche and along the quayside.

An argument developed between a rôtisseur and a man in an apron over which purveyor was losing most through the adjectival decree that food prices had to stay where they were, on pain of whipping; not to mention the order that wine for the bastion workmen was to cost no more than two li-ards—two *liards!*—a pint. The man in the apron pointed out, thickly, that bloody cook-shops supplying bloody food to

155

bloody pioneers at their workings could claim exemption from their whole bloody tribute, while the scare lasted.

The rôtisseur drew to his attention, coldly, the fact that some bloody *crocheteurs* didn't ever pay tribute anyway.

Words passed. M. de Sevigny supported the rôtisseur and won the argument, since he turned out to have a better acquaintance than anybody with the chapter and verse of the regulations. Which was not surprising, since he had drawn them up himself, with the penalties.

After cordial leave-taking the party moved on, but not very quickly. There were men-at-arms still by the river. Dazed, half drunk with spiced wine and fatigue and tension at four o'clock on a September morning, Catherine d'Albon found herself and her mother seated on stools in a bakehouse, watching three arguing men compare methods of kneading. With drunken indignation, M. de Sevigny had refused to produce loaves for a rival. On the block, however, stood three wrought lumps of dough in the happy likeness of M. le Prévôt des Marchands, M. le Prévôt-Général de la Connétablie, and Monseigneur the Cardinal of Lorraine, with his hat on. M. de Sevigny supervised their consignment to the ovens, was embraced by all present and drifted off after Moses, who was making discreet signs from the doorway.

The quay was empty, and at the foot of the steps was the Collège de St Barbe's green and white boat, with the oars mysteriously already in situ. Moses said, 'Can you manage, sir?'

'This night,' said Lymond, 'how can we fail? Wonderfully enriched with shining miracles in confusion of heresy and error. It seems difficult to thank you adequately. I can only say that you have done more than you know. Your father has something to give you. And I want you to take this. If on account of what you have done tonight you or your father are troubled by the authorities, show them the ring and ask them to find me. My name is Francis Crawford, and my brother and I studied at St Barbe.'

'I know that,' said Moses. He took the ring, and stood, the broad grin stamped on his features. 'It is true what you did to all the Professors' boots?'

Lymond stared at him. 'Oh,' he said. 'Yes. I'm afraid it is.'

'Is it true about the mathematical proposition you placed before Orontius Finnaeus that spelt . . .'

'I don't know how you heard about it,' said M. de Sevigny.

'Perhaps you had better not tell me what else you know about my misspent youth.'

Moses said, 'When the ladies of the rue Glatigny were invited . . . ?'

'That,' said M. de Sevigny, 'is what I meant. We have to go. A thousand thanks, Moses.'

They had rowed half-way over the Seine before Moses stopped waving from behind the flood wall and went off, presumably home. Lymond steered them past the Mint watermill and up to the steps at the Tour du Coin, where they had to face an interrogation from the special guard Lymond himself had put on the waterway. The Maréchale's valet de chambre, primed on the way over, told the tale about returning late to the bakehouse, and they were allowed to land and tie the boat to a bollard. Then, without event, they traversed the emptying streets to the Hôtel St André.

By then the Maréchale de St André was almost sober. Standing in her own hall, she spoke to her valet de chambre: a word of commendation, a word of future rewards. Then, with her daughter, she entered the warmth and the light of her parlour.

Francis Crawford, his hat pulled off, and one hand easing over his brow, was listening to one of his own men reporting. There was an exchange of words, and then he turned and crossed to his hostess. 'There have been no alarms. Someone called, but went away when told we were sleeping. And there is good news from the battlefront. King Philip is staying in Saint-Quentin. It looks, mesdames, as if you will not have to learn either Spanish or English.'

'I know English,' said Catherine. Her mother, on first entering the light, had whipped off the tight cap and patting her hair, had begun to loosen the strings of her apron. Catherine stood as she was, face to face with François, comte de Sevigny, and looked at him.

His hat loose in his hand, Lymond returned the look pensively. 'I rather thought that you did,' he said. 'But tonight I think that French would capture it better:

> *Ce Christ empistolé, tout noircy de fumée*
> *Qui comme un Mahomet va tenant en la main*
> *Un large coutelas, rouge du sang humain.*

'It was written by a Catholic against Lutherans, but it ap-

157

plies very well the other way also.' He looked from one to the other of his protégées. 'The City is armed: it is nervous after Saint-Quentin; and any country which has suffered a reverse of fortune instantly turns on its non-conformists. Don't attend such gatherings again, madame, mademoiselle, until the climate is safer.'

The Maréchale said, 'How can we thank you?' with a throb in her voice. 'You too. . . . You too, M. de Sevigny, are a Calvinist?'

'Don't answer,' said Catherine.

'I wasn't going to,' said Lymond mildly. 'I happen to agree with More, that no man shall be blamed for reasoning in the maintenance of his own religion. But that has little bearing on tonight's episode. Half the violence was caused by crowd-madness, and half, as I have said, by fear of the enemy.'

'Who are of the same religion as themselves,' Catherine said. 'Is it true that the Christian King is making a new alliance with the Ottoman Turks, who are Mohammedans?'

'He is hoping for one,' Lymond said. 'Of course, to be cynical is the natural state of a courtier. For the other thing, you would have to look at the Hôtel Bétourné tonight, for example.'

'You find that gratifying? But then,' said Catherine, 'should such meetings not continue? And should women of rank not attend them, to affirm their faith in public if necessary; and if necessary die for it?'

'Of course,' said Lymond placidly, 'there is no missionary as persuasive as death. The Church knows that already. The Church would meet martyrdom by inviting the Inquisition to Paris. The Crown and the people might very well meet it by massacre. Bloodless reformation requires a very delicate sense of statesmanship and timing, and rarely receives it. Praying, on the other hand, can be done at any time.'

He smiled suddenly; and Madame la Maréchale, her eyes half-closed with fatigue, smiled vaguely back. Catherine d'Albon said, 'What prayers do you suggest?'

'In English?' Lymond said. 'I don't know. What about one from Geneva?'

She wondered for a moment whether he would break into song, as he had on the wild journey home, with her mother's chamber valet. But he merely put his hand on the doorlatch and spoke the words gently, and without the cynicism he had spoken of:

> *'And from the sword (Lord) save my soule*
> *By thy myght and power;*
> *And keepe my soule, thy darling deare,*
> *From dogs that would devour.*
>
> *And from the Lion's mouth that would*
> *Me all in sunder shiver*
> *And from the hornes of Unicornes*
> *Lord safely me deliver.'*

She had followed it all, her lips moving. 'And from the horns . . .'

'. . . of Unicorns, Lord safely you deliver. Sleep well. Good night,' he said; and left, without sound, for the stairs to his apartments.

'Good night,' said Catherine d'Albon. A single tear, bright in the candlelight, slid down her face and caught her mother's startled attention. It was followed by another; and then by a stream which bathed her face as she stood there in silence.

The Maréchale said nothing whatever. Only she looked at her weeping daughter and saw her long, glossy hair and pure profile and slender waist, set off by the incongruous garments. Then, retreating silently, Marguerite de St André reached her room and steadily walked to her looking glass.

She was too proud to weep. Instead, she called her daughter's maid and told her to see to her mistress, for she wanted her in her best looks by morning.

CHAPTER 3

Jour qui sera Reyne saluée
Le jour apres le salut, la priere
Le compte fait raison et valuée
Paravant humble oncques ne fut si fiere.

Of the four hundred Calvinists who met to worship that night in the Hôtel Bétourné, half escaped, including the comtesse de Laval and the pastor. Of the rest, five were chosen as an example and condemned to death by burning. Those who remained prisoner, preserved from severe injury by the arrival of M. Martine and his escort, were eventually releasd, upon the intercession of the Protestant Churches in Switzerland and the Protestant Princes in Germany.

The name of Madame la Maréchale de St André was not connected with the episode, especially as it became known about Paris that the lady was confined to her room with an illness. The comtesse de Laval did not take to her bed but on the contrary entered the public eye for quite another reason: her husband the Seigneur d'Andelot, captain-general of the French infantry, contrived to escape from his captors after Saint-Quentin, and a few days after the Bétourné incident he and his wife were reunited.

In Paris, having been refused permission for the third time to join the army in the field, the comte de Sevigny completed the task of enrolling and conveying to Laon the largest company of troops the crown of France had ever raised since the present reign started. He also devised ways of supplying, regulating and supporting the French-occupied fortresses still scattered round the disaster area of Saint-Quentin. Two of these, Le Catelet and the citadel of Ham, fell to the enemy.

By the time they were taken, it was clear even to the victorious Spanish and English that by choosing to stay in the area, they had forfeited wholly and for ever their chances of attacking Paris. Their infantry, unpaid for months, was deserting, most of it to the French army. Their English components, restive over news of Scottish attacks on their homeland, might well find good reason to leave also. And among the troops who remained, lethal quarrels were breaking out daily.

Against which the French army, already large, was swelling hourly. The Duke de Nevers at Compiègne had ten thousand French infantry gathered, and five thousand cavalry and six thousand Switzers, with a regiment of Germans expected presently. M. de Thermes had come with four thousand more Switzers from Piedmont, leaving eight thousand in Lyon as he marched north, to reinforce the defence M. de Sevigny had already left there. Danny Hislop, released from his watching brief, came north and joined Jerott and his wife in the Hôtel de Séjour.

The Duke de Guise left Rome with d'Aumale his brother and Marshal Strozzi and set sail for France with seven ensigns and all those gentlemen who had been fighting with him in Italy. Behind him the Pope, bereft, drew to a hurried conclusion this war waged, he let it be known, owing to misinformation received by him about King Philip and the Duke of Alva his commander, both of whom he now knew to be his obedient sons and excellently disposed towards him.

He received, with gratitude, the return by King Philip of all the states of the Church seized during the campaign, and the Duke of Alva rode into Rome amid celebrations which only ceased when, through an oversight, possibly, of the Pope's immediate superior, the river Tiber flooded, and Rome was inundated to a depth of six feet, including the wine cellars.

The Duke de Guise was indisposed on his voyage to France, and wrote that he would come north to Paris by litter as soon as he was able to travel.

The King of France replied that the Duke was on no account to make himself unwell by hurrying, adding that never was master so pleased with his servant as he with the Duke. He then resumed hunting with his new and charming companion, pursued by couriers from Compiègne, Laon, Amiens, Abbeville and Lyon and accompanied by M. de Vigne, the French Ambassador to Turkey, newly back with advice from the Sultan Suleiman.

The Ambassador, in common with all ambassadors in France, was accustomed to transacting his business on horseback, but not to obtaining decisions with what turned out to be the present velocity. The situation in Turkey was complex. The powerful Suleiman, whose pirate raids in the Mediterranean had been of such assistance in harassing the Spaniards in Italy, was disgruntled. The French, for instance, kept making peace with the Pope without consulting him. He was considering, the Sultan said, invading Hungary and Germany himself in the summer, and if the most Christian King would kindly refrain from concluding his campaign in Italy, the Sultan might be able to spare the Ottoman fleet to support him. He sent a gold cup and a small vase of balsam as, one might say, drink money.

With Spain on her doorstep, it was understood, France had no desire to reopen the Italian war, which had been a crazy venture of the de Guise family in the first place. In the event, no one had to lose face by saying so, for the King's new fair-haired commander merely said, 'You'll get the fleet in any case. My information is that Suleiman is not in good health, and the sons have begun fighting over the succession again. Hungary is in no danger. He won't risk leaving Topkapi.'

'The Knights of Malta will not be pleased,' M. de Vigne had ventured. The Knights of St John, sworn to slaughter the infidel, owed the very island they possessed to the King of Spain. He added, 'Your grace will remember the sad tidings. The Grand Master Claude de la Sengle has departed this world.'

The new fair-haired general, a good seven years younger than Henri, for God's sake, had answered courteously. 'His grace, as you know, is profoundly moved by the news. But the Knights of St John will require a permit for grain. And if Parisot de la Valette succeeds as Grand Master, France has nothing to fear.'

They were in the middle of a close run, and the Ambassador to Turkey could only gasp obsequiously in reply, and observe the King smiling at his commander. The man, he now recalled, had been for a brief period a French envoy to Turkey, and had fought on Malta. There was a Knight of St John, they said, presently on his staff.

He had heard what M. de Sevigny had achieved in Lyon and Paris. At the kill, he saw how the King kept the man by his side, and held him by the arm, and joked with him. And after the kill, the King read the last batch of dispatches, which all reflected the single conclusion: the threat to Paris was over. So M. de Vigne became witness to a moving and extraordinary ceremony: when the King of France placed his hands on the comte de Sevigny's shoulders, and requiring him to kneel, with borrowed sword and gilt spur created him a knight of the royal Order of St Michael.

And that, thought M. de Vigne, was going to shake a few birds from the tree-tops. It was the premier order of chivalry, granted to the great of the civilized world: to kings and princes and generals. There were only 36 Knights of the Order of St Michael. The late King James of Scotland had been one. And Charles V, the great Emperor, now retired to his monastery in Spain, whose son Philip was conducting this war with such lack of confidence. And of course, the de Guise family. The Cardinal of Lorraine was its Chancellor.

Returning to Paris in the wake of the hunting party and watching the King dismount at the Tourelles, his hand on the comte de Sevigny's shoulder, M. de Vigne began, in his head, to plan a number of letters. This was a man to be cultivated, and he knew who would be glad to have warning of it.

During the supper that followed, sumptuous as befitted the ending of a national emergency and the honouring of its manipulators, Francis Crawford asked for and received permission at last to leave Paris, and take up with the army his proper employment.

'That is,' said the King, his soft, wine-moistened lips smiling within the silken black beard, 'we shall expect regular news of you at Saint-Germain. I have told you we are leaving also. The air in Paris is bad. Her grace the Queen is unwell. My daughter of Scotland has been abed coughing these three days, and asking, I understand, why her subjects take no trouble to visit her. I tell her Paris must come before Scotland.'

The Cardinal of Lorraine was not present. 'And the crown of France before her princes,' said Queen Catherine kindly. It was true, she did not look well. The white skin of which she was so proud had a sallow tint round the nose and the mouth: the prominent eyes, damp with the force of her coughing, were downcast.

Then she lifted them, and it was to be seen that the impression of submissive intelligence was one she was well used to conveying. She said, 'Then you do not regret, M. de Sevigny, that our selfish affection has brought you honour in France, instead of in Russia? I remember well my uncle of

163

Albany praising the abilities of your grandfather. Our Scottish friends over here have a saying, *Ecosse notre foi; la France notre coeur*, which moves me.'

There was a third part to that statement which none but her Scottish friends, Danny Hislop hoped, were aware of. Seated far down the company, he tried and failed to catch Lymond's eye.

His mood was sardonic. Short; ugly; sharp as a razor, Danny Hislop the Bishop's by-blow from Ayrshire had owned no superior before joining Lymond in Moscow and still struggled, from time to time, against the knowledge that in Francis Crawford he had perhaps met his match.

He had watched Lymond, under Jerott's furious eye, accept yet another of the golden chains intended to keep him in France, and he wondered what game he was playing. There was no doubt that he had been hell-bent on getting to Russia. Chiselled into each of Danny's eardrums was the precise language Lymond had used when they brought him back from Douai. And now, when you listened to him, the shifty bastard, there was never a damned *fuero* to be heard. Lymond said, 'How could I have regrets, Madame? Thus poulticed with the gold of pleasure, and with such brave consolations?'

He did not, on the word *consolations*, look at the Queen's ladies of honour, nor did Catherine d'Albon glance at him. But a little colour, Danny noticed, rose in her well-bred face as she sat, her hands in her lap, and her mistress, replying, smiled dryly. 'I hear, my lord count, that your wife is leaving for England.'

'She is travelling north,' Lymond said. 'She should pass through Paris in a day or two.'

'While you are in Pacardy. A charming young person,' said Queen Catherine, 'for an Englishwoman. I trust her kin will find her another mettlesome husband. And when she has gone, we must see that you have time for gentle companionship. The Maréchale tells me you have hardly spent more than the night hours at the Hôtel St André, and sometimes not even those.'

'Not from choice, I assure you,' said the King's new commander, and this time, looking across, bowed gravely to the Maréchale's daughter.

The girl acknowledged it with composure but her flush, Danny noted with interest, had become deeper. Pestered beyond endurance for information about Lymond's intentions, Jerott Blyth had let fall a week ago that Catherine d'Albon did not play a part in them.

It turned out that Lymond had told him so. Danny Hislop, who was an unstinting admirer of Jerott's appearance, his wife and his reputation, was still to be overwhelmed by his acumen. Any fool could see that the d'Albon girl and her money were the bargain clause in an invisible contract. And Lymond, being Lymond, would take the girl, he was convinced, whether he settled in France or he didn't.

The angelic Marthe, of course, the viper-tongued glorious step-sister, didn't want M. le comte to remarry. Neither did the little man with the broken nose, Archie Abernethy.

Danny Hislop was not entirely at ease about Archie. Danny remembered a dark night at Lyon, and Archie arriving at the Hôtel de Gouvernement in the small hours of the morning with the printer Macé Bonhomme. They had brought Lymond home, impossibly drunk, and with a clean contusion at the back of his head in which no one appeared to be interested. Mr Crawford, said Archie, had now and then lost his footing.

The type of man who could fool an elephant was unlikely to have the same triumph with Daniel Hislop. It seemed odd to Danny that a menagerie trainer should also dabble in soldiering. Seven years ago, they said, Archie had attached himself to Lymond in Rouen, and had divided his time ever since between the Somerville girl and his lordship.

Jerott, when applied to for enlightenment, merely said irritably that he supposed Archie had required a new owner. Adam, when asked the same question in Lyon, had seemed to view the little man as an ancient retainer. It would be interesting to see what skill, if any, he had in the battlefield.

After Russia, campaigning in France, would be like conducting a war in a chicken-dish. Danny looked forward to demonstrating to the moody Mr Blyth what he had missed by his absence from Russia. He regretted that Adam, anchored at Lyon awaiting the Duke de Guise's arrival, could not be here, equally blessed, to support him. If, as they set off for camp, he noticed Archie Abernethy's knowing black eyes upon him, Danny Hislop paid no attention.

The Duke de Nevers was in the château of Compiègne; the only senior field commander left when the boiling wrack of Saint-Quentin had seeped away, and with him was the veteran de Thermes from Piedmont, who had left Paris only a day or two ahead of M. de Sevigny, bearing with him the agreed plan of strategy.

To M. de Thermes, the plan was his brain-child, and to carry it out thus no hardship. The Duke de Nevers, after four weeks of complying with a stream of equally ingenious projects, was only too pleased to have Lymond in person to help him.

When angling for power in France, tact was necessary. Tact and unremitting success in battle, in bed and in throneroom; with no wake of disgruntled princes to pacify. So far, it seemed to Danny, Lymond's grasp of these principles seemed exemplary.

There followed a week during which he was unable to feel patronizing any longer, or even to watch Archie Abernethy, for the simple reason that he was being run into the ground with hard labour. Eighteen thousand troops were then quartered between Compiègne and the old royal palace ar Verberie, and ten thousand more arrivals were imminent.

There were quarters, and food, and weapons and even money waiting for them all, just as there were provisions and extra men, when they were needed, for all the hard-held towns and fortresses still in French hands around them. Bands of horses went out daily to Corbie and Péronne and Amiens and Abbeville, taking what was required and bringing back information. Other bands departed with special orders. They looked for and routed the foraging parties sent out by the Spaniards whose vast army hovered so near on the frontiers. They harried and hindered the Spanish forces attempting to rebuild and fortify the fortress towns which marked the watershed of the Spanish advance into Picardy; Saint-Quentin, Noyon, Le Catelet, and even Ham itself, where King Philip sat, closeted with his secretaries, his interpreters and his commanders in the citadel.

The object, as Lymond had made it properly clear before ever he arrived in Compiègne, was not to lure the Spanish army out to fight. It was to stand solidly across its path and harass it through the worsening weather of autumn until fretful, unpaid, disease-ridden and weary, the Duke of Savoy's quarrelling army of Germans and English and Spanish should be impelled to give up and disperse.

For a week, Danny was out every night, sometimes with a company of Germans; sometimes with Swiss. Jerott was allotted longer expeditions: at one point he worked out of Amiens with de Lansac for almost two days, and got back to Compiègne with a graze from a hackbut ball that killed his horse under him. He was thankful to find that Lymond was off with a party of German pioneers, doing something inexplicable with a couple of carts spread with tarpaulins.

Jerott had his scratch dressed, slept for six hours, woke, ate and discovered that Lymond had returned and left again for Péronne in the interval, leaving fresh instructions for himself and Danny. A quarrel about precedence had broken out among the German officers and he marched in and settled it, meeting Danny on his way out to collect a new gelding. He had not lost the knack of command, he was pleased to discover.

Danny, who looked hollow-eyed, said, 'Have you heard? He's made the wells of Le Catelet undrinkable. Originality at any price. The Swiss, in their Swiss way, say he knows how to take Dame Fortune by the hair. The Germans, in their German way, say if he wants to lead them again, he will have to bloody well increase their stipend. You know he had all the grain fields laid waste but kept the vines standing to gripe all the Spaniards? The rotten bastard. If I were St Michael I'd disown him.'

Jerott, who was saddling his horse, did not bother to look up at the limpid eyes and teased sandy hair, waning from the baby-pink brow. He was beginning to get the measure of Danny. He said, 'Where are you going?'

'To take some culverin this side of Noyon, and then fall into bed for a lengthy four-minute sleep. I wish I'd stayed in Lyon. I wager Archie wishes he'd stayed in Lyon.'

Jerott mounted. 'We all get out of condition at times,' he said; and moved off at a brisk gait to where his troop of soldiers was waiting. Danny, gazing after him critically, was aware of a twinge of approval. He hoped that nothing about him revealed it.

At the end of the week, a courier from St Germain brought the daily mail from the King, and among it, a hand-written letter from Henri. In it, he commanded the comte de Sevigny, in mock severe terms, to leave disporting himself in the field and return to his master at Poissy, where on Wednesday, 29 September, his Majesty would give the annual banquet for the chevaliers of the Order of St Michael. M. de Thermes, if his business were done, was to return with him.

'Not us?' said Danny hopefully, when summoned for instruction.

'Not you,' said Lymond. 'Or Jerott or Archie. You would drink your soup with your gloves on.' The cracking pace of the week, with its sharp fighting and hard riding and bold exercise of authority suited him, if no one else, and the crisis in Paris had also done. But he was wrong in one respect: Archie did not stay in Compiègne but appeared at his side, without comment, on the far side of Creil. Challenged, he merely opened his black eyes and said that if Mr Crawford was going to play at being a knight, then Mr Crawford would need a squire to hold his petticoats up for him.

If he counted on the presence of thirty men at arms around him to preserve him from immediate castigation, he was, as it turned out, correct. He was still with the newest chevalier of the Order of St Michael when, dressed in white with the one-armed silver cloak and the heavy golden collar of shells, he worshipped with his brethren by the broken marble baptismal font of St Louis in the church of Notre Dame de Poissy, and then walked in procession the short distance to the royal monastery behind the Usher, the Herald, the Clerk, the Master of Ceremonies and the Chancellor of the Order, there to feast under the handsome beams of the Dominicans in the presence of the King, glimmering in pearls and velvet and satin. The next morning, instead of the quick departure he had counted on, the comte de Sevigny, with Archie still in attendance, accompanied the King of France on the four-mile ride from Poissy to the castle of Saint-Germain, there to join the court and to visit the sick-bed of that spoiled young monarch, Mary of Scotland.

It was warm. Whatever decision King Philip might be taking at Ham it would not, unfortunately, owe anything to the inclemency of the late autumn weather. The poplars at the edge of the forest were yellow, but the other trees were barely tinged yet with russet: there were full-blown roses still in the formal gardens round the Old Château, foursquare in its red-trimmed cream stone, with the modern balustrades and urns trimming its roof-walk. Beyond that were the half-built walls of the New Château, rising on its terraced gardens above the loops of the Seine. From there, one could see the roofs of Paris, and even the white towers of Saint-Denis where the royal owners of Saint-Germain would one day be laid to rest. Some kings enjoyed the reminder more than others.

Mary of Scotland received her subject the dilatory Mr Crawford of Lymond and Sevigny in her bedchamber, which had recently acquired a new stucco frieze and a set of gold-fringed bed hangings for which she had been campaigning for months. In the nine years since she had been sent, a child of six, to take shelter with her kindred monarch in France she had never had enough money to spend: never dresses as resplendent as the little French princesses; never a household as lavish; never a governess she had really liked since the King had been indiscreet with Mary Fleming's mother and instead of tolerating it, the Queen and Madame Diane had made her go back to Scotland.

There was no reason in the world why gentlemen should not take their pleasure with ladies of their own rank, provided it was properly done, and etiquette was not openly flouted. But it remained a pity that the King, by doing so, had thoughtlessly deprived Mary of Scotland of Lady Fleming's assistance. And the bastard, Harry, was five, and freckled, and peevish.

She had told them to admit Mr Crawford, when he came, without chattering to him. The chin-cough being intermittent, she was not in bed. She had arranged herself picturesquely in a low, sling-seat chair with a fur rug over her knees and her auburn hair brushed out under its cap, so that it lay like raw silk on her shoulders. She sat haughtily still, because when she moved, it broke into snake-locks. Then the chamberlain's knock came at the door, and Janet Sinclair looked up from her sewing while la Fleming, as instructed, answered it.

Mary of Scotland, who had extremely sharp hearing, noted that she did not chatter, but that the incoming gentleman paused and greeted her with an amiability verging on the irregular. Then he turned, waited for his introduction, and walked forward to kneel, with correctness, by her wolfskin.

He was far fairer than the Cardinal. The hair below her hand was breathtaking in its brightness, and his blue eyes were lashed like a woman's.

'We had expected you before, Mr Crawford,' said Queen Mary of Scotland. 'We wished to congratulate you on your courageous efforts to help his Majesty the King prepare against the enemy, in the absence of Monseigneur my uncle in Italy. He will wish to commend you.'

She had rehearsed it, and so she said it. But Mary Fleming, watching from her place beside the nurse and Beaton, whose mouth was slightly open, guessed what hardihood it had taken.

'Thank you,' said Lymond; and kissed the hand offered him, a little belatedly, and rose. 'Is there some manner in which I may serve you?' It was not, now, the man she remembered from the days of her childhood.

Mary of Scotland moved, dislodging the pools of combed auburn. It was the stifled end of an impulse to rise. She had learned to laugh and talk and even confide in messeigneurs her uncles the Duke and the Cardinal of Lorraine, but although she was a Queen and they were only princes of the blood still they towered over her, golden, invincible, filling the room, like an organ, with the invisible roulades of power.

This man was the same. Perhaps he had been the same six years ago and not the pretty courtier, decorating every bedroom, which the randy gossip of the nursery had made him out to be.

She said, 'You may sit. We have some news from Scotland. The English have tried to seize the islands of Orkney, and have failed with great losses. The Queen-Regent our mother also speaks of French and Scottish raids on the town of Berwick and other places on the Borders, killing five hundred English and taking two thousand prisoners. She mentions particularly the brave part played by my lord of Culter, your brother.'

'Her grace is too kind,' said the comte de Sevigny, the faintest edge on his voice. Mary Fleming hoped that her mistress had noticed it.

'Because of these actions,' continued the clear, French voice implacably, 'the Queen-Regent our mother considers that Lord Grey of Wilton may be summoned back to England, or at least will lose most of his army. Thus those who fight in Scotland serve France as well, if not better than those who remain.'

She made the mistake of pausing. 'My brother is fortunate,' said Mr Crawford agreeably.

However overpowering he might have seemed, he was not, in fact, her uncle. Mary of Scotland's young, timbreless voice lifted half a tone and gained in clarity. 'His highness the Dauphin and I are to be married in the spring time. We shall require the services of wise and brave men to lead our people the Scots in our absence. You have our guerdon, Mr Crawford. His Majesty of France would readily grant remittance of your bargain for that purpose.'

It had been settled today: this marriage which whispering vulgarians throughout the court had been saying would never take place. He was perhaps the tenth person she had told: the sweet satisfaction of it wiped away all her irritation, even when he answered, 'Your grace has my heartfelt good wishes. But does your grace think that the hills of Tweedsmuir will please Mademoiselle d'Albon?'

His voice, even when he was baiting her, betrayed nothing but the politest inquiry. Queen Mary said, 'Your wife knows the Lowlands and has lived there. Would it not be more praiseworthy to take your marriage unrevoked back to Scotland? Or must you wait until your brother is killed in some battle? We are told there is no one else to bear arms but small children.'

'We are all mortal,' observed the comte de Sevigny kindly. 'Should my brother succumb while the children are in their minority, I should have to appoint some kind of regent. My career, like your grace's, lies in other directions. And should France be unable to annul my marriage I shall, with the greatest reluctance, have to travel eastwards.'

He had made the obvious point. The Pope, having made friends with the Imperialists, would be less amenable now to granting favours to the kingdom of France which had abandoned him. Mary said, her hazel eyes direct and pellucid, 'We had hoped your new knighthood might have prompted you to chivalry towards your wife as well as to our mother, Mr Crawford. The comtesse de Sevigny is quite charming.'

It was not etiquette to rise until formally dismissed. But his intentions of shortly leaving the room was as plain as if he had stated it. He said, 'I am an ardent admirer of both ladies. But I do not wish to be married to either of them.'

She said, 'You are impertinent, sir!'

It pulled him up, just a little, you could see. He said, giving her his every attention for perhaps the first time, 'I beg your grace's pardon. I have been redirected so often against my own interests that I am a little wary, perhaps, when all my friends seem to approach me with wheellock arquebuses in their hands instead of handkerchiefs.'

She lost no time in taking him up on that. 'Would it be against your own interests. M. de Sevigny? You have a comté and many other possessions. Few men at the start of their career are admitted as a Chevalier of the Order of St Michael. Your redirection, as you call it, does not seem to have harmed you greatly so far.'

'Quite the reverse,' Lymond said. 'It keeps me also within the light of your presence. Nothing in Scotland, your grace, could possibly provide such an inducement.'

'How can we believe that?' Mary said. 'If we ask you to perform a service for us, and you will not do it?'

'You mentioned two services,' Lymond said. 'You asked me to return to Scotland and I have to say there, with regret, that his Majesty of France has asked of me the opposite; that for the promised twelvemonth I should stay here at his side at the French court. You asked me also, I believe, if I would refrain from annulling my marriage.'

He paused, and Mary did not interrupt. The interview, which had seemed so unpromising, looked like continuing at least with some frankness. It did not necessarily mean, thought Mary Fleming, that she would obtain what she wanted from it.

Lymond said, 'There, I must lay two points before your highness. My wife is English and therefore less acceptable, both in Scotland and in France, than a French lady. And secondly the relationship between man and wife is, I humbly put to you, a private one, and not subject to the wishes of princes. In this instance, must as I revere your grace, nothing could bring me to alter my decision.'

She never really knew when she was beaten. 'We thought,' said Mary of Scotland, 'that a man of war must be flexible? You forget, M. de Sevigny, that we know your wife. She is fully acceptable in France and, as we know from our aunt, has been made welcome in time of peace over the Border. Perhaps we know her better than you do. Would it not help you, before closing your mind, to spend more time with her?'

'Perhaps. But she is on her way home to England,' said Lymond easily. 'And in any case, it does not affect the prime issue. I remain in this country, your highness.'

'I see. Then,' said the thin, clear voice sweetly, 'we must be content, we suppose, with your presence. Since this is so, we may expect to see you more frequently?'

'As often,' said Francis Crawford, 'as my duties and the commands of the king will allow.'

The Queen glanced at Mary Fleming, who came forward.

Lymond, rising, threw her a look of mild inquiry. Jenny Fleming's daughter saw it, but dared not answer it. The Queen said, 'You may leave. There are some persons in the chamber of audience who wish to see you. Fleming will conduct you.'

He made her a full and graceful bow, and looked at Mary Fleming again, as she opened the door of the presence chamber. But the Queen was watching, so she said nothing; only allowed him to enter.

It was a small room. In it was a short, ruddy man with a grey beard whom she introduced as Master Michael Nostradamus, the Queen's barber-surgeon from Provence.

The other person in the room needed no introduction, being the one young woman he trusted had left France and himself for ever.

The Queen, wilful to the end, had sent for Philippa.

CHAPTER 4

Qui par fer pere perdra nay de Nonnaire
De Gorgon sur la fera sang perfectant
En terre estrange fera si tout de taire
Qui bruslera luy mesme et son enfant.

For a girl of twenty to fall in love with an experienced dilet-
tante ten years her senior was nothing out of the way. It was
perhaps rarer for such a girl to make up her mind, as did
Philippa in Lyon in one night of bitterest soul-searching, that
such a relationship was out of the question, and that henceforth his life and hers must lie in different directions.

There had, of course, been sentimental attachments before
in her childhood: to an apothecary, a ballad-monger and a
boy from the Abbey who had shared the same teacher. All
she remembered, looking back, was the delicious anguish, the
laborious subterfuge: to be in the garden when he happened
to call; to be in the market place on the day he might ride
through. The smile one treasured; the box of glutinous oint-
ment one bought but did not use, because his fingers had
touched it.

The boy from the Abbey was the only one who even
learned her name; and he was interested in someone else very
much older. She had produced a tear or two for her pillow
on occasion, and had wasted a great many hours on devious
plans which came to nothing, under the impression that each
tender secret was hers only. She remembered her father re-
marking, on finding the salve, that he didn't know she was
bad with her fetlocks. Later she recognized the loving anxiety
and, very likely, the kindly hysteria with which her parents
had watched all her antics.

It had been painful, but only a little. It was self-inflicted
pain, teamed with excitement and pleasure and an innocent
awareness that one was touching the fringe of something real
which might lie round the next corner. When it came, one

174

would know what to do with it. And meanwhile, one need suffer only as much as one wanted to. It was a game.

It had been so different, her growing interest in Lymond, that she had never connected the one with the other. Brought up by Kate, she had acquired early all Kate's maturity: the maturity which has to do with understanding other persons and, if called upon, putting those who are understood before one's own interests. Physical maturity, although she possessed it, had never claimed her attention.

What had happened therefore was a true awakening: a clear and shadowless light revealing why, through all these years, the condition and wellbeing of one man should so have concerned her.

Subconsciously, she had divined what he might be. That night, turned upon herself and not outward to others, the elements of his identity had been delivered to her, served upon gold, as the bread and meat and wine of a festival.

For an hour, blended with all she could offer, something noble had been created which had nothing to do with the physical world. And from the turn of his throat, the warmth of his hair, the strong, slender sinews of his hands, something further; which had. Though she combed the earth and searched through the smoke of the galaxies there was no being she wanted but this, who was not and should not be for Philippa Somerville.

That her eyes were now open was no fault of his. The pity of it was that, since that evening, he knew it. So, she resolved in that moment, she must remove herself from his circle.

It was then five o'clock in the morning: one hour, though she did not know it, before the Paris courier would come thundering to the Hôtel de Gouvernement door. She rose and, taking paper, wrote a letter to tell Kate, her mother, that she was coming. Then she prepared for her journey home, and for the last service she could perform for Francis Crawford.

To return to Russia, Marthe had said, would mean death for him. Against that, she had only one shot in her quiver, and that so weak that more harm than good might well come of it. She could reach the end of the road in her probe into his history.

If it did him no service he would remain, as seemed likely, an exile for the rest of his life. If it restored to him pride in his family, he might consider working for Scotland. And that, thought Philippa a little bleakly, for an Englishwoman would have to be monument enough.

✱

Once, a schoolgirl in Jerott Blyth's company, Philippa had travelled up the Cisse valley to Sevigny. Riding again through the mild verdant hills, the fruiting valleys, the wide, dreamlike forests, she wondered what had prompted Francis, all those years since, to buy it. Nicholas Applegarth, maimed ex-comrade of God-knew-what battles, had managed it for him, as a Frenchman by naturalization. Now, with the dual nationality granted him, Francis Crawford was master of this and of all the other property with which she had heard the King had endowed him. The farms, the thatched houses, the villages she was passing must be his. She could feel the Schiatti nephews, gallant escorts, surveying the orchards and vineyards and assessing their value. Then they came to the gatehouse, and the avenue of trees from which, under the archangel wings of the beeches, one could see the spired blue turrets and white walls of Sevigny.

It was not, like Chaumont over the river, a stronghold. Sevigny was Italian, and built by Italians as a pleasure house, its walls decorated by bricks, by mouldings of shells, of angels, of foliage; by dormer windows whose interlaced stonework rose to embroider the sky among the slender red and white stalks of its chimneys. Behind, an arcaded terrace bordered a carp pond, beyond which the formal gardens, green and diapered, stretched to where the trees all around closed on the riding paths with arbours set in them, and statuary. There were sunflowers still, their yellow heads yearning westwards.

It had been like that, so Nicholas Applegarth said, when Lymond acquired it, and he had changed nothing, although Nicholas had husbanded it well. Indeed, even indoors there was little in evidence of Sevigny's owner: a library of books which looked as if it had been used; a spinet which was newer than the rest of the furniture in the little parlour in which she found it. Nicholas Applegarth, pink-cheeked and grey-haired, moving unfussily with his stick in the long gown which disguised his infirmity had been expecting them, and made the Schiatti cousins welcome for the night, and saw to the quartering of Philippa's escort. In the morning he took them riding round the pretty property. M. de Sevigny, he said, had rarely had free time in which to enjoy it. Although, of course, when he had his company it was sometimes quartered there.

They had been here when Jerott brought her along, all those years ago, and Alec Guthrie and Fergie Hoddim with them. Nicholas had told her of the disaster at Saint-Quentin, and the news that Alec and Fergie were missing. He told her also of the threat to Paris, and that M. le comte had been summoned there. In private, he used Lymond's christian name, and to avoid an implication which might wound, Philippa had to do so as well.

It was a frightening pleasure, but one she never again could be made to indulge in. She also made and doggedly kept other rules. Nicholas, the most gentle of hosts and the least given to gossip, was told that she was here with her husband's knowledge, to search out his sister Marthe's parentage. She asked no questions about Lymond, or his life at Sevigny. The new flame was already stronger than she could well bear. It would be folly to feed it.

She dismissed with real gratitude the handsome boys who had brought her so competently from Lyon, and set herself to finish quickly the tasks which had brought her to the Loire, and then to leave for the coast and the ship for the Tyne before anyone could prevent her. She wondered what Kate would say, and Lymond's mother Sybilla. Dismissed, though with honour, from the Queen of England's service, she could expect no Court appointment in this reign, although the next might be a different matter. Without the Queen's sister Elizabeth, Lymond would never have reached the shores of France. He had more credit there than he knew of, and his wife probably also.

But none of that, of course, would matter to Kate or to Sybilla. Only one question mattered. When is he coming home? And the answer to that might lie here, in or beside Sevigny.

Such as it was, it did not take her long to find it. With Nicholas and his servants beside her, she rode the few miles through the forest to Blois, and presented her credentials, and had opened for her the five crooked storeys of the carved wooden house known as Doubtance, with its littered forecourt and well, where Lymond had arrived, according to Archie Abernethy, after escaping from a sickbed and a conflagration which had nearly deprived him of life.

Up these twisted stairs, the Dame de Doubtance had received and sheltered him. Here had been drawn up the horoscope which, with others, had been so unaccountably missing from her other house, now Marthe's, in Lyon. From this gallery, perhaps, he had stood and looked over the rooftops to the dazzle of the River Loire and the flat horizon of trees beyond it.

She searched the house with Nicholas's help, stumping painfully from one low-beamed room to another. Marthe had been right. There was nothing here but mould and rotting wood and the shadows of old paintings lingering on the powdered plaster. Philippa walked down from the top of the house and closed the shutters one by one on the antique gold of the afternoon sunshine, and the green, whining motes of the mosquitoes and the bearded seed-quills which passed slowly, lurching; bearing life away from this dusty sepulchre.

The key Marthe had sent her fitted none of the big doors at Sevigny, nor any others in its smooth, tended purlieus. She had not told Lymond's sister that her next call was to be to the Abbey of Notre-Dame de la Guiche, where, paid by Gaultier, the nuns of St Claire had reared Marthe.

Nicholas gave her an introduction to the Abbess. But Philippa made that visit alone and returned from it to find Nicholas Applegarth, anxiety on his kind face, awaiting her.

With him was a royal messenger, with the red lion of Scotland on his doublet and a polite document, which said little, in his dispatch bag. The sharpened edge of the message betrayed itself in the spoken command which accompanied it. The Most High and Virtuous Princess Mary Stewart, crowned Queen of Scotland, sent her greetings to madame Crawford of Lymond and Sevigny, and commanded her to Court forthwith, to take her place as one of the Queen's ladies of honour.

One hoped, said the messenger smoothly, that madame la comtesse was conscious of the greatness of the honour. There was, one assumed, no question of refusing. Or such a refusal, naturally, would incline her Highness's uncles to look askance of any favours required from her husband, in a household which they must regard as henceforth tinged with disloyalty.

She wept all night, for the meeting which now must come, and which she had trusted never to be called upon to endure. Then, being Philippa, she rose and cleaned and tinted her face, and put on the gown and sleeves and cloak in which, she knew, she looked most assured and most elegant. Then, leaving Nicholas silent behind, she rode to Saint-Germain.

＊

The repose of self-command was still there, and the impervious face and the exquisite Turkish grooming when unawares Francis Crawford walked into her presence and stopped dead, his eyes open, his thoughts dispelled, it was obvious, like a mountain torrent striking a boulder. Philippa Somerville said steadily, 'Her Majesty was hoping, I think, to surprise you. It was not my intention to stay in France. But I have been honoured with an appointment it would have been difficult to refuse.'

There followed an interval during which no one spoke.

Mary Fleming closed the door, remaining inside it. Her Majesty, no doubt, had had the satisfaction of overhearing the initial results, at any rate, of her subterfuge. She hoped the Countess, setting aside her restraint, might now settle to gay conversation as she had done before, on her way southwards. The Queen had enjoyed her company. It would be a pity if an old man like Master Nostradamus should hamper them. Then Mr Crawford said, 'I understand. Some invitations are more irresistible than others.'

It was all he said. His stare had shifted to the Queen's physician. She had forgotten, like the Queen, quite how fair-skinned he was. Master Nostradamus, easing the stiff black gown over his knees, settled back in his chair and made professional conversation. 'I hear, my lord Count, that you have been appointed a Chevalier of the Order, on which I must offer you my congratulations. Were you a patient of mine, I should warn you against over-indulgence at their banquets. I have known men attend them who have never recovered.'

'They have not perhaps had the good fortune to discover the right physician,' said Francis Crawford slowly. He looked down at the feathered cap in his hand and then, with a sudden sharp gesture, threw it on the small table, where it landed between his wife and the doctor. 'I speak, I think, to the author of the most famous Centuries, the book of prophecies published two years ago?'

The comtesse de Sevigny, whose luminous brown eyes had been fixed on her husband, turned her head suddenly to look at the Queen's doctor. 'You flatter me,' said the Queen's doctor equably. 'You have heard of my humble works.'

179

He was not, Mary Fleming thought, the aesthetic figure one would have thought from his reputation. Beneath the broad black cap his greyed chestnut hair flowed with his beard over the white, faintly creased collar. His nose was long; his eyes grey under marked brows; his complexion fresh and rosy as a man half his age. Mr Crawford said, 'You are fortunate in your printer. Proof-reading, as Estienne truly said, is to typography what the soul is to the body of man.'

'You are right. I shall convey your compliments to my good friend Macé Bonhomme,' said Master Nostradamus amiably. 'Truly, a man may divorce the one from the other at his peril, and even the best are not immune to mistakes. But the wise craftsman learns from his folly.'

He remained sitting there, rubicund and cheerful, his bright gaze moving inquiringly between the Chevalier and the lady he was divorcing. Mr Crawford sat down. For the first time, Mary Fleming noticed, his eyes returned and locked, momentarily, with those of Mistress Philippa. The Countess turned to Master Nostradamus. 'You make prophecies, sir? You are, then, a caster of horoscopes?'

'But of course, Madame!' said the barber-surgeon, smiling.

'Then if you visit your printer in Lyon, you perhaps exchange visits with others of your profession?'

The barber-surgeon's beard moved once more as he smiled. 'Madame, I know everyone in Lyon. I worked there during the plague. There was only one other lady of reputation who also cast horoscopes and she, alas, is now dead. You wished to ask me about her? . . . I have to visit another case of cocco-lucchia: we might talk about this if you cared to come with me. Disease, they say, is a function of the wrath of God, but in the whooping-cough it seems rather to echo the farmyard . . . The lady you mean dwelt, I rather think, in the rue Mercière, and had a daughter called Béatris, is that not so? who died in '26—I remember it well.'

Mr Crawford did not rise. But the Countess got to her feet, and looking at him said, 'You are not interested, but I still think these things are worth pursuing. May I accept Master Nostradamus's offer?'

Then Mr Crawford did stand. He said, 'You know you have a free hand. Go with Master Nostradamus. Ask what you wish.' Across her head, he was looking at the physician. And Master Nostradamus, Mary Fleming noted, was returning the look with a kind of calm reassurance. Mr Crawford added, 'I may be gone, unfortunately, before you return. I have to be in Compiègne early tomorrow.'

Brighter than all the salves she had employed that morning, the colour burned in Philippa's cheeks. She said, 'I have some news. I had hoped to give it to you. It would save our having to meet again. I know you are busy.'

They disliked one another. It was painful to watch. Mary Fleming shifted uncomfortably. These two would never remain man and wife. Queen Catherine had been shrewder, when she had joked with M. de Sevigny, and reminded him that while he was fighting the English his sweet wife was bereft of company. Could he not arrange a fine suitor for her? He must not be selfish. He had Catherine.

And that was true also. This time, received by the Queen and her ladies, Mr Crawford had paid Catherine d'Albon at last the kind of attention she merited, and she had responded with cool and graceful formality, as a nobleman's daughter should. But when his company was claimed by others, Mary Fleming had noticed, Mademoiselle d'Albon's eyes followed him.

She thought now, for a moment, that he was going to persist in his rebuff. But something of Mistress Philippa's discomfiture must have reached him; for he said quickly, 'I beg your pardon. Of course there are matters to discuss. Send for me when you are ready.'

It was, thought Mary Fleming, watching them leave, a pity they had married, and a greater pity that Mary was bent on tampering with them. She would have to warn her mistress. Queen Catherine wanted Mr Crawford at court, with a French wife. And Queen Catherine, in Mary's view, was more worldly-wise, in this instance, than Mary of Scotland.

❊

Returning from her peripatetic interview with Master Michael Nostradamus Philippa was sick, twice, in the privacy of her own room and then, before her courage could fail her, went to find and face again the patient kindness, worse than contempt, to which Lymond had been reduced, in a profound effort to make his position quite clear without hurting her.

It could not be easy for him, either, to turn aside from the battlefield to deal with a petty family scandal and a case of sudden infatuation. One hoped that he thought of it as infatuation: the burden of withdrawing from it would at least lie on him lightly. When she found him, talking to six other people, he had the look of a man who is trying to forget a crashing headache.

But he did not mention it, and neither did she, when they were walking together out of the château and through the disarranged grounds to the new buildings laid on the terracing. He had been once prone to headaches, and she had inquired about them, she remembered, in Lyon. He had dismissed the subject. And now, entrenched grimly in the impersonal, she could not ask him.

There were workmen everywhere, painting, plastering, wheeling barrows and carrying ladders. An incessant hammering, coming from inside the raw, glistening walls, made her nerves jump. Below, among the galleried steps which led down to the river, they had been excavating the grottos. Some were already mortared into place, with the machinery draped in tarred cloth, silently waiting for some engineer to test its hydraulics. Within the arch of one romantic cavern, half planted with foliage and fitted with descending pool beds, Lymond bent and lifted a corner of canvas. 'What the hell do you suppose that is going to be?'

'I think' said Philippa, 'that it's a dragon. There's another one here with a full-blown organ in it. Would you like to play? I'll pump the air for you.'

'No,' said Lymond. He turned and walked to the half-made balustrade and stood looking down on the deserted flights of steps. 'What did Nostradamus tell you?'

Her throat hurt. Walking to the balustrade, a safe distance away from him, Philippa said, 'He did know the Dame de Doubtance. I think he knew her better than he wants us to know, just at present. I asked him if he knew where all her horoscopes were, and he said one never asked such questions of an astrologer.'

'So he has them,' said Lymond.

'I think he has. He knew a great deal about us. He says that the Lady's sister and her family were of no consequence. And although the Dame de Doubtance herself never married, she did have one daughter, Béatris, who died unmarried also, aged thirty-one.'

'In 1526,' Lymond said. 'And, one supposes, in childbirth. If she looked anything like the Dame de Doubtance it was, probably, all for the best. She was, I take it, my mother?' He spoke as if it was of no possible consequence.

'Master Nostradamus didn't know,' Philippa said. 'He didn't know anything more. Or if he did, he wouldn't tell me. But I have found out something else. The Dame de Doubtance's daughter Béatris was Marthe's mother. The records were there at the Abbey of Notre-Dame de la Guiche, where Marthe was born and stayed to be educated. In 1524, of father unknown.'

Lymond turned and looked at her. Philippa saw, steadfastly returning his gaze, that because he was thinking, the barricade between them was for the moment forgotten. He said, 'Then Marthe and I are probably full brother and sister. Was the Abbess in Scotland quite right? Is everyone right? Does Gavin, second Lord Crawford, proceed to sire brother Richard in his lawful connubial couch, and then move off smartly to lecher in Sevigny with the Dame de Doubtance's daughter Béatris while Sybilla, piqued, makes her own accommodation elsewhere? Marthe is born, daughter of Gavin and Béatris, and left to the Claires to bring up at la Guiche under the eye of the Dame de Doubtance, her grandmother. Two years later I am born, of the same parents, just as Sybilla, by coincidence, has also produced a bastard son, who unhappily dies. In his place, forced upon her by a vengeful husband Gavin, I am substituted. Three years later, in retaliation, Sybilla has Eloise, of whom Gavin is not the father, but blackmails her husband into receiving her as such. It fits.'

It fitted. It fitted so neatly, if you did not know all the people involved in it. She said, 'You assume it was Sybilla's love-child who died. But what if Gavin's son was also named Francis Crawford?'

'You feel,' said Lymond, 'that it would be convenient if I could be discovered to be the son of Sybilla, even if on the wrong side of the French blanket. But if Marthe is born of Béatris and Gavin, and I of Sybilla, how do we come to be so alike in appearance? And Béatris, you say, is Marthe's mother. I wonder if it would be wise to tell her.'

Philippa was not, at that moment, thinking of Marthe. She said suddenly, 'You said Gavin would come to disport himself at Sevigny. But there was no Sevigny in the family until you bought it. There was no reason for him to be ...' She broke off.

He had remembered who and what she was. Philippa, cold to her fingertips, saw Lymond's face change. 'Go on,' said Francis Crawford evenly.

'I was going to say, there was no reason for Gavin to be in the neighbourhood,' said Philippa slowly. 'But of course there was. I don't suppose you know what it is. But the records at Notre-Dame de la Guiche show more than the birth and up-bringing of Marthe. They show that Sybilla was at la Guiche also with the Claires until 1515: her family must have placed her as well as her sister with a religious order. There's no one there now who remembers the Clarisses of forty years ago, but the register says that she applied at the beginning of 1515 to return to secular life. Six months later she left, followed by a peasant girl called Renée Jourda from Coulanges who had served her in the convent and had become apparently at-tached to her. From la Guiche of course she returned directly to Scotland, where she married Gavin, and ten months later became the mother of her eldest child Richard.'

'The third Lord Crawford and, as it turns out, the only le-gitimate offspring. A poor record, even for Scotland,' Ly-mond said, his voice amused. But he was not amused, or he would not have missed the vital, the incredible point in all Philippa had told him.

Philippa said, 'You've forgotten the two papers, the ones Sybilla signed, confessing that the two children known as Francis and Eloise Crawford were hers, but not fathered by Gavin. They were counter-signed by three different people. One was a priest, whom we now know is dead. The second was a woman called Isabelle Roset. The third was Renée Jourda.'

'I see,' said Lymond. He turned, and lifting a fragment of broken marble from the balustrade weighed it in his hand. Then, leaning over, he tossed it over the handrail and watched it bound, exploding, from surface to surface. 'And Renée Jourda still lives with her people at Coulanges?'

'No,' said Philippa. 'She's a widow. She lives alone in a farmhouse near Flavy-le-Martel beside Ham, the town King Philip is staying in. If she still lives, that is. Chaulny was sacked.'

'And if she still lives,' said Lymond, 'she could tell me who Sybilla's lover was. But do I want to know? I am Gavin's son.'

There was a pause. Then Philippa said, staring at him sto-ically, 'I think you want to know. I don't think it matters to you what your parentage was. But I think you need to know the truth about Sybilla.'

Francis Crawford laughed. 'Perhaps I do,' he said. 'But it is an amusement I shall have to deny myself. Even the most Christian King, in time of battle, has to forgo his hunting. I may do it at leisure, when horns are in season. Or I might decide—would you ever forgive me?—that Sybilla's small eccentricities are really of no importance at all. Except, of course, that they prompted you to take so much trouble to put it all right. You love Sybilla. She is fortunate.'

Because she could not speak, Philippa said nothing.

He pushed himself from the staircase and without taking her arm, began to rove back uphill to the courtyards. 'As her foster-son, perhaps I feel differently. At any rate, I find I object quite strongly to being involved in the past any further. Will you therefore, of your kindness, take my vanity into account and let matters lie? We know most of the truth, if not all of it. The rest is better left buried. I shall go on to Compiègne, and you could leave. I suppose, for Dieppe as soon as Queen Mary allows you. It may be sooner than you expected. I think she had a fancy to try her hand at matchmaking, and she is not of the temperament to take kindly to failure.'

'No,' said Philippa. She heard what he said, but over a furious undercurrent of thought of her own. If indeed she had not been so agitated she might have realized that it was unwise to let him sense it.

'Philippa?' said Franics Crawford, and halted.

She could not pass him. She stood, her head up, and said, 'You may be quite sure I shall not stay a moment longer than I have to. I have written Kate that I am coming.'

He didn't evade her eyes this time, or turn aside, or employ any of the graceful, defensive tricks she dreaded. He said, 'You once held me, for a term, to a promise, and I honoured it. Will you do the same for me? The time has come for you to think about your own life, and not mine or Sybilla's. I want you to promise to do nothing more about this. In particular, I want your promise that you will do nothing to try and reach this woman at Flavy-le-Martel. She lives in a battlefield. If you had an army at your back, you could hardly reach her. For all you know, she may be dead already. Let her secrets go with her.'

It was unfortunate. There were some people she could successfully lie to, but Lymond was not one of them. On the other hand, if there was to be no bond between them, there was no ground either for promises. 'Am I accountable to you?' said Philippa stubbornly.

He stood without moving, considering his answer. Then he lifted his eyes once more to her face: 'No. But in the eyes of the world, I shall be responsible if you come to harm through performing a service for me. Even a service I have not asked for.' He paused and said, 'I take it that I am not to have your promise. Or that if you give it, you may feel absolved from keeping it?'

'If I give a promise, I keep it,' said Philippa sharply.

He drew a breath equally sharp, and let it go. 'I beg your pardon,' he said. 'Then in this instance——'

'In this instance, I don't accept your right to demand any promises, in spite of what you say,' Philippa said.

'Did I demand? I tried not to,' he said. 'In any case, promises won't be necessary, or any valiant excursions on your part. Since you think it important, I shall send for the lady.'

'*Send* for her?' Philippa said. 'To Flavy-le-Martel?'

'Why not?' said Lymond. 'On my roll of expenses is an impressive number of entries against intelligencers. If I can't extract one old lady from a Picardy farmhouse and have her brought to me, then I have been wasting my money. You will be content if I promise to send you the results of the inquiry? Like you, if I give a promise, I keep it.'

She let it pass, reddening, and followed him uphill through the rubble without demurring further, or noticing that the promise by which he had bound himself concerned the passing to her of Renée Jourda's information, and not the means by which he might acquire it.

She did not then know, nor did she find out in time, that to dispatch such a mission to Picardy was at that moment out of the question, as it would have been certain death for her had she gone there.

And that, if he had promised her news, there remained only one way for him to obtain it.

❦

He left Saint-Germain later that evening, to the displeasure of a great many people. Archie Abernethy, entering while his packing was being completed, was among the more outspoken. 'The French King's no' very flattered that you're leaving. The Fleming lassie says the young Queen o' Scots is fleein'. And I passed Mistress Philippa. She was all painted ower, but she'd been greetin'.'

'I'm sorry,' said Lymond. He continued to recline with his feet propped up on the window seat. 'It's a general blight of disorientation. I don't know the time, either.'

The boy strapping up the standards opened his mouth to tell him, but Archie got in first, snapping. 'Too late to set out for Compiègne. Tell the loons to unpack your baggage.'

'We're not going to Compiègne,' Lymond said. 'We're going to spend the night at Saint-Cloud. The house is empty, but we have royal permission to stay there. If you don't like it, you can stay on and follow me later.'

'And how,' demanded Archie, 'do you propose to get to Saint-Cloud? Sir?'

One of the servants, grinning where it wouldn't show, left the room with his burden. Lymond said, 'Stop making matters worse. There's a wagon leaving for Paris which will drop us there. If you would help carry down the baggage I should have rather less explaining to do. Or maybe you aren't feeling quite up to it.'

'I'm not. And ye havena taken a civil farewell of Master Nostradamus,' said Archie.

'And I'm not going to,' said Lymond.

There was a pregnant silence. Then Archie raised his voice. 'Chops me!' he said bitterly. 'But ye're a thrawn, bloody, rackle-tongued limmer. I'll come with ye to Saint-Cloud. I'll cut your meat at Compiègne. But there's a limit. I tell you now, there's a limit to what I'll do for you.'

187

CHAPTER 5

*Dans cité entrer exercit desniée
Duc entrera par persuasion.*

It was, perhaps, a mark of Francis Crawford's singular authority that he returned to Compiègne after five days' absence to find his forces well quartered, in good heart and active in harassing the enemy. Nothing untoward indeed had happened, save that Jerott Blyth, returning from a brief Paris leave, had ordered the sommelier to give him the keys of the wine cellars, and had not left his room since he used them.

Danny Hislop, irritated and envious, had made a few attempts through the keyhole to bring him to his senses, aided latterly by Adam Blacklock, newly returned from his duties in Lyon. Neither of them was present when Lymond kicked the door down, although the roar of the preceding musket shot brought them to their feet. What happened after that was mainly inaudible but Archie, questioned afterwards, conjectured that Mr Blyth had lifted his hand to his lordship, and Mr Crawford had knocked him down and kept on knocking him down until Mr Blyth was so beside himself with rage that he was nearly sober. Then Mr Crawford had thrown a bucket of water over him and told him to sit down while he told him a few things the Order forgot to mention.

It was hard to believe that Archie had not actually been present at the interview, but had merely cleaned the room up afterwards, to save Mr Blyth from shaming his valet. In the event Jerott appeared at the supper table, rather shaky and yellow as a Portugese Indian, and listened while Adam described the dying throes of the German threat to Lyon.

Rumour, which at first, naturally, had assumed Jerott's wife to be faithless, had now produced a tale which, if you knew Jerott, had all the melancholy aura of accuracy. He had returned to Paris to find the Hôtel de Séjour filled, not with lovers but with poets, painters, sculptors and musicians and in their midst, impatient with the Philistine intrusion, his beautiful and intellectual wife Marthe.

She had not been interested in Jerott, and Jerott, one could tell, had been far from tolerant of the poets and the musicians and indeed, had probably tried to boot them over the threshold.

The person to leave, of course, had finally been none other than Jerott, who after fulfilling with joyless violence an expensive number of commercial transactions throughout the night had ridden straight back to Compiègne, with understandable consequences.

Among his colleagues Adam Blacklock, himself an artist, an aesthete and a bachelor, had not been over sympathetic. Danny, who had one or two small arrangements satisfactorily current himself, was reasonably tolerant. Lymond, whose own erratic history was all too well known, was not tolerant at all; partly perhaps because the lady concerned was his step-sister, and partly because, with fourteen thousand Swiss and German troops distributed between Compiègne and Verberie, he had little time to waste playing governess to Jerott.

He had none, certainly, in which to make excursions to Flavy-le-Martel, even if he had been willing to advertise his intention, which he was not. Then, little more than a week after his return to Compiègne, there arrived at Court the Queen of Scotland's most senior uncle, the Duke de Guise, summoned from Italy to save France from disaster like Chrysostum restored by an earthquake, and discovering, as he moved from a defensible Lyon to a tranquil court and a confident and liberated Paris, that by some perverse fortune, France had been rescued without him.

Accompanied by Piero Strozzi, under whose aegis the remarkable M. Crawford had been persuaded to return from Douai, the Duke de Guise rode to Compiègne with his trumpets, his banners, his gentlemen, and congratulated M. Crawford, as his niece had foreseen he would, on his hard work, his loyalty and his competence. He then addressed the troops, distributed a limited amount of back wages, and to the sound of cheering, rode back into the castle, leaving M. de Sevigny to take Marshal Strozzi round the foreign detachments.

Taking refreshment, amiably, with the rest of M. de Sevigny's colleagues in his chamber, the Duke invited the Seigneur de Thermes, the Duke de Nevers and M. d'Estrée to describe for him the military situation as they presently each understood it.

They did so, readily. After ten minutes, a member of his own suite, with care, managed an interpolation. 'It seems to me, monseigneur, that most of this repeats the report you already have before you from M. de Sevigny.'

The Duke de Guise glanced at his papers, and lifted out, with manicured fingers, the packet of ribbon-bound documents which had lain underneath them. 'You are right. I have read this with interest. A clerkly hand, and a most meticulous attention to detail. It has been compiled, I suppose, with the expert help of all you gentlemen. Do I take it that you agree with it all?'

The Duke de Nevers looked round the comfortable room and then at the handsome bearded face opposite with its large, considerate eyes and honourable scar.

Still on the right side of forty, descendant of St Louis and Charlemagne, a bold and brave leader of men, wealthy, powerful, head of the most brilliant family in France and next to the monarch and his brother, the man who at this moment controlled France's destiny, François, 2nd Duke de Guise, was a man with whom to walk softly, whatever your rank. De Nevers said, 'The facts are correct. The projects for the future are all the results of mutual discussion. The only one we had cause to dispute with M. de Sevigny was, of course, the first; but he has inclined us to follow his view. We think the time is ripe for expelling the English from France. We think the Christian King should attack the Pale and drive the English out of Calais.'

✤

'You know, of course,' said Piero Strozzi, riding down the lines of huts and pavilions, 'that you have been sent out of the way? That the Duke de Guise has been made lieutenant-general of all French armies inside and outside the kingdom, and that his orders are to be obeyed as would the King's? That having, according to God's Vicar on Earth, accomplished in Italy little for his master's honour and still less for his own, he must urgently re-establish his reputation, and that therefore any campaign, any successes to come in this war will be immediately seized and appropriated? Did the monarch tell you that, when he made you a Chevalier of the Order? Did you know how short would be your tenure and is this, by any chance, why you are wearing so bravely the 100,000-ducat point diamond with which his Most Christian Majesty rewarded the saving of Paris? I have to warn you that it is not the Duke's habit to dispense with rivals by allowing them to leave freely for Russia. He breaks them; and they do not survive the experience.'

'I am relieved to hear it,' said Lymond. 'I thought they were planning to send me with the eight ensigns and 150 light cavalry to Scotland.' A horse coughed in the lines and he turned his head; but the man Archie Abernethy, without requiring an order, had already turned and ridden off to the horse lines. Lymond added, 'You are sorry for me, then?'

'I feel responsible for you. I didn't think you'd last a month,' Marshal Strozzi said cheerfully. 'They may insist on sending you to Scotland, or they may feel they would elicit more reliable service from M. de Thermes. M. de Thermes greatly enjoyed his last spell of duty in Scotland.'

'And you did not. You had a pike in your thigh, as I remember. In any case, I deserve more confidence, I do protest, than you are showing in me. In performance and in humility I am quite exemplary. The Duke cannot break me.

> '*O Lord I am not puft in mynde*
> *I have no scornfull eye;*
> *I do not exercise my selfe*
> *In things that be to hye.*
> *But as a chylde that wayned is*
> *Even from his mother's brest*
> *So have I Lord behaved my selfe*
> *In silence and in rest.'*

Marshal Piero Strozzi, a man with a notable sense of humour, grinned, and then gradually ceased to grin. He said. 'I have another good piece of advice to give you. Have regard to the sources of your quotations. And allow to drop your new friendship with M. d'Andelot. As the Duke de Guise requires credit with the King, so his brother the Cardinal requires credit with Rome. We are all watched. You will be no exception.'

'*Quid,*' Lymond said, '*melius Roma? Scythio quid frigore peius?* Do you have any other advice?'

'Yes,' said Piero Strozzi calmly. '*Bella gerant alii, tu, felix Scotia, nube.* Get a child on the d'Albon girl and make them

191

force your marriage through before the gap between King and Pope becomes any wider. Her father counts for something in the kingdom yet. As St André's son-in-law you would be safe. Or safer.'

'Splendid!' said Lymond gratefully. 'Unless he finds out first that I've cuckolded him.'

The bellow of Strozzi's laughter, rolling back, sang round Archie's ears as he cantered briskly to catch up with his employer. When he could speak: 'Tell me,' said the Marshal, 'why should the little Stewart want your wife for her lady in waiting?'

'At a guess,' said Lymond, to stop me marrying Catherine d'Albon. It would be convenient if, like St Baldred of the Bass, one could be reproduced in triplicate to satisfy every party. What do you think of the project for Calais?'

They had reached the outermost bounds of the camp. 'Do you need to ask?' Strozzi said. 'I wish, not that I had thought of it, but that I were as powerful as de Guise, and could claim to have thought of it. He will agree. He cannot fail. I would break my bâton if I thought otherwise. I see you recommend an immediate reconnoitre.'

'You are an engineer,' Lymond said.

Piero Strozzi's dark, Italian face, eroded with age and weather, pressed itself into a pattern of creases. 'Ah! Pride is not dead in you yet! Yes, I am an engineer. Duke François will not go: I shall be chosen. And for my companion, I will not have my choice questioned. You shall come in person and see if your unchivalrous scheme will indeed work. You do not hold Douai against me?' He looked up, smiling.

'Yes, I hold it against you,' said Lymond, and he was not smiling at all. 'But the days are evil; iniquity aboundeth, and charity waxeth cold. I shall not retaliate.'

＊

Danny Hislop was absent on a mission to demolish the outlying areas of Péronne, and Jerott with Adam as his lieutenant had two companies skirmishing round Chauny when Piero Strozzi and Francis Crawford left unescorted a few days later to ride the hundred miles north to the enemy seaport of Calais.

The Duke de Guise, having given the venture his sanction, had disappeared to report to King Henry. He had little doubt of his reception although the idea, of course, was revolutionary. One did not because of cold, disease, boredom, scarce food, bad roads and impossible transport, wage war in winter. Secure in this belief, the unpaid Spanish armies were already beginning to retrench and disperse at a time when, gathered for defence of her heartland, the French army had never been stronger. The shame of Saint-Quentin, the Duke was to tell his monarch ringingly, would be obliterated. From ruin would come the brightest jewel in France's diadem. This winter, France would be freed of her last English settlement. After two hundred years in and around Calais, the Goddams were to be driven at last into the sea.

No interest in the wholesale exploitation of this idea had, so far, been displayed by the comte de Sevigny. Riding north alone with him on his first reconnoitre the Marshal Strozzi, an ebullient man, set himself to plumb the depths of his partner's precocity.

Lymond bore it without apparent resentment. Having dissected his position on Calais, Piero Strozzi went on to pick his brains methodically on the subject of flat terrain warfare, winter campaigning and the infiltration tactics of Tartars; and listened with concentration to all the younger man could tell him of the Tsar's armies of hired Cossacks and the Janissaries, brought as children from other lands, who formed the core of the Sultan's army.

'You see: formidable!' said Piero Strozzi. 'The Turkish captain fights for himself; for his own advancement. He knows his wealth cannot be inherited. Here we buy our fighting-men over the counter, as the Tsar buys his Cossacks, you say. They come, they steal, they quarrel, they eat the countryside bare, they fight whomsoever you may point them at, even their own fellow-countrymen. Then they go home, leaving their masters satisfied or dissatisfied: and the land wasted behind them. You will never do good with a man who fights for money alone. You know that. He must covet rank and power. Or he must fight for his freedom, as your Scotsmen have done against the English. Or for the good of his soul, or the soul of his enemies, as your Russians have done against the Tartar, and the Knights of St John of Malta against the Mussulmen, and the Sultan's army and fleet against the Christians——'

'. . . Excepting the Most Christian King of France,' Lymond reminded him affably.

'Excepting, of course, the Most Christian King of France,'

Piero Strozzi accepted with equanimity. '*Contre les loups,* the Constable says, *il se faut aider des chiens.* And his merchants agree. Where would religion be, M. mon compagnon, without expediency? But he is the best fighting man that I know, he who goes to war for his eternal salvation.'

'There is another,' Lymond said. 'He who goes to war from revenge.'

The dark face did not trouble to turn to him. 'It is true,' said Piero Strozzi. 'Rangoni taught me well. I have fought in Luxemburg and Mirandole and, given the troops, I could have saved Siena . . . my God, what I could tell you about that! You were at Tripoli. But at Siena they were selling rats at an écu apiece before they surrendered. I have been General of the Galleys of France as my brother Leone was, and for the same reason: to throw out the usurpers who caused my father to die in Florence. And to free Florence, as your nation has striven to free itself from England. You disapprove, Scotsman?'

'Leone is dead,' Lymond said. 'He might have been Grand Master of the Knights of St John and swept the Middle Sea free of Osmanlis, but he chose to put Florence first. The Knights had reason to complain, but if motives count, that must surely weigh on the credit side. There are men, as you say, who fight for rank or power or money. Or even for exercise and amusement, once the hunting season has ended.'

Then the swarthy face with its dark curls did turn. 'So the fish dislikes water. You have about you a stink of Malta yet, mon petit ami. Do you spit on your grandfather, who fought all his life in France and in Italy for love of war and of Albany? And lost all his beauty for it. I saw him in Italy, with his fine yellow hair parted for him by a battle-axe. When he told you tales of his prowess, did you say, *But what were your motives?* Or have you forgotten him?'

'I remember the scar,' Lymond said. 'And I remember his funeral. I was three years old at the time.'

'Devil take you,' said Piero Strozzi warmly. 'You are the only man in this country who can make me forget I am twice his age, and then remind me of it like a mule's hoof in the belly. But I forgive you. If you talk too much, you also refrained from bringing the town guard about me at Douai. Tell me one thing. For what reason do you wish to return to Russia, to become again commander of all her armies?'

There was a short silence. Then Lymond said, 'To enforce peace.'

'Ah. And then?' said Piero Strozzi.

'And then to rule,' Lymond said.

*

They had much in common, aside from the professional gossip: the tales of other men's mistakes and eccentricities and all the low comedy which accompanies warfare. Exchanges of such a kind carried them to Cléry where, in a neglected barn beside a burned-down farmhouse, they found fresh straw and, stored behind some rotting vegetables, a chest holding a change of clothes, a napkin of food, and a wineflask. How they came there, Strozzi did not inquire and Lymond volunteered no explanation: his intelligence service, or, if you preferred it, the number of spies he was paying were his own affair.

They left Cléry rested and refreshed, since it is a stupid man who carries a slow brain and tired muscles into danger. The rest of their journey indeed was enlivened by lurid incidents in which one or other of the King's trusted commanders took a fancy, it seemed, to put the whole enterprise to risk for the sake of an hour's entertainment. On one occasion, to do with a fisherman, a smithy, and three German archers from Arras (*'Eine Deutscher bulet wie ein bawar'*) Lymond rendered even the greatest practical joker in Italy speechless with combined hysteria and anxiety. Only later, when it was all over, did Piero Strozzi perceive that, after all, Francis Crawford was exacting retribution for Douai.

Then they were at Ardres, and ahead lay the Pale, the frontier of the English-held hinterland of Calais.

They crossed it at Leulinghen, whose thatched church once straddled the frontier, its French door in the nave, its English door in the choir. They left after early Mass by the choir door in their coarse jerkins and dusty boots, showing at Sandingfield a pass thoughtfully provided at Ardres by their host for the night. His name had been Haines, and his cousin, Lymond said, leased all the fishing in the marshes between Hâmes and Ardres. He had supplied them also with a mule and a small wicker cart containing six barrels of apples, which they collected outside the church and trundled nine miles through low hills and over the causeway to the moated walls of the city of Calais.

They showed their pass again to cross the drawbridge with the rest of the crowd at the Bullengate and made their way at a dilatory pace to the market place, displaying on the way a happy if illegal propensity to sell apples to any passer-by who requested them. At intervals the mule, a stubborn creature, chose a stance and defied all their efforts to shift it, ending in an act of total resistance at the drawbridge wardhouse of the citadel.

The tang of the apples and the sight of the red waxen mounds were too much for the pikemen on guard there. Yelling and whacking with vigour, Lymond jumped round his mule to find his fruit disappearing in handfuls behind jacks and into stuffed breeches.

He made no effort to consult this trading partner. Howling, he snatched the shapeless hat from his rough hair and jumped on it. Then, stick whirling, he charged at the soldiery.

It was afterwards revealed to Marshal Strozzi that he must have seen the approach of the Knight-Porter and his fifty armed soldiers, returning from closing the Millgate. At the time, the most distinguished muleteer in Christendom stood with the reins in his clutch, breathing stertorously, while his crazy companion ricocheted like an unwashed puppet from cuirass to mailed fist to the flailing wood of reversed and jocular halberds. A couple of hackbutters got to work with their boots and the wicker cart shuddered and tilted. With a bellow, Piero Strozzi dropped the reins and rushed into battle.

'Bleedin' butter-boxes!' said with injured astonishment one of the three men he knocked sideways. 'Bloody Flemish thievin' bastards! Gabbling cutpurses!' He got up, revealing the fact that he had a certain minor authority. He proceeded to prowl up and down in front of the apple-sellers who, in the grip of seven men, had flailed themselves to a spreadeagled standstill.

'I should make faggots of your bones, shouldn't I, me little ugglesome allies? You lay your sticky trotters on us, who come to fight your wars for you? I think you need to be taught a little right feeling, eh brothers? So on your knees, Flemings. And prime your chops, Flemings. You're going to lick the road clean for me and my fellows to walk on. And you're going to pray like two English gents, while you're at it. I'll tell you what to pray. You say, *God save the Queen and f— Flanders.*'

'You bloody donkey!' yelled Lymond. 'D'you think I've

196

been swearing in Walloon? When were you last in London? Never bloody saw it. I wager. Well, I tell you something. I was born by the Pissing Conduit at St Christopher's Parish, and I can tell an English soldier from a parcel of hop-picking yokels from Surrey. What's more, I know milord Wentworth.'

'Do you, now?' said an educated voice. The Knight-Porter and the fifty men at arms had arrived. The grip on the two apple-sellers slackened. Lymond looked up, his two-day stubble stippling his baleful, unwashed countenance.

'That is,' said Lymond sulkily, 'I had an aunty that cleaned out his jakes for him. We're honest traders, my lord. The gentlemen had no call to set on us. We sell sweet apples to those that'll pay for them, but we're poor men. If you take our goods from us by force, why, you take our livelihood, and that's not an Englishman's way. Leastways, not when I was in London.'

'It is still not an Englishman's way,' said the Knight-Porter repressively. 'Release these men. Replace the apples. Set the wagon to rights. You say your wares are for sale?'

'Yes, milord,' said Lymond. He dived nervously for his hat and clutched it, turning it round and round against his coarse jerkin. 'All save a barrel bespoke for the Ruisbank.'

'What price are you asking?' said the Knight-Porter.

'Two sols, milord,' said Lymond. 'Tuppence a pound, you would say. And fit for her highness at Greenwich, bless her dear, saintly heart.' Piero Strozzi, rubbing his arms, let his mouth fall dumbly open.

'We shall take them,' said the Knight-Porter curtly. 'And at three sols, to compensate for your pains. Can you turn the animal round, and bring the wagon into the courtyard?'

Lymond hesitated. 'There's a barrel of them for the Ruisbank. We made a bond on it,' he said.

The Knight-Porter had grown impatient. 'We shall see that you are helped to deliver it. Do you want to take my offer or not?'

'Oh. Aye. Your lordship,' said Lymond, 'is a real gentleman. Milord, you've struck a blow for the honour of England, and when you see those dear green fields again, mind and salute them for me and my uncle.'

Later, sitting below Ruisbank Fort waiting for the ferryman to take them back across the harbour to Calais, Piero Strozzi said, 'I have a strong objection to being described as your uncle.'

'I beg your pardon,' said Lymond. 'I thought perhaps you would prefer uncle to father. It wasn't, incidentally, the regular Knight-Porter. That was Sir Henry Palmer.'

'Ah,' said Piero Strozzi. 'The man who has helped to hold Guînes while my lord Grey has been away with King Philip?'

'Yes. I knew Tommy, the older brother. He held Guînes and Calais appointments as well. Meddled in politics, however, and paid for it.'

'I had heard. I had also heard that my lord Grey of Wilton was in trouble at the same time, but was reckoned too good a soldier to execute, even though he might lean to the Reformers. The English Pale is a useful exile, it seems to me, for the nation's more recalcitrant citizens.'

Piero Strozzi turned and looked at his placid companion. 'You took some trouble to get me this morning to Mass. Can it have escaped your memory that I refused a Cardinal's hat in my youth? That Pope Leo was my mother's brother? That I have a sister an Abbess and a brother a Cardinal at this moment?'

'How could I forget? It was you,' said Lymond, 'who mentioned expediency.' Behind them, the crenellated tower of the fort cut the sky. The garrison had been surprised to receive a barrel of apples, but delighted with it. Rumour had been correct: food stocks were low. And behind the fort lay the long line of the beach and the sea, whose murmur came to them even here, in the busy port. As he spoke to Strozzi he was filing facts as he knew the other was doing: facts about the number and size of the boats in the harbour; the position of the fishing fleet, the notorious drop in the tide, the gun emplacements along the walls and at the Watergate entrance to the city; the flood gates which controlled the intake for the moat of the citadel.

To the right, reeds in plumed, pale banks moved like drowned horses' manes in the marshes. There was water everywhere. Save for the sand dunes the land was an endless, sludge-coloured siade, and above it, the wide pale sky, as wide and as light as in Russia.

'I stand on neither side. I fight with Lutherans and against them. I lead the Pope's army, and kiss his hands, if he will give me soldiers to throw against Florence. I am a man with no God,' said Piero Strozzi. 'And you? You paid lip service at the altar. But I hear that those who would have you in Scotland have so far lit on no inducement.

'Is it conscience which holds you? Yet I believe that the Queen-Regent allows those of the Reformed Faith to live within her daughter's kingdom. Or is it a family quarrel? But your brother the Baron I recall as a charming, a moderate man, and nine years ago your mother the Dowager made me welcome and spoke of you as no man or woman, I can tell you, has ever spoken of me. And yet ... my father was a true man. Tortured, he took his own life so that he would not dishonour himself. He wrote on the walls of his cell, "If I did not know how to live, I shall know how to die." '

The rowing boat was approaching over the sage-grey reflections of the walls of Calais, with behind the sturdy stalk of the Watch Tower and the square tower of the belfry among all the steep tiled roofs and spires. On the east walls the windmills buzzed, active as thread in the stiff breeze, which made fingerprints in the pale water and had silted up every crevice and gradient around them with a thick grouting of peach-coloured sand. Lymond said, 'I too stand on neither side but ... not, I think, without a God. If I went back, I should have to choose.'

'And is that a bad thing?' said Piero Strozzi. 'It is difficult. It would be more gratifying, I can see, to rule all Muscovy than a nation smaller than Paris, with Mother France looking over your shoulder. Politics and religion are no longer fingers on the same hand, and your Queen-Regent's tolerance may not last for ever. Your country may be governed well in the name of a religion you cannot agree with: or badly by those who worship as your conscience also instructs you. You may have to choose between God and your country. Or you may have to choose differently from your family, who wish you to come back. Is this what you fear?'

'Part of it,' Lymond said. 'It is all rather more complex than you imagine.' He got to his feet.

Piero Strozzi rose likewise. 'And your family? If the new religion brings trouble, and your brother were to die, who will they turn to?'

'There is no doubt, of course, of the answer,' said Francis Crawford. 'But considering where we are at the moment, the question perhaps is academic. May I assist you, as my aged uncle, into the boat? I have a note from Senarpont which says that at the sign of the *Trois Têtes* is a very good inn. I suggest we now go and turn our apples into sour beer and naughty doings among citizens and mechanics and other lubberly loiterers.'

As it turned out, the beer at the *Trois Têtes* was excellent. Piero Strozzi, forced against nature to remain dumb, watched his companion rapidly and expertly become drunk, thereafter striking up a bosom friendship with a number of the aforesaid citizens and mechanics, including a brewer called Pigault who described, with a nice turn of phrase, the entire sluice system from Newnham Bridge to Gravelines which, if the silly bastards at the Citadel ever opened it, would drown all next summer's crops and let in salt water round the town that would spoil all the brewing and cause such an uprising that Tommy Wentworth and the bloody Council wouldn't know which to face first—the French or the Calaisiens. The only soldier among them was Willie Grey, and he was away with the foreigners leaving Braying Teddy to hold Guînes, and Guînes, said Mr. Pigault morosely, was a damn sight worse off than Calais.

He called King Philip a number of names, and embarked on a series of dirty songs all of which Lymond appeared to know in several versions. The session ended when Mr Pigault, full of his own beer, slid comfortably under the table. From there, after brotherly leavetakings, the applesellers made their way to the market-place where, under the Gothic towers of the Staple, they filled their cart with cloth, cheeses and tallow and began to make their leisurely way again by Rigging Street and the Shafts and Cock Lane to the Millgate, the east door out of Calais.

Above the portals, a two-line verse had been cut, with some optimism:

> *Il sera vraisemblable que Calais on assiege*
> *Quand le fer ou le plomb nagera comme liège.*

When they were free to speak openly: 'Have you,' inquired Marshal Piero Strozzi of M. le comte de Sevigny, Chevalier of the Order, 'ever witnessed iron to swim like a cork?'

'No,' said the comte de Sevigny soberly. 'But Nature's laws are beyond a simple man's reckoning. If I were asked to wager, I would say that before the new year, iron will swim; and Englishmen with it.'

They left the cob and wagon at Ardres and slept at Cléry

in the same ruined barn, where the food and drink had been replenished and a sum of money added, divided into two purses. Healthily tired, with beer, with laughter, with riding, Marshal Strozzi slept instantly.

Lymond was later in quenching the candle. Waking at first light, Piero Strozzi found by his pallet a neat stack of paper, closely written, with beside it some cards bearing intricate plans: of the Citadel; of Fort Ruisbank; of the four gates and the bulwarks of Calais. He was examining them when Lymond came back into the barn fully dressed and picked up his sword.

Strozzi said, 'I may be old enough to be your unfortunate uncle, but I have my powers of memory yet. Why waste a night's sleep? I shall, if you wish, applaud your skill as a cartographer. My little friend Nicolas de Nicolay produced a plan of Guînes just as pretty. You were his pupil?'

'I was taught by an Englishman. The notes are an aide-memoire, that's all. You will have a great deal to add. I wished you to take them because,' said Francis Crawford, 'you are going straight back to Compiègne, and it will be two days before I can join you. I have some business in the country to attend to.'

'So!' said Piero Strozzi. He sat very still, his broad naked shoulders, stuck with straw, glistening in the dim light. 'A woman?'

'I said business,' said Lymond. 'Remember? The intellectual passion that drives out sensuality.'

'Then a little more spying?' said Piero Strozzi slowly. 'You are in bad country for it. You had better tell me where you are going. Dressed like that, you will be killed: you will not be taken prisoner.'

'Private business,' said Lymond. 'I know the risks. If I don't return, you may give Monseigneur de Guise my deepest apologies. I enjoyed our excursion. I have translated into Italian, by the way, the song you didn't understand. If you ever come face to face with King Philip, you can sing it to him.'

Piero Strozzi roared, 'Body of God, I shall!' and stood up, and slapped the other man on the shoulder and watched as he swung into the saddle and set off through the low scrub on a track which seemed to lead south-east, between Péronne and Saint-Quentin.

It was not a direction Piero Strozzi fancied. A stretch of flat, ravaged farmland punctuated by strong forts: some held by French and some by the varied troops of King Philip. It had been their plan to return to Compiègne via Péronne, where a troop of pioneers and hackbutters under the man Hislop had been given work to attend to. Escorted by this band, it should have been simple to escape or outface the enemy.

The crazy Scotsman had taken no food or wine with him, which meant he was not going far. His motives could not be treachery. They were almost certainly, in spite of his denials, to do with a woman. Which meant untidy watch-keeping. Which meant possible capture and confession, and the end of all their hopes of Calais, unless M. de Sevigny had the will power of Philippe Strozzi, which was unlikely.

Cursing, Piero Strozzi dressed, packed and left very soon after his companion, but unlike his companion, did not give a wide berth to Péronne. Instead, he recruited six men, including Danny Hislop, and set out to track down his imprudent late fellow-traveller.

CHAPTER 6

Dedans les puys seront trouvez les os,
Sera l'inceste commis par le maratre
L'estat changé, on guerra bruit et los,
Et aura Mars attendant pour son astre.

The journey upon which Francis Crawford was embarked
had indeed to do with a woman, but was one which he made
with no prospect of pleasure or profit, but solely for the sake
of a promise. Because an extraordinary degree of self-control
in public and in private through the years had become second
nature to him, he made it without deviating and without
weighing the consequences; or indeed anything but the obstacles which lay before him.

These were not few. Before he had been riding ten
minutes, he had to dismount and hold his horse silently in a
tangle of dew-soaked undergrowth while a troop of mercenaries clattered by, the red cross plain in the lavender haze of
the morning. For some reason, King Philip's troops were
moving early. After that, he crossed open fields only when it
was necessary, taking shelter at the first sound of men's
voices, or the chime of bridle and spurs, or the vibration
which meant hooves beating a way over mud-clods.

There were very few ploughed fields. Wagon trains had
spent the autumn rolling through Picardy, and wheeled cannon, and ensigns of armed men on thick Flemish horses. At
first no doubt, they had paid for the apples they took from
the orchards, and the hay from the barns, and the cabbages
from the kailyard and the nets of onions hanging from the
thatched eaves. They had even paid, perhaps, for the daughters and sisters they tumbled.

And then, of course, however skilled the command and
however well-intentioned the discipline, they would cease to
pay. The farms were deserted; even the bigger ones, built like
a fortress, with walls and towers enclosing the pond and the
barns and the farmhouse. Many were blackened with fire.

Others, the stage for some bitter encounter, had been reduced by both Spaniards and French to a haphazard pattern of stone, picturesque as grey Mauresque fretwork against the red fire of roseships and the ashen drift of seeding blossom from the shelves of marauding black creeper.

He moved from place to place down the swampy track of the River Somme, wary of the flights of small birds; crouched behind some garden wall close to the pale yellow of charlock, or a bed of forgotten pansies, gold and red and dark, bloomy grapecolour or again, in the rushes beside one of the marshy ponds which glittered through all the flat country, with moorhen tracking its jade lichened surface. By then, he had freed and sent off his horse. With the country alive with movement such as this, he was better on foot.

It took him until midday, using all the more primitive skills he was master of, to get himself just north of Ham, the new-taken fortress occupied by King Philip, and the seat of his army in Picardy under the Duke of Savoy, his chief general. Expect that the flag flying now from its square tower was not the personal standard of Philip, by the grace of God king of Spain, England, Sicily, Naples and Jerusalem. The distant trumpets, the frantic marching and counter-marching were all now quite explicable. Philip, last to make his stately entrance upon the battlefield, had that morning become the first to make his stately exit. In case, one week later, he would be forced to leave at a gallop.

It was news, Francis Crawford recognized, to lift Strozzi's heart. It meant his own intuition was correct in thinking the time had come to plan this push against Calais. It meant that de Guise and Strozzi together could force it to a conclusion. Senarpont, the Governor of Boulogne, was a good man, and would see to the detail. In the long stretches of waiting that morning, when thought like a madman in a quarry had to be manacled, he had seen quite clearly the whole possible sequence of action, down to the last company of Schwartz-reiters; the last flamboyant eruption of ambitious noblemen.

And now, so close to his destination, he must think of the business at hand. He must try to find the farm of the woman Renée Jourda, who had once been a village girl of Coulanges and who, ten years before he was born, had left her home at Coulanges to follow to Scotland the lady adored for her wit and her beauty called Sybilla Semple, who had broken short her stay at the nunnery. Who had married Gavin Crawford, the second Baron of Culter. Who had given birth to Richard her heir, who now held the title in Scotland. And who had brought himself up with joy, with laughter, with care, as her second son; although it appeared . . . it was certain, that he was not. A circumstance with which, not being a child, he would come to terms, no doubt, presently.

There were only three farms round the ruins of Flavy-le-Martel, and two of them were empty, except for a starved dog tied to a ring which cried at him as he freed it, its bones arching through its stretched skin. It ran to a pool of green mud and devoured it, before sliding off into the undergrowth. Francis Crawford watched it, and then moved out and on to the last.

The faded sign said *Proyart*; but that meant nothing. If Renée Jourda the village girl had a farm, it was because she had married.

Whoever had married the master of this domain had not led an easy life. Once, a fence might have surrounded it. Now it was fenced only by a ring of dark trees, and the steep, tiled roofs which crowded round the unkempt yard and marbled pond were gapped and ribbed like unravelled jersey-cloth. Lymond walked quietly forward.

The trees in the orchard were not ripe yet for robbing. They stood, brooding and ancient above their rotting wickets of poles, upholding their fruit like green lanterns; and behind them, a row of dry spires strung on withies showed where the vines had been. The house itself was closed and shuttered and cold and the well bucket had dust and dead leaves in it.

A sharp rattle made him look round. A wood pigeon high over his head had flown to its hole above the hayloft door of the barn, paused for a moment, and then vanished inside. Now that he stood still, he could hear the muffled throaty rou-couling. It made him walk to the barn and try the door, whose bolt had been driven home recently, before the webs which muffled the windows had had time to form again over it. He drew it aside slowly and stepped over the threshold.

It smelt of cow. There was no fodder inside but the dung of many weeks, mixed with filthy straw; and in one corner a stack of wood: not the well-mannered cradle of logs one saw outside every yard in Compiègne but boughs hacked and torn and covered still with a shawl of dead columbine. The blunt axe which had cut them stood still against the wall. Outside somewhere, an animal cried out in pain.

But not, this time a dog. And with a call which he did not need to live in a castle to analyse.

With a gesture Jerott would have recognized, Francis Crawford drew off his shapeless hat and threw it high to hang on the topmost twig of the thorn boughs. Then, walking over the yard, he wrenched the bucket free of its framework and swinging it, made for the coppice.

When he came back, the yard was quite silent. Even the pigeons had ceased their low murmur. Above the pond-water a haze of mosquitoes trembled and fussed in the sunshine. Lymond walked to the low windows under the wavering eaves, and laid down the pail. Then, slowly and firmly, he rapped on the worn, sun-bleached shutters.

'Madame,' he said. 'I have brought you milk from your cow.'

Silence. If anyone was there, it must be a woman. A man would be dead, or would have escaped. A man would not have been reduced to cutting that pitiful bundle of firewood, or have tethered the little dun cow where she could graze concealed, and wait for her mistress. If it was Renée Jourda behind those closed shutters, she must be seventy years old, or over.

But that would be highly unlikely. Out of three farms, Renée Jourda need not belong to this one. She had probably been taken away long ago. Or had died, taking her young secrets with her. He tapped again on the shutters and said, 'Madame, I come from Compiègne, and not from the Spaniards. I wish to help you. Come to your window, and I shall give you your milk.'

Nothing stirred. He was talking, it seemed, to himself: to an empty house, in the autumn sunshine, in a land where any soldier could claim a king's fortune for taking him.

I have your mind in my palm. I will crush it. A shiver ran through his nerves and his skin tingled, as if fine wires had moved beneath it. The light, familiar throb in his head, paired with his heartbeats, began to come thicker and faster. He took a moment, breathing quietly, to subdue it; then gripping the edge of the shutters with hard and powerful fingers, he wrenched them both open.

Framed in the lozenged window behind was a face, grey and blurred as if printed on muslin. A face which dwindled, its mouth a dark square as his hands laid their grasp on the windowframe: which emitted, without shape, a long wavering wail as he broke the catch and opened the windows, so low that he knelt to look through them.

It was a small room inside, bare of comfort and almost bare of furnishing. The used air of old age and sickness came lingering out from the window. Below the sill inside was drawn up a pallet, the linen sheet stained and wrinkled, the coverlet sagged on the floor. The woman who had been lying there stood now, her knotted hands gripped white together; her face, framed with soiled cap and tangled grey hair turned to the window; her eyes round and pearly as frog-spawn.

It could be no one but Renée Jourda. And Renée Jourda was quite blind.

Realization withdrew from him the power of movement. He bent his head, and when it returned, and she had fallen silent he said, his hands motionless on the stonework, 'Madame Jourda, I am not here to harm you. I am alone. If you like, I shall throw my sword at your feet, and you may take it.'

Renée Jourda said, 'Give me your sword.'

He had hoped she would not ask it, but there seemed to be no alternative. So he unbuckled the blade and holding it carefully, cast it through the open window so that it fell beyond the bed, on the broken tiled floor of the chamber. The old woman bent. Her hand, moving straight to the sound, uncoiled like a willow wand and touched, warily, the metal pommel. With both hands she lifted and couched the sword on the only tall chair in the room, standing still with the wall at her back and the point of the blade aimed straight and true at the window. Then she said, 'You may come in, Mr Francis Crawford.'

He paused again, momentarily, before easing himself deliberately through the casement. His headache had begun again. He said, speaking distinctly, 'You are not well. Keep the sword, but sit in the chair. I shall bring you some milk, if you tell me where I may find a pitcher. When did you last eat?'

'Yesterday,' I think,' said the old woman. She hesitated; then after a while lifted the heavy sword tremulously from the chair and supporting herself, moved round and dropped into the worn seat. 'They brought a piece of seethed fowl the day before, and some ale, and some cut bread. Today they must have forgotten. I have not been well. It was too far to milk Lisa.'

'Don't they milk her for you?' said Lymond. He had found

a vessel of sorts, and dipping it into the pail, brought it dripping from the window and knelt before her. 'Keep the sword. I shall hold the cup for you.'

But after a moment she freed a hand and took the cup from him, drinking greedily but drawing, at the end, a ragged handkerchief from her sleeve to wipe her sunk mouth. A streak of raw colour had come into her cheeks. 'Without my friends, I cannot keep tidy,' she said. 'The men mean well, but they are rough. And of course, I have not told them about Lisa. A cow, to a Spaniard? They would have her to Ham in a minute.'

'The Spaniards are looking after you?' Lymond said. There was no food in the house. On the other hand, he knew where to find some fat pigeons. He went to the window and lifted in the pail of new milk, drawing the shutters nearly closed once more behind him.

The sudden dimness made no difference to her. She looked in the direction of his movements, a little snatch of fright on her face and said, 'Yes. To an old woman, all foreigners are kind, are they not? All I miss is a fire. When they are here, I have a fire, and it warms me. The evenings are cold.' The sightless eyes fixed on him. 'Would you light one?'

The fire was ready laid on her hearth: neatly set, as a soldier would do it. And beside it was a rack of fine logs, their white faces clean-cut by a woodsman. In one respect, the foreigners had looked after her. He said, striking tinder and lighting it, 'How did you know my name? Because I called you Madame Jourda?'

'That is my nom de jeune fille,' said the old woman. 'M. Proyart died twenty years ago. My neighbours were good.' A stir of merriment, for a second, moved the seamed face. Forgetful, she loosed her grip on the sword and when it fell, stiffened for a moment. But then, when nothing happened, she smiled again and left it there. 'I should not be entertaining a young man. You are a young man? If you are Mistress Sybilla's son, then you must be.'

The fire was burning well. 'You remember Mistress Sybilla?' Lymond said, without turning.

The thin voice had turned to anxiety again. 'She didn't blame me,' said Renée Jourda. 'When I said I must leave Scotland, she didn't blame me. "Renée," she said, "France is your homeland, and you miss it. We shall see each other again. Perhaps, if I need your help, you will come to me."

208

. . . But it was not Scotland I disliked. It was her husband. Gavin Crawford is a name to be loathed. She hated him. And Leonard Bailey, his kinsman. Half the evil in that house came from Bailey. I would not stay at Midculter.'

'So you came back to France,' Lymond said. 'And you did help Mistress Sybilla again. Did you not? Ten years later?'

She smiled. Firelight, blossoming in the worn darkness, gave her face for a moment the thin, pretty shallowness it must once have possessed when she left her home to follow a wilful young mistress back to her wedding in Scotland; and then homesick, had abandoned her to settle here, with M. Proyart and those good neighbours who had now abandoned her.

'When she had the baby?' said Renée Jourda. 'Such a baby! The father had bought her a jewel of a house, there in Paris. It was where they stayed when he was free, and when she could come from Scotland. She was to arrive for the birth of a child. She wrote to ask me to come to Paris. My sister Isabelle who was widowed was already there. She was housekeeper to them both from the start, and kept the house clean and warm, and saw to the bills. She still does it.'

'Isabelle Roset?' said Lymond. It was very hot by the fire. He moved to a low stool and sat there, breathing evenly. It took all his willpower and a good deal of his attention, which was why he was doing it. He said, 'Who does she keep house for?'

There was a rattle outside. The pigeons, fickle passengers, were departing again from the hayloft. The sightless eyes turned on Francis Crawford. 'Why, no one,' said Renée Jourda. 'Only Mistress Sybilla keeps it, for memory's sake. The child was too young to be taken away. I said it should not be taken away, but they would have it. A boy. They called it Francis. She would have no other name.' Fright, for the moment banished, came suddenly back to the empty face once more. 'Your name! But I didn't tell anyone!'

'It doesn't matter,' Lymond said gently. He paused and then said, 'I may not even be the child who was born that day. Did you hear if he lived? You and Isabelle were asked to sign a paper about him.'

She stared in his direction. 'He was too young to travel. But he must have lived. There was a son named Francis Crawford reared at Midculter. Isabelle told me.'

'But not Mistress Sybilla's,' Lymond said. It seemed as if it

209

had all been going on for a very long time. He kept his voice level, and patient, and drained of all shade of emotion. 'It seems likely that the baby you saw in Paris died just after birth. I have seen the death certificate. Then she adopted me as her son, and brought me up by the same name. It makes no difference. There is only one thing that none of us knows. We do not know who bought the Paris house for Mistress Sybilla. We do not know the name of the father of the baby son born to her there. But you did, did you not? It was on the paper you signed.'

'Of course,' she said. 'I knew him. He came to see her in the convent. That, you know, was how they met. His house was near by. Ah, pretty, pretty the pair they made!' She strained towards him. 'You don't hold it against her?'

Lymond said slowly, 'I told you. I was born of a different mother.'

'But with the same name?' Her uncomprehending face remained fixed on his, and then slowly cleared. 'Of course. Then you are Béatris's child, by the same father.'

And she spoke in the same flat and querulous voice, the name he had borne in his mind like a slave-brand through most of the long, solitary years of his life.

It was of no importance. Birth did not matter: heredity was merely a hurdle; one was what one made of oneself: that and no other. Ask one more question, and there would be nothing left to ask, ever, that mattered to him.

But he did not ask it. Instead, he became aware that, sitting opposite him, Renée Jourda had been gripped by a sudden excitement. She said, 'You say you are not a son of Mistress Sybilla's? Then you did not come here to kill me?'

Because of the headache, or because of the state of his thoughts he did not analyse that as quickly as he should have done. He said, 'Of course not. Why should you think I would? To keep my parentage secret?' And then, as his brain took hold, he said, 'Madame Jourda, did someone tell you this? You knew my name. Were you expecting me?'

She sat very still. And now the fire did not renew the illusion of youth but lit, without pity, the blank face of age and fatigue and helpless futility. Renée Jourda said, 'They said they would kill me if I warned you.'

'The Spaniards,' Lymond said; and she did not contradict him. He bent, and lifted his sword and walking quickly and quietly, made his way to the window. It was not her fault.

But he should have remembered that pigeons do not fly for no reason.

The yard was empty but the bolt of the barn door was not driven home, as he had left it.

He left the window as quietly as he had reached it. 'I'm sorry. Goodbye, Madame Jourda,' said Lymond; and unlocking the door, walked out, sword in hand, into the sunshine.

No one rushed on him; no one fired, no one shouted. He continued to move unhurriedly across the strewn yard until he reached the barn door, and if he paused there, it was just for an instant. Then he pulled the door open and walked inside without hesitation.

'Christ, that was quick,' said Piero Strozzi. 'If you needed a woman as much as that, I could have got you a pair at the *Trois Têtes* in Calais. Now we've come all this way, are you going to let us all in to see her?'

He was there, grinning as he lolled in his peasant clothes on the rack of dry boughs, Lymond's discarded hat crammed on his dyed Italian curls. Beside him, less at ease, was Daniel Hislop. And standing about in the sodden straw were half a dozen of Hislop's men from Péronne.

Piero Strozzi said, 'I know. It is bad enough to have one foolish general flaunting his field-skills like a new-made ensign drummer-boy. We all wish to show the soldiery that we can, if need be, cook better puddings than the cook does. I think, however, if you have finished, we should return to Compiègne. The war will be cooling without us.'

Lymond said, 'Did you track me here?'

'Yes,' said Danny. The hair moved on his scalp at the tone of the question.

'When did you arrive?'

Piero Strozzi also had stopped grinning. 'When you took the milk in.'

'Did you see anyone else?'

'No one. No one else followed you. Of that you may be sure. And there is no one else round the farm. Why?' said Piero Strozzi sharply.

'We are in a Spanish trap,' Lymond said. 'Meant for me. But now, of course, they will have you also. I suppose you have all the bloody Calais notes in your jerkin?'

'I left them at Péronne. The girl betrayed you?' said Strozzi. He was moving already, his sword drawn, his eyes on the windows.

'It's an old woman. I lit a fire for her. Better puddings,' said Lymond flatly. Danny had never seen him so totally devoid of all that could be called human emotion. 'Have you horses?'

'No,' said Strozzi. 'And it is too late, in any case. Here they come.'

They were, indeed, Spanish troops; thirty horsemen, under a captain. The Duke of Savoy knew the value of the prize he intended to capture. They combed the trees with their groined shining helmets and took their places in a ring round the buildings, busy as clockwork artefacts of wax and quicksilver. Then the captain rode into the yard and with ten men dismounted beside him, called upon *el conde Criafordo* to surrender.

'They have left their horses in the trees,' said Lymond. 'And they don't know as yet that there are eight of you. You should be able to do it. You must have got your bloody bâton for something other than scoutcraft.'

Which made Marshal Strozzi's temper rise, and events happen commensurately quickly. Danny, obeying orders, kept his mouth shut and saw to it that his six soldiers understood that they were in a good deal more danger from their two leaders than they were from the enemy. And that when they were told to catch pigeons, it meant that they had to catch pigeons, and be quick about it.

In the yard, Captain Alferez Carasco was obeying his orders also. The *Herrervelos* had not been entrusted with his work, nor had Count Wittgenstein's Germans. Only Captain Carasco's light horse could be depended upon to bring back alive and well the important general who, unlikely though it seemed, was to visit this old peasant in person.

Even after the intelligence reached them, the Duke had refused to believe it. Then they had called on the old woman and found that indeed she knew the name of el conde Criafordo and had been nurse long ago to his mother. She was told what to do if the general visited her. And at the first sight of her smoke he, Captain Carasco, had acted.

When, after three summons, there was no answer from the hidden man, Captain Carasco ordered his hackbutters to fire a volley through the shut door of the farmhouse and then, with men on either side, burst it open and began to search through it. He came out redfaced and addressed his lieutenant. 'The woman says he left. He guessed we were coming.'

'*Mi capitán*, no one has left the farm,' the man said. 'It is not possible.'

Which was precisely when the flutter of wings from the hayloft drew their attention to the pigeon holes under the barn roof. His good humour restored, Captain Carasco gave the required orders.

They ringed the barn first; and then called for surrender. Next, after firing some shots, six soldiers burst in and gathered on the wet straw under the trapdoor. Above their heads they could hear quite clearly the enemy general's footsteps in the hayloft. But he must have climbed by rope, and drawn it up after him. There was no ladder.

They reported and returned, their ears burning, with the captain.

It was a very high barn. One of them, upheld by two others, managed to reach the trapdoor and ram it back against no opposition. They saw the top man pull himself up and round, drawing his sword as he entered the hayloft. He rose and moved out of sight. For a moment more there was silence, except for the creak of his steps on the ceiling. Then he howled. Above their heads there broke out a confusion of stamping; the clash of steel; the grunts of two men locked in combat.

Captain Carasco jerked his head. The pyramid reformed. One man and then a second disappeared up through the trapdoor and a moment later, on his orders, a rope came down which allowed the last fortunate three to ascend. 'Remember!' roared Captain Carasco. 'You are to overwhelm him with numbers. He is not to be rendered unusable.'

It was, in fact, the last thing he remembered saying, just before he received an incapacitating blow on the back of his cranium.

Outside, awaiting orders, the ring of horsemen kept their patient vigil, and the group of those dismounted stood in the yard, exchanging muted opinions. From there, the course of battle was agreeably palpable. They listened, impressed by the language before, finally, silence prevailed.

It was not clear whether it was Julian or Diego whose jubilant voice finally reported, shouting, that the prisoner was subdued, and they were about to bind and descend with him.

213

There followed a short wait. Since they had been told to guard the exterior of the barn, Captain Carasco's loyal men continued to stand and guard the outside of the barn. They were still guarding it when the first of them became aware of a strong stench of burning.

The barn windows had all been close-shuttered, which was why unnoticed the burning boughs in the corner, dry as powder, could become a catherine wheel which sparked fire into the litter. Once lit, the straw only smouldered. But the smoke it vented, thick as wool, acrid as ammonia, poured through the seams of the timber and when at last they rushed forward and dragged the doors open, rolled over the yard like the white, stifling fall of some fatal, Ionic volcano.

Figures, retching and coughing, burst from the smoke, joining other spluttering figures in the shrouded, darkening air of the yard. Inside the barn, ribbons of flame fluttered, metallic and bright in the darkness. More helmeted figures burst through them; and last of all a man without uniform: a soot-smeared gentleman with yellow hair and a torn, peasant's shirt, whose two arms were gripped by his captors.

Diego, or perhaps Julian, took time between running to and fro from the pond to congratulate them as they disappeared into the fog. 'You have him!'

'Aye, we have him.'

'Are you sure it's the general?'

'Yellow hair. Can you not see?'

'And a full beard and moustache?' yelled Diego, or Julian, choking. He threw his last helmetful of green water on the blazing barn and prepared to abandon it.

'He admitted it.' Smoke, billowing, closed on the speaker just as Captain Carasco himself, his hand to his head, tottered to the barn door and cried gaspingly. 'To me! To me! There are men in the barn!'

Of the few men left who could see or hear him, five ran towards him. 'There are none, mi capitán. All have run out.'

His breath wrestled through the smoke in his throat. 'I tell you, our men are still upstairs. Can you not hear them? Bring water. A rope. An axe.'

'There is nothing to hold water, mi capitán,' said someone thickly. 'We are using our helmets.'

'Use them, then! We must break our way through to the hayloft. Rope . . . A pail . . . I have seen a pail . . .'

It had struck Lymond, too, that someone would think of

the milk pail He had run with the rest nearly as far as the horses, and seen Piero Strozzi mount, and Danny, and all the Spanish-garbed company, as well as the soldier passed off as himself. Then, merging into the smoke, he dropped back before they could miss him; for he had one responsibility which he could in fairness ask no one to share with him.

So, twisting, sprinting, avoiding the other blundering figures which came at him, black and blinded from the choking seat of the fire, Francis Crawford raced back to the farmhouse and into the parlour, where, taking a moment, he swung the pail of milk out through the window. Then he groped through the white, stifling haze to where Renée Jourda had been sitting.

She was there still; her sightless eyes looking straight at him. Through it all, behind the crazy torrent of movement, he had been conscious of this. Aware that in this shuttered room a blind woman was sitting, assaulted with questions, shaken by trampling vibrations; unseeing, suffering listener to the explosion of gunfire, the clash of steel, the shouting of men in stress and in anger. And last of all, exposed to a choking alchemy by which the very air became bane in her nostrils.

He looked at her, speaking her name: his voice steady over the private, high-spinning turmoil of extreme exertion.

But she did not answer, although she sat erect and calmly, with the long hair ... grey, not black ... straggling over her shoulders; and her eyes open and creamy like milk-glass; and not yellow with straw.

'She is dead. I speak,' said Captain Alferez Carasco from the window, the milk-pail in both blackened hands, 'to el cónde Criafordo? There are three men at the door and one at each window: soon there will be thirty.

'Milord, you are surpassed. You will be pleased to surrender.'

CHAPTER 7

Par grans dangiers le captif echapé
Peu de temps grand la fortune changée.

The red and white chequered fortress of Ham was only five miles to the north-west of Flavy and, powerful as a walled city, had for three hundred years commanded the village, the church and the River Somme whose moat encircled it.

Lymond saw nothing of his arrival there. He came to his senses during the night in a hurriedly prepared chamber in the tower; and in the morning was brought to the low-ceilinged room with its seven-foot window enbrasures where the Duke de Nevers, for France, had so recently given up tenure to the Duke of Savoy, for Spain and England.

Savoy was not there. Behind the massive, dark desk sat a man taller and older whose groomed, silvery beard still rested on the bosom of his richly sewn doublet in the fashion of ten years ago, when he was England's general, commanding the wars against Scotland.

'Ah, M. de Sevigny,' said Lord Grey of Wilton. 'Pray sit down. I am sorry that Captain Carasco had to use force. He was ordered to avoid it. The odds being one to thirty I feel you could, with honour, have surrendered your sword.'

'I was angry,' said Lymond. He remained standing.

'Just so,' said Lord Grey. He rose and stalked slowly round his desk, having reconsidered a tart comment about overplaying one's hand in pretty Spanish masquerades. This might look like the insolent opponent, half his age, of Hume; or Heriot; of Hexham but it was not; as one knew already from the man's record. Lord Grey said, 'I must make plain my regret for the death of Madame Jourda. There was some impression that she, and not your friends, had warned you of your danger. The Captain lost his head.'

It was not all that he had lost. He was in the care of the barber-surgeon at that moment, having had six inches of Mr Crawford's sword passed through his chest wall. Lymond said, 'If you will be kind enough to make out a report of the

216

matter for his grace of Savoy, I shall be glad to countersign it.'

Which meant he wanted Carasco broken. It was probable that he would be. The Duke's orders were to let this man have anything, within reason, that he wanted. Lord Grey said, 'It shall be done. Of course. An army is only as good as its officers,' and having got the man seated at last, clapped his hands for wine, served it, and took a chair this time on the same side of the desk as his prisoner. 'I am glad to see,' said Lord Grey, 'that we have managed to find clothes for you more befitting your rank. I admire your hardihood. Had we not known who you were, you and your friends might have been killed on sight as common soldiers. One hopes they bear you no resentment. They saved their skins, I am told, with remarkable alacrity.'

'It would interest you to know who they were,' said Lymond. 'It would interest me to know who informed you that I might be coming to see Madame Jourda.'

There was a certain relief in doing business with professionals. 'I have no objection,' said Grey. He rose to call Myles, his secretary, and returned to his seat to await him. 'We are unlikely to require his services again. Ah. Here we are. A letter, unsigned, but very circumstantial, as you will see, in its detail. At some time in the next weeks, the Scottish general known as the comte de Sevigny would make a personal visit to a farm near Flavy-le-Martel to settle a family dispute with an old nurse named Renée Jourda. He was likely to come alone, and in private. The writer wished no reward for the information, but would expect half the bounty if M. de Sevigny were secured.'

'To be paid where?' said Lymond.

'At a certain spot in a wood near Chantilly. I have sent a man there. He has orders to stay as long as feasible, in order to see what manner of person comes for it. When he returns, you may question him. There. You may wish to see the letter. You may even perhaps know the handwriting.'

There was a brief silence. 'Yes,' said Lymond. 'I know the handwriting.'

The soul of tact, William Grey, 13th Baron, sipped wine and waited. 'Thank you,' said Lymond. He laid the letter back on the desk. 'You wanted to know about my companions. The leader was an officer from my company called Daniel Hislop, and he and the men under him had been in

217

action for several days outside Péronne. I called on them to give me cover when I saw how busy the district was. Hence they were in military dress and I was not.'

'You give short measure, Mr Crawford,' said Lord Grey patiently. 'I am prepared to believe that you made some excuse to visit the home of an old family servant. I do not believe you would have troubled had her home been, say, in Chantilly. You came to study the fortifications here at Ham. And you did not come alone. I am told there was a second man in peasant's clothing.'

'I believe there was,' said Francis Crawford. 'Let me make you another bargain. I shall tell you his name, when you bring me the address of the man who uplifts your blood-money. *Cuando amigo pide, no ay mañana.* Are we not going to discuss the terms on which I change sides?'

'If you wish.' said Lord Grey courteously. He disguised, with success, his distaste for being hurried in delicate matters. 'You are naturally anxious about your future. His Majesty King Philip must be the final arbiter. But I know that two choices will be laid before you. One of these is to return to Spain with the King.'

He looked up at the other man sharply. No flattered blood mantled Lymond's skin below the cuts and the darkening bruises. They said the lady Elizabeth, sister to Philip's wife, had taken an interest in him. They did not say, but whispered, that if King Philip's wife the Queen of England were to die, the King would seek to marry the lady Elizabeth her successor. 'And the other?' said Lymond.

'Your freedom, upon an agreed ransom. To be effected on the conclusion of peace terms.' Lord Grey smiled. 'You are too skilful an adversary, Mr Crawford, to be permitted to take the field against us any longer.'

'And the ransom?' said Lymond.

Lord Grey of Wilton sipped his wine and put the cup down. He had hoped to defer this. On the other hand, one might as well get the thing over. He said, 'One million écus of gold, Mr Crawford. To be paid in a single sum, promissory notes being in this case unacceptable.'

'I see,' said Lymond.

There was a little silence. It was a round sum, but not a chance one. They had spent an evening working it out, he and Laurence and Arthur. Savoy himself had weighed it up. It represented what they guessed of the total value of all

218

Francis Crawford's possessions: his land, his treasure, his income from his new offices. It added to that, all that was owned by his wife Philippa Somerville. And to that, the whole estate of his mother and brother in Midculter, Scotland.

All these, together with what he might borrow, might possibly raise such a ransom. It offered him freedom and ruin. It put him barefoot in the market again, sword in hand, with this time his brother beside him.

Lymond said, 'I take it my brother is causing you trouble. I'm afraid he will continue to cause you trouble. Nothing, I assure you, would induce him to ransom me. And equally, nothing would induce me to accept any favours.'

'I am sure,' said Lord Grey, 'you would face most stoically a lifetime of prison. I am sorry you feel your brother would do nothing to help you. It occurred to us that the rest of your family might feel differently. And if the money is offered to us, we should have no qualms on your behalf in accepting it.'

'So I go to Spain,' said Lymond thoughtfully, 'or you beggar my family?'

'You claimed once,' said Lord Grey, 'it was Russia your mind was set upon.'

The hard blue eyes did not avoid his. 'Even for me,' Lymond said, 'the price is too high.'

They looked at one another. Outside the door, Lord Grey knew Myles was standing, obediently, to prevent any untimely interruption.

'There is other coin,' said Lord Grey of Wilton carefully.

A smile, irritatingly understanding, broke upon Francis Crawford's mobile, discoloured face. He rose to his feet and looked down, still smiling, at his noble enemy. 'And in the land of Ham for them, Most wondrous woorkes had done? You spoke of two choices only.'

'There is a third,' said the thirteenth baron of Wilton. 'It is my own suggestion but I am prepared, on certain assurances from yourself, to guarantee that King Philip will sanction it.'

'Assurances?' said Lymond gently.

'Indeed. And of a kind which may not be to your liking, unless you have deceived the French as thoroughly as you deceived my unfortunate nephew at Douai. I shall suggest to you the means by which, without money, you may obtain your freedom. In return, I shall require you, enable you, and if necessary compel you, Mr Crawford, to travel to Russia, and stay there.'

'Dear me,' said Francis Crawford. His eyes, resting on those of his captor, bore an expression Grey could not identify. Then he said, 'Was that an inspired guess? I am almost as anxious to leave Europe, my dear Lord Grey, as you seem to be to remove me. Therefore *faisons de fueille cortine et s'aimerons mignotement*. I am prepared to give you your assurance. I promise, once free, to tbandon Spain, France and Scotland in favour of Russia. Provided, of course, that the mitigated price of my freedom is still not beyond me. In place of money, what do you wish of me?'

'Information,' said Grey. He had risen too, and stood by the desk, his patrician fingers lightly clasped at his back, the gold of his chain glinting over the paned yoke of her jerkin. 'But of a most exhaustive nature. What money the French king has raised. What troops he has, and where they are stationed. His intentions in Italy. His intentions in Lyon. His intentions in Lorraine. And finally, of course, his fullest plans for his present campaign in Champagne and Picardy. Whether he intends to disband his troops or place them in winter quarters. Whether he means to try and retake these forts or strike elsewhere, and when and how. His plans for Calais and Gravelines and Guînes. Tell us these things,' said Lord Grey. 'Convince us that what you tell us is truthful, and you shall have funds, baggage, servants, safeconducts and conveyances which will see you in Moscow by springtime.'

'And so,' said Lymond unexpectedly, 'the knot has got to the teeth of the comb.' His eyes were on the tiled floor where, here and there, the pattern had worn down to the terracotta.

'You hesitate?' said Lord Grey mildly. 'With a kingdom awaiting you?'

'I might,' said Lymond, 'make my kingdom Hispania. I wonder if you have thought of that?'

Lord Grey smiled. 'Under Ruy Gomez? Under Alva? Under Arras? You would be dead of a draught, or a stabbing, before the year was well out. Mr Crawford, I have no fear that you will follow the monarch to Spain. I think your prospects in France are less golden than perhaps once you were led to believe. Give me the information which will allow King Philip to finish this war, and I shall convey you to Russia, and your ransom with you. It is an offer well worth considering.' He rang the bell on his desk. 'When you have your reply, ask your guard to inform me.'

'Why wait?' said Francis Crawford. 'You may have my answer now, if you wish.'

'So hastily?' said Lord Grey of Wilton.

'Why,' said the other man, and surveyed him from boots to crown with those derisive, chilly blue eyes. 'I have my eye on a piece of ground called Aceldama. You have found the right coin. I accept it.'

*

He had been taken back to his chamber and they were locking him in when a man in half-armour arrived and came up the stairs running, the guards saluting his passage.

Arrived at Lymond's threshold he took off and gave to a man at arms his gloves and his helmet, revealing fine dark hair flattened by sweat, and a steep-boned self-contained face shadowed, but not yet coarsened by war. Then he stepped inside and motioned to them to lock the door after him.

'Mr Crawford,' said Austin Grey. 'I wish the favour of your attention.'

Lymond turned, smiling. 'My lord of Allendale. Come then, South Wind, and perfect my garden.'

*

The King of France, riding in cavalcade to Compiègne with half the Court, was shown and approved the Duke de Guise's magnificent plan for the recovery of Calais. He commanded that there should be no secret made among the soldiery of the great booty to be obtained there; and he took aside the Marshal Piero Strozzi and placed round his neck a collar worth 800 écus in recognition of the work of espial he had engaged in, at such cost and such risk to himself.

'Nor, when he is returned to us, shall we show ourselves less generous towards M. de Sevigny,' said his Majesty. 'We grieve that France has lost, however temporarily, such a servant. A trumpet will be sent to inquire the terms of his ransom. We have even considered an attack on the fortress, but M. de Guise informs me that it would cost the lives of many brave men, with no assurance of rescue. We are happy at least to have Marshal Strozzi beside us.'

'It was unfortunate,' said Marshal Strozzi. 'Whatever ransom is agreed, your grace will lose the Chevalier's service until the war ends. If the Duke is willing to reconsider, I am prepared to mount an attack against Ham.'

'And risk your life again? We should not allow it,' said Henri. 'In any case, our object at present is Calais. That taken, the war will not be long in ending. M. de Sevigny will return. You will see. And he will be welcome.'

*

In a room in another wing of the fortified château of Compiègne, four men sat round a table and discussed from another viewpoint, the same subject.

'Daddy Cloots says that Ham is impregnable,' said Archie Abernethy. 'But Daddy Cloots doesna want Mr Crawford back again. The Spanish got into Ham.'

'Ham surrendered,' said Jerott Blyth shortly. 'And if you mean the Duke de Guise, I wish you'd say so. Mr Blacklock and I are waiting to hear what Mr Hislop has to say.'

Danny Hislop, newly back from his interrupted duty at Péronne, was aware that he had reached his moment of reckoning. He looked round the table. At the noble, high-coloured face of the merchant of Lyon, the former Knight of St John who had not gone to Russia: who had married Lymond's step-sister and had had to be manhandled by Lymond himself into sobriety.

At Adam Blacklock, long-faced, sallow and gentle, with the scar on his face and the hesitation which appeared now and then in his speech because he was by profession first an artist and only a bad second, a soldier. Who had tried civilian life with the merchants in London, and had found, after all, that this band of men provided him with something he could not yet do without.

And at Archie Abernethy the menagerie keeper, who had played a part, they said, in Lymond's career at its most frenetic: who had supplied him with opium; trained his wife; brought his bastard back home to Scotland.

Danny said, 'Mr Blyth: do I by any chance face some sort of tribunal? We were eight men against thirty, and five miles away from Flavy before we even knew that Lymond hadn't ridden off with us.'

'It w-wasn't your fault,' said Adam impatiently. 'He was crazy to go there in the first place, so close to Ham. Why in God's name did he risk it?'

'Business,' said Danny. 'According to Strozzi. Business with the old biddy who lived there. He must have gone back, I

222

fancy, to rescue her. An essay in strongmindedness expected of Chevaliers of the bloody Order.'

'They were after intelligence,' Archie said. 'Him and Strozzi. They were after intelligence. They left Compiègne on Tuesday together.'

'And took three days to get to Ham?' said Adam ironically. Jerott opened his mouth.

'Wait,' said Danny. 'You haven't heard everything.'

He looked round again at the three diverse, unbending faces. He said, 'Lymond wasn't captured by chance. The Spaniards at Ham knew he was coming before the old woman did. He was sold by someone. And I know who it is.'

Sitting very still, Jerott Blyth looked at him. His face was flushed. 'Strozzi?'

'If Piero Strozzi or I had betrayed Lymond, we would hardly have interfered with his capture,' said Danny dryly. 'In fact, neither of us knew he was making for Flavy. Who did?'

'Outside this room?' said Jerott. His flush had become deeper.

'And inside it,' said Danny Hislop.

It was Adam's hard hand that fastened on Jerott's arm as he scraped his chair back, swearing. He continued to hold him even when Jerott jumped to his feet, dragging the artist half with him. 'You upstart church-get,' said Jerott. 'You serve two years in Russia and run at the first blink of trouble. In all the years we three have fought under Francis Crawford, none of us has left him in enemy hands and come back with a whole skin to tell of it.'

'That isn't fair, Jerott,' said Adam sharply. 'He went back to Flavy and found it deserted. What we have to do is make plans to get Francis out, not attack one another.'

Under Adam's hand, Jerott sank into his seat. 'He made an accusation,' he said. 'Let him substantiate it. Who knew Francis was going to Flavy? I didn't. But of course, I couldn't prove it.'

Adam ignored the sarcasm. 'Nor did I,' he said quietly. 'But I can't prove it either. Archie?'

The black hooded eyes in the scarred face turned on Adam, and then without expression, round them all. Finally, 'Mistress Philippa knew,' said Archie Abernethy. 'But she wouldna tell nor let on my mischance. And I kent. But I dinna chittle.'

Jerott was staring at the tough, wrinkled face. 'You knew, did you?' he said. 'I suppose you also knew why Lymond and Strozzi went off together in the first place, if Strozzi didn't intend to go to Flavy?'

The brown face staring back at him was still impassive. 'I do,' Archie said. 'And it'll be abroad soon enough. They went to spy for the taking of Calais.'

'Lymond told you?' said Danny.

The veteran of many animals and many wars shook his head. 'I overheard. It made no difference. I can keep ma mou' clemmed. Ye said ye kent the informer, Mr Hislop.'

'So I did,' said Danny Hislop. Since Jerrot's outburst he had become formal and very succinct. 'Archie: you and Mr Crawford took two days to come from Saint-Germain.'

The black eyes did not waver. 'We stopped at Saint-Cloud.'

'I was told,' said Danny, 'that you had to stop at Saint-Cloud because Mr Crawford was too drunk to go any further?'

There was a silence. Archie shrugged his narrow shoulders. 'It was too late to go on. He'd had a drop. Yes.'

'Encouraged by you. He'd had more than a drop at Lyon, hadn't he, when you brought him to the door the last night we were there? When the Paris courier came, it took twenty minutes—*twenty minutes*—to rouse him.'

'He had had a fair amount taken,' Archie admitted. 'It had been a hell o' a day.'

'In which he saw a surprising amount of yourself. Considering that you were attached, at that time, to the service of Mistress Philippa. Why did you leave Mistress Philippa and join Mr Crawford at Lyon, Archie? Were two attempts to injure him not sufficient?'

Adams said, 'Jerott, sit down. He's doing it all in good faith. He doesn't know Archie as we do. Danny: what you say isn't possible. But tell us what you think is wrong, and then Archie can answer us.'

'I've told you,' said Danny. His voice was perfectly firm, although the colour had retreated a little, out of temper, from the summer freckles on his undistinguished, snub-nosed face. 'But if you want further details, I have them. Lymond left the Governor's house once, in monk's dress in Lyon. Archie followed him. If I hadn't noticed him watching the house, I shouldn't have noticed Lymond either. They both went up the hill. And while they were up the hill, Abernethy tried to kill him.'

'That's ridiculous,' said Adam sharply. 'You misinterpreted something you saw.'

'Did I?' said Danny. 'When I came upon them, Lymond had Abernethy by the throat and was flinging him over the cliffside. He only stopped because he was persuaded it was all a mistake.'

'Perhaps it was,' Jerott said. He looked, troubled, at Archie who said nothing.

'Perhaps it was,' agreed Danny grimly. 'Then explain this away. Lymond and young Philippa were attacked in the fog that night in Lyon. Afterwards he went off with the Président and one of the merchants to the For Vénus. You know Lymond. There was no secret about what he wanted or where they were going; but Lymond didn't stay in the house. He came out alone and walked straight through a traboule, where I lost him. I came across him again at the waterside.'

'You were playing his bodyguard?' said Jerott.

Danny looked at him. 'I had begun to be concerned for his safety. I ran down the rue de l'Angelle and saw him through the mist in the rue des Hebergeries, making for the Port St Paul steps down to the river. He turned right, down the steps and out of sight. I was still a good way off when Abernethy came dodging down past the Six-Grillets and over the road to the steps, scooping up a rock from the road as he went.' He stopped.

'And?' said Jerott. Adam, looking at Archie, said nothing.

'The story ends there,' said Danny evenly. 'At the moment I was struck from behind, and when I recovered, Archie and Lymond had gone and I was lying on the road with my purse cut. I searched the streets for a while, then made my way back to the Hôtel de Gouvernement. What happened next Adam will remember. Archie brought our revered leader back, helped by a printer friend. He was incapably drunk, and he had a fresh wound in the nape of his neck. The kind of thing made by heaving rocks carelessly. Mr Abernethy will tell you if I've been fair to him.'

There was a long silence. Then Archie Abernethy shifted on his hard seat. 'Aye: You've been fair enough,' he observed. He appeared to be thinking.

'Well?' rapped Jerott. 'What happened? I take it you didn't

assault him. Who did? Who induced him to break all his own hand-written regulations about wine, the mother of all vices?'

'I did,' said Archie Abernethy. 'I wouldna deny it in front of such a number of sharp-eyed solemncholy gentlemen. I flung the stone that dropped Mr Crawford. With the good advice of the printer Bonhomme and yon pisse-pot prophet Nostradamus I filled him with liquor and kept him that way till you got him. Ye complain it took twenty minutes to rouse him. By God, ye were lucky. By God, ye were lucky to be able to rouse him at all.'

Adams said in sudden anger, 'You are talking in riddles.' His hands were pressed hard together.

'No doubt,' said Archie. His voice, his dark skin were suffused as never before with the signs of a towering passion. 'You're friends o' Francis Crawford, ye tell me, but ye take little heed to what is happening to him. You force him to France, and dust your hands of it. You foul his birthright with witchcraft and devilment and see no harm when he walks away whistling. You saw him at his desk, all of you, that morning in Lyon, and thought nothing ailed him but alcohol.'

Danny's skin from white had turned a patchy red. He said, 'He kept still. So would I, if I'd drunk that amount.'

'He kept still. He was empty of blood,' Archie said. 'He kept his hands out of sight, because the cuffs of his sleeves covered bandages. He left the brothel yon night. He picked up glass by the Customhouse. And when I reached him, he'd ripped through both wrists with it.'

*

'*My lord of Allendale,*' said the remembered voice mockingly. '*Come then, South Wind, and perfect my garden.*' And as the cell door at Ham shut behind him, Austin Grey moved forward to see his uncle's prisoner.

He had been rigged out in elegant black, quite unlike the student's buff jacket at Douai. But the sardonic smile was the same; under the same crudely marked traces of fisticuffs. The man's smile became wide.

'*Petite coquette (co co co co dae) qu'esse cy?* Step on the mat, Marquis.'

'What happened at Douai is over,' said Austin. 'I am here to satisfy my own sense of what is fitting. In case Lord Grey was too occupied, I have to convey to you our apologies.'

226

'Apologies? Now that,' said Philippa's husband, 'is extremely novel. I find it even alarming. And as it happens, uncalled-for. I am here, like Rabelais, because I want to be, with my three packets of ash labelled *Poison*. Poison for the King; Poison for Savoy; Poison for Ruy Gomez. I didn't think of *Poison for Uncle*. I thought your gallant kinsman was in Guînes again.'

'We are leaving for Guînes tomorrow. I wished to apologize,' said Austin with a hard-held and meticulous courtesy, 'for the death of your nurse, Madame Jourda. It was inexcusable. I wished to ask what relatives we should send for.'

He had set himself to perform this mission, knowing he would receive little thanks for it. He had not expected the howl of delight with which that was greeted. He stood, concealing his shock, as Crawford seized a chair and flung himself astride it. 'A spark!' he said. 'A riposte! After all these years, a reciprocating witticism! You were due to apologize for the vile stratagem, I would have you know, that led to my capture. Not for the demise of an elderly nursemaid. Forget her and tell me your other reason for braving the cockpit. Or shall I try to guess it?'

'I am sure you could,' said Austin Grey. He moved to the wall and leaned against it, a gentle man whose youth disguised, as yet, a steadfastness which no one so far had had real cause to plumb. He said, 'Your life has taught you how to smell out weakness. Before you whet your claws on me, let me give you some news I have from Scotland.'

'I know that too. I have heard the nightingale herself. My brother is well, my mother failing,' said Lymond. 'And Kate Somerville, I imagine wants her daughter back.'

'She wants you back also,' said Austin. 'And not for her own sake or yours. You know a clash of doctrine is coming in Scotland. The Queen Regent has to tolerate the Reformed religion now, but once the war is over, her French brothers will want her to fight it.'

'Perhaps she'll lose,' offered Crawford. His manner was helpful. 'Wouldn't that intrigue you? I thought the Lord James Stewart seemed an able man. He invited Knox, I hear, back to Scotland. That argues a certain amount of philosophical stamina.'

'Knox didn't go,' Austin Grey said. 'But if he does, Lord James and Erskine of Dun and all those who don't agree with the established Church may well rally round him.'

227

'To rend the surplice, the corner-cap and the tippet, the badges of idolators. Quite. So what agitates Kate? Not the condition of Scotland. As Guicciardini said, there is a great difference between having discontented subjects and having desperate subjects. In any case, being a woman, although unique among women, Kate thinks of the particular and not of the general. Therefore she is afraid for my family, who like Achilles, would rather till the ground than live in pale Elysium. She thinks that Richard wants me to leave my frantic pleasures to come and help him? No, hardly that either. What, then?'

'You under-estimate Philippa's mother,' said Austin Grey. 'Just as you are quite astray, it seems to me, in all your dealings with Philippa. Mistress Somerville thinks the Scottish Queen-Regent needs an adviser. A soldier uncommitted to either side whose opinion she can trust at this juncture.' He could hear with his own ears how pompous it sounded. Crawford's air was one of obedient attention.

'It doesn't sound much like Kate,' he said, damn him. 'It sounds a tempting idea, though, from your viewpoint: to have me sitting in Scotland with jack, knapstall, splent, spear and axe being hit on the head by both parties, while France and Spain kiss and make friends again. You haven't spoken to your uncle yet, have you? He had an even better idea.'

Austin Grey thought of his uncle, for thirty years intermittently guardian of some part of England's holdings in France, when he was not chastising Scotsmen in Scotland. According to Arthur his son, *Hannibal was sworn an enemy to Rome at nine years of age, and my father bred one to France at fourteen.* The mirror of military valour, held up to Austin by his mother since he, too, was less than fourteen. The epitome of the life that he despised and disliked and followed because he would not displease his mother, and because, whatever else it lacked, it upheld honour. He said, 'What did my uncle suggest?'

He knew by the other man's smile that he was going to be baited again. 'That he should connive,' Lymond said, at my escape to Russia, in return for betraying all I know of the French armies and their forthcoming battle plan. A neat device, with advantages to everybody and a built-in safeguard in case I should be seized with a vile urge to egg the bargain. Whether I end up in Russia or Hecate's garden with thricefolding portals of ebony, the King of France will never employ me again.'

Not only the use of the future tense, but something in the other man's mocking, mellifluous voice brought Austin Grey erect from the wall-stones. 'My uncle made you such an offer. And you *accepted it*?' Hard on disbelief had rushed contempt. He did not try to hide it.

Crawford of Lymond uncrossed his arms and rising, twitched round the tall chair so that it faced Austin invitingly. Then he approached. One could recoil. One could allow him, as Austin did, to stretch his hand and move oneself, grim-faced, to sit in it. 'Prepare, my dear child,' said Lymond, 'to receive a revelation. Ham is not a Court of Love. Piero Strozzi is not a true Christian knight and neither is God's silly vassal, the monarch. *Muchos Grisones*, in fact, *y pocos Bayardos*. Modern war is fought by a number of strong, sweaty horsemen with constipation, who have their eyes on power, on wealth and on glory, and who obey the rules just when it pleases them. Your uncle and I understand each other perfectly. I am going to Russia. He has the information he needed. The French are going to Calais.'

Co co co co dae. Austin Grey looked up at the man standing watching him, smiling, his hands lightly folded behind him. He said, 'Can you trust a bargain, then, with no honour?'

'I trust your uncle's,' said Lymond. 'He has his reasons for wanting me to go to the fate which pride and lust prepare. And he seems to trust mine. I have told him all I know. I had just come back from Calais to Flavy when I was captured. The only person which stands to lose by the transaction, indeed, is yourself. Are you still in love with my wife?'

Austin Grey stood up. For a moment he remained face to face with Philippa's husband. Then, turning, he moved to the window and stood there. 'Ham is not a Court of Love,' he said. 'There is no reason why I should listen to that sort of question, or answer it.'

'No, there isn't, but you've done both,' said Crawford. He conveyed a faint impatience. 'I know I shouldn't soil my lips with the name of your loved one, but it occurred to me that I could be helpful, unless, like Antisthenes, you would rather be furious than voluptuous. The young Queen Mary has made her a lady of honour, and restrained her from leaving France while I am here.'

'At your prompting?' said Austin. He had learned to control his face but not his colour, which had left his brown skin entirely, although he did not know it.

The other man sighed. He rambled to the table and picking up a steel pen threw it accurately into the centre of the door where it hung like a shot parraqueet, quivering. It dropped, and he hitched himself on the table corner. 'I know,' he said, 'that Philippa Somerville is beyond earthly criticism. It is not her fault that I have esoteric tastes and I happen to require and consort with professionals. I have resisted, with ease, the temptation to ravish her. I have saved her for you: sweet, jolly, virginal and able to repeat filthy verses in Turkish. There has merely occurred a slight hitch in handing her over.'

'Such as the fact that you are keeping her in France while I am fighting for the opposite side,' observed Austin.

'I am not,' said Crawford acidly, 'keeping her in France in my present situation. *Tu me verrois secher sous le poids de mes fers/Comme un troupeau que voit un berger de travers.* She may promptly depart for Scotland. There is still a slight hitch. The French bought my loyalty with an awe-bond. Unless I fight for them for a year, my marriage to Philippa will not be annulled.'

For a moment, such was his dislike of the conversation, it seemed to Austin that the arrogant, unprincipled man opposite him was asking him to abet an attempt at escape. He said, 'The fact that you have been captured in French service could hardly . . .' and broke off suddenly.

'. . . be held against me? Unfortunately, the fact that I have turned informer most certainly would. There is really only one thing they can do in retaliation, and that is to make sure that wherever I go, I can never legitimately marry. A pity. My mistress, they tell me, has sold her favours elsewhere, but the Tsar had made me another and most attractive offer. You have not, I take it, any intimate acquaintance with Russian womanhood?'

Austin Grey made no effort to answer. Instead he said. 'I think this discussion has ceased to serve any useful purpose. I have to report to my uncle.'

'Because,' said Crawford, as if he hadn't spoken, 'you ought to remember that Philippa has been trained in Turkey and will expect certain standards if you mean to make an impression, whether as her first client or her bigamous husband. I could provide some instruction.'

Austin walked to the door.

'Or a demonstration?' said the other man wistfully. 'You can't be keeping all these randy English contented in Ham without some help from a hot-house. I'm afraid my keepers have locked you in and gone off. Perhaps they are consoling themselves. Have you ever killed anyone, Austin?'

'No,' said Austin. He ceased hammering on the door and swung round, his colour hot in each cheek. 'I am an easy object for all your mockery. I have never killed a man or taken a woman, or betrayed my nation or those who are paying me ...' He controlled himself, hard. He said, 'I have waited a long time for Philippa. I can wait still.'

'You can,' said Crawford reminiscently, 'but I fear the Schiatti cousins won't, whose willingness be the touchstone and trial of their fidelity. I should hurry ... They may sell her by inch of candle if you don't get her home soon, and simply no one can outbid a banker.'

At last, at last the idiot keepers came to the door and Austin left swiftly without speaking, his head high, controlling his nausea. An effusion, gently derisive, tainted the close air behind him.

> 'And from the sword (Lord) save my soule
> By thy myght and power ...'

The door of the prison chamber shut and locked. The voice, lower keyed, persisted floridly.

> 'And keep my Soule, thy darling deare,
> From dogs that would devour ...'

Austin was out of hearing. Alone, Francis Crawford continued, lightly, stubbornly with his amusement.

> 'And from the Lion's mouth that would
> Me all in sunder shiver
> And from the hornes ... of Unicornes ...'

They were watching him through the Judas-grille.

'Oh, *Christ!*' said Francis Crawford on a sudden, harsh breath. His voice split on it, curiously. He flung himself off the table and snatching up the quill pen hurled it with violence this time straight for the opening.

The peep-hole door rattled shut. He subsided with force on

231

a field-chest, his face driven into the arch of his fingers, and might have slept, for all anyone saw to the contrary.

*

Three days later, they moved him under stiff guard from Ham to le Catelet, on his way north-east to safer detention at Brussels. Until Mr Crawford's disclosures were shown to be genuine, my lord Grey was not fool enough to allow Mr Crawford to abscond to Russia or anywhere else.

Austin Grey, Marquis of Allendale, captained the troop that took Lymond to le Catelet, past the reedy ponds and the sky-blue stitchery of the willows; the huddles of russet roofs round their spire, the apples shining like green coins in their flourish of green, the small birds swooping dark on the sky, their bodies glinting pale and short in the sun.

The prisoner ignored his surroundings. But Austin, his imagination already in the dark cell which Philippa's husband must occupy, saw every faint detail of the journey: the verdigris grain on a dry, long-culled meadow; the stagnant pool, high and still, with lily stems twined in its cloudy green depths and the yellow petals of beech arriving and sinking, pensive leaded memorials, to their dissolution.

They rode in silence through it all: a small, swift unit of fifteen men in plate armour, bearing the red bands of England and inviting no attention from the French-held forts of Péronne and of Guise just over either horizon. The only unarmed man, engulfed in their midst, was their eminent prisoner, soberly dressed for better concealment, with his hands bound and the famous hair hidden.

Crawford had not wished to leave Ham. So much had been subtly apparent both to Austin Grey and his uncle with whom the prisoner had been called to a short, unsatisfactory interview the day before their departure. Lord Grey had pointed out briskly that there were some odd discrepancies between the garrison numbers Mr Crawford had given him and those reports which Lord Grey's spies were delivering. Furthermore, Mr Crawford's account of the plan for the taking of Calais appeared to be based on an odd misconception. The Ruisbank fort was not where Mr Crawford's plan showed it.

M. de Sevigny had displayed anger when doubted. But he had not, although he spoke with great vigour, entirely cleared their minds of all suspicion. Lord Grey of Wilton had decided that the safest course was to send him to Brussels. They would look extremely foolish if the attack after all were to be directed against himself at Ham, and Crawford were to saunter out, sneering. It would be in character. Whereas at Brussels . . .

He had not told Austin, because the boy, he well knew, was a milksop. But in Brussels there were ways, denied to him as a gentleman, of checking whether an informant was lying. No doubt Mr Crawford, a man of the world, was aware of them. It would more than explain his present lack of enthusiasm for the journey.

It had not been a silent cavalcade on leaving Ham. Austin Grey, with his prisoner's reins in his grasp, had dropped from his manner all but the meaningless requirements of courtesy. Lymond was bent, on the other hand, on provoking him.

'Why let me have it all my own way? Talk, Tancred,' he said lazily over the hoofbeats. 'Or are you afraid your uncle's men will accuse you of fraternizing? But surely they know you have a mind above bribes, even when your less weak-bellied uncle is sending me to have my bones pulled and my hands broken at Brussels? After all, I have only one thing you want, and you wouldn't find it any harder to get than any other fool with his eye on a married woman. *Toutes serez, êtes ou fûtes/De fait ou de volonté, putes.*'

He laughed at the expression on Austin's face and was going on when Austin called his lieutenant to him and transferring Lymond's reins to his charge, rode off to the head of the troop.

They travelled without speech after that, and no marauding band of French traversed their path; no scout from Guise or Péronne saw them vanish and rode back to try, however tardily, to rouse his fellows.

Instead, as they crossed the broad plateau between the river Somme and the Escaut, fifty men rose out of the ground where for two days they had been waiting, strung across the only possible pathway to Brussels.

Austin Grey knew who they were before he saw the white fleur de lis on the ensign, or the other standard they carried of blue and silver and red, which was quite clearly not a French blazon.

Lymond also knew. Even at that distance, he could recognize the men whom he himself had led into battle, and the four men once his own henchmen: Blyth and Blacklock; Hislop and Abernethy.

The shock of surprise drew the blood from his skin: even Austin saw it, rounding on Lymond in that first, furious second. What he missed was the suffusion of anger that followed it: an anger terrifying because it could find no expression.

Afterwards, Francis Crawford found that in those first moments all the force of his fury had turned, senselessly, towards trying to burst the immutable wire of his bonds. At the time, he sat bound on his horse, his reins gripped in Austin Grey's hands and said 'You may think you can ride over them, but they've got crossbows. Your men aren't going to like that. Or swords ripping upwards as they pass. And there are trees ahead: that, of course, will be where the horsemen are. You may want to ride on, dear boy, but your men are going to think differently. . . .'

It was doubtful if all of it reached the ears of Austin Grey and his men, but some of it did. It no more than endorsed their own opinion. Austin had ordered them to gallop at the line of footsoldiers, but the line of footsoldiers looked far too formidable. Instead, the escort from Ham slowed, hesitated, broke gallop, and swerving, bore to the right.

Ahead of them, another line of men rose from the ground. And behind, yet another.

'Christ,' said Francis Crawford with interest. 'They've got out two companies. You're in a box, Austin. Your uncle will be cross, but we shall tell your mother all about ransoms. And you can learn how to bed an unmarried girl, Turkish fashion. I'll show you, on Philippa.'

Austin Grey heard it as he thundered over the rough ground, dragging the other horse with him. His troop had split up, against all his orders. One by one, as they left him, the French bolts whined through the air and picked them off. He had tried to tell them. The French wanted Lymond. If they kept close to him, they would come to no harm.

And now he himself and only a handful of others were still gathered round Crawford, keeping the prisoner's body between themselves and the crossbows and archers. Silent weapons, not to rouse the near-by garrisons. It had all been planned, all thought out; all most carefully executed.

A man fell on his right, and another. Two had over-ridden the French and reached safety, or had been allowed to escape since there was only one man they wanted. And it now seemed likely that they would free Francis Crawford. That he would return, malicious, triumphant to the fleshpots, to lead the French armies against whatever target they had now chosen—a target which was unlikely to be Calais. To . . .

'*I'll show you, on Philippa,*' said the lascivious, bantering voice, and Grey turned, his blade in his hands as the enemy came rushing towards him, their steel out, their hands outspread for his bridle.

Francis Crawford watched the younger man's sword coming towards him. With Austin's hand hard on the hilt it flashed down to his heart, and then faltered.

'*You bloody virgin!*' said Lymond; and bringing his eyes up, hard and cold, added something further.

Austin had only to lean on the sword. He had only to let it follow its course and his honour and Philippa's would be avenged; his uncle's enemy slain, his nation preserved, his heritage vindicated. And Philippa, tied for ever to this one, hated man, would be at liberty.

And because that was not how he prayed Philippa would come to him, Austin lifted his sword and with his free hand flung the reins of Lymond's horse in the other man's face. Then Lord Grey's nephew turned into almost certain death, and head up, faced the armed men surrounding him.

'Let him through,' Lymond said, and his voice, to Jerott, listening, was suddenly threadbare with tiredness. 'He may as well fail to kill Frenchmen in Picardy as fail to kill Frenchmen in . . . Paris. Tell them to let him go free.'

They did not trouble to watch Austin Grey ride off alone over the marshes, to follow the few who had lived through that ambush. They crowded round Lymond's horse, awaiting his commendation, which he gave them; and then obeyed Hislop's orders and formed ranks ready for marching, having stripped the Englishmen of all their bodies could offer. Jerott, leaning over to cut Lymond's bonds said, 'Jesus Christ, your . . . The wire's made a mess of your wrists. Are you all right?' His face was red with anxiety.

'Perfectly,' Lymond said. 'I am also filled with gratitude. Apart from risking the lives of two trained companies and four principal officers you have contrived to nullify an elaborate scheme which would have sent the entire Spanish army to Lorraine instead of to Calais. It only remains for us all to be caught on our way back to Compiègne, and you will be

235

able to wallow in the fruits of unbridled, emasculated, inadmissible, unmilitary bloody romanticism.'

'Such as,' said Adam Blacklock unfairly, 'the motive which took you back to Flavy-le-Martel in the first place? The trouble with you, M. le comet de Sevigny, is that you're too god-damned autocratic. From now on, you will kindly remember that a good military tactician requires the support of a team. We are your team.'

There was a pause. Then Lymond looked at Archie, and before his gaze passed on to the rest, even Archie found himself flinching.

'Why? You must have other interests?' said Francis Crawford.

They made no answer because, after forty-eight hours of vigil on the sodden plateau for his sake, no possible answer existed. Only Archie Abernethy took his reins and said, 'Oh, Mary Mother. Let us get you home,' quietly.

CHAPTER 8

A l'ennemy, l'ennemy foy promise
Ne se tiendra.

In the interests of the Duke de Guise's winter campaign, the incident of M. de Sevigny's brief capture and escape was not made public. As it happened, the Duke de Guise himself was unaware of the full implications of the event, which were known only to Lymond, his rescuers, and to Piero Strozzi, whom Francis Crawford went to see immediately on his return to Compiègne.

He made no excuses. 'I may have wrecked the Calais campaign. I fed Willie Grey a cropful of spurious information about the forthcoming French attack on the Pale and was rescued before I could be forced to confess otherwise. It may be all right. They were already suspicious of me before we left. But if you want to tell de Guise, I shan't stop you.'

'What did you tell them?'

'This,' said Lymond, and tossed over a roll of paper. 'I wrote it down so that you would know what to expect if by any chance Grey and the Spaniards take it all seriously.'

Piero Strozzi lifted the roll and read through it. Then retying it, he held it out in his ringed, powerful hand towards the man who had written it. 'Take it,' he said, 'and destroy it. With that information you might fool Alva. You would certainly fool King Philip. But Lord Grey and the Duke of Savoy are thinking men. A spy who claimed to have just come from Calais should never have made all these blunders. Did you talk about alternative targets?'

'No,' said Lymond. 'But I became very scathing whenever they mentioned Arlon or Luxembourg. That is where our feint ought to be.'

Piero Strozzi eyed him. 'You came to me,' he said. 'But you have no real fears that they will act on the information you have sold them, and neither have I. Our prime objective

237

remains Calais. We shall take a few extra precautions, that is all. And I see no need why this little history should travel beyond these four walls. Tête-Dieu, I told le Guisard that I was releasing two companies to try with your own men to rescue you for fear you told Grey too much about Calais. I didn't know they would pull you out before you had told enough. What was the bribe? Russia?'

'Obviously,' Lymond said.

'Obviously. But in that case, mon gars, why mislead them? Russia is where you wanted to rule.'

Lymond lifted his eyebrows. 'Perhaps I didn't mislead them,' he said. 'Perhaps I went back to Flavy specifically so that the English would capture me.'

'That's what I thought,' said Piero Strozzi with undoubted cheerfulness. 'It would pay me, would it not, for Douai? On the other hand you would not have come to me and told me this. Nor, of course, would you be prepared to risk your skin with the army at Calais. You are prepared to risk your skin with the army at Calais?'

'If I must,' said Lymond gravely. 'There is also the matter of my divorce. I plan to acquire it before I betray you.'

'Ah, yes,' said Strozzi. 'This marriage to Catherine d'Albon. I advised it.'

'You did not, strictly speaking, advise marriage,' Lymond said. 'And what you did advise had nothing to do with Russia. But don't hesitate to continue.'

'The King agrees,' said Piero Strozzi. 'His grace was impressed by our joint venture as apple-sellers. He has therefore decreed—he will tell you himself—that if Calais is taken, your marriage to St André's daughter may, if you wish, be contracted at Easter.'

'Preceded by my divorce?' said the comte de Sevigny guardedly. His face had changed. Strozzi noticed with interest. The wench was handsome, and wealthy and, in spite of everything, rumour said, still a virgin.

'Preceded,' agreed Piero Strozzi, 'by your God-damned divorce, four months early. And not before time. I'm told every man at court is after your wife as it is. If I weren't so busy I'd be one of them. That charming girl had a wholesome, kind-hearted young man to be husband to her.'

'That's what Austin Grey thinks, but he's busy as well. Really,' said Lymond, 'the only person to be lucky in all this is Cathin d'Albon.'

❀

It was the opinion expressed, and indeed held, by Catherine d'Albon's mother when the Queen summoned her to discuss her daughter's future. 'Not,' said Queen Catherine, the wide, shallow eyes filled with intelligent sensibility, 'that plans could be made known until our gallant lords return from the battlefield. But messages might be passed when next you write to your husband the Marshal. We miss him, as we miss our old friend the Constable. God grant that they will both soon be freed, and peace sent us.'

It was the Duke de Guise's great fear. The news which seeped back to Paris and Saint-Germain and Poissy indicated that before any of France's distinguished prisoners found freedom, the Guisard's troops would mark the autumn, willy-nilly, with a string of successful engagements.

The nature of these was less easy to distinguish. The Duke de Nevers, for example, appeared to have moved out to the frontiers of Champagne, while the Duke de Guise with the rest of the army was hovering between the Spanish fortresses of Ham, Saint-Quentin and le Catelet, intercepting supplies and planning, they said, either to attack them or to advance to protect Doullens.

The King of France's war horses travelled to Senlis; and all the young horses from the Duke de Guise's stud moved suddenly from Champagne to Nanteuil. The Channel ports in Brittany, Normandy and Picardy became unusually busy. In the middle of November the story went about that the Duke de Guise had assembled 20,000 horse and foot to take and fortify Chauny, between Compiègne and Ham. Having done that, he intended to garrison all his fortresses for the winter and dismiss the rest, reducing the troops beside Lyon from 6,000 to 2,000 as well.

Heartened no doubt by these tidings, the lieutenant-general of the Spanish army marched out of Ham, now strongly fortified, and retired briskly to Brussels, burning all he could find as he travelled. The Spanish army, unpaid, for several weeks began, as was its habit, to leave for the winter. A rumour spread that the King of France, who still had his troops and an untoward payroll, planned to justify both with

239

a small foray in or near Luxembourg. They said Marshal Strozzi had been there on reconnaissance.

December came. They said the Duke de Guise was stuck at Compiègne with his men dying off daily. He had, however, sent on his artillery so that if need be, it could be carried to Luxemburg. They said that de Nevers was in marching order for Luxemburg, but would pretend in the first instance to be going to victual Marienbourg.

They said that the Duke de Guise was really staying close to Compiègne with the intention of retaking Ham, and then Arras.

They said that the Duke de Nevers and his troops were in Metz, on their way to do battle in Luxembourg, but had been held up where they were by the weather. There was a sardonic joke travelling round about the Duke de Guise's real hope being to conquer the English in Calais. Lord Grey, who had gone back to his fortress in Guînes, was not in the way of hearing it. The Duke de Guise finally moved out of Compiègne and towards Guise which, they said, he was going to inspect. The army in Compiègne also showed signs at last of striking camp and marching somewhere.

A report came that the Duke de Nevers and 20,000 foot had been seen marching towards Picardy. A further report credited the Duke de Guise with having sent 5,000 German troops by water to Pontoise and a further 20,000 towards Amiens, Abbeville, and Montreuil. Four days later, it was known that the whole French army was marching north in two divisions, and that in the vanguard was an immense body of cavalry, led by Piero Strozzi in conjunction with Crawford of Lymond and Sevigny.

It was the first concrete news for two months of either man, and it reached the young Queen of Scotland just before Christmas. On Christmas Day, Philippa Somerville handed over her duties to Fleming, and attaching herself to a Paris-bound party, took herself unannounced to speak to Francis Crawford's step-sister in Paris.

＊

But for its servants, the collection of buildings known as the Séjour du Roi was empty.

Since Jerott's single crass visit home, he had not returned to his wife Marthe. And since they had joined him in

Compiègne, the rooms allotted to Hislop and Blacklock had been empty.

Clever; self-sufficient; occupied with her own business of antiques and the merchanting of less ponderable beauty, Marthe did not miss them. Only on Christmas day, when her courtier friends were long gone to Poissy and her poets and painters and writers were, for once, at home with their children did she find time, for a space, hang spitefully dull on her hands. She worked alone on a spinet someone had brought in disorder, and then having set it to rights, put on cloak and pattens and went out through the town gate to walk through the grass by the river.

The sharp air cleared her mind and settled her emotions. Satisfied, she returned to the Séjour du Roi and found Adam Blacklock waiting for her on the threshold.

She showed no surprise. She said, 'When I am out, the door-keeper grows rather deaf. I apologize. Have you come to break news to me about Jerott? Or has someone found Francis too inconvenient?'

And that took some courage, thought Adam. Or perhaps sheer, bloody, unfeeling arrogance. With Francis, you couldn't tell, either, to begin with.

He said, 'They are both alive and unwounded. I only wanted to talk to you. I have business at the Bureau de l'Epargne and thought I might pass the night in my rooms.'

'Come in,' said Marthe. And inside, when they were both settled in her parlour: 'I take it, then, that you are here on Jerott's behalf. I hope he is sober occasionally?'

On Adam Blacklock's lean, observing face were the marks of two months of intensely hard work in the saddle. But although he had ridden a long way that day, with one leg which would never be as strong as the other, he was in better training than Jerott to face the bladed tongue, the language sweet and thick as cinnamon quills of the Crawford family. He said, 'I did come on your husband's behalf to see you, and also Philippa. Since your brother came back to Compiègne, Jerott has been wholly abstemious.'

She surveyed him, the dense blue eyes smiling. 'He has found another paramour to chastise him? No. I imagine not. Whatever else poor Jerott lacks, he is loyal. Therefore his sense of responsibility has been jolted. He has had a lesson from Francis? Or . . .'

She was shrewd. Adam saw the thought strike her; and saw

241

her eyes narrow before she produced it, dressed lightly in mockery. 'Or has he been forced to rise to the occasion because his commander has dropped below it? Is Francis prostituting his rare endowments again with pipes and satyrs and spears wreathed with ivy?'

'No,' said Adam. It was childish to feel any anger. He remembered the door closing along the corridor in the Hôtel de Gouvernement, Lyon, and the stories he had heard repeated with envious laughter here in France of the pipes and satyrs and vine leaves of six years ago. He had heard the sound of the Vidame de Chartres' voice, not so long since, talking to Lymond.

Adam said, 'You and Jerott were with Francis at Volos, when his addiction was broken. Do you remember if he had headaches?'

Her eyes were wide open in the fragile face and for once, he could have sworn there was no artifice. Marthe said sharply, 'Naturally. He had opium cramps. Why? Have they come back again?'

'According to Archie,' said Adam. 'It seems that Francis has been having bouts of intense pain.'

Marthe got up. 'I see,' she said. 'Ill-wished by the idols of Themixtitan, whose cement is the blood of small children.' She did not explain. 'It dates back to a chess game. I didn't know its effects were there still. Has he seen doctors?'

'No. He covers it, when it has to be covered, with alcohol,' said Adam grimly. 'He was however examined without his knowledge by Nostradamus in Lyon. Archie told us about it.'

Someone tapped on the door and came in to light the wax candles. Marthe, ignoring him, walked up and down in front of the flickering hearth. 'So what did he say? Whatever is wrong, I am sure with his sense of the picturesque Francis will present a *fadeur exquise* quite adorable.'

The last stand of tapers lit her skin and made it translucent: pure as that of a girl ten years younger. It lit also something else: the fashionable silhouette of a woman standing just inside the open door which led to Marthe's cabinet. The chamber-groom, catching sight of it first, said, 'Oh, my lady. Madame returned with a guest. I . . . We . . .'

'You forgot to tell her I was here,' said Philippa Somerville. 'You will have to make your peace with her about that afterwards. Marthe, I have been eavesdropping. Do you mind

242

entertaining winged virgins with brazen claws? I think divorced wives should appear among the funeral trophies.'

Jerott said she had changed. It was true, Adam saw. Even since London Philippa had altered, not so much in face as in presence. And the spontaneous honesty which had always been there had acquired a disconcerting edge from other, flourishing faculties which seemed to spring up, like dragons' teeth, to meet each fresh challenge of fortune.

The servant, released by a sign, fled from the room. Marthe said, 'Mr Blacklock was coming to see you. You've saved him the trouble.' She held a chair while Philippa sat, her cloak discarded; her furred sleeves folded on the tiled floor. Then Marthe added, seating herself, 'But you have mentioned something we didn't know. Is your marriage annulled?'

Philippa sat very straight but not cross-legged, which would have come to her, as it happened, equally easily. 'Not yet. But the Queen has made it known privately that if the war goes well, Mr Crawford may, if he wishes, marry Catherine d'Albon before his twelve months of service are finished. The Queen of Scotland is furious and even Mademoiselle d'Albon appears faintly stunned. It should be a rather fine match, if they can find a volunteer to go to bed with her mother. You were speaking of Volos?'

'You heard what we said?' Marthe said.

'Yes. I can tell you something else,' Philippa said. 'The attacks began again when Mr Crawford came back from Russia to London.'

'They began at Berwick,' said Adam dryly, 'when his older brother took an enviable opportunity to knock him senseless. Then between us we made it impossible for him to go to Russia. After that, we weren't in the running as confidants.'

'Do you mean that anyone is?' said Marthe coolly. 'Perhaps he'll take all his difficulties to Catherine d'Albon, but I shouldn't count on it. How did Archie find out?'

There were some facts about Lymond that Adam was not prepared to betray to his sister.

'By accident,' said the artist briefly. 'We know the kind of life Francis has led. Concussion also does curious things.'

'These are the reasons a layman would give,' Marthe said. 'I think you should tell us what the prophet of Salon-de-Crau has diagnosed.'

Adam looked at Philippa, who had said nothing. 'I can't

243

tell you Archie's commentary,' he said, 'because it was frankly unrepeatable. But Nostradamus said, according to Archie, that the Gods sell the goods that they give us. We have been shown a fine instrument. But the bow could be overlong bent; the harp lose its voice if its strings were not loosened.'

'I hope he said so in Francis's hearing. Poor Archie,' said Marthe. 'Did he say what should be loosened? His morals?'

'His further pronouncements,' said Adam, his colour a little heightened, 'were confined to lofty admonitions. Francis was to be encouraged to identify the source of his anxiety and assisted to deal with it. Archie, naturally enough, has not brought himself to ask the comte de Lymond and Sevigny what his worries are. He wouldn't do it if God sent him his pardon. Nor would any of us.'

'But of course, we know them, don't we?' said Marthe. 'His family. His thwarted ambition in Russia. His frustration over his divorce. But you say that is to be settled.'

'At Easter,' said Philippa. "If . . . the war goes well.' She sat flat-backed, her hair laced in a caul, and considered the matter, Adam thought, as if it had to do with the fate of a stud groom. 'And once he has his freedom, of course, he will be able to leave for Russia if he wishes, singing the Hosanna. If he doesn't wish, he will presumably marry Catherine d'Albon, which should have the effect of loosening somebody's tension, if only Catherine d'Albon's. The only remaining problem is the family one, which is precisely what I came to see Marthe about.'

Adam stood up. The fire had burnt low. The brilliant light in the uncomfortable room showed traces of dust and of disrepair, eloquent of the crown's somewhat niggardly hospitality as well as Marthe's careless keeping. He said, 'This is private to you and to Francis, but I agree with Jerott. He asked me to come here and put it to you. If you know anything that will help the rift between Sybilla and Francis, you must act on it.'

'Do we?' said Marthe to Philippa, her blue eyes shining, her hair a bright nimbus in the candlelight.

'No,' said Philippa flatly.

'Then there is no need for Mr Blacklock, surely, to dine alone while we discuss it. You know my happy estate I take it, Mr Blacklock? The tactful term is *cloud-fallen*. It means begotten in unlawful bed, of free parents. How free is a mat-

244

ter to which Philippa has been devoting her spare time unstintedly. Stay and listen.'

Philippa said, 'Adam has done enough for the Crawfords without supping off their dirty linen. I am going. I only want to pose you one question. Marthe, do you know, or does Adam, if an old lady from Flavy-le-Martel has been brought to see Mr Crawford?'

Marthe, her eyes narrowed, stared back at Philippa. But Adam answered at once. 'Of course. You knew he was going there. You didn't hear then, that he arrived and walked into an ambush? Someone had told the Spaniards he was coming. They took him to Ham, and he escaped shortly afterwards. The old lady, I'm afraid, died in the fighting. He has written you a note about it.'

The sealed paper was inside his pourpoint. He brought it out and laid it on the lap of Francis's titular wife. She made no effort to open it. She said instead, 'I didn't know he was going there. He told me he was going to send for her.'

'He did?' said Adam incredulously. Then he paused and said, 'Well, his letter may tell you more about it. He hopes, by the way, that Queen Mary will now agree to release you. If she does, I'm to take you to England.'

'Now?' said Marthe, her voice silvery with amusement. 'Is it good for Francis to be without you, Mr Blacklock? Should we not ask him to escort his own wife to England? It would provide a respite for his weakening fibre. And if he succumbs, she can nurse him.'

It was getting late. Adam said, 'He may need us after the campaign, but not during it. He has promised Strozzi nothing less than total success whatever happens.'

'Success in what?' said Marthe sharply.

It clashed with Philippa's voice, repeating his words. 'Whatever happens?'

Adam Blacklock looked at the indigo darkness outside the casements, and then at the hour glass. 'You'll hear of it, I expect by tomorrow. This morning he took the cavalry with Strozzi into enemy territory. Two hours ago he should have made his rendezvous. And by dawn, he will be with the whole French army inside the Pale, advancing on Calais.'

'*Calais!*' Philippa said. Her skin had turned very pink; her eyes brilliant.

'Yes. The rest of the counter-marching was simply to draw the Spanish troops south to defend Luxembourg. If it succeeded, we shall be into Calais and Guînes before any major force can prevent us. If it didn't he's led 21,000 men into an ambush a deal bigger than the one he was caught in at Ham. You needn't fear,' said Adam Blacklock, 'for his weakening fibre. If you'd ever seen Lymond on the battle-field you would know that his private life fades like froth in a furnace-pan. Until Calais is won there won't be any headaches. And if it's lost, more than Francis will suffer.'

He left presently for his apartments, and Marthe went with him, to arrange food and service. While she was gone, Philippa lifted Lymond's letter and carrying it to a small desk, studied the seal and then, slowly, pressed it apart with a paper knife.

She knew the writing well now, with its straight lines and small, balanced characters. There was no preamble.

I have seen Renée Jourda, now dead. She has confirmed all we know. You may tell Marthe, if you wish, that she and I were born to Gavin and Béatris, the Dame de Doubtance's daughter, after Gavin married Sybilla. There is therefore no more information to be sought, and you may go home to Kate as soon as the Queen will allow it. Adam will take you. Adam will also tell you how I was ambushed at Flavy. I have seen the letter sent to Ham by the informer. The writing was Leonard Bailey's.

Until you leave, you must therefore be careful. If Bailey is vindictive enough to have followed me, he may try to find some means of harming you. Adam will arrange your protection. Meanwhile, never travel alone. And leave France as quickly as possible. For Kate's sake, I beg you to do this.

And he signed, as he always did, with his initials.

There seemed no harm in showing Marthe the letter. She read it through on her return, quite unmoved by it. Probably, Philippa thought, she had assumed all her life that Camille de Doubtance was a kinswoman. She might have thought Gaultier to be her father. If it pleased her to discover herself the love-child of a loud-mouthed, lusty, profligate Scottish nobleman, no one would have known it. At the end, she said only, 'Who is Leonard Bailey?'

'A nasty gentleman,' Philippa said. 'The uncle by marriage of Gavin Crawford, the second baron, your father. He was staying as a boy at the Crawfords' castle in Scotland when his married sister gave birth to Gavin. After she died, he and Gavin were brought up together, but he resented living on

246

charity and hated his sister's husband, the first baron Crawford of Culter, who was popular and rather stylish.

'In the end, he made himself such a nuisance that after Gavin's wedding to Sybilla, Gavin's father booted him out of the castle. He took himself yelping to England and made a living, so far as we can make out, selling state secrets. Mr. Crawford discovered only this spring that he had been blackmailing Sybilla for years over the fact that two of her offspring weren't Gavin's. Mr. Crawford got hold of the evidence and has paid him regularly ever since for his silence.'

'And now it appears that Bailey is pursuing him,' Marthe said. 'But with Francis dead or in prison, would Bailey's pension not cease?'

'No,' Philippa said. 'It will be paid by Mr Crawford's bankers, whether he is alive or not, all through Sybilla's lifetime. But that may not be long.'

'Then I wonder,' said Marthe, 'why your Mr Bailey doesn't wait for Sybilla's death before risking Francis's possibly lethal displeasure? Or has Francis never considered that—what, great-uncle?—Bailey should have an accident?'

'He decided against it,' said Philippa smoothly. 'Clearly an error.'

'I stand humbled,' said Marthe. 'And Renée Jourda?'

'She was a maid at the Abbey of Notre-Dame de la Guiche. She left before you were born, Philippa said. 'When Sybilla abandoned the Claires, Renée followed her. Leonard Bailey knew I would probably visit the convent. He must have known about Renée Jourda. It was a safe guess that once I had been to la Guiche, I would tell Mr Crawford. And that when he heard, Mr Crawford would want to visit Flavy.'

There was a little silence. Then Marthe dropped the letter back in Philippa's lap. 'I doubt,' she said, 'if Francis is going to be cured by the heady knowledge that he was sired by the rude Gavin upon the Dame de Doubtance's bastard. It was a romantic idea of Mr Blacklock's, but I know nothing that will help matters, and it is a long time since Volos. What do you suggest? Have you not laid bare some genial morsel of genealogy that will make him whole as Kentigern's robin?'

'No. I remain receptive to ideas,' said Philippa. 'The bladder may be dipped, but never drowned. We have been a sad disappointment to Adam.'

'Ah yes. Mr Blacklock,' said Marthe. 'I have always held that sentimentality is the ruin of the amateur artist. I know a

247

good deal about Mr Blacklock: Jerott and he spent a crapulous evening together. Are you aware, for example, that the scar on his face was caused by a whiplash from Francis?'

'No,' said Philippa. The closed paper between her fingers, she rested in the depths of her chair looking up at the curling smile and the yellow silk hair of her interlocutor. Where Marthe moved, soft as vapour in webs of antique, intangible richness, Philippa sat, still and burnished and clear-eyed, and studied her.

Marthe said, 'Is that wheat repels you? All men on occasion revert to the animal. The Schiatti; the poets; the seigneurs who pay court to you would be no better. What strange Northumberland prudery barred Francis from your bed?'

(Why ask me? someone said. *So that you may ask yourself,* someone replied. *What a silly question.)*

The brown gaze did not shift, or veil itself. 'To be accurate,' Philippa said, 'it was a strange, Celtic prudery. You forget. He did share my bed.'

'Under duress. You were a child. But now you are a grown woman. Would it not amuse you to make him think of you as one? You are his wife, and it is four months to Easter.'

'... And look at the effect a whipping had on Adam?' said Philippa. 'Of course, I am tempted. But, my friends, this is blood, and not the ichor which blest immortals shed. I mentioned before. I am not made for martyrdom. I want to be free to make my choice of husband. And if I share my favours, I forfeit my annulment.'

Marthe stood looking at her, arrested in puzzlement. 'He is only ten years older than you are. I was younger by a generation than Gaultier.'

Philippa played the only card she had left; and the cruellest. 'He is in love with someone else,' she said quietly.

Pride made the next pause a long one; but even pride broke in the end.

'Who is she?' said Marthe.

'He wouldn't say,' Philippa answered. Her gaze unwavering, she drove home her advantage. 'But when he is freed, you are anxious he should not go back to Russia?'

Marthe moved. 'I am averse to waste,' she said lightly. Smiling again, that perverse, slanting smile, she lifted her hand and stroked the quilled porcupine on the chimney-piece. 'Perhaps even frustration is better than being split by four horses in Muscovy. If you don't think so, I am sure Mademoiselle Catherine d'Albon does.'

Reflectively, Philippa studied Marthe. Jerott had said that on Volos, only Marthe had understood her brother well enough to save him. Philippa suspected it had been achieved through competence, but from no natural sense of affection. 'Of course, Mr Crawford has made an impression on her but she is, I think, cool. At least,' said Philippa, considering with equal thoroughness both extra-marital seduction and rapine, 'she guards her feelings.'

'So should I, if the Maréchale were my mother,' said Marthe. 'But he is not cool.'

Philippa looked at her. Was she meant to smile, remembering all the dissolute hosts of his lovers? And yet she was prepared to swear, if Marthe was not, that he had never embarked yet upon a debauch save deliberately, and with coldness.

Elegans est animal. In some men the intellect governed the body, but the spirit escaped from its censorship. In the bedchamber, Marthe was wrong. In every other way, her careless assumption was all too accurate. It was because he was not cool that Sybilla's betrayal had harmed him so vilely.

Marthe was talking again. 'Will you stay in France and help to encourage this girl? Or do the machinations of the nasty Mr Bailey deter you?'

Her eyes on the fire, Philippa sat still and thought about it.

She was free to go if she wished. Whatever had impelled Mary of Scotland to throw herself and Lymond together, it could not apply now, when the Queen of France had taken so forceful a hand in the game. And Catherine d'Albon her protégée was more than a possible bedfellow. She was also a possible instrument to turn Mr Crawford from Russia.

She was free to go. But if, by staying, she could steer these two towards one another; if there still existed any fragment of history which would reconcile him to his family then nothing, Philippa thought, would make her go home but the demand he had made in his letter.

She sat still, and let her eyes rest on it. A dismissive letter. A letter which hastened to say that the case was closed, the facts known, the actors due for dispersal. And there, in Bailey's name, was an excellent reason why she, Philippa, should leave France quickly. Escorted by Adam. For Kate's sake.

She believed in the letter from Bailey. She believed there might be a degree of danger. She believed Renée Jourda was dead and had told Lymond little.

What fretted her about Lymond's note were its omissions. He had told her he would send for Renée Jourda. From Adam's face she now knew the suggestion had never been feasible. To stop her plaguing him, Lymond had gone to Flavy himself. And had been captured. And had led false information, Adam said, which had misfired through no fault of his, and which even now might turn against the whole army.

He had promised to bring her news. He had not promised, in so many words, to send for Renée Jourda. He had at no time intended to send for Renée Jourda.

He had sent her news. He had not sent her the name of Sybilla's lover, or made even the smallest comment on the whole worrying subject of Bailey.

She had wept once because she could not escape, but that was behind her. They had met, she and Lymond, and the skies had not fallen. If she was hurt, she was able to conceal it. If he found matters not to his liking he, too, had the means to avoid her. And meanwhile, there was something at least she could do for him. Perhaps, because of those very omissions, more than she was at present aware of.

For example, this matter of Bailey. It was true, the old man was vindictive. But it was also true that the old man was greedy. The last person, one would have said, to risk his pension for a moment of malice. Or to risk more than that if Lymond caught him. Some of that had been obvious even to Marthe, but Lymond had said nothing of it. If she wished to know more, she must make her own inquiries.

Nor had he said anything, either written or verbal, about what might await him in Calais. She could not save him there. If, as Adam said, the plan misfired, there was nothing she could do except be here, under the same benign sky, and hope when his life drew to its end that she would know it.

Tant que je vive . . . She could not be there. But from Philippa, poor silly infatuated Philippa, a warmth of some sort might perhaps reach him.

To Marthe she said, 'Do you know, I think I might stay in France for a week or two. After all, I want my annulment as well. And I want to prepare Kate for the Schiatti cousins.'

CHAPTER 9

Siege en cité, et de nuict assaillie
Peu eschapés, non loing de mer conflict.

The news Adam brought was the last to reach court before
that vast army of France, coalescing, rolled against the two-
hundred-year-old frontier which enclosed all that England
still cherished of her years of dominion.

Silence fell. The Court moved to Paris for the State Entry
of the Cardinal Legate and in order that the King might
make a public appeal for more money. Adam, bearing what
funds the Treasury could supply, had long since returned to
his headquarters. The restlessness that presages noble events
hung in the air, harassing the attention. In Paris, everyone
had seen the workshops working day and night; the covered
wagons endlessly blocking the portals; the groups of engineers
who would knock up the cook-shops at midnight. The
Maréchale de St André, back from the coast, reported that
a hundred and twenty ships had left, sailing west and laden
with ordnance, and another forty, they said, had arrived at
Ambleteuse with corn and wine and bacon and hurdles and
ladders and cannon-shot. Then someone asked her the nature
of her journey and she became belatedly vague. Her daughter
smiling, turned the conversation.

Philippa helped. Attending functions with her own regal
mistress she made a point of seeking out Catherine d'Albon.
It needed forethought. The Maréchale had found it amusing
that the comte de Sevigny's wife should interest herself in her
husband's next marriage. Her daughter was more reserved.
But because she was more perceptive, in time she saw more
than the Maréchale.

Madame de Sevigny's interest was not crude or childish but
simply friendly. Married only in name, she had no quarrel to
pick with her husband. She did not even refer to him. She
was merely there when one most needed kindness. When the
great military confrontation that rumour talked about sud-

251

denly took to itself a designation. When through all the alleys of Paris the thickening whispers turned and clicked like the wheels of the watermills. *Calais ... Calais ... They go to throw the English from Calais.*

If Calais fell, she was to have Francis Crawford—if he asked for her. One did not speak of it. In this campaign, the Duke de Guise was supreme commander. On that the King and court staunchly insisted. But the cognoscenti in Paris knew differently. Among these, one heard only two names: those of Strozzi and Sevigny.

It was during this time that Philippa, watching the Queen's lady of honour, learned her stature and learned also, with pity, her secret.

So, rashly, Catherine had given her heart before she was asked for it. The daughter of a noble house, trained to court, skilled in all the liberal arts, she was a fitting wife for Lymond and Sevigny. She might enjoy a better fortune than that. She might prove to be one of the most private and exclusive circle of persons to whom Francis Crawford gave, without mocking, his friendship.

If Calais fell. If the Duke of Savoy, less experienced than anyone thought, did not take a piece of suspect information at its face value and prepare for the Duke de Guise's splendid army a reception they would never survive. If, whatever happened, the spearhead of that army lived to see it happen.

Philippa talked to Catherine d'Albon, and played music with her, and read aloud and was read to, and did some fine and useless embroidery and attended all the sacerdotal celebrations graced by the Cardinal Legate, at which the King of France's smile, also, was a little less than spontaneous, and the Cardinal of Lorraine was seen to be thoughtful.

The last of these, with the feeblest of timing, was a Sunday wedding on a cold day in January between the second daughter of the Duchess of Bouillon and the second son of the Duke de Nevers, who was not there to witness it, and might never be.

It was a wedding attended by young boys, by old men and by women. Kneeling jewelled at the nuptial Mass in the stiff, scented folds of their Court gowns: rose and verdet, orange, azure and cinnabar there prayed, smiling and aching, the brides and daugthers and mistresses of all the young and well-born men who today were absent on the shores of the

English Sea, where blood and flesh was their portion; steel their cincture; and gunsmoke, not incense, their mystery.

Unaccountably, Marthe had attended. Enigmatic patron of all the arts, she took little account of her place on the fringe of the court, in spite of the persuasions of those she patronized. As Marthe, she was not invited: as Jerott Blyth's wife, she would have none of it. So, at first, Philippa was disturbed and startled to see the smooth jewelled head held high in that uneasy company. Marthe's escorts she knew because they were acquaintances of her own. Men of song; men of vision; men of ideas were those with whom Philippa also was at home. She knew already, from their talk, how many frequented Marthe's lodging. At court, they were not slow to question her about her husband's step-sister.

That she could deal with. It was foolish also to ignore the obvious. Mirrored in Marthe were some of her brother's most telling characteristics. It was not surprising that Marthe and she should be drawn to the same people.

What troubled her was that Marthe should be here now, at wedding, at banquet and during all the persevering festivities through which, on the edge of the abyss, noblesse meticulously obliged. Since their friends were mutual, Philippa found Marthe beside her, coolly amusing, through most of the long afternoon. The Schiatti nephews, whom good manners restrained to begin with, soon found there was no need to avoid the subject of the comtesse de Sevigny's promised annulment, and returned to exchanging barbed witticisms with those other gallants, rather youthful or excessively elderly, who also wished to appropriate Philippa's attention. With a certain sardonic good humour, Lymond's sister gave them friendly encouragement.

It was not a kindness. Courts English, Oriental and French had instructed Philippa in the peerless art of disguising her feelings, but it was not easy to have Marthe compliment her on her witty composure, or to smile at Marthe's account of the reason.

The Schiatti cousins approved of Marthe. 'She is right. Either Calais is won and your marriage is ended, or it is lost and M. your husband snatched up to heaven. Be merry. We are merry for you.'

Then they looked remorseful, a little; because they had recalled, as they occasionally did, that she was English. That Calais to England was her other frontier; the place where her

253

armies could land, her merchants bring their ships safely, to enter the Continent for trade or for war, asking no other ruler his leave. The open gate at the other end of a thirty-mile drawbridge without which no easy exit was left. Then they forgot again, and were cheerful.

Not so, Catherine d'Albon. Watching her as she sat through the banquet, Philippa sensed the strain which for other reasons oppressed her. If Calais fell, Lymond was hers. But first, he had to live through it.

Philippa wondered if, like herself, Cathin had cajoled the plan of attack from a flattered gentleman of the secretariat. She wondered if, between one mouthful of food and the next, Catherine with twelve thousand horse and foot was also occupying all the marshy passages between Calais and France and attacking their strongholds: Sandygate, Frethun and Nielles, St Agathe, Coquelles and St Tricat. And after that, opening fire at the Newnham Bridge turnpike and charging it with eighty horses, so that the planks of the bridge thudded and splintered, and armour clashed and cannon exploded, and cries of *France! France! Charge! Charge!* twinned and soared with the cries of her countrymen.

She wondered if, when talk lapsed before music, Catherine dwelt as she did on that freezing hour before dawn, when the French great cannon, sailed to Boulogne, opened up on the two key positions: the fort of Nieullay commanding the causeway, and Ruisbank, commanding the harbour. While the army, 35,000 strong, lay between St Peter's heath and the dunes, and the wagons of food and machines and munitions rolled in precisely to order.

Fighting in sand, you had to storm and take Ruisbank, and under the guns of the city 800 paces away, prepare to ford the river belt-high to the citadel. Because of the mud, you had pitch-plastered hurdles to lie on. On account of the marshes, the ditches, the rivers and runnels of water which afforded the Pale its protection you had brought pioneers protected with stakes woven with willow, who cut the ditches and drained the moat water into the sand dunes.

Then you breached the citadel, firing on it from the quarters with your sixty cannon and culverin; and risked the tide to fight your way into it, knowing that once in, the sea would cut you off from all help. Then, if you mastered the citadel, you commanded the bridge into the town, and on that you would turn all your fire.

If, before you fired a shot, the army of the Duke of Savoy, waiting, did not flood from each strongpoint and destroy you.

Catherine did not know what had happened at Ham. She was spared, perhaps, the worst of the beating foreboding that drove all other feeling from Philippa. She had never seen the kind of response Lymond made, from pride or from instinct, to a professional challenge. She feared his death: one could see that, and in each stolen silence, settled her thoughts on him.

Perhaps he felt it. There were moments when, lost in spirit among the thundering gunfire at Calais, Philippa felt within reach of something familiar. As when, long ago, passing Gideon's door, she could sense when her father was there: self-contained, occupied, content in his private absorption.

But Lymond knew her feelings for him were not those of a daughter. Catherine was free to knock on that door: to send to him her thoughts and her love, to be with him through his time of danger.

For Philippa, it would be inconceivable so to harass him. So, in a condition of strange, blank-eyed reserve which alternated, unobserved, with the social demands of the festival, Philippa fought her way through the long, grim afternoon as if she were side by side with the army at Calais, and yet forced her stubborn spirit to bend aside from its homing.

The day ground on towards dusk. The King, with sallow gallantry, led the bride in pavanes and galliards. The Schiatti argued suavely over which, next day, would take Philippa hunting. The nobleman behind her, also a suitor, wished to know her exact plans for returning to Scotland, and by what means he might recommend himself to her family. The Queen of Scots, in an interval, demanded to meet Mistress Blyth, who was so amazingly like to her brother.

They did not take to one another. When, presently, the Queen rose to take part in a galliard, Philippa said to her step-sister by marriage, 'Marthe. Why did you come?'

'For the revelry,' Marthe said. 'Men live, not while they breathe, but while they live well. And to cast an eye, I must admit, on my fellow-women. The girl, Catherine, you can see, adores my splendid Francis. How does he do it?'

'Alchemy,' said Philippa shortly. 'The Maréchale de St André thought he was a shower of gold.' *If you place your cannon on shipboard, for God's sake watch the steep fall of*

*the tide. At ebb your battery will cease to bear, and you will
yourself be under fire from the defenders.*

'I thought you admired the noble Catherine,' said Marthe.
'The young Queen certainly wishes him tied to you and to
Scotland. A monstrous tiger among the silly flocks. How nice
to go through life being male, pretty and wanted.'

*You will have to hinder them when they try to repair the
citadel breach. Watch out. They will cover the work with fu-
sillades, and they seem to have plenty of light artillery.* Philippa said, 'It rather depends what you are wanted for.'

'Ah yes. It is a property of bells,' Marthe said, 'to call others to church, but to enter not therein themselves. . . . If you
are bored, ask your mistress to excuse you. These tiresome
satellites cling together awaiting tidings from Calais, but you
have a home in each country. You, of us all, by divine
bounty are free from all apprehension.'

*Remember, the citadel is a magazine, packed hard with
munitions. While you are there, cut off from reinforcements,
guard against Greek fire from the town cavaliers and bastions. They will be desperate. Remember. Remember.* Rare in
her life, Philippa's temples were aching. 'I might leave early,'
she answered. 'But should I leave you here to suffer? Jerott *is*
with the armies?'

Marthe smiled. 'Jerott goes, like Crassus' lamprey, when
one calls him. His death has no high price on it. It is Francis
whose falling will drag a whole edifice down. Strangled on his
body his concubines and his cupbearer, the master of his
horse and his chamberlain, the usher of his great hall, and his
pastry-cook.'

Philippa rose.

And as she stood, the doors opened and the music wavered
and perished.

Through the noise, no one had heard the growing din in
the streets as the hard-pressed group of horsemen entered the
portals of Paris and rode stumbling along the rue St
Antoine's icy runnels, where the paving had been stripped for
the tilting match.

Even the hubbub at the gatehouse had failed to reach this
long, tapestried room with its bridal banners and flowers and
escutcheons where France dallied, while its manhood, its
prowess, its fortune all hung in the balance.

The doors opened, to admit a manifold uproar and a single
gentleman of the chamber.

256

The words he spoke to the King were unguessable. Behind the sculptured black beard something altered. The King mounted the dais to his chair. Then through the doors in spurred boots and cuirass, mud caked as he had ridden all the long, difficult journey from Abbeville came Robertet; a familiar face, frowning with weariness, and a tread, after the dancers' light feet, like yoke-oxen.

At the dais, he genuflected and the King's white jewelled fingers commanded him. 'We welcome you, M. Secretary. Rise, turn, and tell all my people what news you bring them.'

He rose. He turned. Between all the intervening, motionless heads Philippa could see the mask, grey cracked with white, which the mud had laid on his features. Robertet cleared his throat and then lifted his voice, hoarsely, into the silence.

'Your Majesties, mes seigneurs, messieurs, mesdames . . . I have the honour to tell you that Calais is French once again.'

*

The cheering, beyond all controlling, went on for ten minutes. For ten minutes the Schiatti thumped her shoulders and pumped Catherine d'Albon by the hand. For ten minutes no single fact of the winning of Calais could be learned: the author of the triumph, its course, its culmination, its cost. Many broke into tears. Many shouted, still weeping. Many, like the demoiselle d'Albon, stood silent, their eyes brilliant, their hearts offering prayer.

Marthe said to her step-sister by marriage, 'If you are feeling loyal, then I must ask you to accept my commiserations. On the other hand, you will now be free of your husband by April.'

Robertet had started speaking. The noise died. The words *glorious leadership* and *Duke de Guise* made themselves heard. Philippa said, 'What did he say?'

'He is placing credit where credit is expected. We needn't, however, stay to applaud him. There is a door just behind you if you would like to complete your withdrawal.'

'. . . and Marshal de France Piero Strozzi . . .'

'I can't hear him. He's mumbling. Come on,' said Gino Schiatti. 'I want to see how Paris is taking it.'

'. . . the efforts of Messrs d'Aumale and d'Elboeuf, le Duc de Bouillon and M. de Montmorency . . .'

'There won't be hunting tomorrow, devil take it. He'll

decree a thanksgiving service and celebrations. Mistress Philippa . . .'

'. . . not without cost. Stubborn fighting . . . Aside from those lost in the water . . . The Master of the Camp, who had his foot clean blown off . . .'

'Then that's agreed. This way, Mistress Philippa. No, follow Marco. It is not necessary to obtain permission from your Queen? The occasion is without precedent.'

'I thought you were bored?' Marthe said. 'Don't tell me—'

'. . . Among those whose sacrifice we who survive will long remember . . .'

'Do you mind,' said Philippa Somerville bitingly, 'if before romping drunk in the city I satisfy myself whether I am merely unhappily married or widowed?'

The Secretary's voice came to an end. Marthe betrayed a faint irritation. 'Later,' she said. 'You can hear all the details.'

'Such as whether Jerott is living?' Philippa said. And turning, made a smooth but remorseless passage away from her.

Lymond's sister made no effort to keep her. Over the heads of the courtiers she watched her make her inquiry. But when, hard on that, Philippa walked out of the room. Marthe broke off her discourse and moving swiftly, made her way through the same doorway.

It led to the guardroom; to a passage lined with the white and silver hoquetons of the Archers and, at last, to a long, empty gallery, of which one windowed wall looked over the garden. There had been no time for Philippa to reach the end of it, even had she been walking quickly. Nor had she thought of seeking sanctuary in any one of the rooms which gave on to it. Instead she had simply slowed up and stopped in the middle, and when Marthe came up behind her was standing perfectly still, her hands loose at her sides.

Marthe paused, her hand still on the door-latch behind her. Then she closed both leaves and watched Philippa's head lift at the click of it. She walked forward and spoke. 'Gino is pining. Did you learn what you wanted to find out?'

Philippa heaved a short sigh. Then turning, Lymond's wife faced her inquisitor.

Her face was marked, past disguising, with the clear ribboned tracks of her weeping. 'Yes,' said Philippa thinly. 'And so, I take it, have you.'

Unusually, Marthe was pale. But the mockery lingered,

like a snow-print caught in ice after the thawing. 'Yes,' she said. 'I know that our wanton is safe. And that you love him.'

He is safe. The tears, defying all discipline began again, coursing down her no doubt clown-like cheeks and jumping off through the pearls on her bodice. Philippa said, 'What a perfect day you must be having.'

> *(Estoilete, je te voi*
> *Que la lune trait a soi*
> *M'amiete o le blont poil)*

'I am pleased, naturally,' Marthe said. 'I gather Jerott and the others are equally blessed by fortune.' There was a long cushioned stool in the window embrasure. With a hissing rustle of tissues, she sank on it. 'So. I love the love that loves not me: I am his friend and he my foe? You have been excessively secretive. You were afraid I should tell Francis what you feel for him?'

'I think you should,' Philippa said.

The blue eyes stared into hers. Then unexpectedly, the fair face relaxed. 'And receive my quittance, I gather. So he knows.'

Without speaking, Philippa regarded her. Then she said, 'He has cause to suspect, but tact enough to ignore the situation. He has ties elsewhere. I think I told you as much.'

'You did. You also said the paragon's name was unknown to you. You cannot know how many mistakes he has made. He may be making another.'

'It had occurred to me,' said Philippa briefly. 'I am quite sure he isn't. Otherwise I should hardly be planning to marry again.'

'I see. And who is to suffer in the cause of Francis's nerve-storms? One of the Schiatti? The Duke of Paliano? One of the Dauphin's young titled gentlemen?'

'I thought,' said Philippa, 'of trying them one after the other.' She stood quite still, facing her sister-in-law. 'No one will suffer. Marriage, like law, is a practice. Aut bibat, aut abeat. Subscribe, or get out of it.'

'Like Jerott,' said Marthe. 'And your families? Whatever your choice, you must make your romance convincing. In four weeks, nine Scottish delegates are coming to France to contract for the little Queen's marriage. Pious, religious and unblamable princes who will repeat current gossip like jack-daws.'

Had it been anyone but Marthe, of the open eyes and dulcet voice and sleek yellow hair, one would have taken that at its face value.

It cost something: it cost almost more than she could manage to fight, and to keep on fighting, by this time. Philippa said, 'I hadn't heard, but I am sure that I'm going to. What has Queen Mary been telling you?'

'It was Mary Fleming,' said Marthe. 'A pretty, uncritical creature, and a devoted admirer of Francis. She tells me Richard Crawford of Culter is one of the Scottish bridal Commissioners.'

Lymond's brother. 'Yes?' said Philippa flatly.

Marthe smiled. 'He is coming next month. And bringing with him Sybilla his mother.'

CHAPTER 10

Six jours l'assaut devant cité donné
Livrée sera forte et aspre bataille.

In one matter Lymond's captains had forecast correctly. In
the weeks of brilliant manœuvring which preceded the invest-
ment of Calais, neither they nor their leader had a thought
for personal matters. And even when Calais surrendered,
there was still a rose to replace in the chaplet. The remaining
marshy square miles of the Pale, the last English possessions
in France, had to be overrun and appropriated before the triumph was perfect.

Thus, while the Duchess of Bouillon's daughter was
bedded, the victors of Calais were casting already through the
cold winter marshes, spreading fright and apprehension
among all the lonely, Spanish-held strongholds.

The Duke of Savoy their commander was not there. For
days he had been in Bruges, begging for money with which to
pay the five German regiments hurriedly saved from disband-
ing, and for the 12,000 more foot and horse he would have
to raise, recall or seduce from their warm German ale-houses
to replace the armies he had just dispersed for the winter.

Meanwhile, crowded on the frontier at Gravelines were his
best Spanish captains, each with handfuls of Walloons and
hackbutters. More were marching up from the south, where
the French Jack-o'-lantern had beckoned them, but were still
too far off to be comfortable. Nor could he cull men from
Saint-Quentino or Ham or le Catelet. Those hard-won Spanish
forts were under-garrisoned as it was.

Messages, earnest, courteous and sensible, passed back and
forth between King Philip and his wife, Mary Tudor of England. It was understood that the Earl of Rutland was preparing an army to protect the English possessions round Calais.
They said that the Earl of Pembroke was on his way with
5,000 men to cross the Channel from Dover, and that a further
5,000 were spoken for. It was known that eighteen English

ships, no doubt laden with troops, had had to turn back from Calais because of the disastrous capture of Fort Ruisbank. Preparations were made to receive landings at Dunkirk; lighters and barges were assembled at Dunkirk, Nieuport and Ostend; carts for money and baggage were readied.

The Duke of Savoy, still awaiting his army, laid plans to encamp at Saint-Omer.

Three thousand unarmed refugees walked into Gravelines from Calais, and had to be sheltered and nourished. A lively, well-plenished band of 400 enemy horse rode up to the Sluice before Gravelines, reconnoitred it and Dunkirk, and withdrew, neatly, leaving panic behind them.

Another troop stopped off at the English-held fortress of Hâmes, and called upon Edward, Lord Dudley, to deliver the castle. He refused, even to death. By the back postern, at the same moment, he sent a call of despair to King Philip: for guns, powder and spades, and a standard of three hundred foot-soldiers. No one sent them. The besiegers, on the other hand, had other business to attend to. They made a note to return and rode off, in high spirits.

On Thursday, 13 January, six days after Calais's surrender, the town and fortress of Guînes was surrounded.

Lord Grey of Wilton had seen it coming. In fact, he got Mary, his wife, to ride for help that first weekend, when the French were busy sapping up to the fortress by trenches. It was done properly, with a safe conduct from the Duke de Guise, who would never subject an English Earl's daughter to the inconvenience of a bombardment. All the same, she had a long message to convey to the Duke of Savoy which her husband had induced her to memorize. Unless relieved, Guînes was in great danger of falling. There was food for only thirteen days and powder for four. The French were trenching to drain the defence moats and had occupied the wreck of the town, emptied and burned by Lord Grey himself before they could stop him. The enemy had 35 siege guns protecting his workers while cutting. Lord Grey's total garrison amounted to one thousand English and Burgundians, kindly sent in by the Governor of Artois.

They would, of course, fight to the death for their honour. But the Duke would no doubt see that if Guînes were lost, Calais could hardly be retaken. Whereas (Lady Grey was word perfect on this point) if a strong force were to relieve

Guînes and repulse the French army, the occupiers of Calais might be besieged in turn and starved into submission.

It was all perfectly true. It was not lord Grey's fault that the Duke of Savoy had no army, and that those troops he had, he was saving to protect the Low Counrties, not to lose lives and prestige in pulling English chestnuts out of a peculiarly horrendous French fire. Two small bands of Spanish soldiers were sent to help Lord Grey at Guînes, of whom 35 men got into the citadel and five only lived to get out of it.

By Sunday night, the cuttings had reached the ditches and started to drain them. At dawn on Monday, the bombardment began which was to subject the Mary bulwark between the fortress gate and the town to 9,000 cannon shot in forty-eight hours, dislodge the English counter-battery and breach the bastion.

At two o'clock on Monday afternoon the French sent several parties to wade the moat, now only waist-high, and examine the damage. Later, two bands of Gascons attempted to scale the bulwark and inspect it more closely, and retired, pursued by culvers and hackbuts and pots of wild fire: shortly after, the French resumed firing. The eight deafening salvoes they delivered that evening tore open a breach which exposed all the Mary's defenders.

Night, falling, saved them, but an English captain had lost his life, and a Spanish, and forty or fifty common soldiers. They had then been under siege for five sleepless days before the entire French armed forces. With Lord Grey were his twenty-year-old son Arthur, his cousin Lewis Davie, his nephew Austin Grey, his colleague Henry Palmer, an English captain called Bracknell and an experienced Spanish leader of Alva's called Montdragon. The quality of the leadership was undoubted; and in Grey of Wilton's case, supreme.

He knew the Pale, and its strengths, and its weaknesses. Marsh lay all around him: a wilderness of short, sour grass showing everywhere the white eyes of water, upon which floated the small hill of Guînes.

Marsh protected two sides of the fort's moated ramparts. On the other two, the French were encamped. Lansquenetz straddle the highway to Ardres, which led south from the barbican entrance. And across the west ditch, Frenchmen held the burnt-out husk of the town and by daylight, if they were shrewd, would have ranged their batteries on its maundes, or on the commanding flat stage of the market place. One had only to count the ensigns, streaming from each moving body of troops, and scan the flagged pavilions which spread their skirts from bush to bush to recognize what one was opposing.

There was a particular pleasure, now and then in one's life, in matching one's skill with the best. He had expected to find it when he led the English troops at Saint-Quentin, but that had been a rogue victory, won through an old man's mistakes. Arthur, he remembered had been elated, but he had seen again in his nephew's manner that air of withdrawal which meant he would never make a first-class general, for all his brains.

God knew, one didn't go into this business with any illusions. Over and over again, he had impressed the facts of life on these two boys. One battle in twelve might be won by a brilliant military stratagem. The rest stood or fell by somebody's blunders. Only rarely, there came the feel of a great campaign evolved by a stylist: imaginative, comprehensive, irresistible.

That was the spice in the unseasoned meat of one's livelihood. Savoy had been shown it this winter, and he and Wentworth were the targets. Wentworth had succumbed and so might Guînes, if the troops from England failed to arrive to relieve him. He had sent Mary to beg help from Savoy, but he knew, even if they had help to give, that they would withhold it until the English bands came. If there was to be failure let it be an English failure, as Calais was an English failure. If there looked like being a success, then the troops mustering at Saint-Omer would be marched in to deal the finishing blow.

That night, Lord Grey made a speech to his troops from the bulwark, thanking God for the day's success, praising his men and exhorting them to noble endeavours. In their hands, he said, lay the safety of Guînes; and he took oath before them, and asked his men to take oath in their turn, that the defenders of Guînes would die rather than betray any weakness, or surrender.

After that, they had to erect a new vawmure by entrenching six feet deep in the bulwark, and dawn of Tuesday showed that his forebodings were realized: the enemy had planted a big six-gun battery over the ditch in the marketplace and another of three cannon on the ramparts, making a total of 16 guns aimed at the cathouse and the flanking defence of the barbican. By the end of the morning the cathouse was intact, but not the flankers or the garden bulwark or the curtain wall; and by firing eight or nine regular salvoes an hour, the French were continually crumbling the breach.

The noise was punishing. One's inclination, when it ceased for a moment, was to close the eyes and fall stunned into sleep, and this was dangerous, for the batteries only stopped when another sally was being made. That afternoon it was a regiment of Swiss who approached, with some French, and sent sundry small bands to examine the breach and to try and locate the numbers and stations of the gunners. But Grey was ready, and had the positions concealed. They harassed the reconnoitring party with hackbuts and watched them retire at length with qualified satisfaction: as soon as they were back in camp, the French cannon opened up once again.

The night, once more, they had to spend churning up mud in more trenching. Austin, at one point, came to try and persuade him to snatch some sleep and he did, for an hour: there was no point in leaving his men leaderless. He had no illusions about his command. The Spaniards were good, but they couldn't get the last ounce from the English that he could. Bourne, helpless with gout, had lost his life defending the Mary on a stretcher.

Harry Palmer was able, but still feeling the shoulder wound he took at Bushing last month. He also made the mistake of mixing with the men far too much. They would go with him, but they wouldn't rise, as they might have to, beyond themselves. That was why one talked to them of honour and glory. Men would fight well for their pay, but they would die for an aspiration.

Austin knew that. The trouble with Austin was that he believed so deeply in the chivalrous virtues that he found it impossible to refer to them.

In war—William Grey tried not to sound cynical—in war, it was alas the opposite nature one looked for.

The next day, Wednesday, the enemy opened fire with 24 cannon at daybreak, and the bombardment continued without ceasing for five hours or more, wrecking the curtain wall and driving right through the rampart and the new earthen countermure he had raised on it. He was on his feet all morning, moving between the Mary and Web's Tower watching the effects of the cannonfire, and had just had a bench put down

265

so that he could rest on it while he gave some directions to Palmer, with Lewis sitting side-saddle beside him, when the first telling salvo burst on them.

It was not the first time he had been on the lee side of a direct hit on patched ramparts. Unhewn stone scythed through the air, and a blast of sky-darkening grit swept thudding against them. The bench he was sitting on collapsed, chopped through and broken by boulders. Overturned and rolling, with his hose ripped and his head battered and grazed by his morion, Lord Grey saw Lewis, sprawling, had found some protection behind a crate of currier balls. Palmer, half under the shards of the bench, was protecting his face with his arms, and after that first glance Grey did the same, letting his cuirass shield him as the fall of rubble grew lighter and he could hear, above the ring of the metal, the screams of the wounded and dying.

They suffered their first major losses there by the curtain, and by God's grace only, he and the two men with him were unhurt. Then, immediately, they had to face the first assault in strength by the enemy. At first they came in twos and threes, moving out of the trenches to investigate. Then came the Swiss in close order, stepping into the ditch and marching up to the breach without faltering.

He had done what he could. Twenty of his best shots were in Webb's, and on the other side, a score of Spaniards hidden inside the outworks set up a crossfire when the hand-to-hand fighting was at its worst. And it sufficed, for after an hour with no advance and heavy cost to both sides, the enemy blew the retire and the Swiss left as they had come, and withdrew behind the town's wicker ramparts. Then the bombardment restarted.

Two salvoes brought down Webb's Tower, and killed or maimed all the curriers—his best—who were in it. The firing continued: regular, deliberate shots aimed at the Spaniards still left in the outworks and covering the resting-up and reforming of the assault troops. It was a time for recharging weapons and dragging out balls and powder; for clearing the dead and hurriedly binding the wounded: for the bustle of men obeying and carrying orders, and for everywhere words of encouragement, of commendation, of exhortation before the next big attack should befall them.

He put two hundred fresh men into the bulwark just as the lines of steel helmets appeared again over the counter-scarf and began to move down to the moat. Many more than last time, and well slept and well armed and well led. Then, with pike and bill, it was man to man, face to face and body to body, as the afternoon wore on to dusk. All round, the human voice in all its keys from aggression to anguish to anger, supported by all the music made by metal striking on metal, or the resonance of metal on stone; or the tuneless percussion of metal on hide, flesh and marrowbone.

The fortress held. With his supporting hackbutters dead, his fire weapons finished, his munition boxes made inaccessible, Grey saw his men giving way inch by inch as the French, attracted by the easy fighting, began to cross the ditch unappointed and assail the widening breach. It was then that he thrust hackbuts into the hands of Austin and Harry Palmer and showed them where, concealed by the stonework, they could pick off the enemy.

He knew Harry's trained eye, and his determination. He had watched, over and over again, Arthur's chagrin at his cousin's God-given brilliance with firearms.

Against that, Arthur was a soldier by instinct, and had killed his first man (over a dice game) at eighteen. Whereas Austin, in cold or hot blood, had never taken a life on a battlefield.

Harry Palmer was worried too. His shoulder hurt. From where he crouched, he could see Allendale's dark, delicate profile, bent on to the task of loading powder and shot into his weapon. The boy was a perfectionist. Knew every trick of army strategy from the time of the Caesars, and would talk about them for hours. Rode; jousted; used a bow and a sword; mastered every skill he was set to, like a tradesman. And hated slaughtering men.

Not the person Harry Palmer would choose to trust his life to, out there in the buffeting cold of his niche, bearing down on a scrambling horde of invaders: for if Austin gave way, there would be nothing to protect Harry Palmer when they outflanked him.

On the other hand, Allendale was an oddity. It might just prove that to have a man's life in his hands was the spur that he needed to quieten his conscience. If he brought himself to fire, there was no one else he would trust to do it at all.

Harry Palmer loaded, caught Austin Grey's eye, and signalled. As one, the two long-barrelled hackbuts aimed, paused, and spoke. And on the breach, two of the enemy cried out, staggered, and dying tumbled back down to the ditch.

Swift and sure, Austin's hands set to reloading. He was pleased and happy to find them so steady. He felt still through all his nerves the tingle of triumph he had experienced. Sick with apprehension, he had chosen his target and shot at it. And miraculously, the ball had struck the gold as it always did in the quiet of practice. He had not let his uncle down, or Sir Harry, or the brave and desperate men on the ramparts who were depending on him. He could shoot. He could save lives by shooting. And he had never known before the small, intoxicating glitter of personal victory.

Palmer was looking at him again. Austin smiled, and sighted his weapon, and fired at the same instant as Sir Harry. And two more French soldiers died.

They stayed at their posts firing until nightfall. Between them, they blunted the attack and were part of the reason why the French again called a retire, breasting the cold liquid mud of the ditches, their waterline leaved with the dying. Lord Grey, clapping his nephew on the back, gave him no time to speak or to think, but set him to supervise the repair work on the breach while the dead were thrust aside and the injured roughly tended and the scarce provisions told over.

He called them all briefly together a few hours before dawn, to hear a prayer and his commendation for the way they had fought. 'I tell you,' he said, 'one or two more such banquets will cool the enemy's courage. Hold to your posts. Fight like the men I know you to be.'

The stupidity happened after that in the crowded darkness, as they pushed and jostled about, each with his task to complete before the daylight robbed them of safety. Pain struck as Grey shouldered his way from the bulwark: a pain in his foot so intense that he thought at first it was severed and breathing hard, clutched the arms of the men on either side to prevent himself falling. Then Lewis got to him and he had himself taken indoors, quickly, before he made a fool of himself by losing consciousness. There, cutting off his blood-sodden boot, they confirmed what he suspected had happened: a soldier's scabbardless sword had driven straight through the arch of his foot, severing tendons and releasing a gush of fresh blood which soaked all the cloths that they put on it.

He was not afraid of blood. But he was afraid of the

rumours that start when a commander disappears from the field at the darkest moment and lowest ebb of the battle. He could not stand, but he had the foot cleaned and bound tightly enough to staunch the bleeding. Then he had them bring an armed chair and sitting in it, had himself hoisted like the Bishop of Rome and carried out once again to the bitter wind of the ramparts.

The last day dawned. As the hoar light sifted over the marshes, the Governor of Guînes saw how the enemy had spent the night.

The moat had been bridged. Hurdles, placed across floating casks, spanned the water, already packed with faggots and fleeces. And as he studied it, the day's bombardment began.

It went on until three in the afternoon, and the violence surpassed all they had so far undergone. Borne from place to place, encouraging, ordering, Lord Grey decided by noon what to do. Before the battery ended, he ordered the men in the bulwark to retreat, leaving only a few to make a display of gunfire. Then he sent in his engineers to prepare to blow up the great tower whole.

He never knew whether his plan was discovered. It was perhaps nothing but ill luck that as the fuse was being laid, the assault increased with such fury that no man in Guînes could move, or show his head. And fifteen minutes after that, the enemy's German regiment burst through the bulwark and entering, put all those left to the sword.

There was a moment, at the height of the battle, when Grey of Wilton lurched from his chair and thrusting to the top of the ramparts stood there, exposed in fevered despair and crazily wishing of God that some shot from the bulwark would take him.

It was a common soldier beside him who pulled him down by his scarf, but already his longstanding disciplines had asserted themselves. Calling the rest to follow, he led his remaining suite and their men to the Keep. As the bulwark fell, the men in the base court, Wheathill's Bulwark and the garden rampart abandoned their posts also and fled. Soon all that was left of the defenders of Guînes were together, in the ultimate stronghold. Lord Grey saw the last man inside, and gave orders to ram up the portals.

Many years later the records were to tell how the Duke de Guise's trumpeter, offering parley, came to the moatside that evening; how Lord Grey's men, crowding about him, begged him with tears in their eyes to save their lives by compounding; how, after reading them a homily, he bade them return to their posts, which they did, before his lordship finally sent word that he was prepared to hear the Duke's message.

In fact, there were almost no English left with Lord Grey: they had been cut to pieces defending the bastions. And the Burgundians in the stronghold at Guînes were in no two minds about what they wanted done. The gates were rammed shut. The French advanced and began to lay fuses under them. And Lord Grey's men turned on Lord Grey and threatened to throw him over the walls unless he surrendered.

So that night a single clerk, unaccompanied, was let out at Harry Norwich's Bulwark and waded his way with a pole over the spiked boards which filled the moat round the fortress. He had to plead his own cause on the other side, for Lord Grey's drum had been shot in the leg, and his trumpeter killed as he blew for parley. But they took him at length to the tent of M. de Guise and his brothers, and he spoke up with his offer: to yield the castle, if the garrison might be allowed to march out with bag and baggage and six pieces of ordnance, their ensign flying.

He was sent back to the fort with a refusal, and the soldiers in Guînes threatened to cut his throat unless he returned to the French and made them accept their surrender, no matter what fate befell Grey and his captains. They pushed him out through a hole in the wall, and he, who had been kicked and pummelled by his own side, was kicked and pummelled again by the enemy's Germans before M. de Guise saw him again, and spoke kindly, and took him back to the fort on horseback, laying about his own men with a truncheon.

The clerk's share in the business was finished. Next, the Duke de Guise's own trumpeter sounded below the walls of the fortress, and proposed to Lord Grey a truce, with hostages; and a meeting in the French camp next morning.

Lord Grey agreed. He had no alternative. His chosen hostages, Arthur and Lewis, were sent for at first light. To leave the fort, they had to walk on the naked and newly slain cramming the bulwark, some stirring and groaning yet under the flinching steps of their boot-soles.

In their place, he received the Duke de Guise's two gentlemen. One, tall as a tree, was Jean d'Estrée, Grand Master of the French Artillery, whose guns, the best fashioned and the best directed in the world, had just won the fortress. And the other was the architect of his downfall: the King's new chevalier, Crawford of Lymond and Sevigny.

One does not destroy the dignity of the dead with light words on the eve of surrender. William Grey, thirteenth Baron Grey of Wilton, stood erect, his hand on a chair, his person groomed free of mud and stone dust and powder, and greeted his hostages, his sleep-starved skin lined and as unyielding as horn. 'My salutations, gentlemen. I could have brought my brave English to face no better opponents.'

It was cold. The candles guttered and flinched in the grey light from the unshuttered windows and lit and obscured the undisturbed face and fine cuirass of the man they now called comte de Sevigny so that Harry Palmer, politely inconspicuous with the Grey lads in the background, had his memory and his nerves suddenly jolted.

'Apples!' said Sir Harry involuntarily.

Lord Grey glanced up sharply. The comte de Sevigny, on the point of speaking, paused for a moment. Then turning his head, he met first the pale, closed face of Austin Grey, Marquis of Allendale, and then the bearded one, tinged with fever and accusing astonishment, of the man he had last seen as Knight-Porter of Calais.

'Apples,' repeated Sir Henry Palmer; and took a step forward. 'You were the man with the cart? Were you? In the Citadel? Then . . . Christ . . . No, I'm dreaming.'

'What's this?' said Lord Grey sharply.

Lymond's eyes met those of d'Estrée, and then removed themselves civilly. He said, 'I spent some time in Calais in disguise just before you took me at Flavy. Piero Strozzi was with me.'

'Piero Strozzi!' said Palmer. 'Bloody hell, I sent you to Ruisbank!' He breathed hard for a moment, his hand clutching his aching shoulder. 'Tommy told me about you. Something to do with a tarot game.'

The past history of the Palmer family had no interest for Lord Grey at that moment. He said, 'So, Mr Crawford, you indeed knew where Ruisbank was. And your bargain at Ham, like your bargain at Douai, was a ruse. I congratulate you.'

'Bargain?' said d'Estrée.

Francis Crawford smiled slightly. 'On the contrary. Both times, I told you the truth. I said the French meant to take Calais.'

Lord Grey turned from him. 'Your Scottish colleague, M. d'Estrée, is a master in the art of deception. He gave us information, when we took him at Ham, which led us to think that the Calais attack was merely a feint for a march south to Luxemburg. I told my nephew that he should have given Mr Crawford his quietus at Douai. If he had, Calais would be English still.'

'I rather fancy,' said Lymond dryly, 'that he would have had to assassinate the Spanish high command as well. We know very well, Lord Grey, that but for the Burgundians, we should not be standing here. I might make a guess at the number of times you asked King Philip to support you. Perhaps you should also know that there are no English troops waiting at Dover. Savoy sent ships to bring them over and found that Pembroke's army had been recalled to London. The Queen may wish to retake Calais, but the Privy Council are unlikely to sustain her. When you go to talk to the Duke de Guise, you will find there is no choice. You must surrender, or give up your men's lives for nothing.'

'You speak convincingly for your employers,' said Lord Grey of Wilton. It was time to go. He rose to his feet and faltered, and Austin, catching his arm held him while Lymond on his other side made a swift movement. 'I am exceedingly sorry. You are wounded?'

No one answered. Then, 'It is nothing,' said Lord Grey curtly and moved, with Austin's help to the doorway. His name and his dignity had suffered enough today and in the past at this man's instigation, without revealing that his only wound at the battle of Guînes had come from a sword of his own side, by accident.

*

From pride of a different kind, he refused the first terms he was offered. For the sake of his soldiers he had made every painful concession but one: he could not, without the utter defacing of English credit, agree to surrender his flags to the enemy.

He called the men he had left, and addressed them. 'We have begun as became us: we have yet held on as duty doth bind us; let us end then as honesty, duty and fame do will us. Neither is there any such extremity of despair but that we may yet dearly enough sell our skins ere we lose them. Let us

272

then either march out under our own ensigns displayed, or else perish here under them.'

But it was Burgundians he was addressing, not Englishmen. Burgundians did not see, they said, why they should die for Lord Grey's vainglory. He was to return, and compound. For not one more blow from their hands could he look for.

Austin Grey did not go with his uncle when he limped back to the gates and the French camp, there to offer his total surrender. Instead he climbed to where the two hostages watched on the ramparts, and spoke, his voice controlled, to Francis Crawford.

'But for your guards, the men below would have killed you just now. How dare you defile this place by your presence?'

It was true. There had been a scuffle, put down in anger and fright by Grey's officers. The surety for these two lives were the lives of Arthur Grey and Lew Davie. The seigneur d'Estrée said, 'You impugn M. Crawford's honesty? But what he did at Calais and Ham was quite legitimate in times of warfare. Your uncle accepts it.'

'You have just seen,' said Austin Grey, 'what my uncle has been forced to accept.' His cheeks were dry but his eyes, brighter than usual, told of the strain he was carrying. *Most assured English even unto the death*, Lord Grey had written from Guînes in his last letter to Queen Mary in England; and had taken oath there, on the broken bulwark, to die rather than show weakness or surrender. *Whatever befalls, I am determined to die at my post*, had written Lord Wentworth, the Calais Lord Deputy. And the defenders of Hâmes, who had sworn to hold out even to the death, had, they said, today mutinied and marched away, scatheless.

And he . . . he had killed, and enjoyed it.

'I wonder,' said Austin Grey, 'that you are not crowing with joy at the comedy.'

From the parapet one looked across the bloody ditches choked with dead to the bright banners of the French princes streaming beyond: Piero Strozzi and the three brothers de Guise; d'Andelot and de Thermes, Roche-sur-Yon and de Brosse, Tavannes, Montmorency, de Bouillon, de la Brosse and d'Estrée. Banners which had flown long ago in Scottish air too: whose owners knew no other trade and had been born for this; nursed amid trumpets; rocked in helmets; fed at the spear blade. *As appetite therefore moveth and not as reason persuadeth, men run after vanitas.* 'It will make a good story,' Lymond said. 'So did the Constable's bêtises before Saint-Quentin. It is not advisable to crow. It might be oneself next time.'

Austin Grey stepped to his side at the parapet. He said, 'Warfare and trickery. It is your natural element.'

'You despise it?' Lymond said. 'Montluc would argue with you. *What would a brave and noble soul turn to, if not war? Who would crush the power of the Grand Seigneur? Men would amuse themselves in palaces, and though naturally of good heart, with time become cowards.*' He paused, and then added, without rancour, 'I began, as you did, by defending my country. Then, disinherited, I had to follow the only profession I knew. There are only two roads to power: the Church, and the army; and there are villains in both. It is a moot point which does the most harm. You didn't consider the cloister?'

Austin said, 'The army was our tradition.'

'And so you sacrificed your principles to Allendale vanity. While I,' Lymond said, 'have become ensnared by a lucrative talent for simple organization. We can offer each other some consolation. Without warfare, there would be no chivalry. The weak would be overturned; nations put to the sword, tyrants flourish. I have spent some time, myself, killing tartars and Turks as well as Englishmen. One may say, If I do not do it, another will. There is a standpoint from which to retire with a farmbook or a breviary seems equally craven.'

Until he provoked it, Austin had been unaware that this had been what he required: a defence of war, in the mouth of the man best suited to proclaim it. Less well defined, these were the thoughts he had sheltered behind, in the night of his defense of the bulwark.

It was a strange source from which to receive unwitting comfort. Austin said, 'And what do you say to men who kill, as they hunt, for a pastime?' His body, despite itself, was shivering.

'I try not to speak to them,' Lymond said. 'They generally don't survive very long, anyway. We should go in. You are tired. You know that, when we leave here, you are to be my prisoner?'

'I didn't know,' said Austin Grey.

'And Lord Grey will belong to Piero Strozzi. So that, until your ransom is paid, you can court Mistress Philippa in com-

274

fort. I had hoped to find her back in England, but they tell me she is still at Court in Paris.'

A talent for organization. *Toutes serez, êtes ou futes! De fait ou de volonté, putes.* He had forgotten, for a moment, the words Crawford had used to him, on the unfinished journey from Ham. 'You want rid of your whore. So you are content,' said Austin, 'that an English poltroon should have her?'

A moment passed. Then Lymond said, 'My words at Ham. I apologize. I had a purpose, as I remember, in baiting you. If I thought you required any assurance whatever about her character or her person, you would be dropped from the leet of fiancés. Your uncle may or may not have told you. I owe a long-standing debt to her family.'

'Her mother is rearing your son. But Philippa,' said Austin Grey, 'will be greater than Kate.'

'I am glad you think so. It is for you then,' said Lymond, 'to provide her with her setting. She has wealth. You have position. Between you, you might make of Allendale one of the great political centres of England. You have only to win her.'

'I thought,' said Austin, 'you were doing that for me.'

'Only the groundwork,' said Francis Crawford with affability. 'Does he need me who daily walkest and is conversant among women, seest their beauties set forth to the eye, hearest their nice and wanton words, smellest their balm, civet and musk? Therein is fruit, and palms hanging sheathed in clusters, and the grain with its husk and its fragrance— which of these bounties of your Lord will you reject?'

'None that come from the Lord,' said Austin Grey evenly. 'From the comte de Sevigny, I have no mind to accept either guidance or favours.'

*

That evening, released by a magnanimous enemy, the men of Guînes marched from the citadel. They left bearing their weapons and armour, and every man had a crown in his purse. But they marched in tingling silence, without tuck of drum or music of trumpet, and without the brave dance of their colours, for their flags, like their leaders, had been left captive in French hands behind them.

For the French, it was the end of a campaign which would take its place in history. 'The loss of Calais,' said the Pope, 'is

275

the only dowry the Queen of England will receive for her marriage to King Philip the Second. Such a conquest is preferable to half the kingdom of England.'

Silent in their tents, Grey of Wilton, the three cousins and all their captains heard through the night the tumult of the French camp's celebrations. In the small hours, the sconces were snuffed in the Duke de Guise's gold and purple pavilion. But the lights under the blazons of Strozzi and of Sevigny continued rather longer than that; and so did the outbursts of music and laughter, of talk and singing and the constant coming and going of men, gay and drunken under the chill ruined hulk of the fortress.

Archie Abernethy watched it all, reclined cracking a bone by the wine barrel. He saw them all come to the warmth: d'Estrée and Senarpont and Roche-sur-Yon, lingering, who had known Francis Crawford six years before. Tavannes and de Thermes. The Sieur d'Andelot, whose wife the comtesse de Laval had cause to thank Mr Crawford, and who took him aside and talked to him, holding him close, until he became too drunk to enunciate, and laughing, sprawled and drank some more instead. Piero Strozzi who, his arm round Lymond's shoulders, refought every battle from Sainte-Agathe to Guînes and kissed him, several times, and offered him a choice from his selection of available women, invitingly detailed which, solemnly, Lymond found it politic to refuse.

That night Lymond, too, broke free from the prison he had made for himself. He drank of intent, until one by one the barriers crumbled and let run loose all those qualities he possessed, like Alkabaïdes, of a tarnished and insolent profusion, to set alight in his fellow-men that killing flame of excitement, of passion, of pleasure.

Jerott, released by wine and dizzy with unstopped emotion, argued with him and sang, forgetful of Lyon and Marthe: Danny Hislop, intoxicated wholly by words, plunged in delirium from lascivious songs to long, explicit, unanswered dissertations; Adam Blacklock, barely tipsy at all, looked at Lymond's vivid face and carefree movements and open, brilliant eyes and recognized, as Archie had done, that the shadow had lifted.

If you thought about it, there was no magic in it. War had given Francis his respite, and success had brought him his final reward: the freedom he wished from his marriage. The licence, if he desired it, to go back to Russia. The knowledge, one supposed, that severed from Philippa, he could allow the past to lie in peace, and cease troubling him.

So, in the end, Adam watched them all leave and himself departed, smiling through the tent doorway at Archie, as he exchanged hazy farewells with his master.

Francis Crawford let him go and then, walking slowly inside, put his hand on the tent pole and surveyed, in his turn, the small mahout.

'Archie?' said Lymond. 'It is half past four o'clock in the morning, and I am exceedingly drunk. Do you suppose these two statements have anything to do with each other?'

'No,' said Archie tolerantly. 'And neither will you, come the morning.'

•

Some time after that, the last lights in Guînes were extinguished; the last random shot fired; the last catcall uttered; and only the feet of the sentries could be heard, treading round the encampment.

In an open tent with a Florentine banner Lord Grey of Wilton kept his private vigil, gazing out upon the indigo sky and the fresh-dug graves and the marshes which for over two hundred years had been England's care, and for nearly thirty years, off and on, in his keeping.

And in another tent at the same moment Archie Abernethy began a well-earned night's rest in good conscience, for Francis Crawford was sleeping already beyond him, his guard relaxed, his breathing quiet, his scarred wrists lying free in the blankets.

He was sleeping still when far to the north, dawn arrived in an east Scottish estuary; and with it, a fleet of small ships, come to bear her noble Commissioners to Queen Mary's wedding in Paris.

Part III

Soubs le terroir du rond globe lunaire
Lors que sera dominateur Mercure
L'isle d'Escosse fera un luminaire
Qui les Anglais mettra à décomfiture.

CHAPTER 1

Proye à Barbares trop tost seront hastifs.
Cupide de voir plaindre au vent la plume.

On an elevating cloud of Eleatica the French Army for four
weeks continued its triumphs and indeed consolidated them,
although for the whole of that period none of its officers was
perfectly sober.

The fortresses of Guînes and of Hâmes were razed to the
ground, thereby releasing 300 cannon of brass alloy, 300 of
iron and a prodigious quantity of munitions, much to everyone's retrospective alarm. The fortified châteaux of d'Herbe-
mont, Jamoigne, Chigny, Rossignol and Villemont were attacked and captured. The king of France in company with
the Dauphin, the Cardinals of Lorraine and de Guise and all
the non-combatant nobility of the French Court made a Tri-
umphal Entry into his new town of Calais and handed out
money, preferment and property to all his brave generals.
The Duke de Guise was given the great house of the Staple
in Calais. Marshal Strozzi received the gift of Lord Grey, a
tract of crown lands worth 15,000 crowns' rental, a favourable marriage for an unremarkable daughter, and an appointment to the Privy Council, which was worth all the rest put
together.

The comte de Sevigny was also given land, adjoining the
property of the Marshal de St André outside Lyon. There accompanied it an undertaking by the Cardinal Legate that the
bill of divorce already placed before the Pontiff should be approved and ready for its final ratification by my lord count
and his wife on the day following the Queen of Scotland's
forthcoming marriage. To enable him to entertain as was now
fitting, the crown was pleased to give him also possession of
the Hôtel d'Hercule on the corner of the rue des Augustins,
Paris.

It was one of the great royal mansions of France, and once
housed the Queen of Scotland's young father, twenty years

before also a bridegroom. The comte de Sevigny's friends were not overawed. 'It's known as Plumbago Corner,' said Jerott in a lofty welter of consonants. 'You have to produce a ticket of entry that says you've fought all the statues.' Jerott was drunk as a Templar and happy. Neither he nor Danny nor Adam had had a care in their heads for a fortnight, other than prosecuting with uninterrupted efficiency all the affairs of their companies and ensuing, under the unwinking supervision of Archie Abernethy, that Lymond was never alone.

But then, it transpired that he had no particular desire to be alone, being occupied in congenial company in various activities which happened to satisfy him. The golden optimism, the dreaming absence of stress that followed the campaign of Calais communicated itself to those at Court also. To Philippa it drifted like a temporizing incense above all she did in the four weeks before Lymond came back to Paris.

She made no attempt to obtain her release and go home as he had asked her. To Kate, inquiring guardedly about her non-return, Philippa replied that she saw no reason to miss the momentous spectacle of the Dowager Lady Culter embracing the entire bewildered court of France, if not her difficult son.

In this she spoke the truth. However able, however superb the element of the family Crawford undoubtedly were, individually they were going to require someone's help before this prospective visit to France was completed. She had promised herself to stay with the Queen until she saw some hope of rapprochement between Catherine d'Albon and Francis Crawford. She had hoped to find, before now, a thread of history, however spurious, which might reconcile him to Sybilla his mother.

In this she had been unsuccessful. If Lymond had been right, and his betrayal at Ham had been at the hands of Leonard Bailey, Mr. Bailey had made no other baneful appearances. The only unhappy accident occurred at Court in the first weeks of February when, kept indoors by the snows, the Dauphin shot out the eye of M. de Bouccard his equerry in the course of an afternoon's games, and the King had to ask M. de Bouccard's pardon. His royal bride-to-be watched in smiling commiseration, her jewelled hands hardened together. The most excellent princess Mary, Queen of Scotland, had forgotten her concern for M. de Sevigny's marriage.

The Cardinal of Lorraine, as it happened, had not. Shortly

after his return from the faintly delirious celebration at Calais he had a long, flattering talk with the comtesse de Sevigny about her talented husband and received, with baffled admiration, the same artistic degree of response which Mistress Philippa had learned to allot the Head Eunuch. Considering that nothing but compliments were extended on both sides, it was hard to say how she also made him aware of the fact.

She was not short of employment. The two cousins Schiatti were in Paris still, and the Duke of Lorraine et Bar, and young Paliano, and Arthur Erskine, and a handful of others ready when she might have a free moment to throw snowballs from the town walls, or skate on the ditch, white as tables of Phrygian marble.

Indoors, she indulged the cast of mind she now knew was her own. She listened to Thevet, the Queen's almoner, talk of his travels. She spoke of the Far East to Postel of the Collège Royal; she sat elbows cocked at a table, watching Nicolas de Nicolay design a new map. She listened to Jean Bodin, not yet thirty, talk of politics and astronomy, philosophy, magic, the Talmud.

The answers she carried to Catherine. Already agreeably trained in all the gentle and scholarly arts, Catherine d'Albon received in this interim a new and specialized education in all those areas of the mind in which her prospective husband had chosen to roam.

The daughter of a Marshal of France, destined from birth for highest station, did not admit newcomers to easy friendship. But sitting murmuring over her sewing with this slender girl with the clear skin and brown eyes and coiled chestnut hair Catherine d'Albon found herself moved to converse not as to another girl, but to a tutor. A tutor who brought her not only news and opinion and discoveries but songs and poetry and books, dearly bought and freely given for her to study; so that for part of the day at least her mind was turned from its treadmill. When would he come back? Would he speak? Or would he allow the divorce to take place before he would approach her?

But of that, and the person who filled both their minds, neither of them ever said anything.

The Queen of France was less discreet, or had less need to be tactful. With unerring swiftness she had discerned what Philippa preferred to pass unnoticed: her gift with children.

283

The Princesses Claude and Elisabeth, aged ten and twelve, were brought to her notice; and then Charles and Henri, aged seven and six, and Marguerite, four. Attending her mistress in the Royal Audience Chamber in les Tournelles, Philippa found she spent a large part of her time on the floor with her lute, entertaining and wiping the noses of small royal children. The King's sister Marguerite often joined her. And once, when the Queen of Scots had been called unexpectedly from the room, Queen Catherine crossed from her chair of state and seating herself on a stool said, 'But you play as charmingly as your husband. You have no regrets about dissolving this marriage?'

'None, your Majesty,' Philippa said. 'Marriage requires more than two lutes in counterpoint, felicitous though that may be.'

The young woman, the Queen had noticed before, had a delightful voice: clear and mellow, and allied to the kind of strong nerves which camouflage any falsehood.

However, if that was a lie, she had gone to a great deal of trouble to make sure of her husband's next bedfellow. The Queen of France said, 'I know the Demoiselle d'Albon has formed a great affection for the young man. I should like to learn if his feelings are engaged?'

'I believe ... not yet, Madame,' said the comtesse de Sevigny.

'Then will he marry her? She is already an heiress.'

There was a little pause. Then the girl said, 'He is, I understand, in no great want of money. ... At the same time, his friends would be well pleased if he abandoned his present plan to go back to Russia.'

Catherine de Médicis, Queen of France, settled back on her stool with a certain satisfaction. 'He has sensible friends. I agree with them. It seems a case, then, of encouraging M. your husband to form an attachment in that quarter. I take it he is capable of doing so. And he is, I am sure, a man of honour.'

She raised her eyebrows. Philippa, who had put this precise point only a short while before to her sister-in-law, felt a dim sinking within her. She said, 'Your Majesty knows better than I do, Mademoiselle d'Albon's undoubted attractions.'

The Queen smiled. 'They are considerable,' said Catherine de Médicis. She leaned forward and picked up two gold buttons which had burst from Charles's doublet, and then plucked a third one from Henri's right ear. 'But it is for the rest of us—and you and I in particular—to create for them the opportunities.'

*

The next time she spotted the red-headed man of Applegarth's following her, she drew her valet into a doorway and stepping out suddenly, caused her pursuer to recoil with a yammer.

'You're not very good at it are you?' said Philippa. 'I thought the idea was not to attract notice.'

That was what Adam Blacklock had said when she had complained first about the presence of a perpetual bodyguard, and then had tried, soft-heartedly, to have him asked into the kitchen when the weather got cold. It was a point. If the Court knew the Sevignys had been threatened, they would instantly want to know what they were being threatened with. She stared at the man.

'I wasn't attracting notice,' said Applegarth's man rather sulkily. 'Not until you stopped me, anyway.'

'And how is Mr Blacklock?' said Philippa.

'I don't know, milady,' said her bodyguard. 'There's a man in town pays us. Mr Blacklock's in Artois. So they say.'

So she had to ask, after all, quite directly. 'And M. de Sevigny?'

His face changed, like a cushion with a fat man sitting on it. 'In Abbeville still, I expect. Did you hear what they did on the ice?'

'No,' said Philippa.

'Put the cannon on sledges and hurdled over them. Eight broken legs and four arms that first day, and a culverin fell through and had to be drawn out by horses. Signor Strozzi won eight hundred écus.'

'And M. de Sevigny?' said Philippa with shaming monotony.

'Oh. He put his cap on a weathervane and bet M. Strozzi he couldn't knock it off with the cannon. He couldn't either, so M. de Sevigny got his eight hundred écus back again. Then he took some of them that had been with him in Russia and showed them trick riding. Of course, they're used to the snow.'

His face was shining. She had been a bad-tempered harridan. On an impulse, Philippa put an écu in his hand, smiled, and turning to her valet, continued on her original errand.

It hadn't become any better: not a bit of it. Every day of the long separation had only sunk the well deeper: printed the long, detailed record of his looks and his words, like the dials of the oak, more inexorably into her being.

But to bear it, and in silence, was her privilege. She shared it with many others. Nor was she vain.

*

He came back on Wednesday, 16 February, and put up for the last time with his suite at the empty Hôtel St André, where he found a message from the Prévôt des Marchands awaiting him. It bade him, as one of the victors of Calais, present himself with his comtesse at four after midday on Thursday, to receive the accolade of the city upon the Duke de Guise's great triumph.

With it was a note from the royal maître d'hôtel with the arrangements for the order of ceremony.

Underneath that, was a note from his current wife Philippa.

To Hercules from the Queen of the Amazons. The Cardinal decrees that Monsieur and Madame de Sevigny appear at the Hôtel de Ville banquet together tomorrow. I shall call on you at three of the clock after midday smiling as doth the crocodile, which hath many rows of teeth but no tongue. I recommend to you Dathan and Abiram, whom the earth swallowed quick.

He laughed aloud when he read it, but sent no reply. On the other hand, when Philippa arrived at the Hôtel St André next day, he was waiting on the stroke of three in the Maréchale's parlour to receive her. And behind him was Austin Grey, Marquis of Allendale.

*

It was five months since she had seen Francis Crawford. And in spite of her resolution, it was at him only that she looked.

He met the look, which he had not done in September. All that she remembered was there and something else: a presence bright as a newly sheared diamond. He had about him the hard resilience and the long-sighted vision she recalled from other men on hard-fought campaigns, although he was clean and scented and his hair was fresh-cut and shining. Only his hands, taking hers lightly to greet her, were hard across the palm with the grip of the rein and the sword-hilt, and the filbert nails cut closer than she had ever seen them in the salon. It would be some weeks before he could match Catherine d'Albon with the lute, in counterpoint or out of it.

He looked well. And as if somewhere, lately, he had tasted happiness.

'*Devoted* obedience at the kissing of your holy feet,' Lymond said, lifting a silver cup of Hippocras and handing it to her severely, 'but what do I have to do to induce you to leave France? Stand and pray like St Kevin, until my two outstretched palms both have nests in them? You remember Lord Allendale.'

Philippa turned her gaze to Lord Allendale, on whose fine-skinned dark face was a clearly read turmoil of feeling. She said, 'Poor Austin: you should never have let Mr Crawford buy you. The Vidame de Chartres will challenge you out of jealousy. . . . I am sorry, truly. But you're well; you're not wounded. And Lord Grey?'

'He is in Paris also,' Austin said. 'A little hurt, but quickly recovering. Arthur is with him. Philippa . . . why . . . Kate has been expecting you.'

'Yes. Well, the Queen won't release me until after the wedding,' said Philippa with absolute candour. 'How long are you going to be here?'

Austin, who had also been handed a cup of wine but was not drinking it, looked at Francis Crawford, who was. Lymond said, 'We haven't decided yet. I can't make up my mind what to ransom him for.'

Philippa stared at him. 'Money,' she said, 'is the usual thing. What have you done with Lord Grey?'

'Oh,' said Lymond. 'Lord Grey is half-way up the ladder from grower to buyer, and is remaining in wraps till the market settles. The Crown presented him to Piero Strozzi.'

'And?' said Philippa Somerville. She sat down. She felt very, very happy.

Lymond sat himself also. 'It took two lawyers, a cashier and the Lieutenant-Criminel de Robe-Courte before even Lord Grey could grasp the pattern,' he remarked cheerfully. 'Actually, Marshal Strozzi fixed his lordship's ransom at 7,000 crowns and Lord Grey reduced it by haggling to 4,000 and had nearly reached an agreement when the Queen of

England was moved to send him a noble message of personal love and encouragement, upon which Strozzi added 10,000 crowns to the ransom. Willie Grey was still producing *bouillons* over that when he found himself being led out of the door. Strozzi had sold him as a going concern to the comte de la Rochefoucauld's brother, who wanted him to exchange for the comte de la Rochefoucauld, who had been a prisoner of the English since Saint-Quentin. Are you with me, or are you merely nervous in case we are going to be late for our appointment?'

'I am, unfortunately, with you,' said Philippa.

'I told you it was complicated. Well, the comte de la Rochefoucauld was an unsatisfactory prisoner. He tried to escape. He said he was dying. So to make sure of his money, the Count's captors didn't wait for Lord Grey, but sold him back to his own side at once for a ransom of 30,000 écus. He is here in Paris. Lord Grey is still here as his prisoner. And the family want at least 24,000 écus to go towards the high costs of salvage. Are you ready? It's raining.'

'Look outside,' Philippa said, 'and you will see that the Cardinal of Lorraine has sent his second-string coach for the survivor of Calais to ride in. You don't look very festive, except for that vulgar affair on your shoulders. Tartar barter, I take it? And under it?'

Lying on the rich, sober cloth of his doublet was the exquisite thing she had referred to: a golden chain of linked plaques, each one thick with eastern jewels and enamel. And under it was the black cross-sash, she realized, of his Order: the St Michael: the most coveted of all French distinctions.

'The wages,' said Lymond, 'of insufferable irregularities. The other is my obsidional crown of grass. The clothes are my own. Tant de payis, tant' de Guises. I chose a tactful feuille-morte because the Duke will almost certainly be attired in white and gold velvet and diamonds. Like North Rona: scant of ony religone, but abundant of corne. Who in God's name do these rubies belong to?'

'You. But you wouldn't suit them,' said Philippa. 'Ffarewell Carboncle chosen chief. It's my husband-hunting equipment. What about you?'

'I don't hunt husbands,' said Lymond, getting up. 'It's the other way about.' He stood for a moment, looking at her. 'Has it been very bad?' he said unexpectedly. 'Calais ought to

288

be French. Someone was bound to take it, sooner or later. But you shouldn't have had to watch the rejoicing. I'm sorry.'

He was the only person who had thought of it. Philippa, her eyes very bright, said, 'I didn't enjoy it. But at least there wasn't much slaughter.'

'No,' said Austin Grey bitterly. 'We all surrendered.'

Lymond turned. 'There may be some issues worth being martyred for, but I doubt if the Staple at Calais is one of them. However. Suppose, Philippa my child, you bring Lord Allendale a little English comfort while I see somebody? Then we must leave, or we shall have no food but of thorns, which will neither fatten nor avail against hunger.'

The door closed behind him. Austin said, 'After that, what can I say that doesn't sound illiterate? ... Philippa, the French are our enemies and yet ... Why take service with the Scots Queen? You wrote that you were coming home.'

'I am. In April,' Philippa said. 'I haven't forgotten what country I belong to. But I found some business which needs to be finished and, you know, I *am* married to a Scotsman, even if we are both doing our best to get rid of each other.'

'I see,' said Austin. From deeply flushed, he had turned rather pale. He added, 'So it seems stupid to ask if you need help, especially from me. The Greys have been made to appear very foolish.'

'I don't know whether you know the signs,' Philippa said, 'but Mr Crawford isn't totally sober. From what I can gather, the Greys held out with a thousand men against the entire French, Swiss and German forces for eight days and only gave in when the Burgundians made them. You have no small reputation, I can tell you, at the French Court. Your mother will be flying flags from all the battlements. . . . You look tired. Don't let him browbeat you.'

Smiling, he shook his head slightly and then dropped his eyes to his hands. They were hard, as Lymond's had been, with callouses at the base of the fingers. Philippa, taking the bull by the horns, said, 'And don't let him embarrass you, either. You know why he left the room, and so do I. You can take it that I don't intend to have my friendships either spoiled or engineered by Francis Crawford. Does that make you feel better?'

He was laughing when he looked up, the lines of difficult reserve easing already out of his over-bred face. 'You haven't changed. But what am I to do? The laws of chivalry are silent.'

Philippa rose and walking over to him, placed her two hands lightly on the padded stuff of his sleeves. 'Follow your own mind and heart,' she said. 'I shall be honest with you. And if my suspicions are right, we shall be given plenty of time.'

*

It was not so easy to remain matriarchal sitting in the Cardinal's tall, red velvet coach with Francis Crawford keeping himself to himself less than a foot away from the fall of her furs. From the tilt of his head on the padding, she guessed that his eyes were closed. He said unexpectedly, as she was looking at him, 'Evil the drink and ill the resting place. I am not, unfortunately, asleep.' It was not difficult to guess how he had spent the ten minutes' absence.

A little flame of purifying anger ran through Philippa's veins. She said sharply, 'I suppose you have heard? Your brother is on his way here with Sybilla.'

That lifted his head, his eyes open, from the velvet. Then he said, 'I beg your pardon, Philippa. *Plures crapula quam ensis.*'

'And you have heard?' said Philippa. So often, disconcertingly, he answered not her tongue but her intention.

'Yes. D'Aumale, d'Estrée and I are to take a party to Dieppe to welcome them. We are all moderately good playactors, Richard, Sybilla and I. There will be no unpleasantness.'

'But that is why you are drinking?' The last time he had met his mother, Lymond had turned on his heel and walked past her. And Richard, driven to anguished fury by everything about his younger brother: his high-handed neglect; his utter refusal to concern himself with the affairs of his country had at last attacked and might well have killed his cadet.

Lymond said,

> *And can the things that I have do*
> *Be hidden from thee then?*
> *Nay, nay, thou knowest them all (O Lord)*
> *Where they were done, and when . . .*

'Why am I drinking? I am celebrating the wresting from

290

you of Calais. Or shall I tell you the truth? *The truth is that . . .*'

He had given the words, incongruously, the cadence almost of poetry. Then he broke off hazily and picked up in a more painstaking tone. 'The truth is that I must be in a rather worse state than I thought I was. I apologize.'

'What exactly did you find out in Flavy?' said Philippa.

'My letter told you,' said Lymond. The rain, renewing its force, thundered upon the roof and one side of the carriage. The crowds outside saluted the Cardinal's coach from their windows, or pressed to the sides of the streets under the galleries. Lymond said, 'The old lady is dead. I had hoped to find out where Bailey is living, but Lord Grey's men failed to discover.'

Philippa said, 'Why should Bailey come to France? You left him content with his pension in England. Is he hoping to wring more money from Sybilla than you are paying him? Or could he possibly mean to hint something of all this to Richard?'

'Not if he wants to live,' Lymond said. 'I don't imagine he knew for a moment that Richard and Sybilla were coming here. In any case, neither one of them could afford what I pay to him. No . . . I think he is here by chance, and thought he saw some way to harm me. If Grey hadn't shown me the letter, he would have been quite secure. I expect he has left France by now. But I think you should continue to take precautions. Why are you still here?'

He had not, unfortunately, lost sufficient hold of his faculties. Philippa said, 'The Queen wants me to stay until April. I'm going to have to meet Sybilla. I wish you would tell me the truth. For example, you have said nothing to me about headaches.'

She withstood, for what seemed a long time, an unforeseen scrutiny. At length, 'Who told you?' said Lymond.

'Adam. When he came to the Séjour du Roi.' Marthe was not going to be at the Hôtel de Ville this afternoon. She had not seen or spoken to Marthe since the day the news of Calais arrived, and she had betrayed herself. But then, neither had Lymond.

'I see,' said Lymond. 'I regret I didn't edify you with an account of them, but they seemed to have vanished. Apart, that is, from the normal rewards of intemperance.'

'And at Flavy?' Philippa said. *Don't let him browbeat you,* she had said to Austin.

He drew an impolite long-suffering breath, she saw, to do exactly that. Then he said crisply, 'I learned only one other thing at Flavy, and that is of no possible consequence. Isabelle Roset was Renée Jourda's widowed sister, and she kept house for Sybilla and her master somewhere in Paris. The child Francis Crawford was born there. And so far as I am concerned and you are concerned, Philippa, that ends that matter.'

They had nearly arrived at the end of their unproductive journey. Philippa thought, *Poor Austin.* And said, drawing a long breath herself, 'And who was the master? The father of Sybilla's baby?'

'She died before she could say. A beneficent occurrence for everybody. Here we are,' Lymond said. And looking at him, and not at the Place de la Grève, Philippa knew that she could expect him to say nothing further.

What he had told her up to a point, she had no doubt was the literal truth. What he had not told her, but everything else about him made very obvious was that where once he had been uncertain, now he knew the name of Sybilla's lover.

CHAPTER 2

Le trop bon temps, trop de bonté royale
Fais et deffais, prompt, subit, negligence.

She was afterwards to remember it as the most disoriented day, from moment to moment, that she had ever passed in her life.

In it, she spent nine continuous hours in her husband's company. Hours which, had they been offered her on her arrival from Lyon, she would have found the sense and the fortitude to forgo. Hours which he perhaps would have spared her had he not believed, because he wanted to believe, that her passing attachment to him after five months must surely have faded.

He was not to know, his strung-up nerves doctored with alcohol, that disaster upon glorious disaster was about to befall the City of Paris's Antique Triumph for the Heroes of Calais; or to guess what was to follow it. He had no premonition even when the curving line of royal carriages drew up on the gentle riverside slope of the Grève and rested there closed in the downpour while the City Fathers waited civilly ranked, their plumes and satins and erminetails buffeted like furzy wrack in the cataract.

In time, the rainstorm abated. The City Fathers stood, water running down their humble features. The King's carriage door opened. The King's steps were placed before it. The King emerged and placed his foot, smiling, upon thm. The Town Battery embarked on an offering of deafening salvoes. The King's carriage horses reared, and the King fell out on to the paving.

Lymond buried his face in his hands.

*

The guns were still firing as the Royal family, the Princess of the Blood, the victors of Calais and their ladies moved within the pictured arcade erected about the Hôtel de Ville

293

portals. The Town's fifty standing hackbuts also began their salute, followed almost immediately with a carillon of bells from the church of St Jean en Grève, another from the bell-tower of St Esprit and a third, a little behindhand, from St Jacques de la Boucherie, whose tenor rope had broken.

A small concert of fifes, trumpets, clarions and tambours struck up inside the arcade (Hoc Hercule Dignae and cardboard marble) where the Prévôt des Marchands, his mouth opening and shutting, delivered his message of welcome. The King, his mouth also opening and shutting, could be seen to be persevering with an affable reply. Philippa's husband, crimson with suppressed laughter beside her, was discovered to be talking also.

'What?' Philippa screamed.

'I said,' shrieked the noble and puissant seigneur François, comte de Sevigny, 'thank God the guns are pointing . . .'

Silence fell.

'. . . away from us.'

He had dropped his voice in time, but Marshal Strozzi, also unfortunately commenting just behind, had not. There was an explosion of laughter, abruptly cut off. With her husband, very slightly out of hand, walking beside her Philippa followed the others up the staircase between the breathing ranks of Archers, Arbalestriers and Hackbutters of the Town and past Vicissitude, France In Triumph, the royal arms, the town arms and the motto, GRADATIM, or *gradually* repeated above every third step of an almost imperceptible progress into the Grand' Salle of the Hôtel de Ville de Paris.

They had done their best, with tapestries, with paintings, with fleurs-de-lis and ships on the rafters, to create an Antique Triumph fit for the monarch. Pinned with ivy, painted on friezes were the escutcheons and the devices of everyone: the crescent of the King, the iris of the Queen, the Eclipse of Monsieur, the Gorgon of the King's sister, the thistle of the Queen of Scotland, its purple still faintly running; the emblem, chastely sportive, of Madame de Valentinois, the King's permanent mistress.

Happy fancies abounded. Along each tapestried wall hung ten twinned ivy crescents tied with taffeta: a reminder, had the Cardinals needed one, of the long and useful alliance between the Turkish and Christian kingdoms. At the service end of the room a Latin inscription, big enough to be read by the king and commencing SCOTIA TUTA SUIS, ACCEPTA BOLONIA

. . . extolled the present reign's finest successes. At the royal end hung the choicest offering: a rose-decked goddess with Bacchus and Satyrs and a verse beginning TU DEA, BACCHUS, AMOR . . . and ending, PRAELIA MNEMOSYNE, NON POCULA REGIA CURET, or, *Count only the battles and not the cups the king drinks.*

The names of the Duke de Guise, of Calais, of Guînes were everywhere, interwoven with heroic parallels: Jason; Ganymede; the banner of Caesar with four V's instead of one, signifying that M. de Guise, having come, seen and conquered at last, should this time trap his good fortune by chains in case, as ever, it dodged him. The town had worked very hard.

On the other hand, although twenty years had passed since the Prévôt and Echevins, armed with silver trowels, had laid the foundation stone of the new Hôtel de Ville, it stood still only two storeys high, and its Grand' Salle did not allow any elbow room when its tables were set for a hundred. Those invited by the Prévôt to watch, already admitted, lined the walls of the room on a scaffolding. Those invited by the Prévôt to sup, in their best clothes and early, naturally made sure of their places also.

The King entered, the trumpets blew, the bells rang out afresh from the churches, and the twenty-six merchants' wives already ensconced at the High Board rose, curtseyed and settled again, smiling at their less privileged friends. It was clear where the King was to go, since the royal chairs had been placed on a dais. Where the princes of the blood, the victors of Calais and the great lords of the court were to be seated was for fifteen minutes a matter of frenzy.

Steering purposefully, Philippa found two vacated places just below the Sieur d'Andelot, the Duke de Neveres and Seigneur d'Estrée for the former Voevoda of Russia and King's Lieutenant-General in Paris, who was showing a maddening preference for simply standing stock-still, looking virtuous.

Unfortunately, Piero Strozzi elected to come and sit on her other side. He caught Lymond's eye, which was not hard to do. Philippa Somerville turned to the Marshal and addressed him in succinct Italian. *'If you laugh, I shall kick you.'*

'Signora,' said Piero Strozzi, 'if you care to continue in this field of discussion after dinner, we should have much to say to one another. That is—'

He broke off, his eye arrested by something on her other

side, and then resumed, injured, '... that is, if you had not
brought your Russian retinue with you. *In bocca serrata mai
non entrò mosca.* I give you a friendly warning. You think
M. de Sevigny is drunk. He is not.'

'You might not think so,' said Lymond amiably. 'But in ten
minutes or so, I am going to slip under the table and lie
there.' On his other side, the comtesse de Laval put her hands
over her ears and pulled a face at him. The noise, ringing
back from the beams, was quite dizzying, and so were the
fumes of sweat and scent and wet clothes and incoming food.
The doors, which had been with difficulty shut, burst open
again to admit a group of noisy, wet people. They closed, and
then opened again. There were not enough places at the
table. The benches jostled with incomers. The narrow space
between the long trestles was filled with parties looking for
seats, parties standing or kneeling on seats or parties simply
meeting other parties and exchanging various witty ripostes.

They were all, Philippa saw, minor members of the Court,
who had had no invitations in the first place. Perrot, speaking
to the King, looked extremely flustered. The Maître d'Hôtel
was sweating. More people began to pour in. The superfluity
of blue blood, it was clear, was more than thirty Archers
without benefit of password knew how to control. The reeking air, pushed by the heat from the two raging fires, moved
and swung and swirled up to the rafters where the municipal
chandeliers, specially made in black and white, the King's
colours, tossed and swayed from their herbaceous pinnings.

The comte de Sevigny looked up, his hair, and the priceless
collar he wore neat and spiteful and glittering in the candlelight. 'Christ,' he said. 'Piero. What are *you* going to do when
the candelabra fall down?'

Piero Strozzi leaped to his feet. *'Messeigneurs!'* The roar of
it cut across even that febrile cacophony. 'Messeigneurs
nearest the door! The candelabra are about to fall on you!'

That got rid of twenty-five people. By a miracle of sinuous
movement, Lymond was by the outer doors as the last of
them backed out, exclaiming. The outer doors shut, then the
inner doors. Marshal Strozzi, leaping to his feet, roared,
'Messeigneurs! All has been made safe! The Prévôt begs you
all to sit and be welcome!'

Everyone subsided. Opposite her, Philippa noticed, she had
the god Janus with a key in his hand, and a verse beginning
QUI BIFRONS FUERAM, GALLIS SUM GALLICUS UNA FRONTE

296

DEUS, indicating, she took it, that he was prepared to be two-faced for everyone except Frenchmen. It reminded her of something. Lymond, sliding back, said, 'I've told Jacob if his Archers let another soul in, I'll shout Fire. They'll all jump through the windows.' A braying noise, creeping into the room while he was speaking, broadened, intensified, and began to permeate the clangorous gases.

Strozzi screamed. Lymond, not in the least disturbed, frowned at him. 'I asked the hautboys and clarions to play for us. *Paris, fontaine de toutes sciences.* If you can't lay your hands on three hundred Tartar horsemen with scimitars, I recommend clarions for quelling a riot. What, then?'

Piero Strozzi had screamed again. The Queen's cousin rose to his feet. Below the black hair, tightly curled with the damp, his lips were drawn back in a rictus of passion, displaying his broken teeth. Then, raising one pink and ribboned arm, he swept it across the table and tore from a startled échevin's grasp the silver cup from which he was drinking. Gouts of claret soaked the municipal rust and crimson velvet. The merchant jumped to his feet.

Nose to nose: 'You have many ill-deserved rights as échevin of this undesirable city,' said Piero Strozzi, 'but stealing my table silver is not one of them!'

Someone hauled, with steady violence, at his coat. He rocked, but remained standing.

'Monseigneur!' Where visible through beard and wine-stains, the merchant's face was blotched with fury. 'I demand reparation! You insult me and the city which honours you!'

'*Honours me!*' roared Marshal Strozzi, staggering and recovering with aplomb. He interrupted himself, staring along the crowded table. 'Mon petit François, there is your silver, also.'

'So it is,' said Lymond with interest. The merchant's wife who was admiring a great salt in cut glass and silver snatched her hands back, turning white. The man at her side began to rise slowly, piping like a Chinese ocarina. Lymond, concentrating, surveyed him closely. 'Now I think of it, the shirt is very familiar.'

'My lord count!' said the Councillor.

'. . . But I couldn't swear to it, in a court of law. I don't object. The intention is to make us feel at home.' He lifted a heavy silver-gilt object from the table far to his left and

297

showed it helpfully to Marshal Strozzi. 'There's one of your livery pots.' Marshal Strozzi lunged.

This time Philippa waited until he was off-balance. Then she took a strong grasp of his fur-trimmed coat with both hands and jerked.

With a crash and a hooting of oaths which out-trumpeted even the clarion, Marshal Strozzi fell on his back. It was a gradual fall, broken by the short row of pages behind him. He dropped into a dish of roast swan, and from there into a platter of bustards, and ended with a liquid sigh on the floor in a bowl of small pullets with vinegar. Gilded plumes from the swan quilled, with chic, a bubbling tippet of gravy. From the ruffled merchants, there came a squeal of shocked glee. He lay, speechless.

Across his fallen chair, Lymond gazed reflectively at his wife. 'You borrowed the silver,' he said.

'Someone had to help them,' said Philippa. 'The King invited himself, and left them eight days to get ready. Baptiste had four days to finish the paintings. The tinsmith could only supply so much on short notice. They had to have linen brought in and laundered and buy rose water to scent it, and torch batons and wine, and get a Folder of Linen for the napkins. The master roasters and bakers haven't had any sleep for three days, and Jodelle for four, and they've all been here since this morning, slaving to make everything ready.'

Piero Strozzi sat up, his gravy-stained hands negligently clasped about his steaming and redolent knees. 'But why the comtesse de Sevigny?' he inquired. He was no longer annoyed.

Philippa glanced at Lymond. 'The comte de Sevigny had protected the walls of their city. They were willing to entrust me with their pride.'

'Ah.' Piero Strozzi rose to his feet, righted his chair and removing his ruined coat, seated himself in his doublet. 'I think, mon petit François, that your wife delivers a reprimand and a warning. We watch our conduct?'

'It's going to be awful,' Philippa said, flinching as the King's trumpets, shrieking, announced the general serving of the banquet. 'But if your bone-headed scions make fools of them, the Prévôt and Councillors will never forgive them.'

Piero Strozzi and Francis Crawford looked at one another.

'A hint,' said Lymond, 'sufficeth for the wise, but a thousand speeches profit not the heedless. Did you hear what she said?'

'Unfortunately,' said Piero Strozzi, 'I heard what she said. She spoke good sense.'

'No bloodshed, harrows and ffrayes?'

'I have said this before,' said Piero Strozzi austerely. 'You have no sense of responsibility. Look at those tilted louts at the end of the table who will not sit because they have not been brought wine. Do they not realize that pages cannot pass between the tables if they move about and meet their friends and slap one another, laughing?'

'We have wine?' said Lymond.

'Yes. And some of us have had too much of it. Let us pass it,' said Piero Strozzi, picking up two of the willow-covered flasks standing before him, 'to those more deserving.'

The two bottles sailed through the air. Pursued by three other pairs they made their way, hurtling, from one end of the table to the other. As it happened, there were no mishaps. The young men clambering over the end of the table desisted for the nonce and sat down. A dam of steaming dishes, thus released, proceeded like a millrace down the room and then halted again, blocked by a hilarious group. 'Why,' said the comtesse de Laval on Lymond's other side, 'are the pages four feet high? They cannot see where they are going.'

'And yellow and violet silk!' said Piero Strozzi. 'It martyrs the eye even more than your vulgar collar, *mon fils*.'

'They're children. Whose?' said Lymond sharply.

'The merchants' sons,' said Philippa. The Marshal had been right. He *was* sober. 'The children are serving everywhere except the royal table, to honour the King and allow them a share of the celebration. But of course, they're frightened. And the crowd won't let them through.'

'They will,' said Lymond briefly.

She caught his arm, and then dropped her hand instantly, her colour heightened. 'No. You can't control it for them.'

'No,' he agreed after a moment. He dropped back into his seat. 'But I can dispatch some very dirty stares. Piero?'

'I heard you,' said Piero. 'You have become responsible. *No te quiero. No te quiero, Juliano.*'

'You will,' Lymond said, 'When the Paris Parlement votes us all that beautiful money to enable you to squeeze more victory prizes out of the poor bleeding treasury of France. If you will control that little bastard Paliano at your end, I shall petrify the equerries by the fireplace at mine. Oh Christ, he's going to spill jelly all over us.' He switched to French. 'I see, *mon cher*, you carry this as the King's pages do. I know a better way. Hold it thus, and thus. You see? And smile. The King likes smiling faces.'

Piero Strozzi closed his mouth, which had fallen ajar. 'Of course,' he said. 'You have a son, don't . . .'

He roared. 'I beg your pardon. My foot slipped,' said Philippa. 'Have a date flan, and don't talk so much while the hautboys are playing. If you lose your voice, none of us will know what to do.'

In fact, they did their best to salvage the occasion. The Sieur d'Estrée and the d'Andelots helped. But disaster, like a dropped stitch in knitwear spread running and, torn between sympathy and hysteria, Philippa was forced to watch the evening steadily and formidably falling apart.

Children were sick, burst into tears and dropped dishes. All the marzipan arrived at one table and all the cream dariolles at another. The trestle nearest the serving door captured all the Auxerre wine as it came through and refused to let the serving children carry it further.

The tables further from the serving door began throwing dragees in protest, followed by harder objects: Piero Strozzi at this point collected his own silverware and the Sevigny crystal and put it under his bench, which led to a good deal of excitement from the deprived diners who had to drink out of the wine flasks, share cups or pour wine on their platters and lap it, which some of them unhappily did.

A brief moment of uneasy silence fell during the saying of grace by the Cardinal, and another was accorded the eulogy to the Duke de Guise by the Prévôt des Marchands.

There followed a modest reply by the Duke, the hero of Calais himself, dressed, as Lymond had predicted, in white and gold velvet and diamonds. He made courteous reference, in the course of it, to the able support of his many brave captains and applause broke out all round the tables where Philippa and her companions were sitting.

When the Lieutenant-General had resumed speaking: '*Chacun son tour,*' said Piero Strozzi under his breath. 'You know why M. de Guise kept none of the booty from Calais? A million pounds in gold, he gave to his captains, and 50,000 livres' worth of English fleeces to d'Andelot alone—the painting of Jason there, mon fils, should bear a Coligny face.

Monseigneur required a military success and a popular success both, and you and I gave it to him. O, God in heaven: we are to suffer a fanfare?'

The speech had ended, and the comte de Sevigny's antiseptic blue gaze was turned on his garrulous companion. 'He's going to recite,' Philippa said.

Lymond recited. It was, happily, something she could help him with.

'His prayses with the princely noyse—'
'—Of sounding trumpets blow':
'Prayse hym upon the viole, and—'
'—Upon the harpe also.'
'Prayse him with Timbrel and with Flute—'
'—Organnes and Virginalles,'
'With sounding Cymbals prayse ye hym—'
'—Prayse hym with loude Cymbals.
'—There are times when I feel,' Philippa said, 'that one set of cymbals would be sufficient.'

'But the Duke de Guise,' Lymond said, 'is happy with two sets of cymbals, and *quand le bâtiment va, tout va* . . . Philippa, Philippa, what have you been hiding from us? A plague of demons is attempting to enter the room, a sword of fire out of the gullet of each of them, and every one of them as high as the clouds of heaven. The City fathers have commissioned a Spectacle?'

'Oh dear!' said Philippa, groaning. 'The City Fathers have commissioned two entertainments from Jodelle. But they should have drawn the boards first.'

'They should certainly have drawn the boards first,' Lymond concurred. 'They're going to act in and out of the King's jacket buttons. . . . Oh, Christ. Orpheus?'

'Orpheus,' agreed Philippa sorrowfully. Fighting his way through the crowd, his laurel wreath knocked quite a little askew, trod a singular figure with a carmine smile, a paunch and a lyre. From the shifting shape of his mouth, but from nothing else, one could tell he was singing.

The court, being accustomed to mime, made no concessions. The volume of greeting, conversation and comment rose, intensified and thundered back on itself, carrying Orpheus into masterful inaudibility. A pasteboard belfry jammed in the doorway, tripped, and entered on six dirty feet. A second one followed.

'Francis . . .' said Piero Strozzi.

'Be quiet,' said Lymond. 'I'm lip-reading. *Chantés rochers, et avecq' vostre Orphee, Adorés moy d'un grand Roy le Trophee.* Rochers?'

'Clochers,' Philippa said. 'They ordered rocks and got belfries. Bad handwriting.'

'Hell's own bells too, if I may say so,' Lymond said.

'Rocks with Sirens in them,' Philippa corrected him patiently. 'You're very slow. It's Jason and the Argonauts.'

'No one's handwriting could be that bad,' said Lymond. The Sirens, quavering, retrieved their meandering minims, breathed, and arrived in scratchy unison at their ultimate lines.

O trois trois fois trois fois heureus Orphee
O trois trois fois trois fois heureus Trophee.

A yap of hysteria rose from the audience. 'Francis,' said Piero Strozzi. 'Mon petit François; Madame, I have done my best to help make of this historic Triumph an event which Messieurs of the Ville will relate to their grandsons. I have tried. You have tried. But nothing, mort-Dieu, can redeem this *bella cagata.* I, Hesychast,' said Piero Strozzi, 'am going to lie on the floor and—forgive me—study my belly-button.'

And he did, gracefully, accompanied by the claret flask. Philippa Somerville looked up at Lymond, who had risen and was concentrating visibly on the players.

'Well?' said Philippa kindly.

He turned his head slowly and stared at her. 'Minerva in a canvas shirt of mail and a helm with a cock on the top. There's a gorgon's head on her shield.'

'Oh.'

'She has quite a short ginger beard. She's forgotten her lines. In any case, she can't hear the prompt.'

'That must be awkward for her,' Philippa said.

'Yes. There she goes. You should listen. How about that?'

'... Me suis de ton Paris faite la gardienne
Par ton Pere, qui seul me rend Parisienne ...

'And now,' continued the architect of the battle of Calais, his voice somewhat stifled, 'there is a very large ship attempting to walk through the doorway.'

'Argo,' said Philippa. 'I told you.'

'And you recall those little budge wigs made of lambskin ... ? Could it be Jason?' said Lymond. 'In leopard fur, kicking the belfries in their white satin slops? It's not their fault. They can't see where the door is. But they've got the ship through. They're trying to put up the mast. And who's *that*?'

Philippa craned. 'That's Mopsus, the Argonauts' soothsayer. He was killed by the bite of a serpent.'

'Not this one. This one,' said Lymond, 'is going to be hanged like Mumphazard for saying nothing. You know how Jason died?'

'Naturally,' said Philippa, severely. 'A beam from the ship fell on his ... Oh, dear.'

'Philippa,' said Lymond weakly against the rising gale of anguish and laughter, 'I do beg your pardon, but if I am to attend court again, I shall have to retire under the table with Piero. Gradatim.'

He gazed owlishly at her and she, her eyes brimming, stared back at him. Acutely as she felt for the échevins' suffering, there was a limit to one's powers of civil endurance.

They exploded together, and Lymond slid, as he had threatened, under the table to lie silently shrieking beside the reclining figure of the Queen's favorite cousin while Philippa, covering her face with her hands, sat helplessly through the heroic dregs of the Antique Triumph of Calais.

❦

It ended just before midnight. A little after, wild-eyed with enforced courtesy, Lymond handed his wife into their coach and as they jolted off between their torch-runners, proceeded to relieve his feelings with a total recall of the *Argonautes*, from the warbling rocks to the whinnies of Mopsus.

Half-way home, he remembered that half his possessions were still with Jerott at the Séjour du Roi and the coach was redirected there in the midst of a calamitous declamation by Jason:

> '... *Sentiront que HENRY est leur fatal Jason*
> *Si tu scais bien sauver en un tel navigage*
> *Tout le people qui fait avec toy son voiage*
> *De Geans monstreux, horribles, affamés*
> *Sans cesse sur le sang des petits enflammés ...*'

The coach stopped and Philippa, crying with laughter,

followed him in. He entered, clucking *O trois trois fois trois fois heureus Trophee* and not in the least put out to find himself in the presence of his own English prisoner as well as Jerott.

Naturally, Jerott wanted to know what had happened: Marthe joined them, and almost immediately Danny and Adam. A jug of wine was brought. Sunk, trailing their finery in opposite chairs, Philippa and Francis Crawford related, restored to preternatural gravity, the events of the entire evening, beginning with the welcoming salvoes and going on with the chandeliers and Piero Strozzi's silver.

They ended with the *Argonautes*, Philippa taking the parts of Orpheus, Minerva and Argo and Lymond the rest.

Austin Grey, standing obscured in the shadows, watched it in silence. But it rendered Danny and Adam, who in any case had also been drinking, almost totally helpless. Smiling, Marthe kept the wine flask going round. Jerott, already better fortified, with good reason, than anyone, laughed until his ribs ached so much that he had to fold his arms over them.

For a moment, disconnected by the stitch in his side, he listened not to the sense but to the interplay of the two flexible voices, one masculine and light, one mellow and feminine, unreeling their story, faintly affronted amid mounting hysteria. He opened his eyes.

He knew, because his memories of Francis Crawford went back further than those of anyone there, that Lymond was rather drunk, although he could still disguise it. The quickwittedness, the invention, the faultless comedy timing were present at the price of a little concentration which had closed his outer consciousness for the moment. Jerott, no longer laughing, sat in the shadows and watched the dazzling performance and both the players, blond and brown, artist and acolyte.

Acolyte. But Philippa was a child no longer: he had known that since that single evening in Lyon. The severe, clear-skinned profile turned towards Francis might have belonged to any great lady. The brown and brilliant gaze only quizzed him at intervals: she seemed able, Jerott saw, to sense by instinct the course of his fantasy; and as with Lymond, what she was doing at present occupied all her awareness. Then Francis surged to his feet, leaving his robe, and launched into Jason's querulous tour de force, fractured by interruptions and a mounting fury of incoherent resentment, and finally disintegrating in chaos.

Against her will, Marthe was laughing. Danny sobbed. Adam, his head in his hands, was also weeping with laughter. But Jerott, his attention already caught, watched Philippa Somerville, her gaze on her husband, come to her senses.

He knew how it turned you to water, that unguessed-at well of delight under the bitter intelligence. In his life with Marthe they had found it perhaps as many times as he could count on one hand: never more. When it came, you felt as Philippa looked, her soul in her eyes.

As he watched, she bent her head and crossing her hands, slid them along her forearms to still them. Oh God, thought Jerott. Don't let it happen. She doesn't deserve the torment. The lifetime of waiting, in return for a handful of moments of ecstasy. And standing behind him, always, the ghosts of his other, experienced women. The thoughts he did not share. The knowledge that one had his total friendship but never the key to the innermost door. . . . And there was an innermost door, which Marthe did not have, and had never had although that and that alone was the reason he had married her. . . .

Adam was looking at him. Stupid with too much wine and too much emotion Jerott turned his head, and so caught, without warning, the expression on Austin Grey's face. Then, as he watched, the polite mask replaced the scorn, the hurt anger; and Marthe, still laughing, was prompting Philippa and Philippa, obedient, was rising: 'I beg your pardon. The honestest woolgatherer that ever came to us. What am I? Minerva? . . . *Voyant ainsi, ô Roy, dans ma main docte et foret . . .*'

Lymond put an egg in her hand. 'La mer des cronicques et mirouer hystorial de France. For God's sake don't squeeze it,' he said. 'We've passed that bit: we're into the Masque. What do you want to be, Victory, Virtue or Mnemosyne? It doesn't matter. Dance! Music! Are you men or sedentary blubbers?'

And it did become a dance, of a kind, with Adam seizing a lute, and Lymond seizing Marthe, and Danny and Jerott seizing each other and Austin, because she pulled him out, laughing, partnering Philippa in a storm of blown eggs filled with scent which should have been thrown at the Masque but which had been appropriated, it was to be supposed, by the

Queen's cousin and the Voevoda of Russia, lying under the table. . . .

If he had not for once let himself drink, it might not have happened. He might have found means, changing places in a hysterical vuelta, to escape spinning Philippa as the others were doing. But he didn't avoid it, although he barely touched her. His hands had already left hers when Marthe, cannoning into them, flung Philippa bodily into her arms and then, with her strong, craftsman's fingers held her locked there. 'Come. Be merry. *Kiss her*,' said Marthe.

Lymond burst her grip, dragging her palm through the links of his shoulder-chain. She howled with the pain of it and turned on him like a pole-cat, her hand gushing scarlet.

'Has she the pox?' said Marthe. 'You'll seek out strumpets, fumble with courtiers, fornicate with either parent of the heiress you are supposed to be marrying, but to embrace your wife sickens you?'

The music stopped in the room; and the movement.

'Ah,' said Lymond. His face had emptied. 'From a new host and an old harlot, the good Lord deliver us.' He picked up Philippa's furs. 'Adam, will you see Philippa home?'

Arrested in mid-revel Adam left Danny, whose hazel eyes had abruptly focused. Jerott started forward. And Austin, his skin sallow, made to follow and then stood, his gaze on Philippa.

Marthe moved. Intentionally or not, she now stood fully blocking Philippa's path from the dusty parlour. 'You didn't think Kate or Jerott ever doubted the lady's chastity?' she observed sardonically. 'They were terrified, my gallant friend, in case you or she fell in love with one another.'

'Then reassure them,' said Lymond. 'I am sufficiently served, as you say, with the tag and rag of the streets. Stand aside, please.'

Marthe did not stir. 'Of course you are guiltless,' she agreed, smiling at him. 'But evasion itself can be seductive. Look at her. She is . . .'

Austin moved and was pulled up, hard, by Danny Hislop.

'This,' said Lymond, 'is by no means a game I will play, or consider playing. Move.'

'No,' said Marthe baldly. 'You can shift me by force. If you do, I shall resist, and you will have to injure me a second time. Philippa. Do you want that to happen?'

The folds of Philippa's gown were quivering, but her back

was flat, and her voice very clear and collected. 'We have accepted your hospitality. Mr Crawford owes you his life. While I am here, no one will lay hands on you.'

A spasm like wind on water ran marring over Marthe's intent face. 'Oh God in heaven, I hate you!' she said to her brother.

'I know,' said Lymond wearily. 'I shall stay. Let Philippa go, and the others.'

'Austin said, 'You uncivilized . . .' and was shaken quiet, again, by Danny, his eyes on Marthe.

'It is my wife who is retiring,' Jerott Blyth said. 'Marthe, go to your room.'

'She won't obey orders, you fool,' said Danny Hislop. 'Take her.'

He might have done. But before he could move, Philippa stepped forward and thrust her hands in the tightly clenched hands of Lymond's sister and spoke to her. 'It's too late. It will punish all the wrong people. Come with me. Leave him.'

But Marthe's fists and Marthe's eyes rejected her. And Marthe's voice said, 'Look at her,' to her brother. 'You drunken fool, why do you think she follows you? To be lectured, to take arms, to care for your bastards? She loves you. She's ripe for you. What have you to lose? Embrace her. Then take her home and see if I am right or not,' Her voice thickened. *'Remember me?'* she said. *'The marriage will stand.'*

Philippa dropped her hands and turning, walked to the fireplace. 'Thank you,' she said to the wall.

The Marquis of Allendale broke from his captor, was retaken, and this time was silenced by force. Apart from Adam and Danny, no one in the room either watched or listened to him.

Face to face, Francis Crawford and his sister looked at one another.

'And thank you from me,' said Lymond pleasantly. 'You are an expert in love? In morality? In Christian conscience? How? From the stews of a fortune-teller's in Lyon? From your years as a Muslim, scouring the Levant for money? From your marriage to—'

'Stop it,' said Philippa. She had turned.

'. . . from your marriage to Jerott?' Lymond said. 'Go on. Be our guide. Look about. What other paramours can you find for me, *sister*?'

307

'*Stop it!*' said Philippa, at the top of her voice this time. She faced them, breathing quickly. 'None of you knows what you're doing. Be quiet. If nothing will end it but someone's pride being broken, then as usual, it had better be mine. Mr Crawford. I am sorry to be lacking a beard, but if you will briefly be Jason, I shall do what I can with Medea. With the utmost distaste, let us embrace one another.'

But the eyes he turned on her were as blank and as inimical as the eyes which had swept round them all, and especially lingered on Austin.

'God in heaven,' said Lymond. 'How many more services am I supposed to perform in payment for Marthe's attentions on Volos? Marthe? Step aside.'

'You will have to strike me,' Marthe said. Blood still ran down her hand. She lifted her golden head, braced for his fist and his shoulder.

'Strike you?' said Lymond, and laughed. 'No. I am going to describe Güzel's naked body. And call upon you for corroboration.'

A woman sniggered.

Philippa ran for the door. Marthe, her face sallow, must have twisted out of her way for she reached it: a moment later they heard her footsteps flying down the stairs and then crossing the yard. A horse stamped, and there were voices. For a moment Lymond stared after her. Then he, too, made his way out precipitately. They heard his voice speaking her name; but the sound was overlaid by the rumble of wheels. The noise and splashing receded and dwindled. Lymond did not come back into the room.

Freed at last to move and to speak Austin Grey choked and then, his face yellow, left the room abruptly. No one stopped him.

Marthe also got up and went out.

There was a little silence. Then Danny Hislop heaved a sigh. 'O beau sire Dieu, what a hell of an evening. Jerott, you either want to have another half-bottle, or vomit three ways what you have, like the Rosault.' In five months the professionals Hislop and Blyth had reached an understanding.

It was Adam who found another bottle and helped them drink it, the scar bright and pink on his face. It was also Adam who said presently, 'Listen. It's pouring.' Lymond had still not returned.

'I'll go,' said Jerott. 'It was my bitch of a wife. When

308

Marthe's about, there's always someone puking-drunk somewhere.'

Adam and Danny watched him as he walked out of the room and through the house and down the steps into the downpour.

✱

Outside, it was darker than the slades of the Comté of Oye and muddy, though less so than the Pas de Calais. *The voices of the men were stilled and all mankind was changed into mud.* All the captains who had worked like dogs for the success of Calais had had to sit at table, Philippa said, and listen to the great Guisard claiming the victory. Including Strozzi. Including Francis, the Voevoda of all Russia, who had allowed his work, without comment, to stay in obscurity.

Standing drunk in the yard, while the rain soaked his hair and spread cold through the cloth of his doublet, Jerott thought of the fine design, firmly executed, of the campaign of Guînes and of Calais. And of his own joy and his liberation, after these huckstering years, to be again under the hand of this man, his arts at their meridian.

It had given him courage last night to come home to Marthe: to say, 'I have been wrong. Forgive me. I love you: I wish to stay with you; but I have discovered I am a soldier.'

And she had laughed and said, 'Does the army know? Have some more wine.'

He had not answered because he did not know, as Francis did, how to wound without blows to protect himself.

A fact which Marthe just now should have remembered. She had set out to attack and had been cut down without mercy, and without care for who else besides Marthe might suffer.

He had always known, Jerott supposed, that Marthe had been close, long ago, to Lymond's mistress. He knew no other man who, in cold blood, would have made that threat, or who would have carried it out as Lymond would, ignoring every instinct of decency.

He shivered. The cold was beginning to penetrate. Against the cressets under the archways the rain spangled the darkness like the wild silver threads of horse-harness: as from the passing of heavy cavalry the wind buffeted his cheeks and his flanks and his sleeve-knots. His senses filled with the hiss of the rain, Jerott walked through the ghostly steam of its impact, and through a passage, and, mechanically, into the chain of large courtyards beyond it.

Because of the rain each was empty even of servants. He had found the locked stables and turned, conscientiously, to explore the arcades which enclosed them when he noticed, not in shelter at all, the pale, shallow cup of the fountain.

It was less symmetrical, in the sheen of the rain, than he remembered it. Then he saw that a man rested there on its steps, his head turned on the rim. One coatless arm, lying loose, pillowed it. The arcade lanterns, dimly exploring, found the darkened blond of soaked hair; the fixed flame of strung jewels and the line of wide brow and closed lid and turned cheekbone whose twin he saw, night after night, on his pillow.

The rain fell. For a moment Jerott stood petrified. Then he ran for his life over the courtyard.

Francis Crawford opened his eyes. 'It's all right,' he said without moving. 'The crucifix marque-vin. I've been as sick as a dog. I deserve to be, don't you think? Poor, bloody Jerott, caught between bastards.'

He gave a sudden, violent shiver and, lifting his head from the stone, pulled himself up to sit forward. His hands covered his face. He was so close that Jerott could see the vibration in him: a steady trembling, subdued as the purr of a tomcat.

The effects, unpleasant but normal enough, of anger, and cold, and intemperance. For which Francis Crawford had himself only to blame. Himself and Marthe.

The rain beat Lymond's darkened hair into his hands and the *barmi* produced Russian arpeggios of emerald fire, keyed to all the irregular gusts of his breathing. Beneath his hands, his lips were parted.

Jerott's anger vanished. He placed his palm on the other man's shoulder. The sleeve and the flesh under it were both badly chilled. 'Come in,' he said. 'You can use Adam's rooms.' His hand, moving upwards, drew the fair, tangled hair clear of Lymond's eyes and checked, at the shudder that ran jarring through from his fingertips.

Lymond dropped his hands. He made no protest. He did not look up. But unimpeded at last, Jerott could see the look on his face and give it, sickeningly, its correct interpretation.

'Oh God in heaven,' said Jerott Blyth. 'You bloody, arrogant fool . . .' He sat back suddenly. His own arm, supporting him, was unsteady. 'Why didn't you accept Piero's offer?'

'I don't know,' Lymond said. It was not easy to hear him.

'You ought to know!' said Jerott wildly. 'You're not a priest. You fight. You live on your nerves as we all do. Then you can't touch a girl, in case you leave your senses and take her. Is that what happened?'

'I suppose so,' Lymond said. 'It might have bound me to her for life. It was what Marthe wanted. No light fame shalt thou carry to thy father's ghosts . . .'

'What?' said Jerott.

'. . . to have fallen under the weapon of Camilla.'

He didn't explain. His lids were fringed like a girl's. His tapering fingers, without defences, lay within touching distance. Jerott Blyth, rising to his knees and then to his feet, said, 'Come quickly. I can get you a woman.'

'If you know of a woman,' Lymond said, 'then go to her. What I want I can find for myself. You might perhaps, when you go, send for Archie.'

'Sir?' said a voice, uncannily apt, in the darkness. Jerott turned.

My lord count? Mr Crawford? M. de Sevigny?'

'All of these,' said Lymond dryly. He was shivering still. But he was also trying, Jerott saw, to collect himself. Jerott Blyth hesitated. Then he offered, leaning, an arm, and Lymond took it and stood, as the moving figure neared in the darkness.

It was Archie Abernethy, cloaked and half-dressed as when he had been roused at the Hôtel St André. He said, 'What's amiss?' sharply.

'Drink,' said Lymond impartially. 'The cutthroat of so many men's lives, and the robber of purses. I have been compelled to render my gorge, I have recovered. What is *your* difficulty?'

Archie said, 'Is that true?' and Jerott answered his thought.

'Yes. Nothing else happened. How did you know we were here?'

'Mr Blacklock. He was worried,' said Archie uncompromisingly. And to Lymond: 'I've ill news. Are ye fit for it?'

'A death,' said Francis Crawford. He had thrown off Jerott's arm.

You could see, in the darkness, the pity in the little man's eyes.

'Aye. It's death,' he said.

'Then tell me,' said Lymond. 'Now, and quickly.' The trembling had wholly stopped.

The black eyes of Archie fixed themselves on him in return. 'Your mother and brother,' he said. 'Their ship has foundered.'

There was a little silence, during which Lymond made no movement. Then he said again, 'Tell me.' The amber hair, like the hair of the new born, streaked and coiled round his temples.

Archie said, 'They came from the Forth in a fleet of small ships with the other Commissioners. The wind drove the vessels apart: they put into whatever safe harbour they came to. Two of them made for Boulogne, but never got there.'

He stopped. Lymond said, 'If you go on, you will be finished the sooner.'

Jerott turned his head away. Archie did go on, and his voice, if a little hoarse, was quite level. 'They went to the bottom, crew, passengers, horses, clothes, gifts for the bride on her wedding. They say two men only were rescued by fishermen, and these two were an Earl and a Bishop. The survivors have gone to Dieppe. The King wants the welcoming party to ride to Dieppe in the morning.'

His voice ceased. Jerott said nothing. For a little while Francis Crawford stood unseeing and dumb in the darkness, the icy rain whipping his doublet. Then he said, 'I shall set out now. The others can follow.'

Jerott exclaimed, shrewish in his anxiety. 'Damn that. Four hours' sleep won't hurt you—or them, for that matter.'

But Lymond shook his head and moving suddenly, left the steps and then, walking steadily, the shining circle of lamplight.

Jerott leaped to follow. He had taken the first stride after when Archie's arm, hard as a mattock, barred his stomach, and Archie's lightless black eyes snapped at him.

'What d'ye fear? If ever man valued his life now, it's that one. He has to get to Dieppe. He has to find if there is none left of his name but those fatherless bairns home in Scotland. And he has to decide . . . man, he has to decide what to do about it.'

CHAPTER 3

Des deux duelles, l'un percera le fiel:
Hay de lui, bien ayme de sa mere.

In a trance of fatigue, he would have ridden the hundred miles to Dieppe by post-stage as he was, had nothing prevented him. But, moving into the house from the rain, he found the bright lights of Marthe's empty parlour unbearably dazzling, familiar phenomenon; and the smell of the spilt scent revolted him.

Neither fact augured well for a journey. He wished to be certain at least of completing it. So he let common sense and Archie prevail, and assumed dry clothes and occupied Adam's bed for thirty meticulous minutes while Archie packed saddlebags and an escort was arranged, and money, and a warrant for post-horses.

At the end of that time, Archie came back and questioned him curtly. 'Mr Blyth said ye were sick. How sick?'

'Very,' said Lymond. There was a bowl of soup in Archie's hands.

Archie said, 'We can leave as soon as you like.'

'We?' said Francis Crawford.

'You and I,' Archie said.

With a delicacy he had not expected, Jerott and Danny and Adam were not going to ride north, supporting him. Archie waited, and then said, 'You'll feel better, a bit, when you've a bite taken.'

*

He made the journey to Dieppe without resting except to change horses. Half-way there, his escort began to fall back, and then as fresh mounts became hard to come by, to slow him down quite considerably. One man came to grief on the highway. There seemed no point in compelling six other people to face the mud, the wet snow, the uneven road and the darkness to no purpose. At the next post-station he sent them all home and continued unaccompanied, with Archie.

And that, since it removed a distraction, was an error. One could not talk, but one could think, during the long thudding canters over invisible plains with a sleety wind scoring the face and freezing the hands in their glove-leather. And when the pace slackened, at once he would be aware of the galling fatigue of the saddle, and the growing strain on his shoulders and fore-arms. The post-houses knew who he was. Every fresh horse was strong, and restive and eager.

On stretches such as these, Archie's hands on his reins would sometimes check him; and then, in the lee of a chalk quarry or a tangle of weather-torn bushes the little trainer would pull out aquavite, and a handful of raisins. But the aquavite made him sick, and Archie, when he found out, stopped giving it to him.

Then they began to pass lighted cottages, and laden wains emerging from farmyards and cattle, plodding in to their milking. The sky paled. Over Calais; over Boulogne the new day came spreading: by the time they were in the water-logged fault of the Bray valley, it was quite light. They had been riding at gallop or at canter, for six continuous hours.

To Francis Crawford the rest of the journey was never quite clear in his memory. The wet snow had stopped, leaving a landscape dense and spidery with thin rails of leafless trees, their spars floating and weaving in the cascading grey air. A flock of short, stocky birds rose once, wheeling, blackening, wheeling, and caused his horse, racing flat out, to curvet. He crossed what seemed to be endless undulating chalk fields with the same grey web of trees smudged with mist on the skyline.

Then his horse stumbled again, and very soon after that they saw the hooded thatch of the next posting station, and there was a brief interval of noise and warmth and the reek of horse-sweat and steaming clothes and hot tallow and of fish, from the wicker carts with their two powerful horses on their way to deliver their herring to Paris.

He left the crowded room abruptly when he had only been there for five minutes, and waited for the fresh horses in the squelching cold of the bustling yard. Archie said, when he came out, 'These will take us to Dieppe. But there's no sense in killing them.'

It was the only mention of restraint that he had made, from beginning to end. Jerott had tried to stop him, but not the others. The others remembered another shipwreck, only fifteen months ago in Scotland, when Richard his brother had ridden like this to come to him, but not so far, and in the knowledge, of course, that he was living.

He and Richard had met on the strand at Philorth and like the sand under their feet, all the muddled solicitude which had prompted that journey had in five minutes dispersed through their fingers. Richard, believing him to have come home at last to his responsibilities, had been outraged and wounded to discover that his plans were to leave Scotland for ever. And he had been as careful as he knew how to be, but it had not been enough because he too had been hurt, by a loss he could afford less than Richard. In the wreck had died Diccon Chancellor the English navigator, who had been more than half-way towards becoming the friend he had never quite managed to find and keep, in terms of equality, except sometimes, in passing, with women.

He had thought sometimes to recognize the same affinity with Richard, but circumstances and, he supposed, his own nature were always against it. And of the women, two had died and he had cut himself off from the other.

'This is the Chalk Hill,' said Archie. 'And there's the gate of Dieppe. What do you want to do?'

Below them, running through its cold swamps, was the River Argues with the walled and moated town of Dieppe on its left bank. On the chalky cliffs to the west of the town the blue-capped towers of the castle and citadel stood clear against the grey sky and grey sea beyond: the sea which washed the shores of both England and France, and had become a moat and a graveyard for both.

Lymond said, 'The captain of the gate will know where the Commissioners are. I shall go there first, and then join you up at the Castle.'

He had not realized until he turned then and looked at him, how tired Archie was. The lines in his dark cheeks were deep as knifed clay, and his black eyes were reddened and sunk under the close leather helmet he wore like a turban.

Lymond said, 'A brother, whether I have one or not, could not have done more.'

Then, before Archie could try to answer, he touched spurs

to his worn, steaming horse and plunged downhill to the Porte de la Barre drawbridge.

❋

The captain of the ward knew him, and was flustered by his lack of retinue and the forewarning which was expected on the arrival of a great lord, a King's officer and a Chevalier of the Order to the King's loyal town of Dieppe. It took a few moments of sickening patience to put that right; then Lymond asked his question.

The captain turned up his eyes. The town was full of Scotsmen. He couldn't tell how many each Commissioner had brought with them. And all arriving at different times, some by boat, some by road according to where the weather had landed them.

Yes, he had heard two ships had been wrecked off Boulogne. A fishing boat had brought along the survivors that morning. A man called Rotisse and a man called Rit, he had been told, both Commissioners. The servants had not known how to swim.

He did not know if there had been anyone else in the fishing boat. He had been on duty since dawn, and was only going by hearsay. The principal guests at any rate were in the big house. La Pensée, the house of the late Jean Ango. Monseigneur knew it. Monseigneur had stayed in it before.

He had, in December with d'Andelot. And long, long ago with Tom Erskine, who had married the Fleming girl's sister, and died also, in Scotland.

'I shall go there,' said Lymond. 'Without escort. They know me.'

He had to push his way through the market place at the Puits Sale and steer his horse through the crowds in the Grand' Rue. The town *was* full of Scotsmen. But then, it always was, what with resident merchants and refugees, and fishermen and the ships of both countries carrying wine and hides and letters and practising a little piracy on the side. Speak Scots in Dieppe and anyone could understand you. Knox had been there most of last autumn, and no one had troubled him. At times it was more foreign than French.

Someone in Kennedy livery went by and he almost called to him, and then turned and went on picking his way. After ten hours, one should have patience. And he did not want to accept this, his final loss, in the open market-place.

Then ... here, enclosing the great terraces and the riverside gardens, was the wall he had once swung over, masked on a summer night. And there, gleaming through the bare trees the fountains and statues.

Masterless and directionless after the harsh years of outlawry, he had celebrated his freedom six years ago in ways he preferred not to remember. But it would be reflected in the faces of eight Scottish lords he was about to meet: two earls, two barons; two officers of the Church and two civic leaders, all chosen with care by Mary of Lorraine, Queen Dowager of Scotland, to complete the contracts and attend the wedding of her one living child Mary to the Dauphin of France.

He knew who they were. He also knew their political and spiritual aspirations. Five of them were of the orthodox religion. The rest were not. The Queen Dowager of Scotland had sent to her brothers de Guise three of the foremost sympathizers of the Reformed Religion in Scotland. As wedding guests they might seem incongruous, but there was much that was practical in the idea. It freed the Dowager of their presence for several months, and offered her brothers an opportunity to bribe or convert them. It remained to wonder why Richard, of baronial rank and no fiery beliefs, had been included, and Sybilla his mother along with him.

You might think it a mother's natural wish to send to her daughter's marriage a noble and elderly lady who had cared for the child in her infancy. You might also think that the Duke de Guise wished Francis Crawford to leave for Scotland, and had suggested this as a means of encouraging him.

In which case, it was a pity for the Duke de Guise that the crossing had been so stormy. Or, on the other hand, perhaps the plan of monseigneur mon oncle was going to succeed better even than the Duke had cause to hope.

He touched up his horse and rode up to the gates, which stood already ajar, held by two liveried keepers. The outer yard was swarming with people, and through the archway he could see one of the Scottish heralds running forward, struggling into his tabard, and behind him a hurrying gentleman in a good furred coat who looked like the maître d'hôtel.

The captain of the Porte de la Barre had known better than to let a Chevalier of the Order and a victor of Calais arrive unannounced at the house of Jean Ango. Someone, running by a faster route than his, had roused the household.

The herald was Alec Ross. He had his tabard on by the time Lymond dismounted, had walked through the line of servants into the archway and there paused, to hear his formal welcome. He saw, without looking, that shutters were open everywhere and windows crowded. The maître d'hôtel added a few formal phrases and a succession of apologies. The sieur de Fors had not expected their lordships to come from Paris until Sunday. At that very moment, the Lieutenant-Governor was entertaining the Commissioners and their train to a banquet at the *Écu de France* ... a modified banquet, of course, in view of the sad bereavements which the Commission had recently suffered. ...

He had no idea—why should he?—that the comte de Sevigny was Richard Crawford's younger brother. It was left to Alec Ross to interrupt, pallid with distress. 'I have to tell you, my lord, that it was a terrible shock to us all. The Lyon and all the Commission would want me to tell you. Two shiploads drowned, and they can't even name all the dead.'

The deferential circle in the courtyard moved closer. Under the watching windows Lymond said. 'How many men did they rescue?'

'None, my lord count,' said the herald. 'Aside from the two earls and the Bishop of Orkney. Your lordship realizes that none of the households could swim. It was a fishing boat coming by later that found the three, supporting the lady.'

The vice of pride serves its purpose at times. So, after two heartbeats, Lymond said, 'The news which reached Paris was incomplete. Was the Dowager Lady Culter among the survivors?'

'Why. I beg your ... My lord ... You didn't know?' said Alec Ross. 'My lord count, yes. She's not strong; she's resting, but she's in the house there now. I thought you knew!' said Ross Herald, horror in his worthy face.

'No. But perhaps then, I might be allowed to visit her,' said the comte de Sevigny. 'I am, as you may know, Francis Crawford.'

A scattered cheer rose from the courtyard, as the most ornamental of the victors of Calais walked into the house of Jean Ango. For once he did not respond, although he heard it.

What forces he might still possess he must harbour for another purpose. Of the three children Sybilla had reared, he

318

was the only one living. This time, whatever one's instincts might be, one did not turn on one's heel and walk past her.

✤

Put him, blindfold, into a closed room anywhere in the world, and he could tell if Sybilla was with him. It had to do, perhaps, with her scent. To him, it was more: a breath from the sweetness and peace of his childhood; a sense of light; of understanding; of loving amusement; an air from the flower-filled walls of pairidæza.

Nothing, even now, took from him that first moment as he stood on her threshold. Until the second moment came, and with it his years and his memory. He closed the door, and then turned calmly and looked for her.

He had thought to find her shrouded in shawls, in a chair or in bed, and fortified by companions and serving women. Instead she was alone, playing idly with cards against the grey wintry light from the windows. A charcoal brazier glowed on the polished wood of the floor, and candles bloomed by the warm woollen hangings and the wainscoting, lighting the studs on the coffers and chairs, the toolings of books, the spotless stiffened veil on Sybilla's snow-fair hair, and her fine skin, and the rings on the small hands touching the cards. Then she looked up, and waited.

Which was unfair. In the last five years they had met only once, and then not to speak to one another. And so little had changed: the delicate face, the gentian blue eyes were as he remembered them. Her gaze on him held nothing but repose. But then, he had asked to be received. She had known for a few moments that he was coming, and from her window had perhaps even seen him arrive. His skin and hair were damp from the swift grooming he had contrived for himself, but he could do nothing about the marks of sleeplessness. Yet she showed no surprise.

Then he saw the mourning-clothes and remembered, stricken, what the sight of her, after so very long, had thrust from his mind. He said, without kneeling, without approaching; discarding every preliminary, 'I have heard what happened. I am extremely sorry. If you tell me how I may help in Richard's place, I shall do what I can.'

At the sound of his voice, her hand moved; but otherwise there was no change in her composure. He had said to Phil-

319

ippa that he did not foresee any unpleasantness, and of course this was true.

The candles shimmered. Sybilla laid down her cards and said, 'You look cold. There is a chair by the brazier, if you have time to sit.' And when he had done so, she said, 'You can't have wanted to come. I am grateful that you did. You have heard then. . . . Do you know how many died?'

Her voice was quieter than he had expected, but quite even. And, like his, eschewing all that was personal. She had not even addressed him by name. He said, 'I know only that Richard was drowned. And the servants who could not swim.'

Sybilla said, 'We lost twenty-five men and women from Midculter. I think you knew them all. They were buried at Boulogne. I brought back such relics as were washed ashore, to give to their families. You could help with that, if you mean what you say.'

'I mean what I say,' he said steadily. She had taken the cards again, and was shuffling them with great deliberation. He released his breath and added, 'Then you have written to Midculter?'

'Yes,' said Sybilla. The candlelight, flaring, caught a sudden spark in her eyes which were bright, he now saw, with unreleased tears. She said, in the same low, even voice, 'Is there anything I should add?'

He rose abruptly and walked to a sturdy hutch-table by the wall, with her eternal sewing ranged neatly upon it, with her spectacles. Beside it, also familiar, was a copper kettle he recalled from Midculter. He turned, his hand on the wood, and said, 'I think you know I have no wish to come back to Scotland. I must stay, in any case, until after the royal wedding: the Legate is to dissolve my own marriage. After that, I am free. What I want you to tell me . . . honestly . . . is this? am I needed at Midculter?'

'Honestly?' she repeated; and though her tears did not fall, her soft lips twisted a little in derision, or perhaps in self-derision. Then seeing, no doubt, the look on his face she said quietly, 'That is a question Richard's wife could answer better than I can.'

Their words moved from difficulty to difficulty, as if clearing thorns in an overgrown garden. He kept, among everything else, ludicrously forgetting to breathe. He said, 'Then I shall ask Mariotta. I owe the Culter family a debt.'

And that was too near the bone: he saw her hands, lightly

clasped now, whiten to bloodlessness on the table. Then she said, 'You must know that if you do, Mariotta will summon you for my sake, as well as her own. How then will you reach a decision?'

Behind the careful words lay the question to which he must, for his own sake, find an answer. He also required, but did not intend, to sit down again. The pause which developed was therefore extended by a number of factors and ended by Lymond himself saying, 'It will depend, I suppose, on the condition in which I find both Midculter and Scotland. I had hoped to go back to Russia.'

Upon which, unexpectedly, Sybilla said, 'Perhaps I deserve no candid answers, but I should like to have one. Would you still go back to Russia if Kiaya Khátún were not there?'

The elegant, desiccated body of a gazelle hound for some reason came into his mind. He had forgotten, even, that she would know of Güzel's existence. 'Yes. I should still go back,' he said.

There were no tears in her eyes now but he could see, his own eyes grown used to the light, the fine seams of age beneath her lashes and on her brow and by the soft corners of her mouth. She had always been a woman of ravishing prettiness. 'And,' she said, 'if I were not there, would you go back to Midculter?'

The room became a mosaic; then a dazzlement of grained light and shade, like water-run taffeta. He bore down hard on the hutch table. It was a perfectly logical question. After a considerable time he said, 'It would make no difference.'

'You still would not come back?' Sybilla said. Her voice was no longer quite so low. 'Can you tell me why? If Mariotta needed you, you would return. But not if I were dead or exiled?'

She was the only person ... almost the only person who could manipulate him like this. He said, 'You can't imagine I ... wish for your death. Or your exile. Midculter is your home. Not mine.'

Sybilla said, 'I didn't ask for an emotive answer. You can't imagine, either, that I shall live for ever. What then could keep you away? There can be no personal reasons, except vanity. Or does Russia mean more to you?'

'No,' he said.

It was all he said; but a smile illumined her face as if he, a child again, had brought her some great achievement: the end of a long task embarked upon, beyond his strength and full of dangers, so that the tears spilled over, as now, while she was smiling. Then she said, 'I was not sure. Will you come to the table?'

He hesitated; then obeyed her. It was closer than he had yet approached her. And it brought the grey daylight full on his own face. The wind drove against the thick panes. On the other side of the room, the door-latch snapped suddenly open.

Sybilla said, 'Midculter is mine. But Scotland is yours, and you are needed there. I am prepared to go into exile if you will come back. Whether Mariotta sends for you or not.'

Once, at Midculter, a kitchen-girl had stolen some salt; and walking out when questions were asked, had picked up the cropping shears and plunged the point from one side of her neck to the other. He looked down at the cards on the table and in time, they became clear, and he could see the game she had been playing. It had not, he saw, been a very coherent one.

To leave Midculter, for her, meant leaving grandchildren and friends, servants, dependants; her home and possessions upon which she had lavished such care; the interlocking circles, social, political, scholarly, in which she had passed all her life; the soil of Scotland itself, from which she drew all her worldly and spiritual nourishment.

He said, his voice sounding very strange, 'It would be a sacrifice to no purpose. No one in your circle would let you go, or fail to resent me if I came in your place.'

A line had come between her thin brows; of pain, or of severity. 'If I choose to live in France,' Sybilla said, 'I wonder who could prevent me? As for the rest, you have made your way against worse opposition than a few friends of the Culter family.' She, too, could place her darts.

He shook his head, very slightly because it was painful, and also because he wished to say and do nothing vehement. 'There are other reasons. I meant what I said. Your presence or absence makes little difference. You must believe that—except for Mariotta and Midculter—I do not mean to come back.'

Little difference. Not *no difference.* He saw her note the change of words, the thin, elegant bones sharpening a little. But her eyes searched him, and this time did not let them go. She said, 'If that is so, can you bring yourself to tell me your reasons? Your other reasons? If I were not there, what could still stand between you and Scotland?'

She had offered him the remaining years of her life. In return he owed her nothing but, perhaps, an act of generosity. A glimpse, if nothing more, of the other, private motives behind his refusal. She read his face, who knew him better than anyone and rose, a little colour tingeing her cheeks; and he looked across the table, and drew breath to answer her.

A man's voice, coldly deliberate, said from the door, 'My sword and my right arm will keep him from Scotland. And both, if need be, will preserve you from leaving it. What ill luck, brother. If I hadn't left table early, you would have had Midculter, wouldn't you?'

The cards showered from the table. 'God in heaven ... *Richard!*' said Sybilla Crawford; and stood there, blanched, in her mourning weeds.

For the man in the doorway was indeed the image, older, a little heavier, a little greyer than one had last seen him, of the son she had lost; of the older brother who had drowned at Boulogne. But still with the pleasant grey eyes and broad, big-boned face, little lined; and the fine brown hair, straight and thick and easily displaced, as now, when something had moved him.

It *was* Richard, alive. The guiding hand at one's pony; the voice at one's porridge bowl; the splendid athlete one watched from one's books in the cold tower window, while outside in the sunshine he rode at the ring, threw his spears, matched his sword with the master-at-arms. The brother who had cared for him, a grown man in illness, and defended him against calumny, and who at length, heartbroken at his defection, had turned his back on him a year ago in Scotland.

Richard, alive. Francis Crawford drew a long, long breath and then stopped it, as the oddity of Sybilla's cry came to him.

'God in heaven ... *Richard,*' she had said. Not in gladness, or amazement. But in anger.

He turned.

If she had been white before, now she was the colour of ashes. He cried out, *'Oh, can you not stop? Can you not stop even now?'* He halted. And then, his voice still not his own, he said, 'You let me think he was dead.'

Behind him, Richard said, 'You found out she was alone. That was clever. And still infirm, after the shipwreck.'

His voice was closer. Neither Lymond nor Sybilla looked at him. Lymond said, 'You knew Richard would never let you leave Scotland. You did all that, in order to learn . . .'

'I am paying my price now, don't you think?' Sybilla said very quietly.

He had even forgotten Richard, until at that moment a hand gripped his arm and he was jerked painfully back from the table. 'Will you persecute her yet, in front of me?' his brother said. 'Stand there. I have something to say to you.'

Then Sybilla turned to him at last and said, her voice very tired, 'He thought you were drowned. He came to offer his help.'

'He lost no time,' Richard said. 'The King's representatives, I was told, would not arrive until Sunday. He lost no time in making sure of Midculter and even, I hear, of Mariotta.'

'You misheard,' Sybilla said. 'Francis merely undertook to return to Scotland should Mariotta require him.'

Now, when delicacy was no longer profitable, she could use his name. The pain beating in his brows was beyond belief. He wanted only to go while he was still master of himself; before this primitive desire to devastate them both should overpower him. He took a breath.

'It has all been a misunderstanding. You will allow me to take my leave. I shall see you on Sunday,' he said. He had ridden through the night, without rest and without sleep, for this. It ought, surely, to give someone a moment of wry amusement. He understood—but then he had always understood—how Richard had felt at Philorth.

Richard said, 'But you will be back, before Sunday. It took you how long . . . ten minutes? to persuade Sybilla to hand you Midculter and leave Scotland. What will you not achieve next time? You should be relieved. A lifetime of desertion, and you are still her favourite son.'

'Be quiet, both of you,' Sybilla said. It was the tone with which she had quelled them, squabbling, over the years and which even now could make Richard hesitate, and look at her, and fall silent. She said, 'The fault is mine. I allowed Francis to continue to think you were dead. And I offered to leave Scotland, if he would come home again. If your eavesdropping allowed it, you must have heard him refuse me.'

Neither son had ever blasphemed in her presence before. But Lymond did so now, and caused her to break off abruptly as Richard said, 'I don't believe you. You knew I was alive. Why should you suggest exiling yourself?'

'To see what I would say,' Lymond said and smiling, destroyed all his own controls as they looked at him. 'She had no intention of going. But if you hadn't come in, who knows what she would have learned? Who knows what *I* should have learned? There is no end, is there,' he said to Sybilla, 'to the dues you demand from your children?'

'You have all the weapons,' Sybilla said. Her voice, even yet, was quite steady. But then, she had been prepared for this also.

'You don't know what weapons I have,' he said teasingly. 'What other news is there, that might give you a moment's amusement? Renée Jourda is dead; killed, I fear, because I went to see her. Philippa has paid a call at la Guiche and found it profitable, although she is not as practised as I am in guesswork. Turning to Isabelle Roset—'

He was interrupted by Richard, not by Sybilla. 'You've kept Philippa here! She wrote Kate that she was leaving. What in hell are you doing? You've held that child for four years to this marriage!'

'Then congratulate me,' Lymond said. 'I haven't consummated it yet, but now d'Enghien's dead I may be driven to it. Meydyns' maryage wolde he spyll And take wyffus ageyn hor wyll. How about that, my own brother, my own bright light, thou Igor?'

'And that is bombast,' said Sybilla sharply. 'Richard, pay no attention. She will be free after April. Then she can marry young Austin Grey.'

'Do you think,' said Lymond, 'the youthful Mr Grey can consummate it? Or will her new passion for me perhaps flummox him? How nice to be married with ... how many children, Richard? You don't have quite this problem. You don't have any problems really, do you, sitting there in your lordship pontificating? It seems to be beyond you even to get yourself decently drowned. What did it cost to get Alec Ross to indicate your demise? Or no: that was Sybilla's doing.'

'*Her new passion!*' Sybilla said with great suddenness. 'Be quiet and tell me. Has Philippa become in some way attached to you?'

He raised his eyebrows at her. 'Yes,' he said. 'Naturally, I am doing my best to discourage her.' He had not meant to go so far. Kate, as well as Sybilla, would carry the scar of this news. He held her eyes and said clearly, 'You have a great deal to be responsible for.'

'She gave you birth,' Richard said. 'That was her first mistake. The next was to spoil you. So that everything you want, you must have immediately.'

'I'm glad you noticed that,' Lymond said. Tears, unexpectedly, sprang to Sybilla's eyes but that, he thought, was shock. She had never ceased to command with her attitude.

She said sharply, 'You are grown men, and have commanded men. Childish rivalry does you no credit. Francis is resentful because I chose a painful method of discovering his intentions. I wished to know them for his own good. If he found this intolerable, I can only apologize.'

It sounded well. It sounded rational, even, if you were not Francis Crawford. Put him, blindfold, in a closed room anywhere in the world . . .

Lymond said, 'And that is your only excuse?'

And Sybilla met his gaze with eyes as uncompromising as his own. 'I thought I was the excuse for your whole way of life?' she said calmly.

And nothing had prepared him for that.

After a space he said, 'And who do you blame for your mistakes? Isabelle's master?'

'That's enough,' Richard said. You could tell from his face that the allusion defeated him. His touchstone was the colour of Sybilla's face.

Sybilla said, 'I told you that you had all the weapons. Were we two other people, you would proceed to use them, and I should restrain and placate you in every way possible.'

'. . . But we *are* two other people,' Lymond said. 'Aren't we?'

There was a little pause. Then Sybilla said, 'What you are, I am waiting for you to show me.'

Richard's angry grey eyes . . . honest grey eyes . . . were looking at him. Sybilla was not watching. He supposed she knew that however near he might tread to the crevasse, he did not mean to fall in, and drag Richard with him. Instinct had been right, when last year he had fled such a confrontation. As no living soul could hurt him, Sybilla could.

'What I am?' he said. He laughed. 'Don't wait. Ask anyone in London, or Malta, or Russia.' He made his way to the casement and flung it open. The rumour of a crowd, muffled hitherto by the windowpanes, burst fresh upon them. The

326

courtyard and the road beyond the gardens were jostling with people, and the name they were calling was audible: *Sevigny. Sevigny. Sevigny.*

'Or ask them,' Lymond said. 'I have no concern with Midculter. It has its own master and mistress.. And if it did not, I should still have no concern. If Richard dies of an apoplexy, you should find a good steward and marry him.'

'Then why,' said Sybilla, 'did you come here today?' *Sevigny!* came the noise from the courtyard.

He closed the window. In the swirl of air the candle flames fluttered and guttered. He walked to the door in the silence and turned, his hand on the post.

'I told you,' he said, 'I had a sense, I believe, of indebtedness. But someone trussed it in black felt and kicked it to death, as the Turks do.'

He looked at Richard. 'I am glad you are safe. If you wish any help before Sunday, I shall be at the Castle with M. de Fors. I don't imagine there is anything personal we need to discuss after this, either during your visit or later. On behalf of his Most Christian Majesty, we shall attempt to make your stay in France a pleasant one.'

Neither replied. He closed the door and found a servant a short way off who brought him to the maître d'hôtel and his horse.

Ross Herald was there also, anxious to be of assistance. 'I hear the banquet is nearly over. The Commissioners'll be fashed tae have missed you. But you saw the Earl and his mother.'

The noise was all round them by this time, but somehow, he caught it. Lymond turned. He said, 'I saw Lord Culter. Has he . . . has his title by some chance been altered?'

'God save us!' said Alec Ross, and talked fluently for three unbroken minutes.

Lymond listened, focusing his attention with infinite trouble. Just before leaving Scotland, his brother had been given the Crown lands adjoining Midculter and the barony had been raised to an earldom. Richard was now in rank the first Earl of Culter, although neither he nor Sybilla had mentioned it.

So that Alec Ross had not intentionally misled him. Nor had Sybilla. She had merely discovered that he thought Richard dead, and had continued to let him believe it. *I thought I was the excuse for your whole way of life,* she had

327

said to him. Her ripostes, on the whole, had been more successful than his.

Or perhaps she, too, was feeling like this.

Alec Ross said, 'You see, the word has got round that you're here. You could go by the back ways, my lord, but it'd be a pity to disappoint them. There's an escort from the household waiting.'

There was, in the livery of the corps de garde of the town, and already mounted. Ross was right. For the sake of the Commissioners, if not for himself, he would have to make the short ride across the town publicly. A fresh horse, a little restive with the uproar, stood awaiting him. They had even brushed his heavy coat, soaked with the long overnight journey. It was a day and a night since he and Piero Strozzi had tried to rescue the Hôtel de Ville's hilarious victory feast and since, in Philippa's presence, he had forced Marthe to do what he wanted by the only means at his disposal.

He had better make the ride. One could not outrage everyone: spurn every overture; deny every generous emotion. He had discovered that, if nothing else, before he left Russia.

> *Dunbar, on his heid-ake:*
> *My heid did yak yester nicht*
> *This day to mak that I na micht . . .*

Not everyone was in the narrow streets. Men were about their business, whether it was fishing or privateering, or laying the keel of a new vessel over the river, or drawing an old into harbour, trudging rope over shoulder as the tall masts slid upriver behind it. Work did not stop in the potteries, or the kilns, or the brew houses; or in the yards where, thickly grasping, the rape oil coiled in black reeking boilers.

But there were many who did come to the doors, wiping their hands: the sailmaker; the carpenter with his astrolabe, the women with lace in their hands and flax caught on the nap of their aprons.

> *So sair the magryme dois me menyie,*
> *Perseing my brow as ony ganyie . . .*

The skinners came out, and the Dutch cask-makers laid down their hatchets, and the merchants emerged, with the men who carved whalebone and ivory. And since the catch was already salted, or packed off cold in its seaweed, the fish dealers came and stood on the chill puddled stones with the women and children, to look at the lord who had saved Calais—Paris—all the fine ships and brave men of Normandy from their second occupation by the English. And from the windows of the tall wooden houses, they leaned out and shouted, with cheerful approval, his surname.

That scant luik may on the licht.

The mare they had lent him was playful. She passaged, her ears pricked out of the gateway, and before she had travelled ten yards had called into play, inevitably, all his already over-taxed sinews.

Further on, it was more than a matter of extreme discomfort. The crowds along the Grand' Rue were much thicker, with a good deal of pushing and jostling. His guard broke ranks, struggling to keep with him. A group of white-capped, red-cheeked girls threw down a spray of evergreen from a window, and as he glanced up, cap in hand, his horse jarred back on her haunches, hooves clattering. He controlled her; and again, when a group of boys ran forward from an arched tunnel stacked high with oyster-boxes. The odour of shellfish clung in the air, with the reek of warm oil and resin and the fumes, sunk into clay and timber and grey, salty stone, of the herring slung, russet-shot, over their beech smoke. It lay thick in his throat as the mare heaved, and sidled beneath him.

His name reverberated. The overhanging storeys, closing off the free air, gave back the squeals and the shouting, the clack of sticks and the beating of hands, the carillons of a bell-truss and the hiccoughing roar, over and over, of iron rods raked up and down shutters.

Full oft at morrow I upryse,
Quhen that my curage sleipeing lyis . . .

He acknowledged it all, as he was well accustomed to do. He was a professional, and it was part of his performance. If, in the future, he should require the services of these Dieppois burghers, he would depend on their image of him here this morning.

It would not, however, embellish that image if his horse were to kill somebody, or escape his charge or in any other way betray what were, at this moment, his very real weaknesses.

> *For mirth, for menstrallie and play,*
> *For din nor danceing nor deray . . .*

He had passed the Hôtel de Ville whose doors stood open: the banquet then must be over. Saluting, his eyes sweeping the crowd, he looked for a face he might know and thought he saw one: that of a woman. The next moment, pushed aside by the crowd, it had vanished. The mare curvetted and he did what he could, with his whip and spurs, while the din fluctuated, swimmingly artificial, like the vertigo which ever since Sybilla's onslaught had assailed him.

> *It will nocht walkind me no wise.*

Since endurance and perserverance are also virtues of the military, he employed them until, sooner than he had expected, it became quite certain that whatever happened, the rest of the ride was beyond him. He said to the captain of his escort, 'Your pardon, mon capitaine. I wish to pause here at the church of St Jacques.'

A worthy, if unexpected change of plan. It took longer than he had hoped to clear a new route to his left, and a forward surge of the crowd meanwhile broke through the ranks of his escort and brought them, plucking, pulling and calling, to his stirrups.

He felt the mare quiver and knew, if she reared, that he could not hold her. Then from the tower of St Jacques, the voice of the bell called la Catherine pitched through the screams with the first of her summons to worship. At the first clang, his mare ripped the reins from his fingers.

He saw the whites of her eyes, and felt her muscles bunch. She didn't rear. Nor did she strike with her hooves, or dislodge him. She stood, trembling but still, her reins dangling, with two liveried stablemen holding her.

And at his own knee was their master: a clear-skinned bearded young man in a furred coat who said, pleasantly dictorial, 'I am sure, Mr Crawford, that the Lieutenant-Governor would forgive two well-meaning Scots Commisioners if we delayed your return to the castle. We are with friends in a house over yonder. Will you join us?'

Members of reigning houses have no need to introduce themselves. This was Lord James Stewart, the Scots Queen's half-brother; and his uplifted hand, discreetly steadying, proved that Lord James was not in the right place by accident.

If he was going to be ill, as he was, almost immediately, it might as well be under royal auspices. Lymond said, 'I gather we share the acquaintance of a lady named Martine. Thank you.'

Someone with apparent authority moved forward and spoke to his escort. A pair of double doors opened and closed behind him and his mare was brought to a halt in the peace of a small, silent courtyard. He left the saddle with what seemed to be a great deal of expert assistance.

'I should be obliged,' said Lymond, 'if you would take that horse off and shoot it.'

He had understood he was going to be sick. It was much to his surprise therefore, that before they could help him, he fainted.

CHAPTER 4

La verge en main mise au milieu de branches
De l'onde il mouille et le limbe et le pied
Un peur et voix fremissent par les manches
Splendeur divine, Le Divin près s'assied.

Philippa, who was rarely favoured with the more dramatic ailments of this world, had a head cold of historic virulence.

It assailed her the morning after Francis ... *Mr Crawford* had proposed in public to catalogue the bodily features of his Russian mistress; and by the time she reported for duty had thickened into a turgid, throat-rasping affair which recalled all Gideon used to say, cheerfully, about avoiding claret if your name began with a letter of the alphabet. Madame de Brêne quite rightly turned her away from the little Queen's chamber, and she returned to blow her nose in her room, where Adam Blacklock presently found her.

He, too, was pale, presumably from Marthe's wine and not the Hôtel de Ville claret, and the hesitations both in his walk and his speech were more marked than she had seen them recently. He spoke politely to Célie, who let him in and then retired to the window with her sewing. Then, crossing the room, he said without any preamble, 'Philippa. Have you heard any news yet this morning?'

Francis ... *Mr Crawford*, she thought. No. Madame de Brêne would have told her. Not Kate, either: that would have to come to her direct. Then someone else from the Séjour du Roi: Marthe? Jerott? Danny? Or Austin . . . ?

To her extreme irritation Adam, a diffident man, was still standing, looking at her. She said, 'I haven't heard any news. I've got a cold. Out of his Nois the meldrop fast can rin. What news do you have? I'd prefer something soothing.'

'Francis has gone to Dieppe,' Adam said. 'He left last night, after a false report that his mother and brother had drowned.'

332

Because he was kind, he had put it clearly. But still she said, 'False?' And then, when he nodded, 'And you have sent someone after Mr Crawford to tell him?'

'It was too late,' Adam said. 'He will find them at Dieppe with the other Commissioners.'

Last night, distressed and exhausted, she had been granted at least rest and privacy. While Francis, his condition no better than hers, had taken to the road, with that news for company. And at the end of it, Sybilla. And Richard.

She remembered, looking at Adam, that he knew all about that. The elderly maid had her head bowed. Philippa said, 'The shock might mend affairs between them. Surely, when they see him, they'll be careful.'

Adam said, 'If he is tired, and they put a foot wrong, he will choose the one unmentionable response and make it. He did it last night. I don't know if you or Austin can forgive him. Marthe never will.'

Philippa sat down. 'Marthe's troubles can wait. Tell me what you are afraid of?'

Adams sat down also, his face drawn in the cold light. He also, one would guess, had slept very little last night. He said, 'So far, Richard knows nothing of Marthe. I know, from what Jerott has dropped, that you've been searching into . . . her birth and her background. I can think of nothing more tragic than that Francis should . . . that there should be a confrontation.'

'There won't be,' Philippa said.

Adam glanced over his shoulder and then returned his eyes to her face. 'How can you be sure? Philippa, would you go to Dieppe?'

She had guessed it was coming. 'No,' she said.

'Why not?' The thin scar, as always when he was anxious, lay starkly over his face.

She didn't glance, as he had done, to her woman. She said, 'You heard Marthe. To have me there would only add to his burdens. By now the damage will have been done, or they will be reconciled. And I trust his ultimate good sense more than you do. Richard will never hear of Marthe through him, or anything else that discredits the family. Is Jerott worried?'

'Jerott doesn't know I am here,' Adam said. 'The last thing he wants is to see you in Francis's company. You know that.'

'In case I become corrupted. Jerott and I wish the same

333

thing, for different reasons,' Philippa said. 'But you don't object to throwing Mr Crawford and myself together?'

'I know your upbringing,' Adam said. 'And I know something else. Francis has his divorce and his freedom in prospect, but the headaches have come back. Archie was worried last night. Philippa, this family business has to be laid bare and thrashed out with Sybilla. Not before Richard in a storm of stripped nerves, but with Sybilla, in calm and in privacy.'

'He won't,' Philippa said. 'And I can't help. I don't know the truth and I can't see any way of finding it. I think F . . . Francis has reached it by guesswork and it is quite unacceptable. All I can suggest is that with time, the unacceptable usually becomes accepted.'

'We haven't got time,' Adam said.

The blood left her heated face. She said, keeping her voice steady, 'You spoke only of headaches at Christmas.' And knew from his face that, like herself, he was recalling London.

He said quickly, 'That is all it is. He has nothing worse than headaches, Philippa; although God knows they are annihilating enough. No. I meant . . . He will leave for Russia.'

His eyes were level and anxious. The woman in the window-seat looked up. Philippa said, 'I can only think of one thing that would do any good, and that is to prove or disprove what he has found out about Sybilla.'

'You said you couldn't,' said Adam.

'So the impossible has to become the possible as well,' she said. 'Adam, can you . . . ?'

'We watch him,' Adam said. 'We watch him all the time, and Archie is with him. The other thing he needs is someone . . . anyone at all . . . to lift some of the strain.'

It was, of course, the conclusion that she and Marthe had already reached. 'You mean, to sleep with? I don't think,' said Philippa, 'that professional ladies are adequate. The trouble is,' he doesn't seem to have considered Catherine. In any case, she might well hold out for marriage.'

A faint smile, for the first time, crossed Adam's perplexed face. 'Wise girl,' he said. 'But you know, I don't think we can wait till April.'

'No. Then I think,' said Philippa, 'I had better have a word with her mother. The Vidame is very engaging and I'm sure Condé is delightful but really, at this moment we want something *quieter* . . . What on earth are you laughing at?'

'You,' said Adam. 'Are you as objective about Austin?'

'Yes,' she said simply. 'Don't you think we should suit one another?'

'Philippa, I can't think of anyone you wouldn't suit,' Adam said. 'It depends what, in return, they can offer.'

'I see that. But love, you know,' Philippa said, 'is a very considerable inducement.'

*

She had dinner in her room after Adam had gone and later sallied forth, laden with handkerchiefs, to seek the Maréchale de St André. From there she walked the short distance, in extreme cold, to the rue Marie-Egyptienne, passing the Séjour du Roi as she crossed into Montmartre from the old wall's turreted gate towers.

She did not stop, because Marthe was there, but her heart still sickened, remembering Austin.

Adam, when she asked him, had been reassuring. 'Unlike Francis, he never loses his good manners. He's a gentleman, Philippa. Marthe should never have persuaded Jerott to bring him over. But he hasn't once asked who Marthe is, or commented on her likeness to Francis. . . .

'It was unfortunate that he heard and saw what he did, but he knows now where he stands, and he'll respect you none the less. I imagine he is feeling as concerned for you this morning as you are for him. Needless to say, we are moving him to the Hôtel d'Hercule as soon as possible. If Francis comes back in his right mind, he'll arrange a nominal ransom and dispatch him home instantly along with you, Philippa.'

There was no doubt now that he would try, whether he was in right mind or not. By now, if he rode by post through the night without stopping, as he was quite fool enough to do, he might be in Dieppe. She thought, tramping her way through the frozen mud, of the five enervating things that might happen, and his probable response to them, in the condition he would be in by this time. Adam had begged her to go to Dieppe. To refuse him had been, she supposed, the hardest thing she had ever done in her life.

Célie called, 'Madame! You have walked past the turning!' and she saw, looking round, that she had. She also saw, discreetly strolling behind them, the red-headed bodyguard she had stopped once before. His name, she knew now, was Osias. He shared his duties with another man of Applegarth's

335

with a scarred cheek. Célie or her serving man took them in occasionally and gave them something hot in a cup if she had kept them out unduly in bad weather. It reminded her, in case she forgot from time to time, that Francis—*Mr Crawford*—felt that her association with him might bring danger to her.

But there was danger everywhere in a big city, lawful as well as unlawful. You could be killed by sewer gas from a well, or by crossing the rue Vieille Barbette during crossbow practice. You could be killed by lightning like Célie's cousin, an Augustine, trapped in his blazing belltower with the molten bell mouths and gutters dropping seething upon him a mantle of vermeil and silver. Or you might hold the wrong opinions and be hung bleeding to death like a sheep before your limbs were cut off; or be maimed and nailed to the door of your house, or burned alive, or have your eyes torn out, living.

Down there at the Hospital des Quinze-Vingts Aveugles there was a charity stall for the blinded. There they sold what they had made: the woodwork, the mended clocks, the pieces of wicker and lacework. There was a man who, if you gave him a teston, would play for you on the spinet. He was an indifferent performer.

Célie, waiting for her at the turning into Marie-Egyptienne, said accusingly, 'Look at you! You are acquiring a fever! I told you that you were crazy to come out with your cold in this weather!'

Poor Célie, victim of the Somerville passion for thoroughness: *à fin, fin et demi.* Philippa smiled to reassure her and crossed to the house she was looking for: one of the many lodgings in the old Hôtel de Flandre on the corner of Egyptienne and Coquillière.

It was plaster mud here, oozing white round the sliverstones of the paving. There was more of Montmartre on the white-washed walls of Paris, the saying went, than there was of Paris in Montmartre. On her pattens and cloak hem, she and Célie carried a good deal of it into the porter's house with them. The last she saw of Osias, as the porter conducted them across a yard and up some steps to their destination, was a face, blotched red and blue, peering through the shut gates and scowling.

*

She had not, for some reason, expected the room to be so comfortable. Deprived, by a vanishing servant, of cloak, pattens and Célie, Philippa gazed at the florid little man with the black hat and long beard who came forward to greet her and said, 'Salut, Maître.'

'Ah,' said the King's surgeon-philosopher Michel Nostradamus. 'The comte de Sevigny's exquisite lady wife. As was said of Mademoiselle d'Heilly: *la plus belle des savantes et la plus savante des belles.*'

One became used to this. 'But not comely enough,' Philippa said, 'or else too wise, to become the King's mistress. I hope your gout has improved?'

'It is too early in the day to be put in my place,' the little man said, '—pray be seated—but I shall answer you. It is slightly improved. If you consider me a quack and an empirick, why do you visit me? You do not require a love potion. You may require a cure for your sad attack of the rheum.'

Philippa began to feel brighter. She said, 'You remember our chat in Saint-Germain?'

'About Béatris, the daughter of Camille de Doubtance. I do. You did not, I hope, take the whooping-cough?'

'Not unless I have it now,' Philippa said. She laid on the table the little basket Célie had carried from the Hôtel de Guise for her. 'These are some trifles. It would give me great pleasure if you would accept them.'

Inside the basket were three flasks of wine, a packet of sugar, some cloves, some pepper, some nutmeg and a silk knitted purse with ten pounds in it in double ducats. She sat down while he unpacked it, tucking his beard out of the way. At the end he took out one of the wine flasks and filling from it one of a pair of handsome glass goblets gave her one, observing, 'I am deeply flattered. And for what, Madame la comtesse, am I being bribed?'

Philippa opened her satchel and laid on the same table the heaviest object within it. 'To find,' she said, 'the house in France of which that is the doorkey.

❧

She had been right in thinking the parlour too decorous a room for Master Nostradamus's purposes. The chamber in which she found herself ten minutes later, having climbed a winding wooden stair of no great solidity, was sufficiently like the workrooms of both John Dee in London and the Dame

337

de Doubtance in Lyon to leave no doubts about what it was used for. Running her congested eye over the scales, spheres, astrolabes, flagons, books, crucible, athanor, alambic, altar, fountain, skull and perfuming pan, Philippa said finally, 'I thought they burned that forty years ago. That's the Idol of Isis from the church of Saint-Germain.'

'*Allez a l'idole de St Germain et vous trouverez ce qu'avez perdu.* I acquired it from the person who rescued it,' the astrologer said. 'Why should it worry you more than the sweat of St Anne, or the crystal pipe with the milk of the Virgin, or the leg of one of the holy innocents murdered by Herod, or the bones of the eleven thousand virgins? Isis and Ammon are wise. There is much we can learn from the Egyptians.'

The room reeked of castor-oil, mint pastilles and onions, the symbol sacred to Isis. Philippa, her eyes brimming, thought of a certain Egyptian sarcophagus she had seen in the house of the English astrologer she had once befriended and had her thought divined, disconcertingly, by the little man.

'. . . Or because I do not have so many mirrors, do you consider me less potent than Master Dee? I do not draw up charts of navigation, it is true, but he in turn cannot claim the prophetic gifts of a child of the lost tribe of Issachar. These are Hebrew inscriptions on the walls and floor but you need not be afraid: my family have long since become Christian. And do you still desire a divorce?'

Philippa jumped. 'Yes,' she said. 'In fact, it is arranged for two weeks after Easter.'

'But you have no intention of retiring thereafter, I judge, to a convent for the Mal'Maritate.' He threw something else on the burner, dragged a bronze tripod into the middle of the room and picking up a metal bowl, carried it over and held it under the fountain. He continued placidly. 'And for whom burns then, this white fire which lives without fuel? Bring me a lock of his hair and I will make you a poculum amatorium ad venerem so powerful that, once it is placed in the mouth, he will die frenzied if he cannot either spit it out or seize and master you.'

It was better to show amusement than nausea. 'Would you?' said Philippa with interest. 'Come to think of it, I can tell you the eight people at court you've already sold it to. What's that for?'

He did not seem to be offended. 'The key, suspended by a

Carpathian thread, swings over the filled bowl and taps out its answers by touching the twenty-four letters engraved on the rim. Before that, I have to trace my circle of Floram Patere and then change into linen for the Invocation. You have never offended Anäel.'

'Not to my knowledge,' said Philippa thinly.

'I am glad to hear it. You have a somewhat ready tongue. If there is any doubt in the matter, you may turn right when you leave the building and confess yourself in the Chapel of Saint-Marie-Egyptienne. Many do.'

Above her head, the winter light waned from the skylight. Snow. Philippa wondered what Célie was doing. The reeking pan, vaporous blue, hardly illuminated the floor sufficiently to let the elderly doctor trace his marks on his knees. The black hat travelled over the floor, and the plump hand with the chalk.

Philippa said, 'Would you like me to light you some candles?' and proceeded to ignite a spill and carry it round before he could stop her. A half skull, resting on the top of a cupboard, looked back at her in alarm and created a reaction of such amused irritation that she remembered her cold and paused to deal with a resurgence. She did not therefore hear Master Nostradamus return and was suitably shocked when he reappeared, white as a Turkish headstone in the flickering gloom, booted, turbanned and robed in chaste folds of unblemished linen.

He made her kneel on the ground by the brazier while, cross-legged on the tripod, he stared at the bowl and the key hanging over it. He had put saffron this time on the charcoal. Through eyewatering fumes, she could catch parts of the Invocation. He had a strong Provence accent.

'*Venez, Anäel venez, et que ce soit votre bon plaisir d'être en moi par votre volonté, au nom du Père Tout-Puissant, au nom de Fils très sage, au nom du Saint Esprit très aimable. Venez, Anäel, par la vertu de l'immortel Elohim. Venez. Anäel, par le bras du tout-puissant Mittatron. Venez à moi, Nostradamus, et commandez à vos sujets qu'avec amour, joie et paix, ils fassent voir à mes yeux les choses qui me sont cachées. Amen.*'

The silence tightened. For one trembling moment, Philippa could not tell whether he was going to intone a psalm or burst out naked and dance like the three crazy daughters of Proctus. He looked up and glared sharply at her and she

339

gazed back, stunned, with glazed feazures. Then he took a sprig of green stuff like verbena and with it, touched the long silken thread.

The key trembled, stirred, and then shaking itself, began, uncertainly, to drift over its twin in the lissom dark skin of the water. The little clang of the rim when it homed made Philippa's downy skin start like a hedgehog.

'P,' said Nostradamus, in a flat voice.

The key swung spelling for fifteen minutes, and produced the same sequence of six letters twice. It was not, as such experiments go, quite without fault, but since in no Mappamundi could they find any village called PLARIS, there seemed no ultimate doubt of its message.

'Marvellous,' said Philippa at last, who was feeling cold and extremely tired and wanted to rise from her knees. 'That is, there is a population of 500,000. Do we take the key round them all?'

Which was frivolous, for of course, one simply made the Invocation again, and then asked the key to spell out the street name.

This time, unfortunately, it spelt out CLERASI.

'There isn't any such street,' Philippa finally said, lifting her aching head from the map he had produced and spread out for her. 'I've made a list of the C's. The Quai des Célestins? The Châtelet? The rue Calandre, the rue du Centier, the rue sans Clef, the rue Chassemidi ... de la Chaise ... des Trois Chandelliers ... du Cigne ... Clopin ... Cocqueron.... Hopeless. The nearest is Clopin, and surely even an imbecile like Anäel couldn't turn that into Clerasi? Let's try again.'

Master Nostradamus was remarkably amenable. They tried again, and got the same answer. 'It doesn't even sound French,' Philippa said; then lifted her nose of a sudden out of her handkerchief. 'It isn't French. It's Latin. The hopeless creature has latinized it. What's Clerasus?'

There was a short silence. 'I am afraid,' said Nostradamus, 'that there exists no such word.'

'There must be,' Philippa said; and without warning gave vent to the kind of ignoble whoop which used to ring round the yards of Flaw Valleys. 'The silly ass has put his mad *L* at the start again. It's *Cerasi*.'

'Cherry trees,' said Master Nostradamus.

'Cherry trees ... Of *course*! The rue de la Cerisaye, the

340

street of the cherry trees, between the Bastille and the Arsenal. Clerasi!' said Philippa scathingly. 'He's met William
Baldwyn, and if I'd anything to do with it, I'd make him
damned well languish locked in L.'

'I beg your pardon?' said Michel Nostradamus, looking up
at the wrong moment. He put down the verbena and moving
a step, stood gazing at her in gentle inquiry. 'Madame? Why
are you weeping.'

'Because,' said Philippa, 'I have such an extremely bad
cold. The kindest thing you can do is to pay no attention.'
She blew her nose. 'Now. I don't suppose Anäel is any good
with house-names?'

'I am afraid not,' said Master Nostradamus with apparent
regret. 'But I believe it is a very short street. If I were not so
hard-pressed with my charts, I might have accompanied you
there with my divining rod.'

He was an odd character. He might be a good deal more
frightening than he seemed. But he had been generous with
both his help and his time. And from beginning to end, he
had asked no questions whatever. Perhaps, in an astrologer's
work, that was usual.

She did not want to stay any longer, and it would be less
than seemly to ask him to descend the steep stairs in white
linen. She held out her hand. 'I'm sure I shall find it,' she
said. 'I want to thank you.'

He took her hand, and held it in his two, healthy rounded
ones. Then he looked at her.

'You will not speak of that which is in your mind but I, if
you will allow me, would advise you. Here you have a hawk
of the lure, not of the fist. He will not come to you. If you
would have him, you must lay your heart upon your hawk-
ing-glove; and feed it to him.'

Unfair, unfair. She banished fright from her face with an
effort, but in his hands, her own started to tremble. Then he
said, without waiting for her to speak, 'You are cold. I must
not keep you. What was the question you wished to put about
M. your husband?'

Her mind, then, was still open to him. She said austerely,
'How perceptive. I only wondered why neither of you has
ever mentioned your meeting at Lyon?'

The grey, impersonal eyes gave no impression of shiftiness.
Then, unexpectedly, he removed them and thought, combing
his long grey-brown beard with his fingers. Then he looked

up again. 'Madame, an hour ago I would have told you the bare truth, which is that the gentleman, being incapacitated, had no recollection of that meeting and that it was far from my place to refer to it.'

'And now?' Philippa said. She picked up the key and held it, ridiculously, like a buckler in front of her.

'Now,' said Nostradamus, 'I shall give you another piece of advice. When next you meet M. le comte, ask him to tell you, in detail, what occurred on that evening in Lyon. And if he refuses, as he will, tell him that I, Nostradamus, will inform you.'

'He went to a ... I know where he spent the night,' Philippa said.

'You think you do,' Nostradamus said. 'But I must tell you that I did not find my patient, or treat him, in a bawdy-house. You may remind him of that. I have placed in your basket an excellent remedy for the rheum, and a pot of complexion cream for which, as you may have heard, I have a certain reputation. The inflammation of your skin will require it.'

'Me fera Hecuba en Hélène,' said Philippa rather dazedly. *Rendra*, it said on the pot, *une souveraine splendeur naïve à la face*. It had a familiar smell.

'If used from the age of fifteen,' Master Nostradamus said briskly, 'it will preserve lifelong beauty and enable the skin at sixty to look as young as that of a twenty-year-old. The contents are quite pure. Sublimate, quicksilver, rose-water, and the saliva of a young person who for three days has eaten onions without vinegar. Boiled, I may assure you, for the length of two Paternosters and two Ave Marias, repeated with reverence.'

We used to quote from the Hamasa of Abu Tammam,' Philippa said. She picked up the basket and lifted her eyes. 'We made the fertility potion as well, but the bird-catchers used to cheat with the cock-sparrows. Communications between Stamboul and Lyon seem better than one might have imagined. Did you ever have a dog?'

For a long time he looked at her in silence, and in his red cheeks and his fat turban and his long, forked beard of chestnut and grey she saw, at length, nothing that was trivial or comic at all.

She had invoked the world of Arabic poetry. His answer,

342

when it finally came, was also culled from the lore of Mohammed.

'*If I told you all I know*,' said the Prophet, '*you would flog me with thongs of leather.* Time, Le Boiteux, the Lame One, will release you both. I pray for you.'

'Not to Anäel, I beg you,' said Philippa tremulously. 'He would send us to Purgatory, and even Elohim might find it troublesome to extract us. Maître Nostradame, I am grateful.' And she left him.

She called, too, at the Chapel of Marie-Egyptienne, with the frozen Osias and a disgruntled Célie behind her; but it was full of companionable souls celebrating the religious rites of the local confrèrie and she came away, unable to concentrate. Once back in the Hôtel de Guise she went to bed, swallowed the potion for the rheum and slept for sixteen hours, at the end of which she awoke to find her cold vanished, and a gift from Austin Grey at her bedside.

She sent for the pot of complexion cream. If one had to turn back the clock, one might as well begin systematically.

CHAPTER 5

D'humain tropeau neuf serone mis à part
De jugement, et conseil separez.
Leur sort sera divisé en départ.

The yard which saw Francis Crawford's distinctive collapse in Dieppe belonged to the house of a draper's widow. On the other side of the building, shutters revealed a counter over which, at certain times, the Bouchard employees sold stockings, bonnets, breech-hose, jackets and lengths of velvet, damask and saye from the stacked shelves which ran round the stockroom.

There was cloth also in the room where they carried him. The mellow, powdery smell of it was the first he knew of his surroundings when he opened his eyes: that, and the fact that there was a feather mattress beneath him, and that his travel-stained outer clothing had been drawn off. Then a voice spoke: that of Martine, the beautiful ageing woman who had once governed the high-bred squadron of the old King's permanent mistresses, and whose acquaintance with himself over the years had always been one less of commerce than of friendship.

Martine said, 'I thought when I saw you, mon fils, that the saddle would not contain you much longer. This is Hélène Bouchard, in whose house you are resting. Your Scottish friends have many times been guests under her roof. You may remain here as long as you wish. Master Abernethy is on his way here from the Castle.'

He had already closed his eyes. Archie was not here. Who were his 'Scottish friends'? Memory, fitfully returning, reminded him of Lord James Stewart, who had intercepted him. Then he remembered what had happened before that. There was a movement above him and the firm voice of another woman said, 'This is not good. I will send for the barber-surgeon.'

It was the last thing he wanted. He was saved from saying

so by the bustle of a new arrival and a hubbub of voices among which could be distinguished the uncompromising cadences of Archie's. Then, almost immediately, there was no sound in the room but a door closing, and then Archie's voice again, saying sourly, 'I gave ye an hour more nor that to stay on your feet: ye must be getting soft as saip-sapples. Ye can open your een.' Then after a moment he said, 'Put your hands back, if it helps. You've a bit to go yet. I'll mix ye something.'

He had, as it turned out, a long way to go yet; but in the end it was over, and all that was left was the familiar tenderness at his brows and his temples, and a little numbness in one hand, which would soon vanish. It was by then, he knew, late at night; and he had insisted already on Archie fetching a truckle bed for himself for just this moment. Then, as always, the pain was replaced by a stupor of drowsiness which deepened and deepened until, at last, he relapsed into slumber.

He slept until wakened by the rumble of iron wheels and the sharp clap of hooves underscored by the tinkle of harness bells, as the fish wagons set off again under his windows. He lay for a long time watching the amber glare of each passing lantern, and the patterned light traverse the roof-beams.

Some day, he supposed, the faculties by which he lived would not all return to him. It would put a convenient term on many things, and in the meantime he saw no reason to dwell on it. In two months the royal wedding would be over, and with it, the Commissioners' stay and his own contracted duties in France.

Lethargy both mental and physical sent him to sleep again presently, and next time he awoke in broad daylight, with a savoury smell of hot food in the air and Martine seated picturesquely on a stool by the blazing hearth, smiling at him.

She was wearing the pearls he had once given her. He smiled back, and held out his hand to her; and when she came deftly to his side, gathered her scented hair in his palm during the long interval of her embrace.

Her lips were warm and flexible, and her skin smelt of lily-water and not of the heavy, dizzying aromatics of the East. He avoided responding, because that was his intention, but he did not disengage first. It was Martine who, withdrawing her knowledgeable, courteous hands, placed them one on each side of his uncovered throat and, studying him, said, 'What

345

you cannot say to your confessor, you can tell to me. What is it you want?'

He had not deceived her. But then, he had not expected to. He lifted his own hands and interlaced the fingers smoothly with hers. 'Nothing you can give me this time,' he said. 'Except perhaps your general sympathy. *Par temperance ay acquis grand renom; Cyncinnatus Quintus est mon vray nom.*'

She moved away and sat still, her eyes thoughtful, one hand still in his. 'Then,' she said, 'it is a woman. And at last, at last the right woman, *mon fils?*'

One might not wish to answer but one did not, with Martine, commit the solecism of avoiding her gaze. He said, 'It is a good thing to have friends, says the proverb, but they are unfortunate who are compelled to make use of them. It is best, *ma belle*, if you know nothing about it. Forgive me.'

Martine said, 'You may have had temperance once. You do not have it now.'

She looked at him soberly. 'I shall not kiss you like that again. And I shall not ask you her name. But tell her, from me, not to make you wait any longer. Last night, you were ill.'

'Honest woman,' he said, and lifting her hand, kissed the fingers and held them briefly, smiling. 'There is no need to blame anyone. I had saddled myself, like the callowest law-clerk, with an impossible ride. My blisters will mend with my vanity . . . Tell me about Hélène Bouchard.'

'What do you wish to know?' Martine said. 'She is a draper's widow who likes to entertain Scotsmen. Her last guest was a writer. You can see, if you look, some of his work on that table. And Lord James and Master Erskine, the Scots Commissioners who had you brought here yesterday, are awaiting politely below to talk to you.'

'*Qui maudit soit les pieds d'escot, Et les pieds d'escots qui les suivent* . . . They are friends of yours?' Lymond said.

'They are; but they need be none of yours unless you want it. I saw you in trouble, and I knew this house was near and they could bring you here. The Governor has been told you are being entertained for a single night privately. Should we have said you were indisposed?'

'Would he have believed you?' Lymond said.

She smiled, her handsome eyes watching him. 'Perhaps not. Your reputation has preceded you. You had perhaps better express an interest in cloth.'

'Perhaps I had. But what cloth?'

'Madame Bouchard stocks every kind. I have told you. You are free to choose,' Martine said. 'I am happy to see, *mon cher*, that you have lost none of your wits on this ride.'

'And Lord James and Master Erskine? Are they devoted to cloth, that they also remained all night at Madame Bouchard's? Or have they merely paid a second visit to inquire after my health?'

'They came back this morning. You are an emissary of the Most Christian King. Naturally, they wish you to think well of them.'

'While bearing in mind that *principus placuisse viris non ultima laus est*. Naturally. I think,' he said, 'that I should dress and relieve Madame Bouchard of her unexpected guest ... You are too superb today to help me?'

'I am too wise to help you. I shall send Mr Abernethy.' She rose, and on her way to the door paused by a row of bale-laden shelves, her forefinger touching the velvets. 'I shall have a dress-length of that for my parting-gift.'

'You shall have two,' Lymond said. 'Take them downstairs and make James Stewart jealous. I have a fancy he considers me a sober and well-disposed citizen. I should like to see him lose that impression.'

'I shall tell him the truth,' Martine said. 'That you want ghostly strength and are of a light humour that trifles with women's affections.'

'You have it. Remind him,' he said, 'of Julio Rosso. The only way he would hide in the canon's house was stuffed between two plaster walls, with a stock of hams and a flask and the cooking-wench. You may choose a third length of velvet.'

'I have,' said Martine, smiling; and closed the door gently behind her.

He took time, before he left the room, to glance at the table where, as indicated by Martine, the last incumbent had left lying his writings.

The top page of it, lacking a signature, was headed: THE FIRST BLAST, TO AWAKE WOMEN DEGENERATE. It went on:

To promote a Woman to beare rule, superioritie, dominion, or empire above any Realme, Nation or Citie, is repugnant to Nature; contumelie to God, a thing most contrarious to his reveled will and approved ordinance; and finallie, it is the subversion of good Order, of all equitie and justice.

347

There was little among what followed to flatter Martine and still less, one imagined, the writer's hostess. He read it through to the end before, thoughtfully, he crossed to the shelves and then, collectedly, made his way down the winding oak stairs to where Lord James Stewart and Master John Erskine awaited him.

＊

'Here he is,' said the Queen's brother as the fellow de Sevigny's step sounded coming downstairs, and John Erskine of Dun, seated quietly beside that impatient and brilliant young prince half his age, watched the door for this other young man who promised, they said, to be no less difficult.

In fifty scholarly years, with wealth and pedigree both to support him, John Erskine, laird of Dun and Constable of Montrose, had laid a wise hand on the reins of many a headstrong sprig of nobility, and by his steady intellect and habit of moderation had soothed their elders and steered the throne itself out of shoals in the early, ebullient days of religious upheaval.

He was of those who believed Calvin's teachings, and who wished to hasten the reform of the established Catholic church, but still he enjoyed the Queen Dowager's confidence, he believed, and while she practised tolerance throughout Scotland, he supported her.

In this he knew he had James's agreement—James, who would have been on the throne if his kingly father had not begot him on a married woman, and an Erskine, though not of his family. He was not sure how strong James's personal ambition would grow. He had been left wealthy by his father, and possessed revenues from church offices in Macon as well as in Scotland: he had no claim to the throne, and his belief in the Reformed faith was without question.

Also without question was his liking for power and his ability, it must be said, to wield it. Older men, up to the present, had been able to guide him. It remained to be seen how long he would brook guidance, or require it. For example, how he would handle young Crawford, a rising star of his own generation.

The door opened and in flapped three writhing cloth lengths of loud patterned fabric, loosely furled round a fair, graceful gentleman whose look of simple cogitation gave way,

348

at the sight of Lord James, to a smile of open delight even simpler.

'My dear lord,' said the Crawford boy heartily. 'How can I thank you for your charity yesterday? You have brought me to the best draper in Dieppe.' He lifted his arms, from which cataracts of crude tissues tumbled, and pinched a fold of heliotrope satin between finger and thumb. 'They have seen nothing like it in Russia. Lord James, you must allow me to express my thanks with a bolt of it. Or . . .' He looked doubtfully at the royal robes of black velvet and the black bonnet which barely concealed the royal auburn hair.

'. . . or perhaps it is not quite your lordship's tint. They used to say silk degrades a man and reveals an effeminate trait. But'—unwrapping himself with a slither '—I don't think you'll find any pretty playfellow of mine who couldn't show you a calendar . . . no, by God, an hour glass—to disprove it. You know Martine? Of course: she was the means of our meeting here. You were too kind, my lord; and if you prefer a new pair of stockings, I shall see that they are sent to you. I can tell you, I was never so glad to get out of public view. And this is . . . ?'

'The Laird of Dun,' said Lord James, drawling the words. John Erskine of Dun, who knew him well, was aware by his reticence that he was taken aback, and was beginning to become angry. Erskine said to the yellow-haired, smiling young man who had possessed himself of his hand and was shaking it, 'We met once when you were a boy, at Midculter.' He paused. 'You are not like your brother.'

'No,' Crawford said. He gave his hand another shake and then loosed it with apparent reluctance. 'Richard will never be whipped at a cart-arse for bawdry. I don't know whether you notice, but he wears nothing but mockado and fustian. The graveyard at Culter is full of pauperized mercers.'

'Then all the more credit to you,' said Erskine, seating himself, 'for entertaining such strong family feelings. We heard of your ride. I trust you are now quite rested after it.'

The young man's mouth opened. 'The ride!' He sat down. 'My dear sir, the ride was nothing but the cathartic. It was the banquet at the Hôtel de Ville that did for me. Abernethy will tell you. I suppose I spewed four gallons of claret in Paris before I took to the road, but it proved there was another hogshead to get rid of yet. Ah!' The blue eyes turned from Lord James's expressionless, freckled face to his own. 'I have disappointed you. But if I hadn't been drunk, I should have seen that there was really no cause for hurry. Richard's brats are heir to the title, not I, and they were all safe as it happened, at Midculter. Thank God,' he added piously.

'Do you?' said Lord James Stewart sharply.

In his turn, the Earl of Culter's younger brother looked startled. 'It's a manner of speaking,' he said. 'That is, I don't mind one way or the other. After Easter, I'm going back to Russia. That's where the money is, and the power. And, of course, the ladies.'

'I thought,' James Stewart said, 'that the French crown would offer you an irresistible sum for your talents. Was there not a rumour that the Tsar had found another Voevoda for his army?'

The young man smiled, and leaning forward, he picked up a length of taffeta and draping it elegantly over his knee, leaned back and admired it. 'My dear,' he said, 'shopkeepers listen to rumours. What if Ivan has chosen another favourite? He only exists to be superseded.'

He released the fabric and leaned back, still smiling. 'I know what you are afraid of! You imagine I shall set out for Leith with three regiments, all ready to take de Rublay's place as Vice-Chancellor of Scotland. I shan't deny that there have been strong hints about it. I did consider it. Do you think I should make a gallant figure, armed like Pallas ... Marte, arte et frugibus ... to safeguard the Old Faith in Scotland?' He paused. 'That is Pallas, I believe, was a woman. *Me suis de ton Ecosse faite la prêtresse, Par ton Père, qui seul me rende Ecossaise?*'

From his great height Lord James, who had not yet sat down, looked at the cloudless, delectable face with its intolerable vivacity. 'If you do,' he said, 'you will have to fight Richard, your brother. He has joined the Lutheran party.'

The ravishing smile remained, although the answer delayed by a second. 'Has he?' said Francis Crawford. 'Was that wise of him?'

John Erskine said, quickly, 'I shall save Lord James the trouble of pointing out that it depends whether you are considering his spiritual or material welfare. With Lord James and the Earl of Rothes and myself, your brother signed the Covenant in December by which all friends of the new religion have undertaken to maintain and establish the Word of God and His congregation. He has been our wise friend in all we have done since, aiding us so that preaching and interpretation of the Scriptures may proceed privately in quiet houses, until God may move the Dowager to grant public preaching by faithful and true ministers.'

'I am sure there is a purpose in all this,' Crawford said. With airy impudence he had slung round him a length of chamlet, sober side outwards, and cowled and robed in it was reclining, tented hands pointed upwards. He added, staring at them, 'I shan't induce him to re-enter the puddle of Papistry, if that's what you're afraid of. He hates my guts. In between arranging that the preaching and interpretation of the Scriptures may proceed privately in quiet houses.'

Lord James said, 'We have no doubts of Lord Culter's constancy. We wish to know where your faith stands.'

'Why?' said Crawford with distinct querulousness. He added, 'I thought we were discussing pourpoints.'

Lord James Stewart took a turn to the window and back. He said, 'If you take a ball through your breastplate tomorrow, a pourpoint will not preserve you from hell.'

'No, but my breastplate would,' said Crawford irritably. 'It's a new kind I had made in Russia. Anyway, who isn't going to hell?'

'Richard your brother,' said Lord James ill-advisedly.

'Then that settles it,' said Lymond, satisfied, and began folding his draperies. 'Do you fancy I might persuade a doublet-maker to cut one of these by tomorrow? There must be five Scottish Commissioners still corrupt enough to admire it.'

A rawboned hand, closing fast on his arm, caused the cloth to fall and the young man to look up, astonished. 'You offend me,' said the Queen's half-brother. 'And your memory for favours received seems a short one.'

'There is no argument about the favours received,' Crawford said. He made a single, smooth movement and his arm, without apparent effort, freed itself. 'Good God, here am I with stockings in either hand, panting towards restitution. I merely require you to keep my soul out of the general conversation.'

'And your brother's soul?' said James Stewart. He was drawling again.

'I understood,' said Lymond, 'that you had that in hand.' He rose, collected his draperies, and moved rustling to deposit them on the window seat. 'And, of course, he will fulfil all your expectations. Richard is your man for high moral tone and sound values:

> 'Adieu la Court, adieu les Dames
> Adieu les filles et les femmes
> Adieu le bal, adieu le dance
> Adieu mésure, adieu cadense
> Tabourins, hautboys, violons,
> Puisqu' a l'eglise nous allons . . .'

His smile, full of effervescent charm, was on them both. 'Forgive me, gentlemen. My lapse has made me behindhand already. If you mean to stay longer, I shall leave you and find Madame Bouchard.'

John Erskine stood up. 'Madame Bouchard is not in the house, M. de Sevigny,' he said. 'And the door is locked. I told you I remembered you as a boy. I remember also the face of the Bishop of Orkney when he emerged from a Scottish courtroom ten years ago, and told me of the impassioned plea for nationhoood he had heard from a man then judged guilty of treason. I have watched the same man today degrading his dignity and ours in an effort to deny his own nature. Why?'

Lord James, folding his tall body, sat suddenly down. The gorgeous creature by the window did not move, nor was there a notable change in his plumage. But by some means it was made clear that against the latticed panes of the casement stood a man trained for war, and with skills of a sort which had protected Lyons; had saved Paris; had recovered Calais for an alien monarch. Lymond said, 'To avoid precisely the type of discourtesy to which I now appear to be committed. I am sorry, Master Erskine. I talk to no one behind a locked door.'

John Erskine walked quietly to the door, unlocked it, and returning, took his place, standing, on the other side of the embrasure from Lymond. He did not look at James who had been within an ace, he was aware, of preventing him. He said, 'Our motive in locking it, if it matters, was to spare you the embarrassment of an interruption. Unless the comte de Sevigny of today is really so different from the Master of Culter of ten years ago?'

Perfectly at his ease, the decorative young man he was ad-

dressing leaned back on the shutters and studied him. 'I hope
so,' Lymond said. 'When you were twenty, Mr Erskine, you
killed a priest in the belltower at Montrose. Would you do
so again?'

It made him gasp, a ludicrous thing: he must be failing.
He heard Lord James's harsh voice cutting in: 'You will refrain, Mr Crawford, from pointless—and actionable—accusations. Father Froster's death was an accident.'

Lymond did not even look at him. 'I am sure of it,' he said
directly to Erskine. 'But would you have such an accident
now? At twenty you looked back on Flodden, and on the
deaths of father, grandfather, granduncle and uncle at the
hands of the English. If Catholic Mary dies, and Protestant
Elizabeth comes to the throne, will you feel the same about
the English now?'

Erskine returned the blue stare with a look in which there
was no atom of cynicism. He said, 'If my cause requires it, I
shall court them. From which you may draw two conclusions.
I have shed the brashness of twenty, and I have learned to
subjugate the lesser good to the greater. But I still serve my
country.'

'Mr Crawford also perhaps has learned to subjugate the
lesser good to the greater,' said Lord James abruptly. 'I feel,
John, your approach is too spiritual. The situation is plain
enough to any practical man. While the Catholic powers have
been at war with one another, Lutheranism has flourished
both in France and in Scotland, where the Queen Dowager
has had to countenance it because she required the support of
its adherents.

'Now with the taking of Calais, the wars of France and
Spain and the Papal States may all be drawn to a close: already the Cardinal of Lorraine is urging the King towards
new and violent steps against heresy. In Scotland the Queen
Regent is likely to receive orders from her brothers in France
to take a stand against the new religion. Already there is unrest over the grasp France is exercising in Scotland: the principal officers of State, the main strongholds, are all French
already. There is talk, since her nobles refuse to cross the
Border to wage war on England, of still more French troops
sailing to Leith under the Vidame de Chartres.'

He paused; the pale royal eyes raking the intransigent
figure before him: of the man he had never before met,

whose exploits at fourth or fifth hand he had half heard, half caught like echoes without ever finding a man, except perhaps his dead uncle Tom Erskine, who could attempt to assess their value. Then he said, 'You are a Scotsman: a man of eminence in your own field, who once appeared to interest yourself in the affairs of your country. What you are about to do, and what you are about to leave undone will both affect us. You say you mean to go to Russia. My information is that you cannot survive there. I do not know you. I should expect you however at least to avoid obscure martyrdom.'

'I am perhaps a little more optimisitic than you are,' Lymond said. 'The Tsar is a hard man to cross, but then so am I. *Corsario a corsario*, as the saying goes, *no ay que gañar los barilles d'agua*.'

'... Whereas in France,' said Lord James Stewart, as if he had not spoken, 'you have fame, office and property with only one cloud on the horizon: soon you will be expected to declare yourself openly for the established church or the new religion. If you choose the Catholic Church, your future will be proscribed, for no man, however able, can rise higher in France than the de Guises. And if you choose the new religion, you will court death as surely as in Russia.'

Lymond was smiling. 'Whereas in Scotland, you mean to convey, the possibilities on either side are almost unlimited?'

'That is just what I mean to convey,' said Lord James Stewart.

'And the choice is mine. I can march into Scotland at the head of a French and Catholic army and fight the Reformers at the Queen Regent's side, while retaining all my revenues and my goods in both kingdoms. Or I may abandon all I possess in this country and return to support the cause of yourselves and my brother—if, that is, my brother does not succeed in making a shred-pie of me with his fists or his dagger beforehand. I hardly know which to consider.'

John Erskine said stiffly, 'It is not hard, if you allow material prospects to be your sole arbiter.'

Lymond said, 'I thought, according to his lordship, that we were being practical.'

'We are,' said Lord James curtly. 'Let us continue to be so. Any man joining our faction in Scotland will lose all his French possessions and will find little favour with the Queen Dowager during her lifetime. When her mother the Dowager dies, Queen Mary will stay here in France with her husband the Dauphin and later, one supposes, as joint queen of France and of Scotland. Meanwhile Scotland will be ruled by a regency. And by then, this party will be so strong that the regency will be unacceptable by the Scottish people unless it is a Lutheran one.

'Some of the men you will speak to are despondent,' said Lord James Stewart. 'Some see no future for Scotland save as a Catholic province of France. I have no such fears. No country so far separated from another need call it master. In name, the monarch of France for some time to come may call himself King also of Scotland. But the Regency, and those who brought the regency into power will be the rulers of Scotland, nourishing it on their native wits and goodwill, and leading it to dwell in the pure light of the only true religion. That is our plan. And there were those who told me that you might be man enough to join us.'

'As a member of the Russian Orthodox Church,' Lymond said, 'I could arrange to have the Water of Leith blessed at Epiphany. Otherwise the spiritual yield of the arrangement would seem to be as small as the material one. I am sorry that a drunken ride of mine should have so misled you. I have no interest in Scotland. All I can promise is that I shall not be beguiled into leading an army against you.'

'You will forgive us,' said Lord James Stewart, 'if we fail to break into applause. What if the King of France does use force to put down the new religion in Scotland, and your brother and his house are all slaughtered? Will you not then come hurrying back?'

There was a little silence. Then Lymond said, 'Yes. Indeed, I might.'

The Queen's brother stood up.

'Wait!' said John Erskine suddenly. To Lymond he said, 'You do not trust us, and we have not been open with you. Our people in Dieppe have received letters from Admiral Coligny, now in prison at Gand. We know what you did for his brother's wife in the Hôtel Betourné last autumn. That is our third reason for approaching you.'

He could not tell from the other man's face whether or not he found that surprising. 'I see,' Lymond said. 'And you attributed to me the highest spiritual motives. I am flattered, but I must disillusion you. I owed a slight debt of chivalry to

355

the Maréchale de St André, who was also present at the Communion. Public exposure and confiscation of all the family goods might also have blighted somewhat my forthcoming marriage with her daughter.'

He turned to James Stewart. 'I shall either return to Russia, or, if your forebodings are totally realized, I shall remain in France with my bride, adorning and strengthening, if I may so put it, the court of your sister Queen Mary. She is a fervent Catholic. She will be bitterly disappointed to hear of the course you have chosen in Scotland.'

'You threaten?' said Lord James, smiling.

'Hardly,' Lymond said. 'There is nothing you say or do that is not already known to the Queen Dowager and her daughter, and also, of course, to messeigneurs her uncles. I think you should take care, that is all. Religion in recent years has become a political sport, and politicians are more skilful than honest men at extracting themselves from disasters.'

'I rather think,' said John Erskine of Dun, 'that Mr Crawford intends us a compliment.'

'It is the least I can do,' said Mr Crawford, picking up his neat bales of cloth, 'after your gallant intervention of yesterday. You did not say what colour of stockings you fancy? Or perhaps your faith restricts you to black. Nothing, as every advocate knows, shows off a fine leg to better advantage. Black then, and a lace handkerchief to weep into at the wedding. Have you brought the Crown Matrimonial?'

The unexpected question, as he turned at the door, caused Lord James to look at him sharply. 'The Scottish Regalia are in Scotland,' he said.

'Good. I should keep them there,' said Francis Crawford. 'Gentlemen, until we meet tomorrow, I am your grateful and admiring servitor.'

The bow he made, with the bales, was quite admirable; and presently they saw, from the casement, the same bales being affixed to a packhorse. A short while after that, the comte de Sevigny himself emerged, followed by his man and the woman Martine. He kissed her hand, mounted, and accompanied by Abernethy, crossed the yard and disappeared into the streets of Dieppe below the castle.

A difficult young man, they had been told, thought John Erskine. How difficult he could not have dreamed; nor could

James, standing silent beside him. Then James said, 'A brilliant rogue. We do better without him.'

'Perhaps,' said the other man thoughtfully. 'Indeed, he blocked every sally but one. Until you told him, he did not know his brother was a Lutheran.'

'So? You heard him,' said James.

'Ah, yes. I heard what he said,' answered Erskine. 'But I rather think the interest will lie in what the comte de Sevigny does.'

●

Riding side by side to the castle of Dieppe, Archie Abernethy glanced at his lord and master.

'Ye're fit?'

'For anything. Including another Hôtel de Ville banquet.'

'You're riding to Paris with the Commissioners?'

'And with my mother and brother. Exactly.'

'I hear ye left Mistress Blyth fair put out,' Archie continued. 'And ye ken Master Blyth's no blessed wi' discretion.'

'You are afraid,' Lymond said, 'of an almighty clash between my sister and the rest of my family, and you think I should do something about it?'

'Aye,' said Archie.

They were in the open space approaching the gatehouse. In a moment they would be inside, receiving the salutes of the liveried guard and the greetings of the Lieutenant-Governor and all his people under the laurel boughs and the dressed flags of France and the banners of Scotland. Francis Crawford turned to his escort.

'It was as catastrophic as you think,' he said, 'if not worse. But I have in mind the difficulty with Marthe. There are other pitfalls, too, which a word in the right quarter may shield them from. They will be here until April. And so shall I.'

The cracked, seasoned face had turned scarlet. 'All right,' said Archie. 'Ye should take to mind-reading and write bloody almanacks. But if I've got the night off, there are two addresses yon woman gave me.'

'*Two* addresses!' said Lymond. 'You'll never find strength to climb the hill afterwards. Have you coin for it?'

'Plenty,' said Archie.

Lymond looked at him. 'Well, you'll need more than coin with that face. Take the mule with the cloth. They'll go mad over night-robes in heliotrope satin. They'll stand on tubs, and parade tail to trunk for you.'

'Man,' said Archie crossly. His voice and his stare, as usual, were totally at odds with each other. 'Man, you're a right bluidy antic.'

CHAPTER 6

Coeur de l'amant ouvert d'amour furtive
Dans le ruisseau fera ravir la Dame.

The low, apricot sun of young March lit the rue de la Cerisaye when Philippa first found and explored it. Only in its nearness was there anything startling. It lay, a little closed road among orchards and gardens, on the opposite side of the rue St Antoine from the palaces of les Tourelles and de Guise. Beyond it was the river. Behind it, the cherry trees which gave it its name spread almost to the town wall before being contained by the gates of the Arsenal and the courtyard of the Bastille. And beside it was the great religious house of the Célestins.

One could hardly walk up and down the loveliest street (so they said) in all Paris, and attempt to unlock each front door. Some, in any case, were not on the road, but concealed behind high garden walls and sealed courtyards, as she had seen on her first wary reconnaissance.

That had been while the Crawfords were still at Dieppe, and before the Scottish Commissioners left on their progress to Paris.

News from the north indicated that the scale of festivities at Dieppe castle was quite beyond M. de Fors's expectations, and that M. de Sevigny had sent for his sledges. All one could conclude from this was that M. de Sevigny had not, in public, promoted a scene with his relatives, whether of estrangement or violence, and that he was fulfilling his rôle as royal deputy.

She would know how matters lay as soon as she saw them in Paris. Meanwhile, freed from her worst apprehension, Philippa took the next step in the long path she was cutting for somebody else: a path which, if she succeeded, would lead him quite out of her keeping. She sent the Dame de

359

Doubtance's key to the Célestins with four royal lackeys and Célie.

A dear friend, Célie would say, had died, leaving her mistress a key to a house in the rue de la Cerisaye. The house was unnamed. The commission was pressing. Would the Holy Fathers, so wise, so esteemed by their children, find it in their hearts to help the countess.

With the key, she had sent a gift to the funds of the monastery quite enough to make sure that a friar would be out in his sandals at sunup. No one, surely, could object to his door being tried by a Célestin.

After that she had a difficult day, in the course of which her mistress fell out three times with her dressmaker, and had to receive a lecture from monseigneur her uncle the Cardinal whose effects were felt by everyone, including Mary Fleming, whose charming brother John came, unnecessarily, twice, to talk about it. Half the afternoon was taken up with a council of war about the betrothal ceremonies, over which the Dauphin's mother and the Duchess de Valentinois politely disagreed, and Philippa herself emerged muttering, to find her way discreetly impeded by Catherine d'Albion, looking beautiful.

She carried a letter in her hand addressed to her mother in a handwriting immediately recognizable, as if indited in letters of sulphur. Led apart, Philippa read it, and soon understood why the girl looked transported.

In it, at last, Francis Crawford of Lymond and Sevigny asked leave of Catherine's parents to seek the hand of their daughter in marriage.

Should they agree, the letter continued, the betrothal contracts might be signed on 25 April, on which day his divorce would become absolute.

There followed, briefly, the terms of his own fiscal pledges, which were of a kind to please any mother: even one who had slept with the bridegroom. Concentrating heavily on this characteristically piquant aspect of the affair, Philippa looked up, smiling successfully, and said, 'I'm truly very glad, and so will his family be, when they meet you. Would it seem very odd, do you think, if you came to my room and we celebrated?'

Odd or not, it was what Catherine needed; barred by rank and etiquette from overt excitement. Over the wine Philippa

360

poured she answered, smiling, Philippa's first, sensible questions and then, bit by bit, the guard came down; and it was Philippa who found herself listening, and later, choosing her answers.

And even then, talking because she could not help it, the other girl kept all the qualities of intelligence and instinctive good manners which made her the right choice for this marriage. And observing, Philippa saw as in a mirror all her own deepest emotions reflected as once, in this many-sided glass, there must have been reflected the feeling of those other women . . . of Christian Stewart . . . of Güzel Kiaya Khátún . . . of Oonagh, the mother of his child.

It reminded her, in humility, that she was less to him than any of them. So that she was glad that this accomplished and lovely woman would be the one to whom, at last, he proposed to tie himself, by a deliberate contract which his own code of conduct made it unlikely that he would ever evade. Which promised some happiness for them both. And which, if it did nothing else, would stop him from going to Russia.

She wondered if Madame la Maréchale de St André had passed on the advice she had given her, and whether with a marriage offer in her hand, Catherine would feel secure enough to ignore it. On the other hand, Mr. Crawford himself might feel free now to pay court in earnest. And if he did it was unlikely, thought Philippa phlegmatically, that Catherine d'Albon would succeed in resisting him.

Before she left, Catherine kissed her for the first time, and holding her hands said, 'You, too, will be free: whom will you marry? Whoever it may be, you must try not to leave us. We need you, Philippa.'

Which was generous, but one had to be practical. So Philippa said, 'It's probably as well, or the Vicar of Rome would re-open hostilities. You know I should like to stay, but it poses certain delicate problems of protocol as M. de Sevigny's family will be the first, I'm afraid, to point out.' She smiled. 'Lord Allendale also has other ideas. I am visiting him at the Hôtel d'Hercule this evening.'

'When you know what you want, tell me,' Catherine said. And kissed her a second time.

She returned it with warmth, but no candour. She knew her desire and had just killed it; dispatching it like Ninachetuen upon a scented scaffold of flowers with aromatic fires lit

underneath. There was no reason why anyone but herself
should burn on them.

❋

She spent an hour with Austin, in a small suite of rooms
within the vast, marbled mansion over the river that a grateful crown had bestowed on her husband.

She had been there already, with Adam. The rooms were
guarded, but not stringently so, and Austin was attended by
his own men, and allowed visitors. The negotiations for his
ransom and freedom had, it seemed, progressed not at all
through Lymond's absence. Of what had occurred on the
night of the banquet Austin had never spoken, nor had
Marthe been mentioned.

All that had ever concerned him had been her welfare.
Used to the habit of banter, conditioned to the attacking wit
of Kate's carping tongue, she had never drunk at this well;
known the peace of a deep and loving solicitude, offered with
a delicacy which hardly made itself known.

She had not so far been permitted to visit his uncle Lord
Grey, held in La Rochefoucauld's house elsewhere in Paris.
From other sources however she had learned enough of what
happened at Guînes to explain Austin's pallor, and the
sleeplessness of which he did not complain. He had watched
his country brought low: he had shared his uncle's despairing
surrender: he was the captive of a man whom he had seen in
his most outrageous and despicable moments and whose cal-
lousness towards Kate and herself she supposed he would
never condone.

But he did not discuss Francis Crawford. He brought no
slightest form of bias to the long exchanges in which she
learned all she had yearned to know; about the harvest and
their friends and their neighbours; about the skirmishing on
the Border, and what rumour said of the Dowager, and what
he knew of Mary Tudor's wellbeing, and all the circle she
had left in London. He received letters. He knew and told
her, today, that his mother had been advised of his capture,
and that Kate her mother had ridden to comfort her.

She knew, for Kate had written her too, saying nothing,
this time, of the long wait for her daughter's homecoming;
for she would know that Sybilla, in France, would be her am-
bassadress. Philippa said, 'You would hear: they are all in

Dieppe. Their dispatches came in today. Including one from Mr Crawford himself, asking leave to marry Catherine d'Albon.'

She did not have the energy, at that moment, to soften it; and the sense of it reached him as he bent, serving her himself, to place a glass of sweet wine at her elbow.

His hand, arrested, knocked the glass and tipped it fully over. The wine streamed, stickily golden, over the table and with an exclamation he knelt, his handkerchief out, and tried to collect it. Philippa drew back unharmed and glanced round, concerned, for something with which to help him.

When she looked back he was kneeling still, with one hand closed, gripping the table. The other spanned his averted face lightly, thumb and fingertip closing his eyelids. With a pang of pure distress verging on horror, she saw there were tears shining under his lashes.

One could not degrade him by touching him. Her heart hammering, Philippa dragged a square of dry linen from her sleeve and paused with that half-offered also.

But she had forgotten he was not a coward. The breakdown lasted only a moment. Then he turned, his eyes inescapably bright, and said, facing her, 'I seem to be drenching you in two ways at once. I am sorry. I was taken aback.' He looked down and releasing the wine-sodden kerchief said, 'I shall send someone in to take care of this. Will you excuse me, Philippa?'

Another man had wept, long ago, all through a cold Turkish night: but not for her sake.

Her eyes stretched open, Philippa Somerville sat and watched the wine drip from the table-edge.

There were, sensibly, two courses open to her. She could leave before he came back, which with another man would be kind, but in his case would only prove her mistrust of his savoir-faire.

Or she could stay and watch him sacrifice his pride in order to restore the situation. In helping him, she would almost certainly provoke an offer of marriage. It was what, if you looked at it squarely, she probably wished to produce when, just now, she made that flat announcement. But she had not, of course, taken the trouble to examine her motives. She had acted . . . very probably acted . . . out of jealousy.

Which was not fair to Austin. She was going to have to leave France as soon as her bill of divorcement was final.

Austin, if she guessed aright, would be freed in time to go home with her. Then, perhaps, she could make up her mind whether, by marrying Austin, she would be able to give him sufficient return for all the singular, selfless love he could offer her.

By the time he returned, she had made up her mind; and when the table had been dried and the servant withdrawn, she laid down the fresh glass he had poured for her and said, 'What happened just now was my fault. Saving each other's feelings is all very well, but it might be better to be frank. About what happened in the Séjour du Roi, for example. You may have guessed by now that Marthe Blyth is Lymond's base-born sister. It is not spoken of, as Lord Culter is not aware of it. But that explains her outburst, a little.'

'I see' said Austin Grey. His skin was still very pale against his dark hair but his eyes met hers directly. 'She is jealous, perhaps, of her brother? Or of you?'

'It doesn't matter,' Philippa said. 'What does matter is that she accused me before you all of being enamoured of Francis Crawford.'

She paused. 'You may not have believed her. I don't think the others did. But you ought to be told that she was right.'

Distress; disbelief; alarm; anger ... all these she had been braced to receive and to deal with. But—'Oh, my dear,' he said only, and Philippa's own eyes pricked at the understanding, the compassion of it. She stopped, and then began again, for to break off now would be unthinkable.

'As you know, it ... isn't reciprocated. There was never any question of completing our marriage. Next month he will make Catherine his wife, and we are unlikely ever to meet. He is already at some pains to avoid me.' She looked up, smiling.

'Do you think I am surprised?' Austin said. 'He would charm the fish from the sea, and one needs more years than you have to see what lies underneath. It was a fever. It will one day be over. But you are telling me that, until it is, I must wait.'

'No,' Philippa said. 'I am telling you, my dear, that I have met, unsuitably, hopelessly, and too young the only human being I wish to belong to; that I never will belong to him; but that anyone wishing to marry me should know of the fact. It is a lifelong fever, Austin; and leaves no passion to spare. Only mild love, and kindness, and friendship.'

364

His eyes had darkened and his hands were clasped, she saw, to still them. He said, 'You know, I am bound to say, you may be mistaken.'

'I know you are bound to say it,' was all she answered.

Nor did she break the silence that followed, although she guessed what was coming, and wished, painfully, that she could help him.

Then he said, his head bent, his eyes on his hands, 'Philippa, my love is not mild.'

'I know that too,' said Philippa gently. 'I am not asking anyone to marry me and become to me less than a husband should. I am only saying that ... what I have to offer is flawed. You must recognize that and think about it, before this matter goes any further.'

'Must I?' he said; and looking up, let her see for the first time what she had inflicted on him. 'Philippa,' said Austin Grey, 'why did you have to tell me?'

The wine at her side lay still, deep and bright in its goblet. 'Because, of all those who have offered me love, you would have noticed,' she said.

'I beg your pardon,' he said. 'I was being selfish.' He waited, schooling his voice, and then said, 'But feeling like this, you can have no wish for marriage.'

'Perhaps I need it more than anybody,' Philippa said. 'I can live alone, but it is better to have someone else to concern oneself with; to help and be helped by. There is nothing so strong as a family.'

Sitting opposite her, without approaching or moving or making any attempt to touch her: 'Will you then marry me?' said Austin Grey.

'I want you to be sure,' Philippa said. 'I want you to think about yourself, and not about me. And I want ... I should like Catherine d'Albon's marriage to pass before I make any betrothal announcements. When that time comes, will you ask me again, if you want to?'

'And if I do?' said Austin Grey.

'Then we shall go home,' Philippa said. 'To Allendale, and Kate; and be married.'

❦

Self-respect forbade that Philippa should cry on her way back to the Hôtel de Guise; and when she arrived in her room, Célie was waiting to speak to her.

The Célestins had returned the Dame de Doubtance's key, having discovered the door it belonged to.

The house to which it gave admittance was called the Hôtel des Sphères. And the occupier of the house, who had expressed interest in the Countess's story and who would be happy to make the Countess's acquaintance, was a widowed lady named Isabelle Roset.

*

Long ago, this southern corner of Paris between the Porte de St Antoine and the river had been filled with wide gardens, with white chapels and bowered galleries, with sweating chambers and aviaries, boar and lion-houses, lists and ball courts built for fine palaces. Most had gone, decayed into ruin or sold as separate mansions, but the little roads round the rue de la Cerisaye by their names kept a remembrance of them, and great houses here and there were still standing. A long ivied wall which Philippa passed the next morning held the blue turrets of part of the Palais Royal of St Paul, once the property of King François's mistress; now one of the houses of Diane de Poitiers, the mistress of King François's son. It was a fair haven, long accustomed to lovers.

And here Sybilla had stayed, with the man who had fathered her children. Isabelle Roset was Renée Jourda's widowed sister, Lymond had said. And kept house for Sybilla and her master somewhere in Paris. The child Francis Crawford was born there.

So he had learned at Flavy-le-Martel where the old woman Renée had died; Renée who with her sister Isabelle had served Sybilla as a young bride and who, eleven years after Sybilla's marriage to Gavin, Lord Culter, had witnessed the birth of Francis Crawford here in Paris, and then of his sister Eloise. Who knew, and alone in the world might yet tell her, the name of the two children's father.

This time, Philippa had left Célie in her chamber. There had been a fresh fall of snow just before sunrise and the rue St Antoine was already deep in rimed slush. Beyond it, the small roads lay tranquil and white, edged with ancient walls and speckled groups of brick and wood houses all chequered with snow like cloisonné work. The sky, smoky red behind the Bastille, turned the snow in the gardens to sherbet: the cherry trees bore it like blossom, and the bowers of birch, beech and elm, the weeping thorns and the lilac and vine stems which

366

laced the sky over the gateways. Behind the Célestins' wall there was holly, and the rilled ranks of a physics garden, and a row of Bergamot pear trees as high as their snowy steeples.

Behind her, when she stopped at the wrought iron gates of the Hôtel des Sphères there was only the single track of her chopines, and the flouncing blur from the thick hooded cloak which enveloped her. She had told Célie, before she left, to have Osias called in and given hot soup in the kitchen. Whatever had happened once in the Hôtel des Sphères, there was no reason why anyone remotely connected with Midculter now should know of it.

There was a bell by the gatepost but the clapper was missing, and when she put her gloved hand on the heavy gates, they gave way before her. So, pushing them slowly apart, Philippa carved her way over the creamy snow to a small elegant mansion of patterned brick laid between wrought bands of silvery wood. Above the chiselled door, modelled within a cartouche, was a celestial globe with two winged figures brooding over it. Philippa raised the ring knocker and rapped with it.

The serving-girl who opened the door was young, but well trained in her duties. She asked madame la comtesse to enter, and taking her pattens and cloak left her seated by the fire in the pretty, wainscotted hall, while she retreated to call her superior. Then, before Philippa could receive much more than a pleasing impression of a kind of shining and miniature richness, the maid returned, and she found herself in the parlour, being received by Isabelle Roset.

Unlike her sister's, Madame Roset's eyes had no flaw in them. They stared out, bright faded hazel from the blotched tussore skin of old age, under an old-fashioned goffered cap as white as her hair; and her black dress with its high neck and long, tight sleeves with epaulettes was old-fashioned also, unless you looked on it as a uniform. And indeed, depending from the chain at her waist was the châtelaine's cluster of keys and the hands, broad fingered and knotted, clasped before her were working hands: the hands of a housekeeper or, indeed, a peasant girl from Coulanges. Philippa said, 'It is kind of you to see me, a stranger. Forgive me, too, for approaching you through your neighbours. I had looked for your name at the Hôtel de Ville, but could not find it.'

'You thought perhaps I owned the Hôtel des Sphères. But that is not so,' Madame Roset said. Her voice, thin and girlish was that, Philippa thought, of a talker with no one to talk to. Her eyes, active as monkeys, were brilliant with curiosity. 'Pray be seated, Madame. It is a matter of a bereavement? Allow me to condole with you.'

The chair on which she sat was embroidered, and so were its cushions and footstool: the curtains over the paintings were taffeta, and the little bow window pictured in grisaille the story of Psyche. Philippa said, 'The lady who left me your doorkey was not a relative. Her name was Camille, and she lived in a house called Doubtance in Blois, and another in the rue de Mercière in Lyon. I think you knew her.'

'The Dame de Doubtance?' said Isabelle Roset. She sat down. On her face, still, was nothing but the liveliest interest. 'I remember. I think I remember. She had a daughter Béatris. I nursed her in childbed. Poor girl. In a convent, Madame, one sees many of such cases.'

'Béatris died?' Philippa said.

'Oh, many years later. She herself gave day to a daughter, and died. Fickle men!' said Madame Roset without a great deal of censure. 'And, Madame, Mistress Camille spoke of me?'

The round eyes, staring at her, told Philippa that it was time to say something. She said, 'Alas, Madame, I was not with the Dame de Doubtance when she died. But she left a legacy, as it happened, to my husband, and with it a keepsake she wished us to bring you. Here it is. It comes, I am sure, with her blessing.'

The brooch she handed over was her own, and so was the small bag of money; but Madame Roset was not to know that. She took them both, her cheeks red, her mouth open, and it was necessary to wait, and be patient, while she told it over, and exclaimed, and put questions.

Then it was simple to encourage her to talk of Mistress Camille and Béatris her daughter, and to express interest in what she could tell her.

'And,' said Philippa, 'how many children did Béatris have? Or perhaps you would not hear.'

'Oh, yes indeed, I heard,' Madame Roset said. 'One has many relatives, Madame, in Coulanges. The girl was brought to bed twice in eight years and died after the daughter was born. Marthe, they called her.'

'And eight years before, while you were at la Guiche, Béatris had her first child?' Philippa said. 'Poor thing.

Madame Roset, was it a son? And why was it not on the records?'

'The father did not wish it,' said Madame Roset. A small, lopsided severity had descended, not surprisingly, over the nimble features. 'Madame, if you were a friend of the Lady of Doubtance, did she not tell you of her two grandchildren?'

'*Was it a son?*' Philippa said; and, shaken into subservience, the elderly figure opposite her nodded its head.

'It is of no matter now, Madame, but it was: a fair enough child, but afflicted. He lived ten years with his grandmother before the grand mal carried him off, and his father saw he wanted for nothing. That will be why—' She broke off.

'That will be why the Dame de Doubtance had the key to this house,' Philippa Somerville finished slowly. 'Because the father of the ten-year-old boy who died in 1526 in Lyon ... and the father of Marthe ... and the owner of this house, Madame Roset, are the same?'

It was one point on which she could be contradicted. 'This house, Madame de Sevigny,' said the old woman firmly, 'is owned by a lady.'

He had lied to her. All along, from the beginning, he had lied to her.

'I know,' said Philippa. 'And I am married to her son, who was born here.'

'How clever of you,' said Leonard Bailey, from the doorway.

CHAPTER 7

Au mois troisiesme se levant le soleil
Sanglier, liepard au champ mars pour combatre.

He had changed since last year in England, when he had accepted from his great-nephew Francis Crawford a life-pension to keep Sybilla's reputation unblemished.

Then, Leonard Bailey had been a great, neglected hulk of a man in stained coat and bonnet, living meanly alone with his servants in the estate his treachery had brought him in England.

Now the heavy jowls were the same, and the great nose, spread like a garlic clove, and the odour of unbathed old age, and of malice. But his ribbed doublet and breeches this time were new and uncreased and stiff, and the sleeveless coat lined with some sort of fur, and his trailing hair trimmed under a new velvet bonnet.

He had done well from his great-nephew's pension, had Leonard Bailey, who detested herself and Sybilla, and most of all loathed his great-nephew, who had forced his blackmail of Sybilla to finish. It was his doing that Lord Grey's men had taken Francis at Flavy. It was because of him that Osias and his colleagues had been paid by Francis to safeguard her. It was because of him—did she know it? Or was there merely impatience in the look she was bending on him?—that Isabelle Roset had lost a sister at Flavy-le-Martel this winter.

But she could hardly know it, for she said, looking from one to the other, 'Do you know each other?'

'Yes, of course,' said Leonard Bailey. He did not move but stood, heavily expansive, on the threshold. Behind him two . . . men-servants? soldiers?—had occupied positions at each doorpost in silence. Bailey continued. 'Madame de Sevigny has not had time to tell you who her husband is. You may know him merely as the Count of that designation, but I have to enlighten you, Madame Roset. His own name is Francis Crawford, and he is my great-nephew, the rogue, and that

370

same base-born infant you tell me you delivered here in this house to Lady Cutler.'

He smiled, with his strong lips, at Philippa. 'Sybilla was kind enough to let me have the use of her house while I am in Paris. A charming bower for lovers. Do you not envy me?'

Nymphs, severe, delightful, gazed at her from the friezework. There was a blue Turkey carpet with roses, and roses wreathed the velvet housing of a pair of exquisite virginals. By the heap of books bound in Levantine marocain lay scrolls of music, tinted with sepia. There was a lute in a case, and a box inlaid in sandalwood with garlands of shells and sea flowers. And in marble over the fireplace ran a throng of light, laughing figures, following the spoked wheels of a frail, Roman carriage being drawn by young men between tree stems. Below, were written two fine lines in silver:

I shall harness thee a chariot of lapis-lazuli and gold
Come into our dwelling, in the perfume of the cedars.

The needlework and the music were Sybilla's. But the verse belonged to somebody else. The Hôtel des Sphères was not a living house: it was a shrine. And it was beyond belief that Sybilla could have lent it. To this stupid, imbecile housekeeper Philippa said, steadily, 'This gentleman has no right to be here.'

Madame Roset was offended. Perhaps she had doubts already. 'I have the letter arranging it, in Lady Culter's very own handwriting!'

But naturally. One had forgotten. He was also a forger.

The powerful man in the doorway smiled at her, while the two men behind him stood motionless. 'You see? But of course, if there is any shadow of doubt, Sybilla herself will be in Paris shortly. We have only to place the whole matter before her.' And stirring at last, he came forward into the parlour, rubbing his hands and glancing from her to the housekeeper.

'Are we not fortunate, that you thought to call on us this morning! Such a high-born young lady, and so well connected: in the service of yet another crowned head, they tell me! Do you know, Madame Roset; the young lady and I have a great deal to speak of together. And while we are talking, perhaps a little refreshment might be prepared?' He laughed, his lips spreading widely, at Philippa. 'Madame Roset is a paragon among housekeepers. I have never been looked after so comfortably.'

'Then,' said Philippa, rising grimly, 'it pains me to tell you that you will have to cook your own dishes this morning. M. le comte has asked to see Madame Roset, and I have undertaken to take her back to the Hôtel d'Hercule with me immediately.'

'Indeed? I thought he was in Dieppe?' Lymond's granduncle displayed, perfunctorily, a kind of surprise.

'Did you? He came home late last night. Madame Roset, would you be so kind as to come with me?'

Madame Roset, not unnaturally, hesitated. Her elderly relative by marriage strolled across and laying his hand on the housekeeper's arm, patted it and then held it casually. 'Came home, and sent you out alone so early this morning, and with no escort with you? I watched you come from my window and thought how unchivalrous the young are becoming, these days. Well, well. If he is really here, then his mother and brother ... That is, the dowager and the Earl of Culter must be in Paris also. And what could be better, for I should tell you, my dearest young lady, that when I think of it, there is a little matter I ought to discuss with Sybilla and her two sons, although the morning is hardly the best time to do it. You wouldn't care, my dear Lady Sevigny, to stay and give me your opinion on the whole matter first? I am really very hungry, and Madame Roset does not want to go out into the cold. Indeed, she tells me she had very strict orders not to approach Lady Culter or any member of her family, for which, of course, one must feel the greatest sympathy.'

'Master Bailey,' said Philippa sharply. 'You cannot afford to displease my husband.'

'I should hope,' said Leonard Bailey heartily, 'not to distress any of my fellow-men, far less my own sister's family.' He conveyed Madame Roset to the door, placed her outside, smiling, and closing it, turned back to Philippa. His smile broadened. 'I saw you admiring my doublet. Do you think I could afford these buttons on a mere three hundred pounds every twelvemonth? No. I have M. de Sevigny's bond that so long as I maintain silence about his unfortunate conception, I shall receive such a pension, and I am not ungrateful. But now I have additional sources of income. I am no longer the pauper I was when we met last in England.'

'The fees for betraying your own sister's family to the English?' Philippa said.

He smiled again. 'Partly so. I am sure, for anyone so able, the incident at Ham proved merely a temporary inconvenience to my gallant great-nephew. And I am glad to say that my payments have continued without abatement. Your husband is a man of his word. Only in the event of my breaking silence, he ruled, would it cease. A step I should not lightly take. But a step I should not now require to avoid, if I felt it necessary. . . . I have been waiting for you to come, my dear, ever since your impulsive husband rushed off to Flavy. I made sure Renée Jourda would tell him everything, and you would find a way of extracting it from him. But instead, you used Camille's key?'

Philippa said, 'Renée Jourda died before he could learn this address. How did you know he was going to Flavy?'

'I have friends in Coulanges,' Bailey said. 'I knew as soon as you went to la Guiche what you would report to him, and that he would go to see Renée Jourda. I only wish I had been there to hear that overweening self-esteem pricked at last. And what do you think now of the honourable, clean-living Scottish family you have married into? Small wonder I hear you cannot wait for a divorce.'

It was, somehow, not so desirable to stand up. Philippa found a tall velvet chair by the fireplace and sat in it, taking some time to dispose of her petticoat and overskirt and hanging sleeves with their expensive gemwork. *I shall harness thee a chariot of lapis-lazuli and gold* said the thin silver writing, glittering in the weak sun striking white through the window panes.

The man—the person—the shapeless vessel of envy and malevolence seated opposite her believed that Francis . . . *Mr Crawford* . . . had learned the truth at Flavy, and had imparted it to her. Whereas what Lymond had written was that Béatris and Gavin Crawford were now proved his parents, and Béatris's daughter Marthe his full sister.

But Renée Jourda could not have proved such a thing to his or anyone else's satisfaction. Béatris's only son had died, aged ten, in the year Francis Crawford was born. And Lymond and Marthe must therefore have come of different mothers.

They were alike because the same man had fathered them.

A man whose real identity, it seemed, could not be coun-

373

tenanced, even for Sybilla's sake. An irresponsible and, one supposed, irresistible man who must therefore have sired four different children, two to Béatris, the Dame de Doubtance's unmarried daughter and two to Sybilla, already the wife of Gavin Crawford and the mother of Richard.

The daughters had been named Marthe by Béatris and Eloise by Sybilla. But the same name of Francis Crawford had been given to both the sons: to the beloved child born in this house to Sybilla, and to Béatris's ailing child of ten years earlier, who had died of grand mal and whose death certificate his grandmother, the Dame de Doubtance, had kept.

'What!' said Leonard Bailey and Philippa looked up, after too long an interval, into those seamed and glistening eyes. 'You are silent. Can it be . . . can it possibly be that your husband has not admitted you to his confidence? Do you not know, even yet, the name of the man who betrayed Sybilla's good husband Gavin? Who enticed her again and again from her marriage vows, and lodged her here till brought to bed of each bastard?

'Do you not know that Gavin was cuckolded by his own father?'

*

A lie is a broad and spacious and glittering thing, sweeping belief before it from its very grandeur. But the truth fits, like an old man cutting cloth in an attic.

And that, Philippa did not need to be told, was the truth, which Lymond had guessed long before her. The only circumstance in the world which now accounted for Marthe, for Eloise, for the erosion of all that lay between Lymond and Sybilla to the point where, brought face to face without warning, he could not support an encounter. And dear God, who would blame him . . . who would force him now to come back to Midculter and Scotland?

When, at Flavy, he had learned the true facts for certain he had lied to her. And with every reason.

Your father's two sons will not meet in this world again, the Dame de Doubtance had said, with cold-blooded accuracy. And Francis, believing her, had stayed in Russia rather than put that prophecy to the test. So the meeting on the sands at Philorth for him had been terrible, indeed.

Francis Crawford had known the truth, and he had continued to fight. It would be a pity if she could not do the same.

Sick in every thread of her body, Philippa stared the man direct in his suffused and ponderous face and said, 'I don't believe it.'

'Don't you?' he said; and smiling, moved to the small inlaid cabinet she had already noticed, set upon a side table. He opened it. 'Of course, you have only to ask Madame Roset. But you might remember, there is written proof as well. Your husband burned the copies of these. Here—I would prefer that you do not touch them—are the originals. I found them, after a very short search, where you see them. A methodical creature, Sybilla, except in obedience to the laws of her Creator.'

And there they were, displayed in each powerful hand:—the two papers written by Sybilla and witnessed by Isabelle Roset and Renée Jourda so long ago. The papers in which she confessed to have borne a son and a daughter, Francis and Eloise, of whom her husband Gavin was not the father.

And there, completed now in her writing, was the name of her lover, and the father of Francis . . . and Gavin. The name of Francis Crawford of Lymond, first baron Crawford of Cutler. The gay, the gaillard, the remarkable man who died when Francis was three, and whom all the world thought his grandfather.

She read the words without speaking. But as he turned to put them away she said, 'Why have you shown me these, Master Bailey? My woman knows where I am. You must know that if Mr Crawford comes here he will take them, and kill you.'

He finished what he was doing and turned round. His smile this time was pitying. 'You think me a fool. What do you know of the world, my dear? I have no intention of keeping you. If you wish, you may leave forthwith: I have no objection. As for finding the papers . . . Do you imagine I mean to store them here? Hardly. Before you have reached the Hôtel de Guise, they will be out of the house also, and on their way to safe keeping. And should anything happen to these, I have made copies and sent them to London. Not as convincing perhaps, as the originals; but enough, if published, to create quite a scandal.'

'Then you want more money, I take it', said Philippa. 'In that case, why not approach Mr Crawford himself?'

'Because I wished to give myself the pleasure of entertaining you,' said Leonard Bailey.

There was a stool by her feet. With surprising smoothness for a heavy, elderly man he seated himself on it. 'I dislike your husband. It pleases me that he should know, when he looks in your face, what you feel about that impious coupling.' He took her hand unexpectedly in both his own and toyed with it. 'Tell me: now you know, could you lie with him?'

He was the sort of person one could with justice kill if only—if *only* one had had the sense to bring a weapon. He was the sort of person who, if one offended him, was quite capable of destroying the whole house of Cutler. Philippa withdrew her hand and said, 'If I did, I should never obtain my divorce. Am I to give him some message?'

'No,' said Bailey. He picked up the cuff of her long sleeve and admired it. 'I told you, I think, that I was no longer on the edge of pauperdom. I did not mention that it was because I have received a congenial—a most congenial commission. I wonder if you can guess what it is?'

'I have no idea,' Philippa said. 'Except that it will probably be damaging to the Culters. Is that it?'

'You understand me,' said Lymond's great-uncle. 'It is going to be, if I may so term it, a labour of love. And lucrative. The only disappointment is that in the end, I shall have to forgo your husband's pension. . . . He has, you must know, many powerful enemies.'

'And what then,' said Philippa, 'are they paying you to do that they can't manage themselves? Challenge him face to face?' The floorboards outside the doorway creaked. Bailey's men were still standing there.

'I fancy,' said Leonard Bailey, 'any man of birth might be excused from challenging M. le comte de Sevigny face to face in a very short time. No. I have been asked to investigate the circumstances of your husband's progeniture and collect all possible evidence which will reflect against himself and his mother with the object, in the end, of making it public.'

'By whom?' Philippa said. 'Or could I guess?' Coming from Bailey's house in England, once, she had been followed. She remembered the livery the soldiers wore, and the look of Lymond's face when she had told him. Of all the powerful enemies Francis had made, one family had the most cause to hate him, and herself. Long ago in Scotland, Lymond had exposed the renegade Earl of Lennox to ridicule and later, in

France, had discredited both him and his expatriate brother. And over and over, through the years, had stood between Margaret Lennox, the Earl's half-royal wife, and the lands, the power, the kingdoms she coveted. Margaret Lennox who, rumour said, had once appeared on the long list of Lymond's mistresses.

There was money there, enough to give even this shocking old man satisfaction.

But he was not going to answer, or to give away anything at the moment. He smiled, his pores sweating a little from the warmth of the fire and said, 'Perhaps you could. The Crawfords always picked clever girls.'

'And they know the truth, your employers?'

'Not yet,' he said. 'They undertook to pay me for the duration of my researches, and so far, I have not been in a hurry. They do not, for example, know where this house is. But of course, I know the truth and I have all the evidence. It remains only to choose a time to hand it over. The arrival in France of Richard Crawford and Sybilla herself makes the present moment seem singularly appropriate.'

'Then your payment from all quarters would cease, and Mr Crawford would kill you,' said Philippa.

'Oh, he would try to kill me before that,' Bailey said. 'As soon as you leave here and tell him of this conversation, he would never rest, would he, until I was done for? That is why I have written some very special instructions to go with those papers I showed you. If your husband or anyone else touches me—if I suffer injury, or die by violence, or even if Madame Roset is concealed from me—Sybilla's confessions will be opened and published in London and Paris.'

Philippa stared at the flushed face. 'But, Mr Bailey ... if you sell to the Lennoxes, Mr Crawford has nothing to lose. Do you think you could possibly escape him?'

'They have paid for my bodyguards,' he said. 'And promised protection in England. He can't go to England. He's in French employment.'

Philippa laughed. It was a little sawtoothed, but she was glad she could manage it at all. 'Mr Bailey,' she said. 'I'll remind you again. You are pitching yourself against the best-known professional in Europe. If he wants to kill you, he will have it done. What are the Lennoxes paying you?'

He had dropped her sleeves, shifting uneasily on his stool. He did not appear even to have noticed that she had guessed who his employers were. He said, 'I have ten pounds a month so long as I am in France, and a written bond for six thousand more when I hand over the proofs, quite complete.'

'I shall give you ten thousand pounds for them now,' Philippa said.

His eyes shone, and then he dropped his wrinkled lids over them. 'And have your husband send to kill me tomorrow?'

'Hardly,' Philippa said. 'If, as you say, your death will make everything public. In fact, whatever we arrange, Mr Crawford need know nothing of it. Your pension from him will continue, and you will tell the Countess of Lennox that you cannot help her. Then you will be both rich and safe, so long as you keep perfectly silent. Otherwise you are a dead man, Master Bailey, no matter what the Lennoxes promise.'

She looked at him, without drawing back, and without, she hoped, showing fear of contempt or any of the black rage burning within her. 'You will have to choose, Master Bailey, which of us to trust. But I can tell you that I should put your chances very low of ever seeing the six thousand pounds the Lennoxes may have promised you. The present Queen of England, we now know, is childless, and her sister has no love for the Lennoxes. When Elizabeth comes to the throne, that family will need all their wealth to keep themselves out of prison.'

He was interested. He said, 'You could bring me ten thousand pounds without your husband knowing of it?'

'I have my own resources,' Philippa said. 'Give my bankers three days.'

He had stopped smiling at last. He got up, and taking a turn, stood again in front of the fireplace. *(Come into our dwelling, in the perfume of the cedars.)* He said, 'It is all very well, madam, but it is a matter of staking one's life and one's money on the word of a schoolgirl. I am not going to decide such matters in a moment.'

'How long does it take,' Philippa said, 'to decide whether you want ten thousand pounds in your hands directly or not?'

He walked up and down again, the stiff folds of his coat swinging and buffeting the delicate furniture. 'It would suit you to know now, hey? Well, it would suit me to ponder the business. There's no hurry from my point of view, mistress. Every week I stay is twice paid for. And Sybilla and her dear son will be here, won't they, at least until the royal wedding?'

Philippa got up and said, 'What, then?'

378

He walked forward and took her arm, just above the elbow. He was a big man, taller than she was, and broad with it even in age. His flat fingers, the joints bunched and reddened, moved a little, smoothing the silk on her sleeve. 'You make a good case,' he said. 'Considering the Crawfords are no business of yours, and that piece of misbegotten trash is just divorcing you. Why spend your savings on them?'

'I can't think,' Philippa said. 'My mother always said I had more money than I knew what to do with.'

'Aye,' he said. He did not let her go. 'They have all the old arts of enticement, that family. So my sister Honoria found out, and her son Gavin, although the Crawfords never bewitched me, among them. Is there anything you would not do, Mistress Philippa, for Francis Crawford?'

Courage, Kate always said. Nine-tenths of every attack is bluff. The art is to know when to call it. She did not shake her arm free. She merely said, 'The offer is ten thousand pounds, Mr Bailey. Nothing more.'

Kate, Kate ... This time it isn't bluff. She felt his other hand rise and settle, first on her arm, then, sliding up, on the bare skin of her neck ... and over ... and down. Then the broad padded mass of his doublet closed upon her, hard as a bolster, and his breath steamed on her face as his open mouth descended quickly.

If she used the flat of her hand, or her knee, or the heel of her shoe, he would throw her out, and do what the Lennoxes wanted. She got her head free then, and snapped at him: "If you indulge yourself now, Master Bailey, you will not have your money, for I will not send for it.' And, the pressure continued: 'It's your life you are risking,' said Philippa clearly. 'If you go on, I shall make it known to Mr Crawford, whatever the consequences.'

'Ah,' he said. He disengaged very slowly and stood breathing thickly. 'I remember. You said there would be no divorce if he mounted you. So ... is it possible? You jib because you have a maidenhead still to barter?'

'You should take a beginner's course in almost any well-run seraglio,' said Philippa shortly. 'It would adjust certain gaucheries in your language.'

He ingored that. 'A virgin under this monarchy, and with a fortune! ... I cannot believe it!' said Leonard Bailey; and in his voice, quite plainly, was a puzzled excitement. 'What milksop lovers have you had, that you have reached twenty without a single passage, a single conclusive joust in some antechamber, or grotto, or window embrasure? I have known no man born who could not achieve his business with a woman at court, if he felt like it.'

'Perhaps my approach is too subtle for them,' Philippa said. 'Master Bailey, with ten thousand pounds, you can buy all the court ladies you want, and the window embrasures to put them in.'

He smiled. His nostrils spread, and his lips; and you could see that his mind had shifted, for the moment, from the promptings of his appetites. She waited, holding her breath, and staring at him.

'But that would not hurt the Crawfords,' he said. 'No. Go home, Madame de Sevigny. Collect all the money you have. Wait. And, in my own time, I shall tell you the price. If there is one.'

She was free. She tempted fate by using no more arguments. 'It is your life, Master Bailey,' she said. 'I should advise you to put off no time in safeguarding it.'

The men still stood on guard outside the door as she passed through. She supposed Bailey called them his servants. There were two more in the hall waiting, he said, to escort her over the snow to her lodging. Which was shrewd of him. For that way she could not linger and watch who left the house with the papers.

She hoped Madame Roset would be safe. She should be. He wanted to stay in that house, and she was a witness: he needed her. And there was no way of removing her, that she could think of.

He squeezed her fingers and kissed them, taking his leave, and she walked from the house with her keepers, the three sets of prints tumbling and gouging the smooth, sparkling white of the garden. The bodyguard answered no questions, but stood while the gatehouse porter, scolding, brought servants running to guide her over the swept, slippery flags of the Hôtel de Guise courtyard.

As she entered the doors she saw them still there outside, watching.

Her grace of Scotland, said Célie, had sent for her.

It was, as one had guessed, a matter of the dressmaker's continued shortcomings. Philippa did what she could, through the raging pain in her head, to rectify it.

The headache lingered a while but did not approach, she

380

was glad to find, a degree of virulence which might incapacitate her.

For that, you had to expose your sensibilities to attack for very much longer; and take no one into your confidence: least of all those already nearer to you than you wanted.

She was busy all day but at night found herself too tired to sleep. When she finally closed her eyes before dawn, she was awakened almost at once by the noise of somebody frantically sobbing. It was not until she felt Célie's brusque arms around her that she realized that it was herself.

CHAPTER 8

Freres et seurs en divers lieux captifs
Se trouveront passer pres du monarque.

Conducted by the glittering red and blue tabards of the Lyon
Court, the procession of the nine Scottish Commissioners for
the Queen of Scots' wedding wound into Paris some three
days afterwards, impeccably escorted by François de Sevigny,
brother to one of the Commissioners, and by Claude d'Aumale, brother to the great Duke of Guise himself.

All the way from Dieppe, the names of de Guise and of
Sevigny had filled the air, through the speeches and the noise
of the hackbuts and cannon. Lymond had sent for the
Tapkana, his specially built canopied sledges, and the first
part of their journey was spent Russian-style running over the
flat snowy chalkfields, with pennants streaming and bells ringing in the crisp air.

He was not averse, his brother noticed, to reminding the
populace who he was. Even d'Aumale's jewelled hats and
furred cloaks drew fewer eyes than the Voevoda Bolshoia in
his black fox fur hat, balancing on his light sleigh, reins in
hand. Along with everything else, Richard Crawford
concluded, Lymond had come to enjoy adulation.

Except once, long ago, over an estrangement with his wife
Mariotta, Lord Cutler had never been jealous of the young
brother he had seen grow from babyhood. Until the moment
Francis had left home at sixteen, a prisoner of war to the English, Richard knew him solely as a blond and delicate boy,
interested only, it seemed, in reading and music, whose apparent fragility concealed a will of steel, and a turn of phrase
which could wound like a sword-cut.

Most of all, he remembered the hatred which lay between
Francis and Gavin, his father. It was on the violent, heavy-
witted older man that Francis had practised his verbal play,
to no benefit to himself. Some of the floggings Sybilla prevent-

ed, for of course, Francis was always her favourite, and the favourite too of Eloise his sister.

But he had failed often enough to weather the storm, and had had to stand by while his books burned, or his lute lay in splinters. It was to be expected that when he became in turn a leader of men, Francis should prove hard on others; should observe no laws; should fight, regardless of method, for victory.

Hence had come the misunderstandings which had led Richard once to hunt down his brother in order to deliver him to the justice he thought he deserved. Later, learning to know him, a friendship had grown: odd, irregular; at times surprisingly deep. And at times marred, it seemed wantonly, by Lymond's excesses and his own lack of trust towards Richard which again and again had caused his older brother anger and misery.

No one in Scotland was ignorant of Lymond's growing stature: in France, in Malta, in his embassy for France to Turkey. It had seemed possible that he might outgrow his wildness: that the virtues he did possess, and the depth and constancy of his relationship with Sybilla might bring him at last to safe harbour.

But then, Francis had not come home after Turkey, and the tales of his doings there and in Africa were not slow in coming to Scotland. There followed Russia, and his brief visit home where it became finally clear that he had changed: that all the ground gained during those painful years had been lost. And most distressing of all, that the sheet anchor had gone: that he had made up his mind to break for all time with his mother.

It was this discovery which had led Richard last year to attack him: a futile reaction, and one he would never have been driven to make but for all the years of growing attachment between. For what Francis was doing to Sybilla, Richard believed there was no forgiveness.

He had hoped, after that bitter encounter at Dieppe, that the schism, painful but wholesome, would now be complete on Sybilla's side as it was on Lymond's, to see her through the coming difficult weeks. And certainly, the bloodless formality of the relationship Francis had since maintained with them made it easy for her to keep her distance, and her thoughts to herself.

But although she could dissimulate, Richard was wiser than

once he had been. He watched her when Lymond was there, moving cordially among his eminent countrymen, agreeably talkative, encouraging Beaton or Rothes or Cassillis or Seton to tell him about their troubles in Scotland; amusing young Fleming, who still worshipped him; impressing, you could see, the Bishop of Orkney who once, for God's sake, had tried him in Edinburgh for an outlaw.

James Stewart and Erskine of Dun, one noticed, were less communicative. Rumour had it that they had already had a brief encounter with Lymond on his first day in Dieppe; and had caught him, perhaps, in the same temper that he had displayed in the house of Jean Ango. At any rate, the magic had failed to work in this instance.

In which case why, of all the company, did Sybilla choose to spend most of her time with these two?

Because, his observation told him, she saw, as he did, that something lay between them and Francis. And because, as ever, the matter of Francis occupied her still, to the exclusion of virtually everything else.

After that, everything he saw confirmed it. The rejection he had hoped for had not taken place. Thrust into her son's daily company Sybilla faced, in the weeks ahead, a test of endurance far harder to bear than his desertion.

After Berwick, after Dieppe, one was not fool enough to go to Francis, cap in hand, and plead yet again for a reconciliation. On Lymond's part the separation was quite clearly final, and had been before he left Scotland. What Richard needed to know were his reasons. And then, to the best of his powers, to convince his mother that Francis would never return to her.

To be private with anyone in the midst of such pageantry was not easy; and less so if every obstacle is placed in your way by your quarry. It was not until Rouen that Richard found his brother alone; and then only by dint of following him into his bedchamber when he walked in, divesting himself of his elaborate surcoat and proceeding swiftly to change it for some plainer clothes, brought him by Archie.

It appeared he had an appointment with a sculptor called Hérisson, and was not willing to linger. Neither did Archie show any sign of budging. Richard closed the door and said, 'Perhaps you can give me an answer while you are dressing. What is the source of the trouble between you and Sybilla?'

'Ask her,' Lymond said. Archie, unfolding garments from a coffer, did not look round.

'I have. She says I am not to concern myself with it. It seems to me, in view of her age and frailty, that I must concern myself with it.'

'Is this supposed to be something new?' Lymond said. He picked up a shirt and slid into it. 'You seem to have charged often enough at that particular target to be fit to stop a bull by his horns in full fury.'

'Is it to do with Eloise?' said Richard bluntly.

Lymond's full attention was being given, briefly, to the knotting of his shirt-cords. 'Did Sybilla say it is?' he said. He looked for his doublet armhole, found it, and slinging the garment on, began to fasten it.

'No.' Richard, harassed, turned to look at Archie and Archie's black eyes, unwinking, outfaced him. Richard said, 'I don't want to hear your miserable secrets. But for Sybilla's sake I want some answers. I once accused you of wanting your sister dead. I did you, perhaps, an injustice. The fact remains that she told me . . .'

'I'm sorry,' Lymond said. 'Unless you wish to follow me into the street, I am afraid we must abandon our gossip. So full of fruyte and rethorikly pykit. Gloves. And no, the other hat. Money?'

Richard said, 'She told me one night that she had no wish to go on living, and that if she did, it could only harm you. She was thirteen years old. . . . Can you not stand still, and look me in the face, and give me an answer?'

'No,' said Lymond. He had gone now, fully dressed, to the door of this room where he turned, Archie behind him. 'If you are asking, did Eloise make no effort to avoid the explosion which killed her, the answer is probably yes. If you are also asking, was I her lover, the answer is no. After all,' said Lymond, 'that would be incest.' And with a click, the door closed finally after him.

That night, Richard retired early and drank himself grimly insensible while Lymond, with faultless bonhomie, was adorning his third Hôtel de Ville banquet. He did not know that Sybilla, who had also excused herself, took the occasion to trap Archie Abernethy at last in her room and confront him with an inquiry. 'I believe, since Richard is incapable for the first time in fifteen months, that my two sons have had an encounter?'

385

'I wouldn't know, my lady,' said Archie.

'But you do know about Mlle Marthe,' Sybilla said. She had never uttered that name to him, or to either son, until that moment.

Archie's lined face did not change, but his black eyes were not without pity. 'Aye,' he said. 'Ye'll ken, she was wed to Master Blyth.'

Sybilla said, 'I know you are attached to my son, and must therefore regard me as an enemy. But I should like you to tell me. Does Francis mean Richard to meet her?'

He knew her and respected her, and had nursed her grand-child as his own, but he was also a man who spoke his mind, and sharply if need be. 'Lady Culter,' said Archie Abernethy, 'only a man who hated you would do such a thing.'

She stood up then, staunchly upright in spite of the seventy years she carried, and said, 'Forgive me, Mr Abernethy. You see, I have no guide lines left. I can do nothing to help him. You cannot know what it means to me that you are with him.'

There was a pause. Archie did not drop his eyes. Presently he said, 'His defences are good. But it is his friends that will bring him low, not his enemies, Lady Culter. Keep you out of his way. That's the best advice I can give you.'

*

At Paris, they were met outside the gates by a hundred gentlemen and a band of Archers of the King's Guard with pipes and tambours and escorted to the Place de Grève for the City's welcome; and thence over the river to the Maison de l'Ange, the large residence in the rue de la Huchette which the Crown utilized for its more important guests. There, they were received by the King's Maréchal des Logis; and there took place the ceremony of the Corps de Ville's gifts. The Commissioners received the double quarts of hippocras and boxes of dragees and gilded cotignac, the yellow wax flam-beaux and the pâtés of Mayenne ham and the double marzi-pan of Lyon, gilded; and listened to and replied to the speeches. Then, at last, the nine official representatives of her Majesty the Queen Dowager and the Three Estates of the Realm of Scotland were allowed to retire and compose them-selves.

Lymond went straight to the Hôtel St André.

He knew, by the abandon with which the gates were flung open that his suit was known, and had prospered. Before he reached the top of the steps Marguerite, Maréchale de St André was waiting there, dressed more splendidly than he had seen her in Lyon, as befitted a noble lady, the mother of a courted heiress. Only her eyes, as he bent to kiss her hand, dwelled on him in a manner less than maternal and her voice, scolding him, was softer than was its wont.

'*Cher ami,* I hear you have been extravagant to the danger of your health. You must not act *à la bizarre* when you are wedded to Cathin. I trust your mother and the Earl are in good health?'

'You shall meet them before very long. I have your permission, then, to address your daughter?' said Francis Crawford. 'I should try to make her content.'

'I know she will be content,' said the Maréchale de St André. 'I am not happy, my dear; but if one should have you, then I should prefer it to be a child of my breeding. She is waiting for you.'

*

How long she had been waiting he could not imagine but she was there, sitting upright and alone in the smallest boudoir, with her black hair shining over her shoulders and her skirts of rosebud velvet spread all about her. Crystals, circling her throat, were her only ornament.

No one accompanied him into the room. He closed the door gently behind him and saw her colour rise as she turned her head, but she kept her perfect composure.

'A wife, a spaniel, a walnut tree,/The more you beat them, the better they be. I learn,' said Lymond, 'that you are willing to undergo unmentionable risks?'

She had risen to curtsey to him. Now, standing, she faced him, unsmiling still. 'It is my mother's assent which brings you here,' she said. 'I have said nothing yet, M. de Sevigny, for nothing has been said to me.'

'It is a principle of Archidamidas,' Lymond said, 'that he that knows how to speak, knows also when to speak. You know, I think, who and what I am. I have the word of the King that on the day after the Dauphin's wedding I shall receive the final annulment of my present marriage. When I have my release, may I hope that you will become my wife?'

She had studied her mirror. She knew how the candlelight enhanced the excellent line of her throat, the shape of her cheekbones, the balance and mould of her body. She said, 'It seems a poor way, Mr Crawford, to ask for a lady's hand in marriage. Can you not manage a quote or two from the poets? A note of devotion? A fleeting salute on the cheek?'

'A masquerade?' he said lightly. 'Would you think any better of me?' But his hands were still and he was looking at her.

'Is happiness a masquerade?' said Catherine d'Albon. 'Or do we not speak of it? I am sure my mother did not.'

'We shall speak of it,' he said. 'I trust I may be able to give it to you. Aside from that, I make few demands on those close to me. I shall not encroach on you.'

She said, 'You are telling me, I think, that you mean to lead your own life.'

'I hope you will lead yours,' Lymond said. 'And that mine, where it touches us both, will not be displeasing to you. But if you hold me in horror, there is no reason why this contract need be completed. And if I have offended you, forgive me.'

There was a little silence. Then, 'You make no pretence,' she said quietly; and saw him recognize and accept the bitterness she could not quite keep out of her voice.

Then he said, 'No. Pretence makes a poor foundation when you are hoping to build.'

'Do we have anything to build with?' said Catherine d'Albon.

'Yes,' said Lymond. 'There are my good intentions. And there is your wit, and your kindness, and your beauty.'

'What do you know of them, Mr Crawford?' said Catherine d'Albon.

For the first time in an interview which had fallen out not at all as he expected, Francis Crawford hesitated. Then walking towards her he raised her hand, and kissed it, and leading her back to her chair, seated her, and placed himself thoughtfully on the little rug at her feet. He said, 'If you wish pretty phrases, and true ones, I should say that your beauty I can see and your wit I am coming to know in this meeting. Your kindness, clearly, I do not yet qualify for. But I should be honoured if you would allow me to try.'

'As you say,' she said, 'you are able to make polite speeches when brought to it. Why are you divorcing Mistress Philippa?'

His eyes were blue: a dense and brilliant cornflower, and his hair was leaf-gold under the flattering light. He said, 'Doesn't she want to marry the worthy youth Allendale? I don't know her plans, but I rather thought that was her intention. I am divorcing her, lady, because our marriage has never been more than a formal one. I don't bed with children.'

'Rumour says,' said Catherine d'Albon, 'that you did. Or are the Knights of St John all mistaken?'

'You know too much,' said Francis Crawford slowly. 'Shall I amend it? I don't bed with young girls who are virgins, unless they ask me, and unless I am married to them.'

'I see,' said Catherine d'Albon. 'You must be asked?'

'And married,' said Francis Crawford.

'That is easy,' she said; and for the first time he saw her lips tilt in a smile which recalled nothing at all of her mother. 'If you ask me, I expect I shall marry you. But as for what comes after that, who can forecast?'

'Nostradamus,' said Lymond. 'And I myself for that matter. In fact, I would be willing to take a small wager.' He looked at her, the levity fading. 'If you have doubts, Catherine, there is no need to go on with it all.'

'I have doubts,' said Catherine d'Albon. 'But they appertain to myself, not to you. No. It is a match. How could I fare better?'

She felt his recoil as if it were physical. Then he said, with a kind of suppressed anger, 'I know it should be different. It will be, if you will give me time. I promised you happiness; and I meant it.'

'But you have no expectations,' said Catherine d'Albon, 'of receiving any from me?'

His self-possession, unlike hers, was in place again. 'I should like you to try,' Lymond answered with gravity. 'I shall tell you, from time to time, how you are succeeding. Meanwhile, I suggest we summon your mother. There is a common belief that left behind locked doors, I don't stop to ask anyone anything.'

She rose. 'You mean,' Catherine d'Albon said, 'I have agreed to marry a libertine?'

'Everyone marries libertines,' Lymond said comfortably, rising and taking her elbow. 'But not everyone knows it beforehand.'

◆

News of the impending marriage, discreetly disseminated, produced a number of different reactions.

Her grace the Queen of Scotland was extremely displeased.

389

The Prince of Condé, a fairly regular recipient of the Maréchale de St André's favours, was a little put out and began instead, belatedly, to pay a good deal of attention to her daughter. A number of other noblemen followed suit.

Piero Strozzi, who heard the news out of town, was delighted, and added spice to the general interest by inquiring of all those he met as to how *son petit François* had got the branch budding so promptly. Jerott Blyth, offended by Lymond's lack of frankness, quarrelled with Adam Blacklock and stalked off to the Hôtel d'Hercule, to be told that M. de Sevigny was absent on business. Danny Hislop, calling later, was told the same story.

Madame la Maréchale de St André, who had better means of judging its accuracy, called and was admitted, but left without having arranged, as she had hoped, for the necessary meeting between herself, her daughter, and M. de Sevigny's family. His mother, M. de Sevigny said, was still recovering from her journey.

Catherine d'Albon began to spend a good deal of time in Lymond's company. Her dramatic good looks, daily enhanced, became breathtaking. So her mirror informed her, and her mother, and the comte de Sevigny's eyes, sometimes, resting on her. But so far, he had done no more than kiss her hand.

I don't bed with virgins unless they ask me, and unless I am married to them.

There was time enough, in spite of what her mother might say.

Jerott discovered that Lymond was in fact in residence in the Hôtel d'Hercule but failed a second time to get himself admitted, upon which he walked instead to the rue de la Huchette and sent his name in to Lymond's mother.

Sybilla received him. She remembered him as the fiery, black-haired young Knight of St John who had concerned himself so passionately about Francis's affairs in Malta and Scotland. She saw now the same young man in the guise of a Lyon merchant, and married to the girl of whose existence her older son Richard knew nothing.

She said, 'You wish to talk to me about your wife; about Francis; and perhaps about this wedding of his, which everyone seems to be speaking of.'

She had always been a splendid person: bright as a silver

penny. Jerott said, 'Have you seen him? I've been shown the door twice. Did you know about this marriage arrangement?'

It was typical Jerott Blythe, if not the overture which courtesy perhaps demanded after an interval of five and a half years. Sybilla, amusement in her tired eyes, said, 'We travelled south together, but he didn't speak of it. Don't you approve? I know of nothing against it.'

'It depends what his plans are,' said Jerott. 'If you want my view, he should have stayed in Russia.'

'Why?' Sybilla said. Her tone expressed kindly interest.

'It was good for him. It would have kept him away from Marthe. And that poor lass would be married long since to her Austin.'

'You speak of Philippa. Is she in love with Austin Grey, Jerott?' said Sybilla. 'I hear he is a prisoner with Francis.'

'She would have been,' said Jerott bluntly. 'As it is, she has to get Francis out of her system first. He held on to that marriage far too long, and she's paying the penalty, not milord of Sevigny. You know she wanted to trace Marthe's birth?'

'Yes, I knew that,' Sybilla said. After a space she added, 'And has she succeeded?'

'Not while she was in Lyon,' Jerott said. 'If she found out anything since, I don't know about it.' Now it had come to the point he hesitated, his face rather red.

'She is not a child of mine, Jerott,' said Lady Culter quietly. 'Nor can I tell you anything about her that you don't know already. But whatever irregularity there has been, I think it would be best if Richard knew nothing of it. So far as Marthe herself is concerned, I have a favour to ask you. I should like to meet her.'

He had not expected that. He gazed at her miserably. 'She would hurt you,' he said.

'She resents me? Or Francis? Or both of us?'

'She resents the birds in the trees,' said Jerott bitterly. He pulled himself together. 'They are very alike. In times of dispute it's best not to get between them.'

'What are they disputing about?' Sybilla asked. 'The new marriage?'

'In a way. Marthe is set on a union between Francis and Philippa.'

'Is she? Why is that?' Sybilla said.

'Revenge, perhaps. She won't say.' The flush on his splendid, jutting profile deepened. 'You know the life he has led,

Lady Culter. He is ten years older; he has a son, and a mistress in Russia. Even the girl he is marrying—' He broke off.

Sybilla sat, fragile and composed, watching him. 'If it affects Francis, you may tell me,' she said. 'If it concerns Catherine, not.'

'In Lyon,' Jerott said, 'he was her mother's lover.'

Sybilla dropped her eyes. 'I see,' was all she said. There was a long silence. Then she said, 'I should still, in spite of all this, like to meet your wife. Do you think, Jerott, you could arrange it?'

But, of course, he couldn't. And so, at last, he had to tell her the reason.

*

Alone among Francis Crawford's friends, his wife made no effort, on his arrival in Paris, to see either him or his mother.

Fresh from the Hôtel des Sphères, she knew she could not face Sybilla just yet; or be sure of concealing her knowledge from Lymond. Instead she bestowed on him, from a distance, the kind of protective attention which, through Osias, he had conferred on her; and for the same reason. Leonard Bailey had not so far, to her knowledge, made any move since their interview. When he did, she wanted to hear about it.

So she learned, before the Scots Commissioners had been two hours in Paris, that there had been no reconciliation between Lymond and his family. She knew when he first called on Catherine, and the growing number of meetings that followed. She knew that on his visits to the Hôtel de l'Ange he did not present himself to Sybilla, but performed his duties towards the nine other Scottish delegates on the well-worn treadmill of ceremonies, sight-seeing and conviviality: at the Louvre, the Bastille, the Palais de Justice, les Tournelles, the Church of Notre Dame, the Abbey of Saint-Denis and its treasures.

She used, as Sybilla had, the best intermediary she could find; and asked Archie Abernethy to meet her.

From him, she learned of the brief illness at Madame Bouchard's house in Dieppe.

'And Lord James and Mr Erskine?' she asked when he paused. 'What did they make of it?'

'It would seem nothing out of the way. He had had a

hundred-mile ride, and a long day and a good evening's drinking before it.'

'. . . But?' said Philippa.

'But he was postit for six hours till the pain eased; and weak for about as long after it. Barring him and me, no one knew of it. They're strong men for the Reform party, John Erskine and the Queen's bastard brother,' said Archie. 'They must hae been blithe tae get the chance tae speak wi' him.'

'What did they say?' Philippa said.

'He didna confide in me, but I think I can guess without having a nosebleed. He also said that the meeting with his ma was more vexing than he expected.'

'Hence the nerve-storm,' said Philippa.

'Maybe. He was already pitched unco high leaving Paris, from some event in the Séjour du Roi, I should fancy. Master Blyth wouldna say what it was.'

'I know what it was. And now, Archie?'

'There's a truce, for the moment, with the family. He has himself well in hand. It's just a matter of wearing out the few weeks to the wedding.'

'With or without help from Catherine d'Albon,' said Philippa reflectively. She paused, and as Archie said nothing, she finished what she had to say. 'If you need him, Nostradamus is in Paris.'

'You've seen him?' said Archie. His voice had sharpened.

'In passing,' said Philippa smoothly. 'Which reminds me, Archie, what happened on your last night in Lyon? Master Nostradamus said I should ask Mr Crawford.'

'Did he indeed?' said Archie Abernethy. He paused. 'Well, I wouldna ask him the now or you'll get a right nippit answer. . . . Ye ken Master Blyth's lady's banged out the house and left him for good? Leastways, she hasna come back again.'

'No, but I'm not surprised,' Philippa said. 'I don't need to ask what Master Blyth is doing. Is anyone looking for her?'

'Mr Hislop. He likes a problem,' said Archie. 'I'm told Lady Culter wants to speak with her.'

'Oh,' said Philippa. She felt her nose growing red. After a moment she said, 'Do you think that's a good idea? Marthe won't let Lymond down publicly, I'd swear, however much she attacks him in private.'

Archie didn't say anything. She wondered how much he knew, or suspected. Enough, certainly, to know that it was a question of Lymond's birth and Sybilla's honesty. He had no means of discovering anything else. Her face must have reflected her thoughts for Archie's voice, striking through them, said suddenly, 'I take it you have no good news to give him then?'

And recognizing the question for what it was, Philippa said, 'He knows all there is to know, and none of it is good. Archie, he isn't lacking in character. In the end, he has to learn to support it. I am sure he will.'

The wise eyes, unflinching, stared into hers. 'There is a man in him that could support it,' Archie said. 'True enough. But it is maybe a man the world could do without. I don't know. I wasna in Russia.'

CHAPTER 9

Sera connu d'adultere l'offence
Qui parviendra a son grand deshonneur.

It had been tempting on a scale positively Biblical to confide in Archie, and it was with some wistfulness that Philippa watched him leave after that interview. But for all practical purposes, he and Francis Crawford must be considered a single person, and on one matter she had made up her mind on the day she left the rue de la Cerisaye.

While there was hope of settling the matter in any other way, Lymond should not be told of Bailey's threat to his family. The misconduct he had uncovered was far more serious than any Archie could have envisaged. Misconduct of such a kind that, whatever strength of character Francis Crawford might possess, he was at this moment barely keeping his balance in face of it.

If affairs went according to plan, she would not need his help in any case. If they did not, she at least would not be blinded by passion into taking some action which would throw secrecy to the winds and Sybilla into the hands of her persecutors.

It made no difference why Sybilla, of all civilized women, had so abominably betrayed her marriage. Or why she had chosen to set down in black and white the name of the man who had begotten her two younger children. It was done, and it was for those who loved her to protect her and her family from the consequences.

But not—whatever happened, not by trusting Leonard Bailey. He might sell Sybilla's papers to her. He might sell to the Lennoxes. Most likely of all, he would cheat, to wring from the situation the maximum money and the maximum injury to the Crawfords.

The obvious course was to move quickly, and cheat before he did.

So Philippa, from the moment she left the Hôtel des

Sphères put her intelligence, her imagination, her considerable energy to work with one end in view: the tracking down of the two sets of papers containing Sybilla's confession.

There were copies in France, and in London. In whose hands? Someone empowered to reveal the contents if Bailey met an unnatural end. Someone, then, with authority.

What sort of agent would Leonard Bailey trust, sufficiently moral or sufficiently wealthy to be immune from bribery? She did not know the name of Bailey's bankers, but she did know Francis Crawford's, who paid to Bailey each month the fee he had claimed for his silence.

She sent a page to invite the Schiatti cousins to supper.

In twenty-four hours she had the name of Leonard Bailey's bankers in Paris and London and the information, extracted she understood by alcohol rather than violence, that a package, with instructions and password, had been confided by Mr Bailey to their Paris house recently. She also had, drawn upon her own funds in France, the sum of ten thousand pounds in Venetian ducats.

She had a day and night watch set upon the Hôtel des Sphères, operated by a number of cheerful gentlemen of questionable reputation, found for her by some good friends in the stables. This served a number of purposes. If, for example, she could stop Bailey sending out instructions, she could postpone if not prevent any little hitch occurring, such as Bailey deciding to sell the papers to Lady Lennox. Or Mr Crawford receiving a similar offer, and half or wholly killing Master Bailey so that the whole mechanism of publication was set in motion.

She attended a long, polite discussion on procedure between the Cardinal of Lorraine, the Queen, the King's sister and his mistress, and then arranged for the Schiatti cousins to attend a contest of jeu de paume. During the ensuing tête-à-tête she related a highly credible tissue of falsehoods which brought her, to her momentary shame, instant promises of manly succour.

Gino Schiatti, the older and wealthier, was going to borrow the Paris documents for her. Marco Schiatti, the better scribe, was going to write a persuasive letter to someone in London, which she proposed to enclose a still more persuasive letter of her own to Sir Henry Sidney. In this, she did not intend to mention Lymond's name or to lie; but merely to say that the loan of the papers was a matter of life and death to a friend of Diccon Chancellor's.

An excellent method of transmitting both letters to London occurred to her.

The Commissioners arrived in Paris, and she saw Archie.

In the interests of Master Bailey's health she absented herself from an excruciating reception for the King and Queen of Navarre, newly arrived for the royal wedding, at which the comte de Sevigny was expected to be in attendance.

She paid a visit to the Hôtel de La Rochefoucauld, and at last obtained permission to see Lord Grey of Wilton, the captured English commander.

*

To the thirteenth baron Grey of Wilton had fallen none of the galling luxury daily enjoyed by his nephew Austin, under the régime of the Hôtel d'Hercule.

Not that he lacked either food or common necessities. For a nobleman of his rank, on parole to a brother-in-law of the Prince of Condé, such treatment would be unthinkable. Besides, since the Queen of England had displayed such a loving concern for him, he was worth a thumping good sum of money.

His health was therefore well looked after, even to the healing of the unfortunate cut in one foot. Only the comte de La Rochefoucauld, with recent memories of a stringent six months' captivity in Genap, was a little less accommodating in his hospitality than he might have been.

Philippa, having passed the scrutiny of a porter, a captain of arms, a maître d'hôtel and finally, surprisingly, a quartet of the King's own bodyguard, still required to pass through two locked doors and satisfy the double guard at the threshold of another before a key was inserted and turned and she was ushered at last into the presence of Austin Grey's uncle.

'My goodness,' said Philippa Somerville appreciatively. 'They *are* frightened of you. You've got more pikemen than they took Calais with.'

His lordship of Wilton, rising abruptly, gazing at the vision before him and said, with caution, 'It *is* Philippa Somerville?'

'It was,' the vision said, removing with aplomb a mesmerizing cloak of ermine and Anatolian green velvet and handing it to a servant, who left the room, locking the door carefully behind him. She sat down, her extremely costly dress spread about her. 'Now, as you certainly know, it's Crawford of Lymond and Sevigny, the name of your favourite enemy. I'm sorry you don't get on better together.'

Lord Grey of Wilton also sat down, without removing his eyes from his visitor. The straight brown hair he rather remembered, although not dressed and knotted in this style. Her face had thinned. Her eyebrows had changed. He had seen paintings at Whitehall Palace with eyes like that. Come to think of it, these were probably painted too. The rubies round her neck were worth a fortune. And she was wearing scent. A smell of pepper and musk, faintly discernible, made the room pleasant.

Lord Grey said dryly, 'Perhaps for England's sake it is as well that we do not. Your husband appears to possess an uncanny gift for seducing his enemies.'

The versatile brown eyes gazed at him limpidly. 'I have a confession to make. Did you know I brought him to France in the first place? I thought it might be cheering to watch France and Spain waste their money on one another. I didn't, I'm afraid, think of Calais.'

'No. And you have, of course, remained in France.' Spare, and cool. It was the way he got the truth out of many a young ensign.

Young ensigns did not say candidly, as this girl did, 'But I haven't taken arms against you, truly. It was the only way I could obtain my annulment. And in less than a month I shall be free to leave for England again, if he doesn't contrive to get rid of me sooner. I beg your pardon?'

'*You should know*,' said Lord Grey, adjusting his sight to the folded paper he had just raised from his desk, '*that I am tied to the Hexham Saphronia, who combines total chastity with a jackal-like taste for digging up my family history. With twelve barons Grey to research she should be rendered peacefully harmless, with no sharp quality of heat, either biting the tongue or offending the head. She will also bring you a fortune in dowry.*' He looked up.

The girl, he was pleased to see, had turned a deep and uniform crimson. 'He's sent you a letter,' she said.

'Mr Crawford has indeed taken the trouble to write to me,' said Lord Grey of Wilton. 'Soliciting, it appears, my aid in the event of your making a match with my nephew. I have seldom been more astonished.'

'So have I,' the girl said. She was still scarlet. 'That is, it's

398

true that Austin has mentioned marriage, but nothing has been settled as yet. And in any case . . . although of course I know he would want your approval . . .'

'He is of full age, and requires no one's permission to marry. Quite,' said Lord Grey. He recalled, but did not refer to the succession of powerful families into which Audrey Grey had attempted in vain to marry her son. He continued, gazing at the girl, 'That is not the point exercising your husband. He appears merely to be anxious that the match should not fail because of what he calls *any undue delicacy surrounding the use of the young lady's dowry.*'

'For your ransom?' said Philippa. Her face had become even brighter. 'I hadn't thought of that. He knows Austin better than I expected. But he doesn't know how anxious . . . That is, I don't think Austin would allow the money to interfere with his plans.'

'Then I,' said Lord Grey with heavy humour, 'am tempted to be equally magnanimous. This attachment, then, is of some standing? It explains, of course, Austin's behaviour on a number of occasions. I am sorry the boy did not see fit to confide in me. If he had, I must admit that I should have put forward several objections. There is, forgive me, some difference in rank. The boy is unworldly. And you yourself, Mistress Philippa, have been married for some years to a man of some notoriety; a Scotsman who has many times fought openly against us, and who has made powerful enemies in England.'

'But you know Gideon,' the girl said quietly; and under her gaze he felt his colour rising. She said, 'In any case, as Mr Crawford has so tactfully pointed out, I should expect my money to mend my lack of status. And if he has powerful enemies, Mr Crawford has friends even more powerful. If you have any doubts, speak to Austin, however. I don't want to be accused of kidnapping both my husbands.'

Lord Grey said, 'Friends more important than royalty? It isn't my place to repeat scandal, but you must know of the Lennox feud with your husband. It dates back to '42. They have land in the north next to Austin's. And Lady Lennox is the Queen's cousin.'

'But I hear the Queen is failing,' the girl said. After a moment she added, 'Also, it isn't my place to repeat scandal either, but in '42 Lady Lennox surely was in her late twenties, while ... Mr Crawford was a prisoner in London.' She had lost a little of her poise.

'He fought at Solway. He would be sixteen. Quite old enough,' said Lord Grey, 'for this kind of trouble. The initial fault may not have been his. Lady Lennox is an ambitious and powerful woman, who has been the downfall of more than one comely boy in her day. About his subsequent career, however, there is no ambiguity ... I would allow to lead my army, Mistress Philippa, a man who had begun life like that. I would not give him any maiden I respected in marriage. I still do not know how you could so defy your upbringing.'

'It was done to preserve appearances. The mail from Turkey was rather slow,' the girl said flatly. She was shocked, Grey saw. The platonic marriage, which he had hardly believed in, suddenly appeared to be very likely a fact. Mistress Philippa, worldly as she appeared, was an innocent. Come to think of it, Austin would have chosen no one else. He wondered, as he had wondered so often, how his good-sister had come to give birth to a saintly fool.

He said, 'Well. You have been far from home and good guidance, but perhaps your mother's excellent sense has stood you in better stead than would appear. As you say, large changes are possible which may overturn many who today feel most secure. I hear peace is spoken of. That, too, should make your match more acceptable.'

He knew, when she did not contradict him, that there was some truth in it. He kept his ears open. He knew Calais was already being repopulated from the wreck of Saint-Quentin, and that there seemed no prospect now of his own side recrossing the water to take it. King Philip, lumbered with unpaid troops and overdrawn credit, had no wish either, it seemed, to launch a new venture. The war was in abeyance.

But you couldn't talk of peace without recalling that the Duke de Guise and his brothers flourished on war. And although they might have retired for the moment, that the armies of France were fresh, and well armed and plenished.

Until the Queen of Scots' marriage, rumour said, no one would lead those armies into action, and talk of truce no doubt would keep both countries pacified. After April, with Scotland in her purse, there was no knowing what France might rush at. He wondered if he could slip a word of warning in his next letter to London.

He further wondered if the girl's reference to the Lennoxes

had been quite fortuitous, or if she had reason to know how much he disliked them. He supposed his private persuasions were fairly well known by this time, although the Queen, fortunately, took no account of them. He added, since she made no rejoinder, 'Peace. A dangerous thing. It gives the politicians time to get into mischief.'

'You wouldn't say that if you were a Deputy in Rouen or Toulouse,' Philippa said. 'France is exhausted with taxes.'

'She'll be taxed whatever happens,' said Grey of Wilton. 'Well fed, vigorous men with nothing to do in the house—if they can't go to war with someone else, they'll fight each other. Take this new religion, now. They say it grows. They say it thrives, too, in Scotland.' He looked at her. There was a gleam in her eye.

'There are those in Scotland who don't like French rule,' Philippa said.

'There are always, of course, the nationalists and those who want personal power. There are some, too, who have honest beliefs. If there is peace between France and Spain,' said Lord Grey of Wilton reflectively, 'and England no longer has a Catholic queen on the throne, I see both France and Spain might think her a tempting morsel. Then our sole bulwark may be those of the Reformed faith, from whatever land they derive.'

He had called her innocent, for this he believed was her nature. But the brown eyes watching him now were those of a clever young woman, versed in diplomacy. She said, 'He won't go back to Scotland, Lord Grey. And if he did, how do you know which side he would take?'

'I hoped you would tell me,' said Lord Grey of Wilton.

'No. I don't know. He may not know himself.'

'Ah. There,' said Lord Grey, 'if I may say so, I think you are wrong. These are profound issues. A man of intelligence will not fail to have considered them. Discuss it with him.'

'No. That is for you to do. You forget,' Philippa said. 'I am not his confidante: only the subject of an act of propriety, shortly to be excused.' She rose. 'If Austin asks me to marry him, do you truly think you could find it supportable? I swear that whatever happens, at least Mr Crawford will never suborn him.'

Within the brushed and silvery beard, he smiled at her. 'I believe you. I see it may be a good match. I shall not stand in your way,' said Lord Grey of Wilton. And in the same kindly mood took the packet she gave him; and agreed, patting her arm, to send it to London with the envoy arranging his ransom. He wondered, examining the very firm seal, why she was writing to Henry Sidney, but he didn't break it. It might, after all, be to do with her dowry.

He stood at his window and watched her depart. She looked preoccupied.

She was preoccupied. She had just asked Lord Grey for leave to marry his nephew. But as she saw it, the time was coming nearer and nearer when she might have to wed one of four bankers.

*

The youth with the scarred cheek who alternated with Osias followed her home and she made it easy for him, wryly conscious of the fact that, like two fortune-tellers at a fair, she and his master were playing the same game. Except that these men were paid by Lymond for the straight-forward purpose of protecting her, while her duplicity was rather more complicated. She returned anxiously to her boiling pots, but found that no message had come to her from Bailey or the Schiatti cousins; and the men watching the Hôtel des Sphères reported that the old man and his four henchmen were still inside, and there had been no unwonted activity.

One could not be certain, with all the passing traffic of a large and busy household, that no other messages slipped in and out. One could only hope that Bailey's own men would handle the important matters.

A note came from Richard, brief and friendly. The Commissioners were coming to kiss the hand of their juvenile monarch, and he looked forward to seeing her. Sybilla would not be there.

She hadn't called to see Sybilla yet. Had it been possible, she would have been missing from Queen Mary's reception as well; but the inquiries about her health last time had been too many and too embarrassing to perpetuate. Her task was not to draw attention but to present an appearance of unruffled serenity.

By the day of the ceremony, the strain of maintaining unruffled serenity had put her off her food and sowed a doubt in her mind as to whether she was going to be capable of attending anyway. The presence of Richard presented no unsurmountable problems. He knew from Kate, presumably, that she was in France for her divorce, and at Court through Queen Mary's persuasion. She had always been able to handle Richard, and most of the other Commissioners were familiar to her as well, from her frequent sojourns in Lymond's absence at Midculter.

What frightened her was the knowledge that now she must fake and deceive Lymond himself.

Since her far-off moment of self-discovery in Lyon she had seen him only twice. Once when, lying to her, he had told her at Saint-Germain that he was the son of Gavin Crawford. And once through the long, dizzy evening at the Hôtel de Ville which had ended in that explosion of violence and loathing in which he had flung at Marthe the name of his mistress.

Since then, he had endured the reunion at Dieppe described by Archie as *vexing;* and the brief prostration afterwards which had seemed so easy to account for, but was not.

Since then, she had found out at last the nature of the canker he lived with; the scourge which accounted for everything he had ever said or done. And worse, she knew that at any given moment it might be broadcast to all the world, unless she herself could prevent it. And all this, by whatever means, must be kept from him.

The last time they met, she had rushed from the house like a schoolgirl. Dressed today by the Cardinal's decree in stiff blue velvet to offset the Queen's impressive cloth of silver she stood with the rest, and begged the mute gods of the Masque to uphold her as she watched the Commissioners enter, two by two, while trumpets like golden-voiced drakes quarrelled together.

And there was Richard, brown and heavy and grave, and a glimpse of fair hair, picked out by the low winter sun. Then the half-brothers entered, almost together.

And, knowing their parentage now, you could see Sybilla in both her sons; but more clearly still, the legendary presence of the first baron Crawford of Culter: blurred through two generations in the square, brown-haired person of Richard; and undiluted in Francis, the love-child.

Richard, seeking her as soon as he stepped through the door caught her eye and smiled, before filing forward to make his salute to the Queen.

Francis Crawford looked only at the Chair of State, and if

the arc of his gaze included the demoiselles of honour, he gave no indication of it whatever.

It was beyond Philippa to look anywhere else in those first moments. He had become a romantic figure in the country, they said. The pale, pleated taffetas with their exquisite needlework and the channel of cabochon emeralds on the short, reversed cloak confirmed the suspicion that he was living up to it. His manners during the presentations were of a courtly perfection verging on the caricature. When he chose to assume the high style, as when he chose to be vulgar, he could always equal or outdo the professionals.

Of the illness at Dieppe there was no trace, unless it were in the weight of his gaze, modishly languorous. But when, stepping back, he did allow his eye to be caught and bowed delightfully to his countess, every nerve from his mouth to his fingertips was unquestionably within his control.

He was not alone in that form of dexterity. Into her answering curtsey Philippa put a matched degree of suavity and slightly more distance: Richard, she saw, grinned; and Lord James Stewart, also observing, was watching her critically. Then the speeches began and ended, and Lymond rejoined his compatriots and she was left with the Provost of Edinburgh, whose royal ancestors had bequeathed him a certain amount of conceit which she suffered, because he was brother to one of the four little Maries. But she had always thought George Seton facile, and now the charm barely covered the drift of his questions.

Of course, her interest for them all lay in her marriage. But she was thankful instead of wary when at last Richard came and displaced him. 'Dearest Philippa, you would take away the breath of any right-minded man who was not talking politics. You must come to see Sybilla. She misses you.'

Kind as of old, but greyer and a good deal more adroit, he was studying her as he was speaking. She leaned forward and kissed him. 'Of course I shall come soon. Is she well, Richard? And Mariotta at home, and the family?'

'Come to the Hôtel de l'Ange and you shall hear,' Richard said. 'Yes, we are well, and Kuzúm is flourishing. Kate has been looking every day for your letters. We thought you were coming home before now. But after this, of course I see what is keeping you. I hear the royal marriage would founder without you.'

'I hope not,' Philippa said, 'or you would all have to go home. What did the Queen say?'

'She asked,' Richard said, 'if I thought my brother really intended to marry the Marshal de St André's daughter. You know, of course, about that?'

'Yes,' said Philippa firmly. 'I think it's a splendid idea.'

'So do I,' Richard said. 'I told her grace that he might not marry the girl if she lost the use of her limbs or her dowry; but I couldn't think of anything else that would deter him. You must be mortally glad to be free of the whole business at last. Is he always tiresome, or has he attempted at least to be civil to you?'

It sounded innocuous. Late in life, Richard had begun to master the game played so well by his younger brother. But Philippa, who had Lymond for her fencing-master, saw suddenly through it. He had been told of her attachment, and was probing it.

In the seraglio, one learned the trappings, at least, of a golden diplomacy. 'Not in the least,' Philippa said. 'But *le mal preveu ne donne pas grand coup*, as they say. Perhaps he will mend his manners now that the Bishops are here, and God will come with feet of wool, surprise him asleep, and waken him with an iron arm. Archie won't like it at all.' Who had hinted at the state of her feelings for Lymond? Jerott, maybe. She knew Jerott had called on Sybilla.

But it was not Jerott. Lymond had seen what was happening; and softer footed than God, was standing behind Richard Crawford, speaking gently. 'Everything she says is a lie, and the arm of iron which pushed me into Catherine d'Albon's embraces did not belong, I would have you know, to the Deity.'

He stared straight at Philippa. 'I tried to convince my furious friends you had a weakness for me.'

Damn him. Damn him for letting her down—in what drunken access of fury? And damn him for insisting now, belatedly, on redeeming it. Philippa said, 'If I had, I grew out of it early. Like the Etrurian mule who ate hemlock, any poor ass seduced by a Crawford—' She broke off abruptly, remembering.

'... is apt to wake flayed alive,' Lymond finished. He had himself well in hand. Archie was right as usual. He said blandly, 'You can be expected to recall the fate of each of my mistresses. Even Richard gets muddled up sometimes. Why don't you call on Austin Grey instead of corresponding with him? You won't meet me. Like yourself, I seem to be permanently occupied with other people's errors of judgment.'

He was correct: fear of meeting him was the main reason which had kept her from the Hôtel d'Hercule. But not, as he must suppose, because of the manner of their last meeting. The others had moved away, leaving Lymond and herself for a moment standing together. She said, conscious this time of being under an undiluted and possibly suspicious regard, 'Tell Austin I haven't forgotten. I shall call on him presently.'

'He will be deeply moved, while preserving a gentlemanly fortitude. You could either marry him here,' Lymond said, 'or go home with him two days after the Dauphin's wedding. In any case, leave instructions for Willie Grey's ransom. Advise the Queen when you are going. And write to Kate. She thinks I am keeping you in Paris instead of vice versa.'

'There are times,' said Philippa shortly, 'when I feel like the entire Russian army.'

'There are times," said Lymond equally shortly, 'when I wish that you were. It would solve the whole Tartar problem and save Ottoman Turkey for Jesus.'

'My dear Mr Crawford! *Caelum, non animos mutant, qui trans mare corrunt.* So near dissolution, and still bickering!'

The voice, a sacerdotal one, came from behind her. She recognized it, but would not entertain it. Lymond, on the other hand, not only identified the owner but took steps to deal with him. 'Why, naturally, my dear Master Elder. *Chi Asino va a Roma, Asino se ne torna.* Have you not preserved your habitual qualities? And how is your sweet charge, and the Countess of Lennox?'

The Countess of Lennox.

An ambitious and powerful woman, who has been the downfall of more than one comely youth in her day. Such as a fair, haunted child of sixteen, with a French degree and his first major battle behind him.

She had known of the association. She had not known how it began. And looking at the worldly courtier smiling beside her, she wondered if Lymond had forgotten. She turned.

Master John Elder was secretary to Lady Lennox, and her son's tutor. Philippa knew and disliked him of old. He stood, waxily smiling with a new black cap clapped over his lugubrious ears and a new black robe knocking about his slippered ankles. He said, 'I come bearing my mistress's loving greetings to her charming niece, the little Queen so soon to enter matrimony. And my young pupil, I thank you, is well. You know he and the Queen have exchanged verses in Latin?'

'How delightful,' said Philippa kindly. 'And will you stay, Master Elder, for the wedding?'

'I have been invited,' he said. 'Am I not fortunate? The Earl of Lennox is distempered and his dear lady must needs stay and nurse him. But she charged me, did I see you both, to tell you that she trusts you remember her.'

With curses, as she well knew, sending that decorous message. And delivering it, John Elder must be hugging a private pleasure known, he believed, only to himself and to his semi-royal mistress.

For Margaret Lennox was not only the woman who had taken a sixteen-year-old boy and ruined him. She was the woman who, to strike this formidable antagonist and his relatives from the path of her family, had promised Leonard Bailey six thousand pounds for the public proof of Lymond's base parentage.

Only John Elder did not know, unless Bailey had told him, that she, too, was in the market for the same information. Philippa said, 'Do you know Paris well, Master Elder?'

He smiled. The lean, Caithness face, untidily bearded, had nothing generous in its lineaments. 'I know some parts better than others. I visit friends. I was not so fortunate as some, to be educated here. I come of humble parents, Madame de Stevigny. Humble but law abiding. I cannot aspire to the splendid caste of your husband. A lowly priest stands in awe of a descendant of the superb, the stainless, the magnificent Crawfords. I can only draw maps and string some Latin together and nurture my noble young prince, who may surprise you all one of these days.'

His eyes, bright with malice, flickered from Lymond to herself and back again. He had hoped to hurt. But had he known the real truth, Philippa thought, he would have cut very much deeper. And had he known that she knew it, he could not have resisted the temptation to taunt her.

It meant that Bailey had not betrayed her interest. It probably mean that the existence of the Hôtel des Sphères was still unknown to Elder.

Lymond, his gaze restful, was allowing a pause to develop. The irony could not have escaped him, even if he perceived, as she did, that it was founded on nothing solid. Then he said, 'He certainly should. With his education and heritage, Harry Darnley will be the only turncoat in England who can practise sodomy in Alcaic stanzas. Now he can't write any more winsome verse to his cousin, how are you going to impress his charms on the little French princesses? Or would you like me to speak for him?'

Between the strands of his beard, Elder yellowed. It was a cut, you had to allow, of inspired virulence. Darnley was twelve: a suitable age for betrothal. But to flatter his character at the French court Lymond was the last person Lady Lennox could depend upon.

'You are too kind,' said the priest at last. 'Indeed, I shall send word of your offer to her ladyship. And meantime, perhaps I may perform the same office on your behalf with your future wife, Mademoiselle d'Albon?'

'Why,' said Lymond, surprised. 'I should appreciate it if you would. There are some items in my early history which Mademoiselle d'Albon has yet to hear about.'

Fool. After carrying it off, he had allowed Elder to sting him. Philippa, exasperated, marched up to the blaze with a hand-squirt. 'There are a few episodes in your later history she ought to be warned about as well,' said Lymond's wife with acidity. 'She may be hoping for Lug of the Long Arms but what she has is the family Crawford, *qui peut de tous bois faire flèches* in order to sit in the butts and shoot hearty rounds at each other.'

The blue gaze had swung round upon her, but Master Elder's shot arrived in the meantime. 'And when,' said the priest, 'am I to wish Madame la comtesse well of a new marriage?'

'My good man,' said Lymond. 'Don't you know the court has opened a book on it? At the last hearing there were eight separate contenders, and offers still coming in from abroad, like wolves forced out of the forest by famine. I hear the odds at the moment are in favour of a triple union with the Schiatti cousins.'

So he knew about that. 'I am making no secret of the truth. The incumbent will be properly selected by open competition,' Philippa said.

'Jesus Christ ... And the rules?' Lymond said. Someone approaching, blessedly spoke to and led away Master Elder, who bowed and retreated.

'No rules. Just mincing knives,' said Philippa aggressively.

408

Common sense told her at any cost to avoid the personal. Deaf to common sense, she said, 'I gather you are holding a competition as well. We are dazzled by the goguettes and gaudisseries.'

'*Osse sur Olympe et Pelion sur Osse.* They call me the darling of the masses,' Lymond said. 'Has Richard asked you to visit Sybilla?'

His gaze, full upon hers, was as searching as she had feared it would be. Returning it with unblinking candour, Philippa said, 'He didn't require to ask. I am going there in a day or two. I'm glad to note that Catherine is managing all her own marital arrangements. You wouldn't expect me to make social calls if you had the remotest idea of the work entailed in bringing two unfortunate persons to the altar.'

Careless words. 'It takes ten minutes, in my experience,' Lymond said. He glanced round. 'I must go look after my lordlings. We shall meet on the happy day of our annulment. I should be glad, by the way, if you would kindly refrain from escaping Osias. Your excursion the other day, wherever it took you, cost him a whipping.'

'I shall allow Osias to follow me to my private engagements,' Philippa said, 'if you will allow Célie to follow you to yours.' She took a deep breath. 'You haven't heard any more from, or about Grand-Uncle Bailey?'

'No. Platfut he bobbit up with bendis and then went home. Or so it would appear. My men can't trace him. It doesn't alter the fact. I still require you to—'

'. . . In all my doings to offend none but to please the godly. And the brightness of the light of the sun of our Justice and Equity hath caused the darkness of Injuries and Molestations to vanish away. I am sure,' said Philippa with that particular acerbity called forth by the deceived from the deceiver, 'that there must be a psalm to fit the occasion?'

There was; but not of the kind she had expected. He recited it, staring at her:

> 'And with a blast doth puffe against
> Such as would her correct.
> *Tush, tush* (sayth she) *I have no dread*
> *Least myne estate should change.*
> And why? for all adversity
> To her is very straunge.'

'Are you implying,' said Philippa coldly, 'that I enjoyed being brought up surrounded by eunuchs?'

'No,' said Lymond. 'But I expect you enjoyed it more than the eunuchs did.' He hesitated, and she waited.

'To be condemned eternally to choose his words in her company must be as irritating to him as it was painful to herself to suffer it. She knew she would hear nothing of Dieppe, or of Catherine, or even of Marthe's disappearance, since it related to another of the disasters in their relationship. He had made no effort to excuse himself for that either, although she thought the faintly febrile nature of his conversation today owed something to his awareness of it.

He said, 'I remember Gideon, your father. Austin is like him. He dislikes war. But he fought a fine battle at Guînes.'

To no one else, probably, would that sound like an apology for interference; and a question. Philippa said, 'If . . . When he asks me, I propose to accept him.'

'Lord Grey will be relieved to hear it,' he said. 'Don't be afraid of the Lennoxes. They are out of favour in France.'

If that was all he had observed, she was safe. 'The smylere with the knyf under the cloke? I'm not afraid of John Elder,' she said. 'But I'd be both i-hangyd and to-drawe before I'd turn my back on Margaret Lennox.'

'Or on anybody,' Lymond said pointedly. 'Instead you prefer to sit in the butts, de tous bois faisant flèches, letting fly at them. In a day or two, with unusual economy, I shall be giving a banquet for the Commissioners which will also serve as a betrothal supper for Catherine. Do you wish to be present?'

Philippa allowed polite regret to inform every muscle. 'Whatever day it is on,' she said, 'I feel I have a previous engagement.'

'May I congratulate you,' he said agreeably, 'on your evident popularity.'

'Anything I can do,' Philippa said, 'to save you from the exhaustions of pluralism.'

She watched him go, in a running flash of costly minerals.

He had seen no special threat in Elder's presence. He had had three or four instructions to give her, and that was all that concerned him. He had gone as soon as he could. He had no way of knowing that the Lennoxes were tracing his parentage. Or that until she intervened Leonard Bailey had been on the point of selling them all he knew.

It was to pull down Francis Crawford and not merely to attend the royal wedding that John Elder was in Paris. And it was for her, with all the skills she possessed, to deny him that extravagant pleasure.

Part IV

*En bref seront de retour
sacrifices.*

CHAPTER 1

Second et tiers qui font prime musique
Sera par Roy en honneur sublimé
Par grace et maigre presque demi eticque
Rapport de venus faux rendra deprimée.

Very soon after that, M. le comte de Sevigny, Chevalier de l'Ordre, gave his promised banquet for the Scottish Commissioners to Queen Mary's wedding, combining it, as indicated, with a supper for his future bride, Catherine. The economy also indicated did not leap to the eye.

Nearly thirty years before, a boy at the Sorbonne, Richard Crawford had hurled river-pebbles over the decorated wall of the Hôtel d'Hercule at the corner of the rue des Augustins. It was then already fifty years old and one of the finest houses in Paris, owned by the Prévôt of the town and his family. When the last du Prat died, it became the palace in which the Crown housed the foreign visitors it most wished to honour. He little thought then, that one day he would ride through its gatehouse arch with the flower of Scottish nobility at his side, to pay court to his young brother Francis.

The yard was arcaded, as he expected it, with majolica Roman medallions inset below the frescoes which gave the Hôtel its name. The stable officers, the grooms, the footmen and the ushers who waited there were all in livery, but not in azure and argent with the pheon and phœnix of Culter; or did the achievement over the doors display the invected bordure denoting a younger son of that house. Instead: 'The chaplet proper of Sevigny,' said the Lyon King of Arms beside him. 'A French coat of arms, of course, and perfectly correct, although it only tells half the story. The two achievements to which he is entitled should be conjoined paleways. I should be happy to advise him.'

The Earl of Culter did not answer, nor did his mother, to whom he gave his hand as, alighting, they made their way in procession through the square hall and up the wide caissoned staircase to the first floor of the mansion.

The entrance to the first of the Hercule's sequence of galleries was enclosed in a porch of white wrought Gothic marble, in which the form of the hero arched and strove in the exercise of his classic talents. Sybilla shivered. 'If he shows you any shadow of discourtesy,' Richard said, 'I shall leave, and take the Commissioners with me.'

For some reason the strain left her face and she smiled at him. He did not understand her. He wished she had not insisted on accepting the invitation. Braced for anything, he led her from the porch and into the delicate warmth of a long, exquisite room lit by sunlight through which moved, smiling, the faces of friends: Scottish friends. Men he had known long ago, before they left Scotland to teach and to study in France; to go fighting or merchanting; to join the French King's royal guard of Scottish Archers; to serve the court or take up an inheritance. Important men like young Arran, whose company had fought at Saint-Quentin and who, after the Queen, was in direct line to the Scottish throne. And important men who were not Scottish at all, but had spent much of their lives fighting for Scotland in Scotland: the Sieur d'Estrée, M. de Thermes, the bonhomme M. de la Brosse . . . Pierro Strozzi, whom he and Sybilla had cause to remember best of all.

It was Strozzi, catching his eye, who gave a halloo and bounded towards him and Sybilla who, touching Richard's arm, reminded him of the man at his side, waiting to receive him.

It was not Francis, but his master of household; an elegant, elderly gentleman, who, smiling delivered to all the Commissioners a perfect Court bow. 'His lordship bids me give you his particular welcome. His home is yours; his servants are here to be treated as you would your own. He will give himself the happiness of joining you in this salon shortly.'

'Your brother,' said Lord James Stewart, drawling, 'keeps regal style.'

'He's kept you waiting as well, has he?' said Piero Strozzi, arriving definitively and in a single movement bowing to all the Commissioners present and saluting Sybilla twice on either cheek. 'You are the most beautiful Scotswoman in the world, and I adore your son's effrontery. But see the pleasures he has in store for us all. Lord Cassillis, there is your old tutor, Master Buchanan, locked fast in disputation with Nicolas de Nicolay over the Ptolemaic concept of the heavens. Do you think a poet and Latinist can persuade France's leading cartographer that the Earth is the immovable centre of the Universe . . . ? Lord Fleming, your goodbrother the comte d'Arran stands beside Daniel in the Lion's Den without flinching; and my lord Orkney will see a few scholarly faces he recognizes by the statue of a gentleman—or is it a lady?—with the head of a hawk.'

'God in heaven,' said Richard Crawford, gazing at the gentleman with the head of a hawk. Moving with pleasure to their appointed encounters, the other Commissioners and those who followed them stepped past and were accepted into the gathering. Wine was being handed. From the calm of the statuary, Richard gazed at the long tables of marble and bronze and the burden of treasure upon them; to the gold and coral Chia Ching porcelain and the jewelled silver-gilt Venetian mirrors and candelabra tall as two men, upon which the symbols were none that the Christian church would recognize.

'. . . You are looking,' said Jerott Blyth, appearing vaguely in front of him, 'at the spoils of nine cultures. The more threatening objects came from the Dame de Doubtance's house in Lyon. Lord Culter will remember the chair.'

Lord Culter did remember the chair, a tall spired object in which the old witch had seated herself while claiming to tell him his fortune. To his knowledge, Sybilla had never heard of the Dame de Doubtance. It did not prevent her from giving the chair all her attention. She had become rather pale again. 'You're a merchant now. Did you collect these for my brother?' Richard said. He had a very clear recollection of Jerott Blyth who was at present, he saw, slightly intoxicated.

'He doesn't need my help,' Jerott said. 'Every piece in harmony with the room and its neighbour: nothing on display for reasons of ostentation alone. Unlike my bitch of a wife.'

'I think,' Sybilla said, 'I see Adam Blacklock. How very nice. You are well? I thought you intended to stay with the Muscovy Company.'

Lean, brown and diffident, with the remembered halt in his walk, the artist bent over her hand. 'Hullo, Lady Culter. I did. Just as Jerott here meant to remain a Knight of St John, and then thought he would become a merchant. We all finish by working for Francis. Which reminds me. Jerott, come and settle an argument. George Seton says all the Knights of St John have turned Lutheran.'

'It's Sandilands,' said Jerott Blyth, changing colour. 'Just because. one man in Scotland turns his coat in order to fill his own pockets . . .'

'Yes. Well, come and tell George Seton,' Adam said, drawing him gently off. Sybilla watched him go.

'The Blyth boy?' said a high-pitched voice in her ear. Bishop Reid of Orkney had returned to chat. 'I remember the family well, before they left for France. He was a well-set-up youngster. I had a word with Daniel Hislop. He has turned out remarkably well. A cynic, but a cynic with a head on his shoulders. I knew his father.'

'The Bishop?' Sybilla said, with composure.

He caught it, despite his deafness and the noise in the room, and laughed. 'The Bishop? Yes. it is not a mishap so uncommon that the Church can afford to ignore it. Our friend Beaton's uncle had . . . how many? Nine children? And Bishop Hepburn had ten, all, I am assured, by different mothers. Hislop has no need to feel shame. But I came to congratulate you on the skill of our host. He has assembled here not only the full number of those Scottish students I know best, but a cousin of my dear Will Lubias, all the way from Dieppe. We have been speaking of Honey Plums, and Arbroath Oslins, and wallflowers, yellow and bloody. As I remember, you at Midculter are also conducting a romance with horticulture?'

'We are not so prolific as you with our Bon-Chrétiens,' Sybilla said. 'I'm glad you think Francis efficient, but I shouldn't read too much into it. He was also proficient with Russians in London. The conducted tours of King Arthur's Round Table, I am told, were a sensation.'

'He is a man of energy,' Bishop Reid said. 'And will use that energy, for good or ill as we know, wherever he may be. Do I please you with the moderation of my language? A gentle bedewing instead of a glutting rain?'

Many years had passed since, as President of the Court of Session, the Bishop of Orkney had arraigned her son Francis for treason, and his language then had not been moderate. He had only been pursuing his duty, and she had come to understand and to be reconciled to it, as he had come in the end to respect, she thought, the man he had tried.

Sybilla said, 'Yes, you please me. The more modest your

expectations, the less often you will court disappointment. Richard, I think you should write that down while we all understand it. Tell me, what has stopped?'

'The music,' said Richard Crawford. 'There was some music in the next gallery. It seems to have halted.'

'They've come to the end of the pieces they know,' offered Danny Hislop, mystically appearing in the Bishop's company again. 'Good evening, Lady Culter. We met in Edinburgh. If you say *Favouzat, cavouzat,* they may start playing again.'

Beneath Danny Hislop's sparse sandy curls operated one of the brightest brains to grace Lymond's company; but all the same, Sybilla had not reared three children for nothing. '*Favouzat, cavouzat,*' she repeated promptly, her blue, limpid gaze on the little man.

The door opened.

'Hercules?' said Danny tremulously. 'Isosceles? The triangle? The Angel Apostate?'

'On the contrary,' said Richard Crawford dryly, and dropped to one knee. The rest of the company, ceasing to talk, turned variously and then sank likewise into obeisance.

In the doorway to the next gallery stood his young brother, fair and quiet in nacré velvet, with the black sash of St Michael knotted slanting from shoulder to waist and the Little Order glinting upon it. Beyond him glimmered the arched and gemmed headgear of his house-guests: the profile of the Maréchale de St André, and the lovely, composed face of a young woman: Catherine, Richard supposed. The heiress. And a beauty.

But although she was to marry Francis Crawford, Catherine d'Albon entered behind him. For by Lymond's side as he moved into the long, scented gallery was his monarch, the fifteen-year-old Queen of Scotland.

'... My mother, the Dowager Lady Culter,' Lymond said. 'And my elder brother, the Earl. Her grace honours us for a short time only.' Below the sash and pinned by another decoration he was wearing a small doeskin glove, its cuff covered with jewels.

'We met my lord Culter the other day,' the Queen said. 'You have recovered, Lady Culter, from your mishap? Our mother writes lovingly of all your family, and we remember well your kindness in Scotland. There was a riddle you taught us, but it does not translate well into French.'

'I am glad to hear it. I believe it was my son,' said Sybilla, 'who was responsible. But it was long ago.'

'Indeed. You see my glove, how it is small. But still,' said the Queen, 'your son defends us. It is gentle of you to spare us his presence.'

'It is my privilege, your grace,' said Sybilla steadily; and sank in a perfect curtsey as the Queen, with Lymond escorting her, moved to the next group of her countrymen.

'Then—we meet at last,' said the handsome, scented lady who had entered the room behind Francis. 'We know the requirements of royalty: Francis is unable to divide his attention, so I shall take it upon myself to introduce myself and my daughter. I am Marguerite de St André, Lady Culter, and this is my only child Catherine.'

Her lustrous eye, as she spoke, was upon Richard, and Richard, approaching after his mother, decorously kissed the Maréchale's hand and then, gravely, her cheek.

Catherine d'Albon offered, guardedly, only her hand, but was drawn by Sybilla into a little embrace, as loving as it was gentle. 'You are used, of course,' Sybilla said, 'to being told that you are beautiful, and I knew, if Francis had chosen you, that you must be so. I also know, if he has chosen you, that you are clever and honest and kind. . . . Richard and I wish to thank you for accepting him.'

The Maréchale, a student only by hearsay of Scottish sentimentality, was shocked to see in her daughter's composed face the signs of undoubted emotion. She said, affably. 'He is a gallant creature: all France knows of it, and I believe they will make a famous couple. Of course, we are all very fond of the little wife. It is not always that a first contract can be broken so easily.'

'Philippa isn't here?' said Sybilla, a little distractedly. Behind the young Queen, she noticed, had entered the four young attendants called Mary and virtually all of her suite who were Scottish.

'No. It would not have been discreet. She has engaged herself elsewhere, I understand, for the evening. You know that the Queen herself was not invited? It is an escapade. The maids of honour wished so much to go, since their relatives are among the Commissioners. I am told that she simply sent word to M. le comte this afternoon that he was to fetch her. Even the rest of the Court is not aware.'

'Christ,' said Danny Hislop, behind Richard, but not very

loudly. And when Richard, by no means a stupid man, turned and glanced at him he added brightly, 'It's going to play merry hell with his table plan.'

But, it seemed, the matter was taken care of; and when, her slow progress ended, the Queen of Scots reached the end of the gallery, the double doors opened before her on another room, a vision of paintings and delicate, open-work plaster in which supper was laid, quite differently from any supper she had seen before, on garlanded damask, with confections spun glistening high among the candles. And creams and curds and sugared flowers and sherbets and little and thin, woven bread rolls, and before every plate a stem of green cryszal, with a pink salted rose in its sheath.

In the middle of the long principal board stood the chair of state, and to this her host directly led her. 'This evening, Madam, you are at home with your countrymen. Pray do them and me the honour of presiding over us.'

So she took her place beside him, and looked under her long lashes at all her unknown subjects, while the Bishop said grace, and the chaplet proper of Sevigny made a nimbus of the bright canopy over her.

❋

'What are they talking about?' said the Provost of Edinburgh irritably, to his step-sister Mary Seton.

'You, probably,' said the maid of honour and smiled, for the fourth time, at Fleming's older brother.

❋

'They are, as you see, somewhat subdued,' said the comte de Sevigny to his guest of honour. 'Brought on by respect for the crown, and a certain natural diffidence. It poses a problem. If we contrive to bring each man to his nature, then he will be happy; but he will no longer be quiet. Do I have your grace's permission?'

'For what?' she said. The flecked hazel eyes regarded him, as in after years perhaps she would regard her chancellor, her treasurer, the president of her council of Scotland. 'Is there any king living with the right to deny his subjects happiness?'

'There are tribes today,' Lymond said, 'who find happiness in lust and cannibalism and the worship of idols. Doesn't that open up a whole familiar pattern of argument over the purpose of kingship? I shall spare you all of it. These are baked

421

crabs, and these are primrose cakes, made of honey and almonds and saffron. The primroses are real: I shouldn't advise you to eat them. And the liquid is Russian, and called *Gorelka*.'

'It looks like water,' said the Queen of Scotland. 'Surely, if his subjects' souls are in danger, it is the duty of a monarch to correct them?'

It did not taste like water. Mr Crawford said, 'But then he will make them unhappy.'

'In this world, yes,' said his Queen, ejecting a primrose.

'It is this world,' said Mr Crawford tranquilly, 'that we are discussing. In any case, who decides whether their souls are in danger?'

'The Church,' said Queen Mary indistinctly. 'Who will advise the monarch.'

'And if,' Lymond said, 'there are two churches? If one tribal witchdoctor says you may make a meal of your grandmother, and the other says burning is holier?'

'You are talking,' said Mary, 'of savages. To civilized nations, there is only one church, and a Pontiff to whom we turn for guidance. And if you question that, Mr Crawford, it is blasphemy.'

'I know I'm talking of savages,' Lymond said. 'Have savages no right to be happy? Presumably, also, savages have souls. So what is a savage monarch to do for them?'

She did not balk at it. More than the food or the vodka, the lure of the argument pulled her attention. She laid down her cup and her knife. 'If he is a king, and is offered conflicting advice from his ministers, then he must seek the truth himself. He must find others outside the tribe who will enlighten him. This is the work of our missionary priests, Mr Crawford.'

'He should take the word, then, of the first man he meets? All religions, Madam, have their missionaries.'

'Then he must speak to many men, and weigh what they say. If he is King, he must have judgement.'

'Not necessarily. But if he is King long enough, he will usually attain judgement. For example, you have reached a sound conclusion and one day, I trust, will have sufficient judgement to apply it. These are anchovies. May I give you some? There will be an entertainment for you shortly.'

She gazed at him over the anchovies. 'You lecture me, Mr Crawford?'

'I,' said the comte de Sevigny, 'am attempting to offer you foodstuffs. It is you, your grace, who insists on conversing of cannibalism: chacun à sa marotte. You are going to live on an olive a day, like the Stoics?'

'Did they?' said Mary.

'I have it on the best authority. You know what they say. Feed a horse or a poet too well and neither will ever do anything. Lord James, your royal kinswoman requires nourishment. Forbid her to talk, and while she eats discourse to her on the duties of kingship.'

'No!' said Mary.

'A masque on the glorious union soon to take place between France and Scotland?' Lymond said hopefully.

She glanced at him sideways, her expression commendably close to the gracious. 'You have prepared one, Mr Crawford?'

'No,' said Lymond with regret. 'What we have for you are love songs. They need not keep you from eating. Simply recognize the singers, now and then, with a wave of the hand, and allow Mr Hislop, there, to join in the choruses.'

She laughed; and through all the company, the volume of talk rose a little, and then rose again as, nerves assuaged and stomachs full, each man began to come, as Lymond had undertaken, to his natural self.

'I am sad,' said the Bishop of Orkney to Lord James Stewart as the tables were gently drawn and the floor cleared and the candied ginger passed from place to place. 'I am sad because we live, you and I, on two sides of one river. And whoso list to hunt, I know where is an hart we both covet.'

'There is a remedy,' said the Queen's half-brother.

'Is there? I doubt it,' said Reid of Orkney. 'There might have been, in the past. But this hart is ten years too young, I fear, for his destiny.'

*

The entertainment, which came with the sweetmeats, consisted of feats of skill, performed by jugglers, dancers, acrobats and illusionists. All were dark or yellowskinned and none of them spoke any language that George Buchanan tried them with. Each act was executed in its proper order and without any visible flaw. None of them had been seen before. The guests stood, with the inclusion of the Queen of Scotland, to applaud their last exit.

The dancers did not perform a symbolic masque, and the

423

consort of players was in tune. The singers entered unseen and Piero Strozzi jumped to his feet at the first surge of tight-pleated sound; at the low, throbbing band of the bass, and the counter-tenor planing, slow and bird-high through the harmony.

'Hunno! Oswald! Andreas!' Piero Strozzi yelled at his host, through the busy hum of a party astonished to be enjoying itself. *'Fou enragé*, you have sent for Les Amis de Rabelais?'

And '—Why not?' murmured the Earl of Culter to Adam Blacklock, sitting beside de Nicolay behind him. 'I don't think I've ever heard better.'

'It's a long story,' said Adam; and glanced across the handsome room to where he had last seen Jerott Blyth. He added, 'And not one to mention in Austin Grey's hearing. Francis once used Les Amis in order to try and leave France.'

'And now, final irony, he is patronizing them. Where is Allendale?' Richard said.

'In the house somewhere, I believe. It isn't the kind of celebration a sensitive prisoner would intrude upon. If Philippa were here, it might have been different.'

'But she is here,' said Nicolas de Nicolay behind him.

Adam stared and Richard, swinging round, examined the cartographer coldly.

'You have failed, my lord, to allow for local deviation,' said the little man blandly. 'She came in five minutes ago, with Signor Strozzi. You will see, if you look, that the company has expanded itself in other directions also.'

Adam peered across the gentle, candlelit width of the salon. 'The Prince of Condé,' he suddenly said. 'And el Vandomillo . . . the King of Navarre his brother. Christ.'

'I also see,' said the cartographer, 'the Sieur d'Andelot and his wife and Monseigneur de La Roche-sur-Yon. And, I believe, M. de La Rochefoucauld. The Bourbons are here in strength. Who can have invited them?'

'I did,' said Piero Strozzi, coming and dropping with a thud on the cushion beside them. 'This of your brother's is too good a party, my lord, to keep to oneself. I sent out one or two discreet messengers. Mon petit François, I am sure, will bear me no ill will for it.'

'You invited them without Lymond knowing?' said Danny Hislop. He wriggled into the circle. 'Can I be there when he hears about it?'

'He cannot fail to know. We are not all blind,' said Nicolas de Nicolay cheerfully. 'But with the Queen of Scotland at his right hand and the King's sister—you observed, of course, Madame Marguerite?—seated at his left, there is little he can do but appear delighted by it. At least, *mon cher*, you were obliging enough to refrain from increasing our numbers until the food was finished.'

'It was not perhaps so discerning,' said Richard coolly, 'to compel his wife to celebrate the occasion. How did you induce her to come?'

'Why, by telling her that mon petit François had sent for her,' the Marshal said cheerfully. 'There was a moment of, shall we say, incredulity when they met, but both parties rose to the occasion. She is being looked after by a number of attentive gentlemen from her own court and, of course, by the next incumbent, the charming Mademoiselle d'Albon.'

'Christ!' said Richard under his breath, and rising unobtrusively to his feet, began to make his way, with native persistence, to where Philippa Somerville, he now saw, was seated.

Danny got up as well.

Piero Strozzi, a single earring swinging against his dark face, looked up and grinned at him.

'Why are you going? France is a civilized country. The two wives of the comte de Sevigny—does my poor Earl doubt it?—are fond of one another.'

'I know,' said Danny Hislop. 'I want to see them being fond of one another. I want to see everybody brazening it out. And then I want to see what your petit François does to you when the party's over.'

❖

For her part, Philippa Somerville watched without pleasure her husband's older brother picking his way purposefully towards her while displaying to Catherine d'Albon, several eminent noblemen and one or two mesmerized students surrounding her, all the overtures expected of a selfless and hard-working guest, together with evidence that she had never spent a happier evening in her life.

The moment when Piero Strozzi's messenger had found her, released from duty, drinking wine and reading poetry and discussing theology in the little house belonging to the mistress of a young medical graduate named Jacques Grevin, had been in itself sufficiently macabre, denoting, it seemed, some royal death or disaster.

The message he actually brought—that Francis Crawford wished her presence at his reception—was in its way even more worrying.

Since there was, she was assured, no time to change, she hurried to the Hôtel d'Hercule as she was, in a high-necked gown of unadorned russet velvet, with her unbound hair lying brushed over her cloak. Her mind, occupied furiously with possibilities, first reached the conclusion that some kind of unthinkable climax had occurred between Sybilla and Francis, and that, unable to ask another's help, he had had to send for her services. Or had Jerott, too fuddled to remember the niceties, said something of Marthe to Lord Culter?

Or worse than anything else ... Had Leonard Bailey left the house in the rue de la Cerisaye and chosen tonight, of all nights, to make public the scandal surrounding the Crawfords?

Even when her escort pushed his way through the crowds to the brightly-lit house, and she heard the music and laughter drifting from the tall windows, she still thought it possible. It was the dénouement a vengeful man would choose ... before an audience of Sybilla's own countrymen. And with even the Queen, it seemed, there to hear it. Bailey could have made his threat. Lymond might be waiting helplessly, even now, for his arrival.

So she came quickly into the room, her furred cloak fallen back; and saw him see her at once, and with an apology to the Queen at his side, rise to walk swiftly towards her.

And from his manner, she knew instantly that there had been no disaster. St Michael killed his dragon, gold and green, on the spotless velvet of a man who was totally at home, and in command both of himself and of every circumstance of his surroundings. And in his eyes was no personal apprehension, but only a faint, well-masked concern whose reason was perfectly obvious.

He had not expected to see her.

Philippa did not even speak. Her eyes sought Piero Strozzi and found him grinning, his splendid shoulders raised in expansive expectation of forgiveness.

Following, speechlessly, all the play upon her face and, turning, on the Florentine's, Lymond divined, still without words, what had happened.

Then he smiled, betraying no anger, and said, pleasantly, 'I see that Piero has been at pains to make fools of us both. There is no need for embarrassment. Come and make your salutations to the Queen and Sybilla and then I shall bestow you on Catherine for companionship.... Take your cloak off. Your gown and your hair require no adornment.'

It was direct flattery to restore her shaken confidence; but none the less, she was grateful for it. And when Catherine, smiling, came to lead her to a low cushioned hassock beside her, she was grateful, too, that Francis had chosen a bride of sensibility as well as intelligence, and that she had made a friend of her.

Someone was singing.

> The fruit of all the service that I serve
> Despair doth reap, such hapless hap have I.
> But though he have no power to make me swerve
> Yet, by the fire, for cold I feel I die.

Richard, coming to question her, was diverted after all: she thought by his mother. Lymond, bending courteously, was talking to d'Andelot's wife, reclining near her husband on a coffer-seat.

> In paradise, for hunger still I starve;
> And, in the flood, for thirst to death I dry.
> So Tantalus am I, and in worse pain
> Amids my help, and helpless doth remain.

Danny Hislop, twining among quilted backs like winter jasmine, arrived and seated himself nonchalantly in her circle. The Queen, and everyone else in the dim, scented room were listening to the singers. And as thought returned, and the flush died at last in her cheeks, Philippa listened to them too.

> Help me to seek, for I lost it there,
> And if that ye have found it, ye that be here
> And seek to convey it secretly.
> Handle it soft and treat it tenderly,
> Or else it will plain and then appear;
> ... Help me to seek

The theme of the music was earthly passion. The songs

sprang from every country and age, their story told sometimes by the music and sometimes by the singers and sometimes in mime by the dancers, grave of face and tranquil in
manner, and faultlessly clothed, as were all the performers, in
pale, clear colours which spoke of spring, and of young lovers and sunlight.

> *. . . I wis it was a thing all too dear*
> *To be bestowed and wist not where;*
> *It was my heart. I pray you heartily,*
> *Help me to seek.*

It was a display of art unmarred by slovenliness. One wept
indeed for Jodelle, and for every masque born of Alciati and
Giraldi and d'Avrigny, and presented, woodenly fixed to the
drawing-board. Skilfully brought to this moment with wine
and food and pleasure, with dim candlelight, and the warmth
of their own kind, in talk and company, the guests were quite
silent, watching and listening.

> *As hound that hath his keeper lost,*
> *Seek I your presence to obtain.*
> *In which my heart delighteth most*
> *And shall delight, though I be slain.*

Come cold upon it, Philippa saw it with clear eyes, and
was pleased to be critical.

Cunningly done, O Francis, puissant comte de Sevigny.
Nothing crude. Nothing too rich, or sickly, or posturing.
Songs like a lost hearth-fire, that one had known from one's
childhood; songs rarely come upon, and the rest like new lovers, moving in their unfamiliarity. Songs which spoke direct
to the heart. To the heart, and not to the intellect.

She looked at Lymond.

The dark wood of his chair defined his head. His profile,
pure as the flowered spurs on his porcelain, was turned from
the singers. His lids at first she thought were closed; and then
she realized that he was fully occupied. He was watching
time, and his guests; and guiding noiselessly through his
maîtres d'hôtel the weaving pattern of footmen, pages,
sommelier. Tonight he had no hostess and equally needed
none. He had done this, somewhere, many times, and it was
effortless.

> *I fold thy gentleness within my cloak*
> *The flying wit I braid with jewellery,*
> *I span thy courage with my bravest clasp*
> *And sip the sweets of thy integrity.*
> *They think thee fair.*
> *They see not what I see.*

The guests sat close. The gold in Strozzi's earring flashed, above the girl's hair coiled across his breast. The white hand of de La Roche-sur-Yon stroked, down and down, the charming boy who sat beside his feet. Condé watched Catherine, and the Maréchale watched him until, with a soft movement, the demoiselle d'Albon rose and moved to Lymond's side.

Then he looked up, and smiled, and watched her as she settled by him: black hair, white neck, and azure skirts spread all around the floor.

> *When her loose gown from her shoulders did fall*
> *And she me caught in her arms long and small,*
> *Therewith all sweetly did me kiss*
> *And softly said, 'Dear heart, how like you this?'*

The music rose again, and his hand moved and stilled, as Catherine leaned her head against the carved chair-arm. *Aşk Olsun* sang the plaintive, sweet voices to the undulating airs one had heard inside Zante, through Thessalonika, within the gates of Topkapi itself. *Aşkin Cemal Olsun* . . . Let there be love. May thy love be beautiful. May thy beauty be light. *The truth is that thy body is free of all shadow./To soul and brain from thy abode comes the perfume of Paradise./O thy beauty!/The brightness of the day and the night/Are made timid by thy hair* . . .

The words used by the Bektashi in the ceremony of the tekke: how could any group of student singers know these?

No longer cold: drugged with musk and amber and the dizzy languor of fasting emotion, Philippa looked hazily round her.

Jerott she could see nowhere, but she caught Adam's eye, and felt that for some minutes, he had been watching her. Even then, when the next song had started, he did not look away.

But by then, anyway, she knew who had written those

words and set them to music. Once, Francis Crawford had sung with Les Amis de Rabelais.

Looking at him, she saw that Catherine, smiling a little, was still sitting below him. And that his absent fingers, their movement almost imperceptible, were caressing the smooth, creamy skin between her neck and her shoulder.

Andreas was singing alone. Philippa looked away, her face drawn, and watched him. 'Wyatt,' Danny murmured beside her.

It was Wyatt's verse. It was also the bitter outburst of a wronged and unforgiving mind much nearer than that of Wyatt:

The piller pearisht is whearto I lent
The strongest staye of myne unquyet mynde;
The lyke of it no man agayne can fynde,
Ffrom East to West, still seking thoughe he went,
To myne unhappe! for happe away hath rent
Of all my joye the vearye bark and rynde.

It was a safe scourge to use. No one beyond himself and Sybilla should have been present to know its significance.

Sybilla was weeping, the tears running so fast that she placed both hands over her face. Richard, astonished, leaned to put his hands on her shoulders. And Lymond . . .

Lymond, his golden head bent, listened smiling to something Queen Mary was saying while his hand, with that hardly visible movement, told over promises on Catherine d'Albon's beautiful neck.

Soon after that, the Queen left, her host escorting her. The doors closed. The company rose from its various obeisances. The atmosphere brightened.

Piero Strozzi, disentangling himself from his girl friend, seized a lute from the consort, drained his wine and uplifted his voice in the first verse of an interminable Court lampoon aimed at Condé. His audience, still on their feet, faintly dazed, took a moment or two to revive. Many trays appeared, laden with goblets. Concupiscence gave way to satisfaction, and the first chorus had a commendable complement, if one not quite so melodious as that of the professionals:

Ce petit homme tant jolly
Tousjours cause et trousjours ry

Et tousjours baise sa mignonne.
Dieu gard' de mal le petit homme!

Madame de St André was laughing. So, fortunately, was the little man himself. Philippa Somerville said to the other little man standing behind her, 'Where is Jerott Blyth?'

Danny jumped. 'Asleep under a piece of paper saying *La musique recrée l'homme et lui donne volupté, signed Calvin.* I laid him to rest under the gryphons. He can't sing a note; he can't really.'

'Your nerves are weak, aren't they?' Philippa said. 'So tell me. Where is Marthe? Or haven't you dug her out yet?'

He was reluctant to talk. Four of the sixteen verses about Louis de Bourbon were achieved before she told him what she wanted, and eight more before he had agreed to it. They were still roaring the chorus when she made her way across to Sybilla.

'How do you stop them?' said Robert Reid, Bishop of Orkney, when Lymond, free of his royal guest, returned to the midst of the gallery.

'I distribute large sweetmeats,' Lymond said. 'As you see my footmen are doing. And I ask the wittiest and most senior statesman present if he would honour us with a short closing speech.'

'Ha!' said Reid of Orkney. 'You know what you are about. Not a long, sodden aftermath exchanging coarse epigrams about one's betters? I have heard the one about de Brissac three times already.'

'No. Let us save everyone's faces,' Lymond said, 'while we can. And before Master Buchanan is hurled to the floor by either Nicolas or a thunderbolt from the late Copernicus.'

And so, smiling, in English and in Latin, the Lord President of the Court of Session thanked his former prisoner, in elegant terms, for the quality of his hospitality; and the comte de Sevigny, also in English and in Latin, turned in a graceful speech which brought three graded roars of laughter and a howl at the end when he sang, quickly and lightly, four lines from *Ce petit homme*'s chorus, neatly warped to malign Piero Strozzi.

Strozzi himself leaped over a bench to reach him, as they all began to make their farewells. 'You are mollified! I knew it! To Scotland, arse of the world, I bring many well-endowed

431

patrons, and allow you to impress them. *Par le mort bien,* many a gentleman would embrace me.'

'I shall let you know,' Lymond said, 'when I am ready to embrace you, and with what. In the meantime should you seek a favour, ask elsewhere.'

Antoine de Navarre, smiling, held out his hand. *'Feu contre feu.* It is becoming a legend: Sevigny and Strozzi. How did you cease to fight each other long enough to conquer Calais?'

'I cannot quite recollect,' said Piero Strozzi, his face contorted in thought. 'The Duke de Guise could tell us. This Sevigny, you observe, works only to become one of the four Marshals of France, and then he must say *bon soir et bonne nuit* to Fortune, for there is nowhere to progress but downwards.' He sighed.

'I have your example,' Lymond said. 'Madame Marguerite?'

'You have become too eminent to sing?' said the King's sister. 'Or might one invite you to perform in private? I should like to have the musician and poet who wrote and arranged this entertainment to visit me with you.'

'We are all honoured,' Lymond said. 'The only obstacle is our natural modesty. Mademoiselle d'Albon and I wish to thank you for joining us.'

Richard caught the words, waiting with other Commissioners to take his leave, Sybilla beside him. The inexplicable storm of tears had ceased without trace: the tensions of evening, he supposed, had over-tired her. There had been no exchanges with Lymond. He was glad that Philippa had come, at last, to spend some time at Sybilla's side. He had left them to talk quietly together and on returning, had found the girl gone, so that he did not require to offer his escort back to the Hôtel de Guise. One supposed there were plenty of gallants who had leaped at the opportunity.

He moved forward with Sybilla, hearing Lord James's slow voice ahead, making all proper remarks to his brother. The girl Catherine stood at Lymond's shoulder and his hand had come to rest lightly on her waist. The mother, creaking with jewels just behind them, looked positively hilarious. He had heard about Marguerite de St André. It was not surprising, he supposed, if she clung to her youth. St André, they said, was a *harquebuzier de ponant.* It was the rottenness at the French court which had ruined Francis.

Then it was his turn and he bowed, without approaching for an embrace; while his brother returned the gesture with practised, careless courtesy to them both. The decoration pinning the Queen's glove, he now saw, was the gold Medal of Calais. He wondered if the Queen knew he had another glove donated last year by Madame Elizabeth of England. Neither Francis nor Sybilla avoided each other's eyes, he noticed, although neither was smiling. The two delicate skins even yet could look identical: milky-fair in the dazzle of ruff-gauze. There were oyster shells made from silver spools, a pretty conceit, half concealed by the seaming and arm-hoops of Lymond's nacré velvet and within each a white pearl, tastefully glimmering. The St Michael, they said, was the most privileged Order in France, and opened the only sure doorway to power.

Sybilla said, so quietly that none but he and Francis could hear it, 'You brought me here, it seems, for one purpose. If it pleases you to ask me again, you must not be surprised if I refuse you.'

Richard felt the heat rise through his face. Erskine of Dun, damn his eyes, was just behind him. He said harshly, 'What? What did he do?'

'Richard my dear: so universal a boiling and bubbling: one cannot talk here. Call on me in the morning. My lady mother is waiting to leave. Mr. Erskine, you see Marshal Stozzi provided you with even more congenial company than I had thought of. All the same, I should not advise you yet to throw your black stockings out of the window. Mademoiselle d'Albon, as you see, is prettier than Sir John Knox.'

Lord Culter left, with his mother.

'I know which guests were not of your inviting,' John Erskine of Dun observed quietly. 'You have taken infinite trouble to pleasure us. It is no small thing to bring a nation together on foreign soil and send its members from your doorway arm in arm.'

'But with its eyes set firmly, I fear, on material values.' It was surprising what, deaf as a bell-founder, the Bishop of Orkney could follow. 'Did they aspire to spiritual perfection, Mr Crawford, in such a degree as you have shown them the other kind, we should be a nation of souls fit for Paradise. But there was no passion but the passion of the human senses. I looked for a rallying-call, such as I heard once in Edinburgh.'

433

'I am sorry you were disappointed,' Lymond said, 'but I notice that a merry man is seldom disposed to give thought to the higher issues. You have to catch him feeling low. You quote an example in point.'

'When you were an outlaw and an excommunicate you were a Scot, and now you are a Frenchman? Perhaps you are right. At least I see,' said Bishop Reid, glancing at the girl on M. de Sevigny's arm, 'that you are a happy man.'

Lymond bowed and glanced, smiling, at the dark head beside him as the Commissioners passed. The number of guests waiting now was only a handful. They stood side by side, he and Catherine, and she curtseyed and smiled as they said, over and over, the same things. Her mother, placing a ringed hand on Lymond's shoulder, had already announced her departure to bed, and hinted that Catherine, her duty done, should do the same. 'In a very few weeks you will be contracted. The child must not lose her looks!'

Her colour higher than usual, Catherine smiled at her mother and did not wince, as she might have done. Tonight, they were to sleep in the Hôtel d'Hercule. Tonight, she thought, her head full of his love songs, she might not sleep alone; or at all.

The last guest left, and they looked at one another. 'Pleasant communications and merie conceits, and in everie mans countenance a loving jocundnesse. And on every woman's also, I trust,' Lymond said. 'A last cup of wine? And then I have to wait a moment for de La Rochefoucauld. He called upstairs to reassure Allendale. They are taking his uncle to Onzain, and the old man seems to think he'll be dropped in an oubliette.'

He had signed to a servant, one of the many who now moved softly about, opening windows and clearing the debris. But when the tray came, Catherine refused the offered goblet. 'I think,' she said, 'I shall go upstairs. I shall be in the way, and they are occupied. Perhaps someone could bring me wine later.'

'Perhaps,' he said. A trace of colour showed itself, also, on his pale skin. He emptied the cup he had been given and lifting another, took her hand and led her to the door. 'I might bring it myself.'

'And your lute?' Catherine said. 'I should like you to play to me.'

434

'I was not,' said Lymond, 'proposing to waste time with a lute.'

He watched her go and then, turning back, proceeded automatically with the last duties of such an evening. He spoke to the Count of La Rochefoucauld, to his maîtres d'hôtel and to his ushers and then, descending to the kitchen, to the principal staff. The singers were still there because he had asked them to stay. There was nothing new to talk over, except by way of post mortem, because, God knew, he had rehearsed them enough in the preceding days; but they were loath to go, and he did not wish to hurry them. He drank while he was with them a great deal, but was still able to guide, control, and even help half-carry them, high as tilers, to the courtyard, where his groom harnessed a cart and set off with them.

The wax lights in the gallery were already snuffed when he re-entered the house, but the wall sconces had been left alight on the staircase and up the further flight to the next floor where his rooms lay, and those of Madame la Maréchale, and of young Austin, and of Catherine.

Someone had put Jerott to bed and Adam had volunteered to stay until morning to look after him. None of his principal guests would have cause to be sorry for themselves on rising—the results of thorough planning practised, of necessity, in Russia. But this evening had had an importance much beyond the entertaining Güzel had done for him at Vorobiovo.

Or that he had done for Güzel. Compared with that, Catherine, *grande dame de maison* though she might be, was formless clay. Some of her gifts he now knew, and some he would have to find and foster. He had done it often enough, but never before for himself that he remembered.

That tonight should see that start of the process was by Catherine's decision, not his. He had laid down for himself the rules to follow, and he had obeyed them. The theme of the music tonight had been so arranged not for her sake, but to make as deep an impression as possible. He had wanted the young Queen to remember it. The young Queen who had not been invited, but whose curiosity had been excited by so many innocent means that he knew she could not resist it. What happened now remained to be seen.

What happened now . . .

To Adam Blacklock, at his door with Jerott snoring behind him, it was like a nightmare recurrence of tragedy: of the

435

time when he stood thus in a Dumbarton tavern, and watched Lymond come walking like this to his chamber, though not with the sash of St Michael on his pearled doublet, and his eyes darkened, smoky blue in his pale, brilliant face. Adam stepped forward. 'Francis?'

'Yes?' He was slow in turning and reluctant, Adam knew, to be stopped. Then he said, 'Adam? How is Jerott?'

'Asleep. Francis . . . There is someone in your room.'

A valet de chambre, with an extra stick of candles, came out of a doorway and, when Lymond glanced at him, said, 'When my lord count is ready.'

'I shan't need you. Go to bed,' Lymond said. And as an afterthought, 'Where is Mr Abernethy?'

'In bed, my lord. You said . . .'

'Yes, I know. Adam, you should follow his example. Thank you for warning me, but I have been held up, that's all.'

The servant was barely out of earshot. 'I brought her some wine,' Adam said. 'You took your time coming up. She's probably asleep.'

'How very indiscreet of everybody,' Lymond said. 'But thank you for advising me. Did you think I would scream?'

'What are you doing here?' he had said to the naked child in his rooms, that night in Dumbarton. And going in, had induced her to serve him all night as his desires inclined, crude as old Cranmer's vase de necessité.

The eyes of both men met. Then, as Adam said nothing, Lymond walked past and entering, closed behind him the door to his chambers.

Inside, waiting for him, was Philippa Somerville.

436

CHAPTER 2

Le grand credit, d'or d'argent l'abondance
Areuglera par libide l'honneur.

He stopped as if he had walked into glass; thus affording
Philippa much satisfaction.

She sat in her russet gown on his bed, her ankles crossed
and Adam's empty wine glass in her hands, and said, 'Catherine is still waiting for you, in a blue velvet *robe de nuit* with
clasps on it. She put on a white one at first, but her mother
made her change it. You can go to her when I have finished
with you.'

'Thank you,' said Lymond. He came several steps into the
room and stood looking at her guardedly. 'At least she isn't
sitting on my bed.'

'No,' said Philippa. 'It isn't that kind of conversation. In
fact, after tonight, it won't be that kind of conversation
again. A great many inferior people, Mr Crawford, have
helped you over the years in your well-publicized career of
adversity, but you mustn't be surprised if the circle begins to
diminish. To go by what happened this evening, the man who
has finally emerged from it all isn't worth helping.'

'I see,' he said. In the few moments she had been speaking
he had flushed and paled again. The verbal attack, when all
his senses had been prepared for something different, had set
him adrift, it was clear, for a moment. When he moved, she
could smell the wine on his breath. He said, resting his fingers
on the chimneypiece. 'So you think I am cruel to Sybilla?'

'My dear man,' Philippa said. 'It seems to me that you
have no spirit left but the spirit of resentment. In a few years,
there'll be nothing to choose between you and Leonard
Bailey. Tonight, Sybilla came in good faith as your guest, and
you broke her down publicly. Justify that.'

'A drunken whim,' Lymond said. He had taken his hand
from the carving. 'Probably unjustifiable, as you say. I shall
apologize for it, if you like.'

437

'You were sober when you arranged it,' Philippa said. 'And "*probably* unjustifiable"? What would justify it? If she had whipped you daily instead of protecting you all your childhood? Would you have let her off if she had confided in you, as you grew up, that you were a bastard? Or will you never really let her off because she cared more for her lover than she did for any child he might leave her with? Have you ever tried to analyse her motives or yours, *or are you still standing outside your grandfather's door, kicking it?*'

'Oh, Christ, Philippa,' he said, after a little check, as of a man suddenly winded. When he sank, his hands gripping his elbows, into a wainscot chair, it was with such economy that the golden eye of the Calais medallion shone without interruption. 'How did you find out?' he asked.

'I guessed.' If it was a half-lie, he was not to realize it. 'The seal on the death certificate. I saw the first baron's arms on it, although you broke it so quickly. I found out that Sevigny had been leased by him for many years, before much later you bought it. And if you were his son, it accounted for your likeness to Marthe. I have told Sybilla, by the way, how to reach Marthe. She wanted to speak to her.'

He allowed the spate of words to pass over his head, sitting compressed and unmoving, his eyes on the table below him. Then he said, his voice kept, with evident care, still quiet and ordinary, 'Did you tell Sybilla that you knew the truth?'

'No. Not in words,' Philippa said. 'Not in any other way I could help. But of course, she has been left in no doubt that you know it. She is being quite adequately punished, so far as I can see, without your assistance. She also asked, by the way, if your marriage to Catherine was one of convenience only. I said that on your side, it was.'

He let his arms loose then. They lay, the embroidery glittering, on the table. He said, 'You must remember. You wanted me to marry Catherine.'

'She is in love with you,' Philippa said.

'It is not usually,' he said unwisely, 'an impediment to successful matrimony.'

The click as she set down her glass rang through the quiet room. Springing from the bed she walked to the shuttered window and back; then stood before the low fire looking at him. 'Successful matrimony?' she said. 'You told me once you loved someone else.'

'Did I?' he said. 'Ah, in Lyon. I remember. But it is no

438

one, I promise you, who will interfere with my marriage to Catherine.'

He seemed able, in spite of the wine, to keep his voice perfectly normal. She found she resented that. 'How many of those songs tonight were yours?' Philippa said.

The light lay on his rings, and the curve of his lowered lashes, and the gold and green of St Michael, killing the dragon. Presently he said, 'Some, of course. But the purpose of the evening was political.'

'I am well aware of that,' said Philippa grimly. 'If you are made to leave France, what will happen to Catherine?'

Again, he did not answer at once. Then he said, 'While armies need captains, I am not likely to be asked to leave France.'

She said, 'That is not, I think, an honest answer. And since the purpose of the evening was political, the songs were not for Catherine either. Although, it seems, they brought you their reward. You're right, of course,' Philippa said. 'I did help to bring this marriage about. And now it appears you are cheating her.'

And still, he kept his head, and his temper. 'It does not seem,' he said, 'very different from your marriage to Austin.'

'No,' said Philippa. Then, because she had demanded honesty herself, she set her teeth and said, 'But I have told Austin that if I marry him, he must accept the fact that my interest, too, is given elsewhere.'

His hands moved together and clasped themselves, lightly. 'And you have told him, of course, the name of the fortunate man?' His voice had changed, a little.

Philippa's face muscles trembled. She stilled them. 'I thought it fair. Do you think I was proud of it? I didn't think he would still want to marry me.'

He stood up, with his own very studied grace. 'But he does. And you arrive uninvited at my house—'

'Uninvited!' Her voice scraped. 'Now that is—'

'. . . You arrive without warning at my house and hear what you were not intended to hear: a number of things which are painful in the extreme, because they all have a bearing on my possession of Catherine. You—'

'I pushed you—'

'Please allow me to finish,' he said. 'You asked me to analyse my motives. Look at your own, Philippa. This visit tonight hasn't been about Sybilla, except in so far as you

439

wanted to punish me. It hasn't been about Catherine either. If Austin will forgive you anything, why should . . .'

He stopped in mid-sentence. Sick with miserable anger, Philippa glared at him, her lips shut, waiting. And incredibly, all the hostility melted out of his face. His hands loosened. And he gave a laugh.

'The wine speaking,' he said. 'I beg your pardon. It appears that I am in no position to lecture you on that particular subject. Come.' His smile was unforced: and sweet as she rarely saw it. 'I shall find someone to see you home.'

'And that,' said Philippa, 'is a little capricious, isn't it? You were going to inform me why I was here.' She was still very flushed.

'Scorpio,' Lymond said, 'does not caper. He stings. We are damned, as the man says, of nature: so conceaved and borne as a serpent is a serpent and a tode a tode, and a snake a snake by nature . . .' He looked at her again, a little wryly. 'And you, I suppose, are the Crab. It doesn't matter. If you want to bite, bite.'

Her colour burning she said, 'I pushed you into Catherine's arms. Jealousy is one motive you really can't accuse me of.'

There was a short silence, but not an unkind one. Then Lymond said, 'Brought face to face with reality, it can make a difference.' Then as she didn't speak, he said, 'I was on my way to her room when you stopped me. You know that, Philippa.'

'You can still go,' she said stiffly.

He gave a very faint smile. 'Yes,' he said. And then, gently, 'It was a natural reaction. Piero's fault, and mine. It won't happen again, and soon you will be home. Don't worry.'

She had been led into behaving like a female. And she was being dismissed as a female. But she had charge of his good name, although he might not know it; and she had work to do, although like a fool she had lost sight of it. Philippa said curtly, 'Hanged with clooth of gold, and nat with sarge. I apologize, but you needn't be so forgiving about it: your behaviour did you no credit. Which reminds me. After you left me, how did you spend your last evening in Lyon?'

He was lifting her cloak when that reached him. He set it down and turned. After a long scrutiny: 'Hanged with serge next time, I think,' Lymond said pleasantly. 'Why do you ask?'

'Nostradamus suggested it,' Philippa said.

There was a silence this time of some weight. Then, 'Nostradamus? How interfering of him.' Lymond said. 'Not having my present resources, I passed the night at a house of entertainment. You don't want the details, I take it.'

She fixed on him, without a qualm, the lucent stare which had so distressed the eunuchs. 'Nostradamus is to tell me the truth if you avoid answering. He said you'd avoid answering. He was right.'

'And you, of course, instantly assume my conduct was execrable. Whose eyes continually burn with the unquenchable flames of the deadly cockatrice, whose teeth are like to the venomous toshes of the ramping lion—'

'. . . and whose whole man, body and soul, go always up and down, musing of mischief. What happened?' said Philippa relentlessly.

And he answered her lightly. 'A piece of foolishness. The mouse instead of the mountain of gold. You will be disappointed. I left the house with a headache, and a drunken fall in the street knocked me senseless. Archie conveyed me to a printer called Macé Bonhomme, and Nostradamus tended me there. Such things are not supposed to happen to leaders of armies, so nothing has been said about it.'

It tallied with what she had overheard in Marthe's house. Philippa said, 'Like the headaches you had in London?'

'Fortunately,' he said, 'not at all of that order. They are common, according to Nostradamus, in individuals with a chronic inability to suffer reverses. He is hoping, I am sure, that someone will keep a matronly eye on me.'

And that, set beside what she knew, was a little too specious.

He had turned round, as he had in Lyon, and put his hands out of sight on the edge of the table behind him. Philippa said, 'I should like the truth. I haven't had it yet.'

The truth. *The truth is that* . . .

'But I am not your business now,' he said calmly. The train of thought vanished.

Philippa said, 'Perhaps you are not the best judge of that.'

'And you are?' he said. 'You should have let me go to Catherine.' And then moved to sudden anger perhaps by the wine, 'Everything I do seems to be exposed, like a bloody carcass picked over by . . .'

'. . . jackals,' she said. 'You have me followed. You interfere with my affairs. I am not allowed to say to you, I am not your business.' She paused, and then said very firmly, 'Do you tell me? Or do I ask Nostradamus?'

'I shall tell you,' he said. 'Why make an occasion out of it? I devised a somewhat arbitrary way out of my own difficulties that evening; and Archie stopped me. The headaches are an extension of the kind I had in London. At the height of each attack, I am blind.'

All the servants by now were in bed, and even the quayside must be empty. Outside the room there was no sound at all; and inside only the thud of her heart, jarring the air, the tapestries, the bedhangings; and her view of him watching her, braced a little to recoil, in case she moved towards him.

Then the innermost sense reached her of what he was saying.

In the only voice to which she had access, a reedy one, she said, 'You tried to . . . ? How?'

'In the time-honoured fashion,' he said. 'My cuffs are too tight to gratify you with a view.'

Her eyes, wide open, remained on his: brown eyes, like Kate's. And the curl of her nostril deepened, although she did not know it; and the line, like Kate's across her clear brow.

Then Philippa turned and reaching the twisted marble pillars of the chimney-piece sank down before them, her back to him; her hair, fire-lined, drifting over her shoulders. She said, 'Of course. You have always tried to escape.'

'And I have always harmed the friends who have tried to stop me,' Lymond said. His voice was uninflected. He added, 'I have tried many times to warn you not to come too close to me.'

'Naturally. Level-headed and constructive to the end,' Philippa said, 'in confronting all your personal problems. And now? A trifle of hemlock? You can always evade Archie.'

He said, 'You might spare me a little. I did give you the whip of my own accord. In Lyon, I had no other means of escape. Now I have several; and responsibilities which I mean to honour. There is no need to agonize over it.'

'And the blindness?' Philippa said. 'What capable plan have you devised to deal with that?'

'Archie knows,' he said with a weariness she could just hear. 'And keeps me drunk, or drugged or otherwise insensate at intervals. No one else has discovered. Except, of course, Nostradamus.'

Her hands, deep in her lap, were clenched bone to bone upon each other. 'And Nostradamus?' she said. 'Your involuntary nurse? What can he do?'

'Inform you, it seems,' Lymond said. 'I suppose with some purpose. He might have left me with a little more dignity and you with a little more peace of mind if he hadn't.' He halted; and then said, 'There is no treatment for heterocrania, but it is only intermittent. It seems drink can start it, or emotion. And sudden exertion can sometimes stop it; or a woman. It's inconvenient. But it's manageable.'

You should have let me go to Catherine. 'I see,' said Philippa. 'Your men walk round you when they notice you drunk, drugged or blind on the battlefield?'

'It hasn't happened as yet,' he said quietly.

'It's a pity they don't know how lucky they are. Do you think Catherine will notice?' said Philippa.

He said, 'Look . . . I do realize the implications. I shall not allow it to endanger other people. I shall honour my obligation to Catherine. Meanwhile I know very well my own limits. De Thermes has gout. Strozzi has jaundice. I have headaches. We are all capable of adjusting our lives to our defects.'

'You are?' Philippa said. 'And you can't adjust to bastardy?'

He said evenly, 'Give me, perhaps, until tomorrow instead of today to achieve it.'

'Rubbish,' she said. 'You've guessed it for years.'

'All right. I've guessed it for years,' he said. 'Philippa, that's enough.'

'And done nothing about it. You sit on trouble, don't you, until it blows up in your face? You turned on Sybilla. You'll turn on me soon, once it strikes home that someone has censured you. You are proving, aren't you,' said Philippa contemptuously, 'that to be base-born makes you a fourth-rate son of a fourth-rate little country?'

She did not see how swiftly he moved. She only felt his hands on her shoulders, twisting her firmly to confront him.

And then, of course, he saw confirmed what only the fire had heretofore seen: the ceaseless cataract of her tears, pouring and pouring, without hope of concealment down her young face.

He said, 'Oh God help me,' in a voice so low and so tired

that she barely heard it. Then dropping his hands he rose and left her.

She cried after him then. 'Wait! Wait. Where are you going?'

He was already far from her, but he halted. He turned to her, and the silver oysters and the jewels and the medallion all showed blindingly how he was breathing, like an escaping hart bayed down by staghounds. He said, 'I've upset you. We're both tired. And I don't know how I can help matters.'

He had at some time pushed his hands unseen into his hair. Threads of it spangled the dampness on his brow, and his open eyes were without light. He went on with difficulty, 'My birth is the least of my troubles. The rest you must allow me to support by myself. I shall try to be what you wish me to be, and do what you wish me to do and if I fail, you must believe that I have tried. . . . Philippa, it is so late. Let me call Adam to take you home.' And then suddenly, his voice raw with desperation, *'Here is non hoom. Here nis but wildernesse.'*

And at last, the pain was more than she could bear.

'It's Kate. It's Kate, isn't it?' Philippa said. 'Not Güzel. Not Mariotta and Midculter, whatever Richard may think. It's Kate, and because of the blindness you never would tell her. You wouldn't take Gideon's place. But your music, your verse was for my mother. And when I showed on the steps at Lyon what I felt for you the breakdown came next. and the blindness. How I must sicken you,' Philippa said; and put both hands over her face, and sat, choking.

There was no response. After a long while she dropped her hands, and opened her eyes.

He was standing quite still, his eyes resting on her. All the violence that had driven him from her side seemed to have left him. His hands were steady and his voice, when he spoke, was clear also, although not at all loud.

'Music, the knife without a hilt,' he said. 'But for Piero, I suppose none of this would have happened. Since it has . . .'

He hesitated for the last time, his voice dying away. Then he said, 'Do you know, Philippa, what an unsuitable match is? It isn't the kind I shall have with Catherine d'Albon, or even the kind you will make with young Allendale. When one human being is trapped in the net of another's grand passion: then it comes about; and it is tragedy. It happened to Gavin and Sybilla. It is happening to Jerott and Marthe . . .'

444

'I had no expectations,' Philippa said. The tears stood still on her face. 'This is one lesson I know by heart already.'

'You are young,' said Lymond gently. 'You will change. I don't take lightly what you feel for me, but it wasn't the kind of passion I was speaking of. You asked me a question, and I think we have come to the place where I must answer it. For one thing, you are being hurt. And for another . . . as you see . . . I seem to be losing the knack of concealing things from you.'

She said, 'I was wrong. Don't tell me.'

'No. You were right,' he said. And as the chill spread through her nerves and her flesh, he said, *'Tant qu je vive . . .* I said too much that evening, didn't I? It was not, of course, Güzel. Or Mariotta.'

'Kate loves you,' Philippa said. 'It's all right. She has always . . .'

'Philippa, no,' he said. He stood in an island of space, as isolated as he must have been, directing his forces in Guînes or in Calais. 'You were right to ask, and wrong only in your conjecture. Kate is my friend. That is true. But the songs were for her daughter. And the passion, for ever. That is why we are parting.'

The words reached her, without bringing the sense any nearer. He would think her very slow: even in the middle of the night; even with undried tears bloating her eyes and her cheeks. She appeared to be on her feet, facing him. 'But I am her daughter,' Philippa said.

Like some obscure and difficult text, the look in his eyes was too complex to read at a distance. She said, 'You can't mean . . . ?' and then, as he did not speak, answered herself. 'No.'

He was as pale as the sheened marble masks on the chimney-piece, but a ghost of the old self-derision pulled his mouth, as she saw, at the corner. 'No? Then let us leave things as they are,' he said; and moved to the table. There, he poured two glasses of wine. One he laid where she could and did take it. Bearing the other he turned and dropped into the chair he had once already occupied. He lifted the goblet. 'To marriage,' he said.

She stood where he had left her, the wine disregarded in her cramped fist. *Kate is my friend, but the songs were for her daughter. And the passion, for ever.*

This was not true. So why should he say it?

445

She scanned at him as he leaned back, the wine in his ringed hand, watching her. He looked nearly prostrate with tiredness, but with no trace of malice about him. Yet he was trained to dissemble. He had spent an evening acting, downstairs.

'Think, *Yunitsa,*' he said abruptly.

He had called her that once before, back in London. Her legs were trembling. There was a chair just behind her. She sat in it, and tried to see where, through the years, had grown the cruelty which would inflict this upon her; or the signs which would stand witness to what he was trying to tell her.

For of course, she had begun by detesting him. Loathing the arrogant horseman, discussing a corpse in a ditch outside Boghall; the enemy who had defeated her father; who had forced his way into her mother's house, where, a child of ten, she had baulked and betrayed him.

And he knew it, and had not retaliated. Lying drenched by the whipping-post at St Mary's he had said, 'You had good reason to hate me. Don't build up another false image.' He had not been acting, then.

That was when, discovering his quality, she had set out to redeem all the damage she had done. When, blundering, she had helped him retrieve Kuzúm, the child who now lived with her mother. At Algiers it had been her fault when, losing his temper, he had knocked her proffered cup into the ocean. She had been sixteen. He had sent her home then, or had tried to.

He had not been acting in Stamboul, when, expecting to die, he had said, 'I am offering you my name. Then, as you choose, you may divorce me.'

That was after he had slept, drugged with opium, sharing the same great crystal bed in Topkapi, and in his nightmare had cried out the words she did not follow then, but all too clearly understood now. *Poor Eloise. Tell me. I can't understand. Why did you do it?*

But Sybilla had not told him yet.

Sybilla. Struck by a sudden thought, she looked at him. He was still watching her. 'Go on,' he said; as if she had been speaking, not thinking of him.

As she had thought of him so often, when he was absent. As, sleeping, she had dreamed of him making just such an avowal, only to wake to desolation and anger, that the cruel impossible should so have taunted her.

And still it was both cruel and impossible. What evidence was there to suggest otherwise? Think . . . Of what? The time in London, for instance, when he had upbraided her for meddling once again in the history of his origins? *This matter is mine, and not yours or Kate's, do you hear me?*

That had been the voice of fear and of pride, not of love. Love did not make for the long absences, the abrupt avoidals, the lack of all physical contact, except where wine, or excitement, or gaiety made him forget . . . the Hall of the Revels at Blackfriars Monastery; the flight through the fog in Lyons; the banquet at the Hôtel de Ville and after . . .

The truth is . . .

That was where she had heard him quote those words, without realizing then what they were. *The truth is that the body is free of all shadow. To soul and brain from thy abode comes the perfume of Paradise . . .*

He had spoken them to her, and broken off when he remembered. And after, when Marthe had tried to force him to embrace her, he had used, in his need, the only weapon which would both stop Marthe and send herself, quickly, out of danger.

Love did not require to act like that.

But hunger did. Hunger, decently denied, accounted for everything. Looking back, her eyes unsealed and open, she saw proved over and over what she should have observed long before but for her dazzlement. He wanted her. And as he had just said, had determined to spare her the net.

He did not know, but could be told, that to her, his reasons for abstaining were baseless. That nothing mattered but this: that the moon was here, in her fingers.

Through the jolting in her ribs and the agony in her throat Philippa said, 'I am not crying, I would have you understand, because I am sad; but because I believe you. I also have a little . . . sermon of my own to deliver.'

His wine glass was empty. He set it down carefully, its foot between two slender fingers. A little colour had come to mark his cheekbones, but his eyes remained on the goblet. 'I know,' he said. 'You are not either Sybilla or Marthe; and you know better than they do. But I am Gavin in everything but name. . . . Indeed, I am his brother.' He looked up.

'How long did Marthe's love last, I wonder? A few months; a year or two at the most. Perhaps it would take you a little longer to find out you wanted a different husband, nearer your own age and interests. But since you have loyalties, unlike Marthe, the conflict then would be unsupportable. It might do you great harm: it is certainly more than I could contemplate... And there are other factors against me, that you know of.'

She would have spoken; and then felt, rather than saw, that he did not want her to.

He said, 'I opened this door so that, understanding each other, we might shut it together. There are many men who feel about you as I do. When there is time and distance enough between us you will choose one, or be chosen, and have a life as good as Kate's was with Gideon. Meanwhile ... We have very few meetings left, and those all in public. It should not be too impossible. And at least you know ... that it is not Kate; and that you do not sicken me.'

He paused to breathe, and to smile; and ended with the same persistent steadiness. 'And we shall manage very well, as long as we are sensible. Restraint is the remedy. Restraint, and not exaggerated gestures of self-abnegation.'

'And that, I see, disposes of my future,' said Philippa. Her chest was heaving. 'So let's take yours, and see what we can do for it. The blinding headaches, for example?'

He said, still steadily, 'Perhaps marriage to Catherine will cure them.'

'Until April, you are married to me,' Philippa said. 'Perhaps four weeks of matrimony would cure us both.'

She saw his breath leave him silently. There was a space. Then he said, 'We should simply lose our annulment. I have had eleven months to think of all this. There is no basis for marriage between us. And that is quite final, Philippa.'

She was breathing almost as quickly as he was. But she kept her voice calm. 'As you say, I'm inexperienced. On the other hand, you are not always right. Please listen. Please think. Are you sure, when it matters so much, that you know my feelings better than I do?'

'No,' he said. 'I'm not infallible. You might, without my crediting it, fall deeply in love and for ever, with some warped hunchback whelped in the gutter. I should equally stop you from taking him.'

She couldn't speak. Her breath wheezed in and out. With extreme deliberation, and indeed restraint and moderation as well, Philippa raised her glass and dashed it on the parquet.

448

Crystals frosted the carpet between them, and the wine lay like blood.

Speech came back. 'God in heaven,' Philippa said. 'Do you think that I care?'

He looked up from the mess. 'I know you don't,' Lymond said. His eyes were black, not blue; and there were red splashes on the white velvet. 'But you must excuse the hunchback, who does.'

*

The crash of broken glass was heard in three rooms and brought the Englishman, Austin Grey, to his door.

He saw Adam Blacklock walk to his host's door and tap on it. It opened on de Sevigny himself, standing in a blaze of silver and white, his face like hammered quartzite. And on a tearstained girl behind him, her gown sparkling with glass, who bent suddenly, snatching a cloak, and ran past him into the passage.

It was Philippa. Disbelieving he saw Blacklock speak, and then hurrying after, catch the girl's arm and begin to guide her downstairs. When they were out of sight, de Sevigny turned and Austin confronted him.

His eyes on Lymond's face, the Marquis of Allendale stretched out the velvet sleeve of his night robe and stroked the black taffeta cross-sash with its fine jewel on the other man's doublet.

'So what do they give you this Order for?' said Austin Grey. 'Fornication?' And hooking his fingers beneath it, he ripped the sash from Lymond's shoulder. The little glove also pinned there fell with it.

'With my *wife?*' said Francis Crawford without moving; and Austin, lifting his hand, struck him over the face.

Or intended to. Just before the blow reached him, Lymond caught his wrist. Nor was he gentle. The grip on his wristbone made Austin gasp, before pride and anger shut his lips and drove him to bring all his strength to bear on M. le comte de Sevigny.

They were better matched than they had ever been before, because the more experienced of them had his reactions deadened by drink and by weariness. So it took Austin longer to lose, as the struggle took them back and forth on the stone steps and in the end, half over the low wooden coil of the balustrade, so that for a moment death stood, unattended, on the squabble.

Then Lymond made a sudden, violent move and Austin, his arm limp, released him, and staggered, and sat on the steps.

His assailant, breathing very hard, stood and surveyed him.

'That was a pity,' Lymond said. 'You always seem to come upon me doing the wrong thing, in the wrong place, with the wrong person. I goaded you quite unnecessarily, and I accept total responsibility. I was only having a somewhat dissident discussion with Philippa. She will tell you tomorrow. I have made no attempt to enforce my dwindling conjugal rights.'

He was, Austin saw, shivering from the exertion.

If Philippa was to corroborate, then he spoke the truth. Giddily, Austin Grey rose to his feet and tried also to control his heavy breathing. 'Then it seems,' he said, 'that I should apologize.' He waited, and then said, because his breeding and nature against all his desires demanded it: 'You are married to her. Have you no wish to cancel the annulment? Have you never thought of taking her to live with you as your wife?'

'No,' Lymond said. His back to the wall, he looked up to where Austin was standing, a step or two up the staircase. 'I am going to marry Catherine d'Albon. If she'll still have me. She has been waiting for me, by my reckoning, for about three hours this evening.'

Austin's face whitened and then flushed again. 'I see,' he said. 'But perhaps you had no reason to think of it. If you were told, for example, that Philippa—'

He was interrupted.

'... if I were told, for example, that Philippa was inflamed with an unlikely love for me, I should still marry Catherine d'Albon,' said Lymond gently. 'I shall never, divorced or married, in this country or another, live with Philippa Somerville as my wife. If you want my oath on that, you can have it. No plans you can make will have my shadow on them.'

The golden heads on the ramp of the stair stared at him. 'I think,' Austin said, 'I saw Mademoiselle d'Albon just now, outside her chamber.' He gave a wry smile. 'Perhaps you should get Philippa to explain matters tomorrow to her as well.'

'Oh, *Christ!*' Lymond said, his voice splitting. 'So long as she isn't in my room. I haven't the address, or indeed ...' he looked down at his sashless, dishevelled doublet '. . . the attire for it. *In the battlefield he was a lion wielding a dagger; and in the banquet-hall, a cloud raining pearls.* I seem to have combined both activities. Does your arm hurt?'

'No,' said Austin, lying.

'Call Archie if it does. Her door is closed. What fickleness. *Strange birds cry in the air Today! Today! and vanish.* I go,' said Lymond heroically, 'to take my rest after the manner of the Antabatae. Sleep well.'

Austin could not remember who the Antabatae were.

*

When Archie entered Lymond's room ten minutes later, he was seated in his shirt sleeves, writing a note at his table. He did not look up as Archie entered, but signed it using, the mahout noted, his first name; and then powdered and folded it and wrote the superscription. Then he held it to Archie.

'That will test your stamina,' he said. 'I want you to slip it under Mademoiselle d'Albon's chamber door. If she opens it and throws an axe at you, come and tell me. If not, you may go back to bed. I don't require to be coddled, and I promise you I shall be in excellent shape in the morning.'

Dark and disapproving, Archie Abernethy stood still, the note in his hand. 'If it's an assignation,' he said, 'ye'll make a right sumph o' yourself. Look at your hands.'

Francois, comte de Sevigny and Chevalier de l'Ordre, spread them out, and watched his rings trembling. 'It was an apology,' he said. 'Not, I must admit, in my best handwriting. I said that I had been overtaken with sickness.'

He broke off. Archie stood, watching him narrowly. Then without saying anything, he left the room with the note.

When he returned, the door was locked. He tried it gently, once, and then did as he was bidden and went back to bed.

I promise, in Lymond's vocabulary meant exactly that. Violence, Nostradamus said, often resolved the worst of the head-pain. He had left some mild opiates in the room: the boy could use them if need be.

He lay in bed, worrying.

Elephants gave you less bother, any day.

CHAPTER 3

Grand ennemy de tout le genre humain
Que sera pire qu'ayeuls, oncles ne peres.

Two days passed, reverberant with repercussions.

On the afternoon of the second day Jerott Blyth's truant wife Marthe, idly scanning the street from her refuge, witnessed a convoy of servants approaching, escorting two persons. One of them was Daniel Hislop. The other was a small, regal lady, cloaked and hooded in lynx fur. Both were making, beyond possible doubt, for her threshold.

She was gripped successively with a mind to vanish, and a vindictive anger against the man Hislop. Then dismissing, sharply, her cruder emotions she picked up her bell and, ringing it briefly, walked over, smiling a little, to her mirror.

To the servant who came: 'Ask the Dowager Lady Culter and Mr Hislop, when they arrive,' she said, 'to wait for me in Master Nostradamus's parlour.'

❦

The sensation of being watched from above had already attacked Danny Hislop as he conducted his astonishing companion along the rue de Marie-Egyptienne to the house of the astrologer Michel Nostradamus.

He had promised Jerott's wife, having traced her here, not to tell anyone else where she was. He had not promised to refrain from bringing anyone.

He had promised Lymond's wife, for whom he had a deep and inconvenient admiration, to enable Lymond's mother to talk to Marthe, and to be present himself, if humanly possible, throughout the meeting. And that, he couldn't deny, he was looking forward to.

The stigma of bastardy, to Daniel Hislop, was of no particular moment. The person and intellect of Lymond's sister by this date were engaging all his spare attention. And the prospect of watching the Crawford family at grips with itself was something that, blissfully, he wanted very much for his birthday.

His attitude to Sybilla, naturally, was that of a kindly colleague willing to perform any small service for Philippa. He had heard enough of Lady Culter to form his own opinion: *haute à la main et un peu superbe*, like her bloody son. The ease with which she attracted large numbers of diverse guests to her chair at Lucullus's eye-opening reception had been interesting. She had the family charm, it was clear, and did not often stop talking. In fact, on the present short journey, it had been extraordinarily difficult to slide in the questions he wanted to ask, because of a continual kind of placid effervescence which did not halt, even on Marthe's doorstep.

'How exciting!' said Sybilla happily. 'I declare, I can smell the Occult from here: or is it a sniff from the medical side? Hot goat dung for sciatica. Dioscorides always held, but I always felt you would acquire sciatica waiting about for it. Have you met Nostradamus?'

'No,' Danny said. He had given their names to the porter and they were inside the hall. 'He was out when I called on Mistress Marthe.'

'Neither have I,' Sybilla said. She gave up her cloak. 'I saw his picture, of course, in his Prophecies. I suppose he *might* have been kissed in the woods like Apollo, when he was very much younger.'

Darting a glance to either side, Danny Hislop had a sudden feeling that the whites of his eyes were beginning to show.

'Suppose we go upstairs?' said Sybilla comfortably. 'I think the steward is waiting to take us. That is, if you really want to hear us talk about our intimate family affairs in your presence. Otherwise I am sure they will make you very welcome elsewhere.'

She *was* like her bloody son. And he wasn't, after all, going to get away with it . . . Or was he?'

Upstairs, a door had opened. A moment later, Marthe's voice, coolly welcoming, floated down the turnpike. 'Lady Culter? Please allow Mr Hislop to join us. A third opinion— don't you feel—can often solve many problems?'

'She's perfectly right,' Sybilla said. *'Durant les grandes chaleurs, on recherche les ombres des grandes arbres.'* The blue, innocent eyes dwelled fondly on Danny's spare form,

453

and Danny's resemblance to a magnificent tree faded, marginally.

Sound sense, at this point took over. Danny halted. 'Lady Culter,' he said. 'I deserve it. I beg your pardon. I shall stay downstairs.'

'No,' Sybilla said slowly. She was looking, not at him, but upstairs where Jerott's errant wife stood waiting. Marthe was dressed, Danny saw, not in her usual gown but in a loose velvet robe not unlike a man's night-gear and her yellow hair, capless, was knotted just clear of her shoulders. She had never looked more like her brother.

Lady Culter brought her gaze back to Danny, and smiled at him. 'No,' she repeated lightly. 'I wasn't fair. I required to be rapped on the knuckles. If Mistress Marthe has no objection, I have none to your joining us.' And turning, she climbed up and entered Marthe's parlour.

With something astonishingly approaching reluctance, Daniel Hislop followed her, and sat down when so invited and heard Marthe say to the woman she had never met, 'I assume you asked Mr Hislop to bring you. I shall be glad to do what I can for you if you will tell me your business.'

'That of a mediator,' Sybilla said calmly. 'On what terms, Mistress Marthe, would you return to your husband? He will do anything that you wish.'

'You astonish me,' Marthe said; and Danny saw that she had, indeed, been taken by surprise. She laughed. 'An unusual mission, Lady Culter. Why should Jerott choose you?'

'Perhaps,' Sybilla said, 'because I have had some success with other members of the family. He is, I know, a most irritating young man with a great deal of emotion and very little self-discipline. On the other hand, you can't be tired of helping him, because you don't appear to have tried. Why not?'

'So the blame is mine?' Marthe said.

'Yes, of course,' Sybilla replied. 'But you know that perfectly well. Since you are intelligent you also, presumably, know why. There is no point in anyone trying to bring you together without knowing your reasons.'

'I am glad you realize it,' Marthe said. 'My reasons are excellent. And private.'

'Then I shall have to guess,' Sybilla said. 'It isn't really very hard. Or perhaps at this point you would be happier if Mr Hislop really did go away?'

Danny's mouth, metaphorically speaking, dropped open. He got to his feet.

'No,' Marthe said. 'To anyone with Mr Hislop's thirst for knowledge, the reasons must already be obvious. Each partner in our curious marriage has married the other as a substitute for somebody else.'

Danny sat down.

'And that, I take it, is supposed to shock me?' Sybilla said. 'May I take it, instead, a stage further. If either you or he were married to the person of your choice, would you fare any better?'

'Perhaps you would answer that,' Marthe said. 'If you have the experience.'

There was a little silence. Then Danny, paralysed, saw that the blue eyes of Lymond's mother were actually smiling into the blue eyes of Marthe, her tormentor. 'I began to wonder,' Sybilla said, 'how long it was going to take. Of course I can answer it. My son took many years to learn the simple truth. You cannot love any one person adequately until you have made friends with the rest of the human race also. Adult love demands qualities which cannot be learned living in a vacuum of resentment. Mr Hislop, I am sure, will confirm it.'

Mr Hislop swallowed. 'Jesus,' he said. 'Don't drag me into this.'

Marthe ignored him. Her curious gaze, instead, was wholly bent on the small, erect person opposite her. 'You mean,' she said, 'that Francis has come to terms with his birth? In such a short time? I congratulate you. Why so alarmed, Mr Hislop? You knew, surely, that Mr Crawford and I are brother and sister.'

'I thought ... I was under the impression,' said Danny huskily, 'that you were his step-sister.'

'No,' Marthe said. 'Mr Crawford and I, it seems, are both the offspring of Lady Culter's late husband, and a French-woman. Mr Crawford was fortunate in being adopted and reared as the legitimate son of the late Lord Culter, and has readily overcome his disappointment at learning his true condition. I was brought up in France in the full awareness of my bastardy and have taken longer, I freely admit, to learn to love the human race.'

'You have always known that Béatris was your mother?' Sybilla asked. No sympathy showed on the fine-coloured face;

455

only a firm and gentle command, expressed also in the tone of her voice.

'No,' Marthe said. 'Not until our mutual friend Philippa came investigating in Lyon and la Guiche. Then we found the death certificate of the first Francis Crawford. And the rest your son discovered at Flavy-le-Martel.'

Danny pricked up his ears. 'That old woman in the farmhouse? The Spaniards killed her.'

'Renée Jourda, her name was,' Marthe said. 'She had followed you, I think, from la Guiche when you left to marry Gavin.'

The heavy lids had dropped over Sybilla's pale face. 'And she is dead?' she said.

'Francis went back to try and save her,' Danny said. 'That was when he was caught and taken to Ham. Some bastard had warned Lord Grey in the citadel and we were nearly all taken. If I ever find out who it was, I'll have him roasted alive in the pig market.'

'Then go and find him,' said Marthe briefly. 'It was a man called Leonard Bailey.'

There was, for various different reasons, an abrupt silence. A woman's voice, remote and clear, said, 'Fool.' Danny looked about him. Then Sybilla said flatly, 'How do you know.'

Marthe raised her fair brows. 'It was in a letter from Francis to Philippa. She showed it to me. You know, of course, about Philippa's attempts to discover the three witnesses?'

It was too much for Danny. 'Witnesses to what?' he said.

'That is what Jerott asked,' Marthe said. 'But neither Francis nor Philippa, I'm afraid, felt inclined to tell us. That must have been before he learned to trust everybody.'

Sybilla ignored it. 'And did she find her witnesses?' she asked.

'Don't you know?' Marthe said. 'I suppose she did. One of them, a priest, was dead. I presume Renée Jourda was another. And perhaps she found the third by means of the key.'

Leaning back, her golden head gleaming, her eyes half closed like a cat's, she looked at Sybilla, and Sybilla said peacefully, 'Well?' You are either going to tell me or not going to tell me. What key?'

'The key we found with the death certificate, in my grandmother's chair,' Marthe said. 'If I lack finesse, you must make allowances. I was brought up by the Dame de Doubtance and her minion, not at Midculter Castle. I cannot bring myself to love and tolerate my drunken husband. I am living testimony of the fact that men resemble their age more than they do their fathers. You must not expect me to respond quite in the same way as my brother. What have we in common with each other?'

Danny jerked.

'I beg your pardon?' said Sybilla kindly.

'I said, *The face of a hoore and the tongue of a serpent*,' said Mr Hislop mutinously. 'Ask her why, if she resents Mr Crawford so much, she's dead set on his staying married to Mistress Philippa.'

'Do you know,' said Sybilla thoughtfully, 'I don't think I shall? Or is it unfair to spare Francis and Philippa and place poor Jerott on the bill of fare for View and Search Day? I thought Austin Grey and Philippa were fond of one another and Francis was satisfactorily betrothed to the Maréchal de St André's daughter? *C'est tout de même que de manger la poule et puis son poulet?*'

'You know about that?' said Danny, fascinated.

'And approves, I am sure,' Marthe said. 'His wife, who adores him, cannot compete with the St André wealth and the St André prospects.'

'Nonsense,' the Dowager said calmly and Danny, intoxicated with horrified pleasure, wriggled back in his seat. She continued, with equal austerity, 'Philippa, as you well know, is worth two of Catherine d'Albon with her mother thrown in for good measure, but Catherine will do Francis very well. They know the world, and they will conduct their own lives with perfect discretion, and no one will get hurt. I am not having anyone tied to Francis who is as vulnerable as Philippa is.'

'You mean,' Marthe said, 'that she might take to the bottle or the bordello, as Jerott does? And yet you suggest Jerott and I should remain tied together?'

'I mean,' Sybilla said, 'that a marriage between Francis and Philippa was highly unsuitable in the first place, and they are both intelligent enough to know it. Whereas your marriage to Jerott, so far as I can see, has been based mainly on undisciplined emotion and prejudice, and has had no kind of proper test of all. I am willing, on your behalf, to give Jerott a talking-to. He has had a severe fright, and is ready to be taught a lesson.'

'And what,' Marthe said, 'do you suppose you can do about my prejudices?'

'I can answer a question you have not asked me,' Sybilla said.

Marthe laughed. 'You are going to tell me about Gavin,' she said. 'The bold, brown, loud-mouthed Scotsman who made himself so disliked about la Guiche, and yet persuaded the Dame de Doubtance's daughter to go to bed with him?'

Sybilla rose. Thoughtfully, she moved over the indifferent parquet of Master Nostradamus's hired house and seated herself gently at the other end of the heavy, cushioned settle Marthe had occupied. 'What do you know of the Dame de Doubtance?' she said.

'That she was my grandmother,' Marthe said baldly. A strand of the yellow hair, too quickly pinned up, had come coiling like silk over her shoulder. 'That she believed herself to be an astrologer. And that I am grateful for only one thing in our relationship: that at least I was not her daughter.'

'You know then how she directed her daughter's life,' Sybilla said. 'Perhaps it would not even surprise you to know that it was she who arranged for your father and Béatris to become lovers. Then when you were born, she took and reared you. I went to her and asked her to let me have you, but she refused. And since Béatris was her daughter, I could not insist. Then, two years later, Francis was born and Béatris died.'

'And this time, you had no trouble in obtaining her permission?' Marthe said. Derision glittered in her blue eyes.

'None. It was what she wanted. But, although I asked her again, she still would not release you nor, until she died, would she let me come and see you. I wonder,' Sybilla said, 'if you can tell that I am speaking the truth? You must have some of her skills.'

'No!' said Marthe sharply; and then, with an abrupt change of manner, gave a harsh laugh. After a moment she added, 'How can I possibly tell? All I know is that for thirty years you lied to your own son.'

'I was held by a promise,' Sybilla said very quietly. 'It has not turned out, as you will notice, to my advantage.'

'It has not turned out to his,' Marthe said. 'Do you think I envy him? At least I was reared without tenderness and without expectation of it. During all that time, you were breeding a hothouse love based on deception. You suffer now because he has withdrawn it, you imagine. He has not even done that. When the news came that you were lost at sea he set off to ride all night to Dieppe, although he had been so sick he could barely walk over the courtyard.'

'I can't remember why,' Danny said.

The look Marthe gave him would have caused a less brazen spirit to recoil. Undeterred, he went on blandly. 'I take it, if I may interrupt, all this competitive planning on Mr Crawford's behalf, that neither of you has heard what happened after the Hôtel d'Hercule reception the other night? The town is agog with it.'

'After we left?' Sybilla said quickly. 'What?'

'There are two versions,' Danny said. He was enjoying himself. 'One, from the servants, says that the young English prisoner went berserk in the middle of the night and having discovered the comte de Sevigny in bed with both his present and future wives at once, hauled him from between the sheets and attempted to throw him down the staircase. The two ladies ran away screaming and the Marquis of Allendale, having come off worst in the subsequent battle, is now in his priest's hands, having been given up by his doctors.'

'Mr. Hislop?' said Sybilla patiently. The attention of both women, he was pleased to note, was rigidly upon him, whatever they might choose to say.

'The other version,' he said regretfully, 'belongs to Adam and Archie, who say that Philippa was in Lymond's room for an hour, talking, a fact which did not escape his fiancée, with whom he had an assignation. Catherine, so it seems, had the good sense to retreat to her own room and has not been heard to refer to the incident subsequently. Austin, who also witnessed the whole thing, ill-advisedly tried to attack Francis and got, of course, what he asked for.

'However that may be, Francis certainly didn't appear until after the d'Albons had both left for home the next day, and Austin Grey is in bed with a badly broken arm. I rather think,' Danny said, 'that you should cease concerning yourselves too much with Mr Crawford's marital problems. If he is going to take an active hand in them himself, then no gentle feminine influence is going to make itself felt in the general conflagration.'

'What were they talking about?' Marthe said.

It was so far from what he expected that he did not understand. 'What?' said Danny fluently.

459

'What were Francis and Philippa talking about?' she said again, abruptly. 'Adam must have seen Philippa. Why was she there so late at night?'

'I don't know,' Danny said. He hesitated, and then said, 'She had been crying for a long time. Adam said her face was all swollen, but she said it was her own fault and nothing to do with Francis. And after that, she didn't even seem to hear what he said, which was perhaps understandable after a drunken session with Francis on his way to someone else's bedroom.'

There was a little silence. Then, 'Did he go?' said Sybilla softly.

'Adam says no,' said Danny, his confidence steadily dwindling. Sybilla did not look at him while he answered but at Marthe, who sat, her golden head high, sustaining the long, clear regard.

'I see,' Sybilla said. She rose, her eyes still on Marthe, who rose also, her eyes masked for the first time by their lids. Sybilla said, 'It has been enough. I am going. When you have no one else to turn to, come to me.'

The lids lifted at that, to reveal blazing eyes. *'To you?'* Marthe said. 'I would sooner . . .'

'Yes? What would you sooner do?' Sybilla asked.

And as Marthe did not reply, Danny spoke, with less assurance than at any point in the preceding discussion. 'And Jerott?' he said.

Sybilla had begun to walk to the door. She stopped and turned; and when she spoke, it was to Marthe. 'I shall tell Jerott,' said the Dowager, 'that it is better if you do not come together. He will find solace in war.'

'And I?' Marthe said.

'It is for you to begin your studies afresh, although I am not sure of your present choice of tutor. Do you know, Mr Hislop, the expression, *A pen is walking in the chimney behind the cloth?*'

He had already observed the badly-hung hung tapestry, but without Sybilla's quick intuition behind the observation. 'This?' said Danny Hislop; and striding forward, ripped the cloth aside.

Behind the arras was a door, and beyond that a small antechamber, in which stood a single chair. Master Michel Nostradamus, his expression entirely undisturbed, was sitting in it.

'Ah,' said Sybilla. 'Behind the prophet, the analogist. And behind the analogist, the eavesdropper. We have not met before, I am glad to say. Which of you thought of this first?'

'I asked Master Nostradamus to come,' Marthe said.

'And I came, believe me, with no evil intention,' the astrologer said. He rose and, moving through the door, stood before the Dowager Lady Culter. 'I wished to see the chosen vessel and learn why it was chosen. Now I know. Of all the matters you spoke of, there was nothing of which I was not already aware. Mistress Philippa has already been to see me.'

Danny waited, and then as the vital question remained for some reason unasked, put it himself. 'What about?' he said.

The astrologer smiled at him. 'I had promised to tell her how Mr Crawford spent the last evening he passed in Lyon,' he said.

Danny Hislop's pink freckled skin turned slowly the deep scarlet of pure anger. 'And you did?' he said sharply. 'You told . . .'

'Do you, too, enjoy your monopoly?' Nostradamus said. 'I propose to tell no one else, in this room or out of it. I am concerned, as you are, with her future, and with the curing of my patients.'

'And Mistress Marthe is a patient of yours?' said Sybilla. 'As you were a disciple of her grandmother's?'

'We have an understanding,' Nostradamus said. 'Francis Crawford will come to no harm through me; nor will your son Richard.'

'Is that a prediction, or merely a pious intention, I wonder?' Sybilla said. 'I am not sure that I care to have either of my sons' affairs in your hands, and if Marthe were a daughter of mine, I should remove her.'

'If I were a daughter of yours,' Marthe said curtly, 'I should probably go. If it makes any difference, I am willing to accept what you have told me.'

'You should. It is true.' Nostradamus said.

'But it didn't occur to you to tell her,' said Sybilla. From the formidable, her expression had changed to the highly exasperated.

'Yes, it did,' said Nostradamus mildly. 'But I realized that it would come better from you, provided you had the courage to talk to her. I had not then had the experience of meeting you.'

'You must,' said Sybilla coldly, 'come and overhear me

461

again. It might endow you with sufficient of the same to sit and listen to me in the open another time.' She made a slight, perfect curtsey to both her host and her hostess and rising, turned to the door. 'Mr Hislop!'

'Yes,' said Danny, and bowing, hurried after.

Making their way in procession back through the network of streets to the river: 'I feel,' said Danny casually, 'that irritating though the lady may be, she is worth helping.'

'That is why you traced her, isn't it? Of course she is worth helping,' Sybilla said. 'Perhaps Nostradamus will do it as well as anyone.'

'Or Philippa?' Danny said. 'She's good sense incarnate.'

'She is also,' Sybilla said, 'in love with Francis.' The adverb dangled, ambiguously, in the air. 'No. Philippa cannot help,' her mother-in-law continued soberly. 'Philippa herself is engaged in battle that nothing must stop her winning.'

*

At the time she was speaking, the battle which Philippa must win had continued through two nights without sleep and a day of such stupefying abstraction that her royal employers, impatient of the sudden failure of the strongest horse in the wedding team, gave her a day's leave from her duties.

It saved her physical health if nothing else, for the struggle was with herself; and her chief necessity was peace in which to concentrate.

Do you think that I care?

No. But you must excuse the hunchback, who does.'

With the emotional extravagance of a clerk of the Court of Session notifying a transumpt, Francis Crawford had placed briefly on record, for her sake, the one factor in their relationship of which she was ignorant. Then the door had been closed; and she was alone in the dark with her shock.

Restraint is the remedy. So little . . . Nothing had been put into words. Of course he had been confident of the scale of her love, having borne time and again the calf-love of others, men and women, and having watched them suffer because of it. Of his own, he had told her nothing. Perhaps he knew, having lived with Güzel, how short a time earthly passion lasted. She only guessed, from his words, that for him, it must have started in London.

And so he had tried to escape. And she had prevented him. And thence had come the strains which she, as well as his

462

friends, had so officiously set about assuaging. And the blindness which Archie knew about, and Nostradamus, and herself.

She had offered herself as his cure, and he had refused her. To overcome that refusal demanded more than a convincing protestation of life-long devotion. It demanded that she should recognize the steadfast integrity which lay behind the refusal; and destroy it.

And that she could not do. Without a tremor, Francis would bring his spoiled heritage to Catherine, the daughter of two people who in their time had indulged in every form of costly licence. But to herself, a girl of twenty, reared by Kate with wisdom and wit and endless, clear-sighted love, there was no path that pride, regard, convention, self-respect and even, she suspected, an odd, well-disguised quality of self-distrust did not block for him.

She could not be his wife. She must shut the door, as he asked her, on all the crowding memories: the words and actions each now apparent, like shot-silk, in a different colour. her task, for which she needed all her strength and her common sense, was to protect him.

Adam came to tell her what had happened at the Hôtel d'Hercule after she had left. Believing the battle won, she went to find Catherine d'Albon.

She was alone in her chamber. Philippa sat beside her quietly and said, 'I want you to know that Piero Strozzi brought me to the Hôtel d'Hercule the other night with a false message from M. de Sevigny. And that I went to his room, without warning him, because I was upset about some rudeness he had shown to his mother. Austin lost his head.'

'I know,' Catherine said. The lustrous grey eyes within the coiling black hair remained bent on her needlework. 'He apologized, I believe, the following morning. No harm has been done.'

'Except to Austin,' said Philippa lightly. Her own eyes, concerned, were watching the bent head. After a moment she said, 'Catherine?'

The needle flashed once, twice, and then was pushed firmly home. Catherine took her sewing and rose, and lifted from the wall a small looking-glass. Then, reversing it between her long fingers, she held it so that Philippa saw, reflected there, her own perplexed face.

'I know,' Catherine said, 'that the encounter happened by

accident, and that you did not intend to be thoughtless. But since it happened, have you watched the change in your eyes?'

Philippa flushed. She felt the blood rise in her skin, and lifting both hands, took the mirror from Catherine's hold and laid it, face down on the cushion. 'I didn't know,' she said.

'You don't hear, either, when we speak to you; and the children think you have a fever. The rest of us believe it is an affair of the heart.'

'How embarrassing,' Philippa said. Her eyes and her voice were both steady.

'But you have not called on Austin Grey,' Catherine said. She paused, and then said, 'It is Francis, isn't it?'

She had made this girl her friend. And Lymond, knowing all that he did, had asked her to be his wife and still meant to make her so. Philippa smiled, wryly, and said, 'Yes. I'm glad you didn't notice before. He wants his divorce, and the marriage with you. It won't matter. I shall be in England, with Austin probably.'

'I noticed,' said Cathering slowly. 'He has always encouraged the friendship between Lord Allendale and yourself.'

'I told Austin a long time ago,' Philippa said, 'that I loved Francis Crawford, but that there was never any question of our marriage being completed, or of his being interested in anything but ending it as quickly as possible. If, after Easter, Austin, still wants to marry me, I have said I will listen to him.'

'I see,' Catherine said. She picked the glass from the cushion and resting it on her knee, looked at herself consideringly in it. Then, laying her arms on top, she gazed, smiling a little, at Philippa. 'And one word with your husband and you revive like a garden of flowers. Why ... I wish I knew why he does not want to keep you?'

'Look in your mirror again,' Philippa said. And felt sick, while she said it. And wondered, then, how often Francis must have felt this same deadly loathing.

You told yourself that it was a convention: a marriage between two worldly people whose amorous inclinations could without harm lead in opposite directions. But the truth was that this girl loved Francis Crawford with something which might approach, for all he knew, the passion he talked of. *What makes an unsuitable marriage?*

This, she thought as she left Catherine's chamber. One-sided love, where each side hurts and is hurt, like Jerott and Marthe . . . Gavin and Sybilla.

As her love was not. This love which, it had been decided for her, was to die as the child killed by the mutes at Topkapi had died, for the sake of the greater good.

To make that other decision in Turkey he had sacrificed everything: the integrity of his body and the sanctity of his spoken vow; and had been strong enough, in sort, to recover.

Now he demanded an equal sacrifice of her, as well as of himself.

But no. Her thoughts better schooled, she reminded herself. The smothering of an adolescent attachment was all he believed he was asking of her. The self-control which for eleven months had kept his own desires in perfect concealment also made nonsense of her fears for Catherine.

He was not Jerott or Gavin. Catherine would not be allowed to suffer. And in the calm of such a marriage he might find the relief he had himself suggested: a cure which, storm-ridden with remorse and self-loathing, no union with herself could ever offer.

He was right. He had already trodden this path and found it barred: he knew the landscape and was already, in his pain, accustomed to it. It was she, blinded by the brightness of the flame, who could not yet believe that there was no way of dwelling in it.

•

She returned to find the court already packing to travel to Fontainebleau, the ancient hunting box to the south-east of Paris, which the King's father had emerged from his Spanish prison thirty years before to recreate with all the glories of Italy.

The object of the visit was to enable the Tourelles, the Hôtel de Guise, the Louvre and the Palais de Justice to be adequately cleaned, aired and renovated before the royal wedding. The Parliament of Paris had already been requested to sit at the Augustins for that reason.

Fending off agitated jewellers, dressmakers and goldsmiths whose one mule had gone sick, Philippa rallied her flock under the confused Madame de Brêne, and prepared them as well as human agency could for their exodus.

When Danny Hislop called to see her he found her newly released from a lengthy conference between Charles de

Guise, the bride, the Bishop of Paris and the King's consort, sister and mistress. It was clear that the discussion had not been harmonious. Philippa was undeniably jaded; and the dark skin under her eyes told of sleeplessness which owed nothing to this interminable process of bringing the next King of France to the altar.

He said, 'You look, if I may say so, just like Sardanapalus, that beastly epicure, the morning after his orgy. You know he has left Paris?'

Philippa nodded.

'He's taken Jerott and Archie with him,' Danny said. 'And they say that Strozzi has joined him. Wherever they're going, I'm glad I'm not there: it'll be a Franco-Italian blood-bath. And talking of Jerott . . .'

'You've taken Lady Culter to see Marthe. What, then?' Philippa said. And listened while, succinctly, the elements of the encounter were laid before her by Danny.

So Sybilla now knew that Leonard Bailey was in France, and that she, Philippa, had the key to the Hôtel des Sphères. And Sybilla's first reaction, being a valiant lady, would be to trace Leonard Bailey if she could, and forestall any trouble he might be planning. And next, to call on Isabelle Roset in the rue de la Cerisaye and make sure that her secret was intact.

At least, with Danny's willing co-operation, the inevitable meeting between Sybilla and Marthe had taken place under supervision. Philippa said, 'The Commissioners are departing, aren't they, for Fontainebleau also? Or Moret. At least, they will leave Paris shortly?'

'We all are,' Danny said. 'They want to wipe the finger-marks off everything before the wedding. You still want Lady Culter stopped if she shows any signs of wanting to go to the Arsenal area?'

It had been the recurrent nightmare, the arrival of Sybilla alone at the Hôtel des Sphères, and of Leonard Bailey opening the door to her. 'Yes. Has she tried?' Philippa said.

'No. She hasn't had a chance, and Lord Culter is generally with her anyway. She wouldn't send a servant?' said Danny wistfully. No one would tell him why Lymond's mother should not be allowed to visit the Arsenal area.

She wouldn't send anyone, nor would she take anyone with her. She organizes witches' Sabbaths every full moon,' explained Philippa tartly.

Danny said, clearing his throat to cover an unaccustomed awkwardness, 'Nostradamus told us you had been to see him.' Then he blushed.

Philippa looked at him. 'How did you know?' And then, as she read his face. 'Is Marthe with Nostradamus?'

'He couldn't get a raven,' Danny said. He cleared his throat again. 'I gather he was indiscreet about Mr Crawford's ... accident at Lyon. Don't let it trouble you. While his mother and brother are here, he's not going to do anything daft: even Archie is satisfied.'

'He doesn't look very satisfied,' Philippa said. 'And after his mother and brother go home?'

'Well: he'll have his divorce,' Danny said. The pink, putty face steadied on her. 'If he leaves for Russia, will you try to stop him?'

'No,' Philippa said. 'I've cut the string. Didn't you know? If anyone wants to stop Mr Crawford from doing anything, they should now apply to Catherine d'Albon.'

●

She called on Austin. His arm, strapped under his doublet, was still useless. He had tried to tolerate it unsupported when he learned she was to visit him, but had been forced, sick with pain, to replace the bandaging. He had no cause for complaint: he had begun the quarrel. And Philippa had explained to him the reason for her visit to de Sevigny's room.

He had little news to give her, beyond that he was being well cared for at a prescribed level, Philippa gathered, which fell tidily half-way between the generous and the patronizing. It was a relief that Lymond was absent. Before that, the house had been filled with secretaries and couriers and advisers. And since the reception, the number of fellow countrymen calling had trebled, even though de Sevigny had seen very few of them. He asked, hesitatingly, 'Was the evening very ... flamboyantly Scottish?'

'No. He avoided that,' Philippa said. 'But he has a popular reputation, and I expect people like Orkney and Erskine have sounded him out and vouchsafed some sort of general cachet of approval. Being sought after is no novelty.'

'No. I suppose not,' Austin said. He glanced at his hands and added, 'The marriage with Mistress d'Albon is then to go on?'

467

'She hasn't changed her mind,' Philippa said. 'And neither, of course, has he.'

'Philippa,' said Austin Grey. 'If something were to go wrong and you have need of a friend ... only a friend, will you think of coming to me?'

He knew nothing. He merely loved her, and intuition told him she was in trouble.

Her eyes bright with tears, Philippa Crawford walked forward and touching the empty sleeve at his side, kissed him on the cheek. Then she left quickly.

❄

Waiting for her in the Château with Gino Schiatti with a packet. Inside, heavily sealed, was the pair of folded documents which Leonard Bailey had deposited at his banker's shop on the day that she had visited him.

Master Schiatti, who had just to his surprise received a very warm kiss, showed her, a little flushed, how to slit the seal with the minimum of disturbance and left, on the reassurance that the packet—or one very like it—would be returned to him within twenty-four hours, or even earlier. He received another kiss which led him to wonder, hopefully, if the English bastard at the Hôtel d'Hercule was dying.

Alone in her room, Philippa unfolded the papers. And then, laying them down, to the detriment of her paint, her powder, her dress and her hair, she wept aloud, with wet, incoherent sobs like an imbecile. For the papers had nothing written upon them at all.

With native cunning, Leonard Bailey had not confided Sybilla's affirmations to his banker in Paris, but had simply made of the bureau a decoy. These were blank. The true papers had been hidden elsewhere.

And although, in due course, she sat up and blew her nose, and rinsed her face and restored, so far as possible, all the vista of equanimity laced with severity required by her present duties, she knew that the reverse she had just suffered was a major one.

Someone in authority must hold Bailey's documents, but to find him now at short notice was virtually impossible. There remained only one gleam of hope. Perhaps Bailey had lied. Perhaps no second copy existed. Perhaps it was the original which had gone, not to a Paris bank but to England.

She would know, when she received Henry Sidney's reply.
And meantime, time was running out.

'Collect all the money you have,' Leonard Bailey had said,
'And I shall tell you the price. If there is one.'

CHAPTER 4

Mort conspirée viendra en plein effet
Charge donnée et voyage de mort
Eleu, cree, receu, par siens deffait,
Sang d'innocence devant soy par remort.

Painted, portly, bellicose as puffins in ungainly flight from
their feeding-ground, the Court rose from Paris and settled,
pecking, in a fresh set of burrows at Fontainebleau.

Built to rival the gilded palace of Nero, the blue-roofed
château of Gilles le Breton lay in its park like a scarab, encircling harmonious courtyards fit for the muster of armies,
and enclosed all about by the noble forest teeming with game
which had first determined its building. Behind the palace,
beyond the Basse-Cour and the Convent of Mathurins which
enclosed it, was the town, once a village, which had grown to
serve the court with its inns and its tradesmen, and in which
domestics and guards and officials, decorators, artists and ar-
chitects could all find lodging. There, also, were the private
houses of the officers of state and the wealthier noblemen: La
Rochefoucauld and La Roche-sur-Yon: the Cardinal de Bourbon and the House of Guise and all its offspring.

Those who could find no harbour there were forced to
travel the forest to Moret-sur-Loing, a pleasant small riverside town with a castle, in which the Crown housed its official
guests on occasion, and where its permanent foreign ambassadors were also expected to stay. There the nine Commissioners from Scotland were lodged, and divided their time,
in chilly March weather, between Moret and Fontainebleau
itself.

The Royal family and all those dear to its heart were
housed in the windowed white geometry of the palace itself,
with squared gardens and fountains and lake water to look
upon. They included the brothers de Guise of whom, in the
nature of things, Philippa saw a good deal. It was the Duke
and the Cardinal who arranged all the wedding ceremonial,

470

including placing in hand the six silver-sailed ships of gold tissue and crimson velvet suggested by Signor Primaticcio in the wake of which she could foresee, with a cynicism born of experience, a long tunnel of hopeless catastrophes.

She saw them also at the succession of informal entertainments for the growing numbers of wedding guests already gathering. And she saw them when, supervised by Cardinal Charles, the Scottish Commissioners embarked upon the series of conclaves to discuss and ratify the marriage agreement between their child Queen and the fourteen-year-old Dauphin.

They brought the bridegroom in from the hunting field for some of the meetings. Standing behind the young Queen, Philippa saw the nine Commissioners each in his own way covertly watch him: this pallid snub-nosed boy with the heavy head and perpetual catarrh who slept, or sat groaning with earache, or would run out when released in an access of useless energy and seizing a horse, ride himself into a collapse, and the palfrey to death.

One listened then to the interminable voices, the Scots and the French, pondering all the matters at issue: the dowry Mary was to be given; the pension she was to receive and the lands; and the repetition in three tongues of the terms of the treaty made in Haddington those ten years before, by which her highness *contracted, agreed and obliged herself that she and her heirs-successors should observe and keep the Freedoms, Liberties and Privileges of the realm of Scotland and the laws of the same siclike and in the same manner as in all King's times of Scotland of before*; and to provide that if she died without issue, *the righteous blood of the Crown of Scotland should succeed without any impediment.*

Then one looked at the slim back and auburn hair and pale, pointed face of Maria Dei gratia regina Scotorum, and wondered how Cardinal Charles had so trained and shaped and moulded a volatile, emotional fifteen-year-old that she, too, was more attentive to paper and ink, to legal concession and legal commitment than to flesh and blood. But then, Philippa reminded herself, the manner of ruling comes easily to the young, and is a balm to their pride, until they learn better.

The articles drew towards their final drafting. Towards the third week of March, attending the Queen on her retiral, Philippa caught the ring of Piero Strozzi's ebullient speech

471

somewhere in the long, painted galleries, in competition with another assured voice, equally unmistakable. Francis was back.

He brought the Commissioners to their assignation next morning. She heard him speaking, with a little unwonted emphasis, outside the room, and knew she had been given a warning. Then he walked in with the rest.

As always, the fair hair, brushed and orderly now, asserted itself among the others. But this time his eyes also came to her instantly, open and dark as they had been on that night in his chamber. She had not known until now, in her isolation, that after closing the door he had not walked away from it.

Later, she received a smile and a bow, but both were formal. He looked tired but moved and spoke firmly, as if brought back to tone by air and exercise. Where he had been she had not yet discovered, except for the fact that he had spent four days on horseback. He was helpful but noncommittal in conference. From John Erskine, with whom she had formed a pleasant acquaintance, she heard after a week of such meetings that on the journeys to and from Moret he would go further.

'We pick his brains,' Erskine said, 'and he is not unwilling, I think, to advise us. He believes—and I think we are all agreed on it—that the next key figure in Scotland will be Arran, the present heir to the crown. Unhappily, if we identify him too closely now with the Reformed party, the Queen Dowager may well bequeath the Regency to Lennox. Elder, his secretary, is here. Perhaps you have seen him.'

'I've not only seen him,' Philippa said tartly. 'I fall over him every time I walk through the door to the Presence Chamber.' She added, quelling the twitching nerves of her stomach, 'Do you think both religions can co-exist under Arran?'

'I hope so. Under Lord Lennox, of course,' Erskine said, 'the whole country would be Papist, and moved to it by burnings. It also remains to be seen how tolerant the Queen Dowager will remain after this wedding. With the might of France legally behind her, she may feel differently towards heretics like ourselves. Your husband also says—'

'He has a theory that if France and Spain end their war, they may make some sort of Holy Alliance together. What is true,' Philippa said, 'is that the King of France has borrowed a great deal of gold from the clergy, and they may want to see something soon for their money. Also, it would be nice for the de Guises to have a niece who is Catholic Queen of three countries, provided England can be overrun satisfactorily. I'm glad your expatriates are being useful to you. I thought Francis was remaining aloof from his countrymen.'

'You will find,' said John Erskine, 'that he has changed his policy in a number of things since he came back from Thionville—' He stopped.

'Thionville? You might as well go on,' Philippa said. 'If anyone has overheard us, we are due for the gibbet already. It's a town on the Moselle, isn't it, on the eastern frontier with the Archbishoprics and Champagne?'

'It is one of the strongest held by Spain, and threatens all that region of France. It has already stood up to at least three assaults, but the Governor of Metz thinks that if the King will raise some German levies, he can take it. Mr Crawford has just been to see him, with Signor Strozzi. I have not, of course, heard the details, but it will form the main part of the French spring campaign, to open, I imagine, after the wedding.'

'And Francis is arranging it?' Philippa said.

'If you were to ask the Duke de Guise, he would answer you differently,' Erskine said. 'But from what I hear, there is very little that our friend is excluding, at the moment, from his daily round. D'Aumale tells me that he has been given rooms in the palace.'

Philippa knew that. Since his return from Thionville, Madame Marguerite had seen to it that he honoured his promise to visit her. From the other royal apartments also, one would hear of an evening the remote strains of *Du fond de ma pensée*, and *Ne veuillez pas ô Sire*; and laughter. M. de Sevigny had become of the magic circle with whom the King steamed daily in his suite of hot baths. Even Mary had asked him to come and play for her, and Philippa had watched while the two sat and conversed. She did not know what the topic was, but she did observe that Monseigneur mon oncle was not altogether pleased when he arrived and discovered them. That evening, the Queen was invited to retire rather early.

For themselves, they never talked, save for a commonplace exchange in public. Yet she saw him every day, or heard him spoken of. She knew, without turning round, when he had entered a room: she could pick out his voice, or his music, or his laughter from any concourse. He had spoken of the few meetings still left to them. He could not have foreseen that they would have to share the same house, however vast, in the weeks before their parting.

It tired her beyond reason: the more that she observed for the first time the ceaseless, invisible care with which he treated their relationship. He avoided what meetings he could, and made the rest simple. She tried very hard, seeing his glance on her, to seem calm, but knew she did not always succeed. And even on his face sometimes, or in his manner, she caught a shadow of strain, so well disguised that she could not be sure of it, until Archie's angry black gaze told her that she had guessed correctly.

Once, she saw him leave the room abruptly half-way through a recital of indifferent music. No one else, she thought, observed it: the singer, undeterred, continued hooting mournfully: *The fruit of all the service that I serve . . .*

The tone, there was no doubt, was excruciating. The following day he was occupied as usual, she was told; and spent the morning in conclave with the Duke de Nevers and the King's leading Treasury officials.

The wedding drew nearer. No saving letter arrived from London. No message, no sign came from Leonard Bailey to warn her which way his concupiscence would lead him: towards herself, or to the Countess of Lennox through Elder. For the first time since the evening at the Hôtel d'Hercule, she was thrown together with Sybilla at a formal dinner for the Commissioners and for foreign ambassadors, held in the monumental ballroom with its ten painted window bays and caissoned ceiling, its bronze satyrs and white and gold stucco and statues and swirling frescoes of nymphs and heroes and goddesses.

It put her, as usual, off her food and made her want to escape later on to the gardens. There she found Bishop Reid of Orkney and Lady Cutler contemplating the Michelangelo Hercules at the edge of the pond, with the fountain spray unregarded soaking their garments. 'For an atheist,' Sybilla said, eyeing it, 'Signor Strozzi is blessed with quite excessive good taste. You ought to ask him to tell you about his collection of antique books and weaponry. I believe the Queen has her eye on them.'

474

'The weapons?' Philippa said, joining her after a small hesitation.

'Well of course, perhaps; but I don't think she'd need them,' Sybilla said. 'Stekit to deid on ground lay mony man: she has her own methods. Bishop Reid and I were having a comfortable discussion over how we are ever going to enjoy other people's gardens if we don't continue to teach children the classics. Also, we agree that those are Bears'-ears.'

Philippa surveyed the flower plot gravely. 'And, undoubtedly, Affodyll Daffadilly,' she said. 'And do I detect a seedling or two of Love-lies-bleeding?'

The heavy, black-capped head of Robert Reid with its grizzled beard was tilted towards her. 'Amaranthus caudatus,' he said loudly. 'You are an atavist. You are a snivelling follower of those Cambridge lackwits who think Adam spoke English and we can do no better. . . .'

'Philippa,' said Lady Culter blandly, 'is one of Roger Ascham's favourite pupils. We all know every onion in Beauly can reel off the Georgics but it can all become a little excessive, as the elephant said when he fell in love with the herb-wench. I hear Lord James has been refused the Earldom of Moray. A second Lombardy.'

'I didn't hear you,' the Bishop said.

'I thought not. The Queen said it was a secular title, and Lord James is supposed, of course, to be Prior of St Andrews. I hope he received the news meekly.'

'I suppose James might receive the Second Coming meekly,' said Bishop Reid, his hearing suddenly recovered, 'but I doubt it. I have to go indoors.'

'Then Philippa and I will walk along and see the Atlases in the Pine Grotto,' Sybilla said. 'There is no doubt about it: the spectacle of large gentlemen striving to uphold vast blocks of monumental masonry does wonders for the digestion.' Then as, parting from the Bishop, they walked side by side through the pine garden, she said in quite a different tone, 'I shall not keep you long. I have no right to keep you at all. I only wanted to beg you to contrive that Francis is taken to see a doctor.'

Philippa ceased walking. 'I know he isn't well,' she said. 'But I doubt if a doctor can help him. He has already been told the cause of it. They say he has a chronic inability to suffer reverses.'

It was not very kind. It was better than saying, *Go and see*

Nostradamus. Get him to tell you what he treated your son for.

Sybilla, who had halted also, began walking again. 'You cannot possibly take anyone's part in this but his,' she said. 'I spoke to Marthe: perhaps Mr Hislop has told you. The wisest advice anyone could give Francis now is to turn his back on us all, and marry Catherine d'Albon. Do you think he will?'

'I think so,' Philippa said. They had reached the blockish ranks of grey sandstone giants and stepping inside the vault of the grotto she sank down on the marble beside one of the two little fountains whose trapped light, released in fine spray, illuminated the crystalline walls and the frescoes embedded within them. He slept in the château, and not in Catherine d'Albon's bed, where once it had seemed so desirable to direct him. Nor, she knew very well, would he bring himself to go there now, before the obligations of marriage made it necessary. She said aloud, 'He finds the time of waiting troublesome, I think. We all do. But it will soon be over.'

'I asked,' Sybilla said, 'because I have seen him like this before ... once; when he elected to take everyone else's business in hand and return it to them correctly aligned, like an artist with a child's drawing.'

She stopped talking. Standing by the murmuring spray, her eyes downcast, her hands clasped together under her cloak she said nothing more for a long time and Philippa, waiting, finally said gently, 'What happened?'

Sybilla looked up. 'He left the castle,' she said. 'He was only a boy. Everyone in Midculter looked for him. Richard had no sleep for two nights. It was Eloise who finally found and brought him back.'

'His sister?' Philippa said. The girl who had died in a gunpowder accident in her Scottish convent while still in her teens, during the last English wars. The girl who was also no daughter of Gavin Crawford's and who, perhaps had known it. *Poor Eloise*, Lymond had said.

Eloise had brought him back ... from what? And now Sybilla wanted her to do the same. But not to remain married to him. She had made that quite plain as well. Philippa wondered how much she knew, or guessed about her son, and what she would say if she were told that Lymond had made his choice, and had turned his back on that also.

Then, looking at Sybilla's bent, fair-white head, Philippa

476

realized that what she had just heard was such a pronouncement. Sybilla guessed, even if she did not fully comprehend, that Lymond's feelings were somehow also engaged now. And knowing Francis, saw the barrier better even than she did.

Philippa said, 'After the annulment, I am going back to England with Austin.' A shaft of sunlight, entering between the triple arches, lit the enigmatic smile of a green-haired lady emerging from a large cockle shell to one side of her. She added, a little desperately, 'There are some details Francis doesn't know, and I haven't told him. The Hôtel des Sphères is locked up and shuttered: Madame Roset seems to have gone away. So I threw away the key.'

Sybilla looked up. Against the sunlight, Philippa could not read her face. 'Thank you,' she said. And then, after a moment, 'I hear that Leonard Bailey is in France.'

It was a question, although it didn't sound like one. Philippa said, 'He made an attempt to have Francis taken by the English at Ham, but that seems to be all. He has probably gone back to England. Even if he does appear, Francis will do nothing to harm him, nor shall I.'

Her voice, stoutly lying, echoed all around the twelve-foot vault. Someone once told her that the mirrors set into the niches had been made as peepholes for a royal observer. It hardly seemed necessary, with all the explicit romping taking place from wall to wall in every room. De Brissac had told her that the bath-house paintings had taken his mind off his gout for the first time since he got home from Italy.

She had lied to Sybilla, and would go on doing so. What good would it do to say, 'Within four weeks, unless he accepts my bribe or unless I can steal the evidence, Leonard Bailey will have sold all he knows about your extra-marital affairs to the Lennoxes in England?'

If Bailey were going to accept money, she could find or raise as much as Sybilla. If he were not, it was better that Sybilla should know nothing about it. It was for herself, a free agent, to attempt whatever felony was needed to remove the evidence from Bailey's reach.

So she thought, looking at Sybilla, and Sybilla said, 'From limbo, you cannot say *forgive me*, unless you can also say you regret what you have done. I have no regrets. I have nothing to tell you, except what you know already: that love is a powerful master. For his favours do you pay tribute and toll while flesh endures, and no doubt after.'

I have no regrets. Against the sunlight the slender, erect body looked for a moment as it must have looked thirty years before and more, when, careless of any consequences, and herself another man's wife, Sybilla had followed where love dictated.

'I shall do what I can,' said Philippa baldly; and rising, walked out of the grotto and quickly, back to the palace without her.

There, she found in the succeeding days that nothing had changed. The peace overtures continued slowly to cross and recross between Fontainebleau and Brussels, with offers of mediation from the imprisoned St André and the Constable. M. d'Andelot travelled north to arrange for the fitting out of vessels to secure the French coast from possible English invasion. Fifty infantry captains left to raise companies to go to Scotland and Piedmont. An army of 15,000 German infantry and 4,000 cavalry began to collect at Metz, and for several days, Lymond was in every room that one happened to enter, from the King's post in the basse-cour to that of virtually each man holding senior office under the crown, in addition to a number of others lodged in the town outside the gates.

Philippa, mediating in an agonizing war of precedence between Alec Ross and du Boulay, the Lorraine herald-at-arms, during the final draft of the order of procession, was aware of it. The dispute dragged on into the Monday of Holy Week, when a new irritation beset her. Mary, already committed to eight minor engagements to do with her wedding garments and trousseau, was instead removed from her suite and closeted for the entire morning in the Cardinal's room with the Dauphin, the keeper of Seals and two secretaries.

Madame de Sevigny dealt herself with the callers, a last-minute injunction by Madame Diane, and a visit from the Queen which lasted an hour. Then, returning limp to her room for some much-needed letter-writing, she found Archie Abernethy standing there, awaiting her.

Célie was there. She sent her out, and shut the door. 'What?' she said.

'Now I need help,' Archie said.

She could feel all the blood leaving her face. 'I thought he was out with de Nevers,' she said.

'He was. He has just come in. He'll be out again shortly,' Archie said.

478

I have seen him like this before. Philippa said, 'Is he ill? Archie?'

And Archie said, 'Ill? He hasna the time tae be ill. He's thrang as a tick in a tannery.'

'Too busy?' Philippa said.

'Aye,' said Archie. The black eyes scoured her face, and his voice was quite deliberate. 'He's like a man making his will: and in a hurry over it.'

She had kept from Sybilla, to spare her, the knowledge of what had happened in Lyon. But Sybilla, closer far to her own son than she could be, had already seen where lay the danger.

Her throat dry, she said, 'What has happened?'

Master of camouflage, what had he to fear from marriage to Catherine? His cure lay there, if he wanted it; and the responsibilities he had promised to honour. The path to Russia lay open. All around him now, unlike that evening in Lyon, he had means of escape. He had said so himself.

Archie shrugged. 'All I know is what's going to happen.'

Philippa said, 'What should I do?'

And Archie said, *'Break him.'*

❧

That afternoon she was chained to the Queen: there was no one to take her place in all the Holy Week ritual and Mary, normally so full of laughter and invention, was unsympathetic. She saw no reason why Mistress Philippa should visit her husband; and she remained all day obdurate as an unrepentant wine drinker, his head full of fumes from his tankards.

It was early evening before the mood lifted. Released, her heart beating, Philippa ran.

Archie opened the door to the comte de Sevigny's expensive apartments.

'You're late,' he said.

'Well, I'm here now,' said Philippa sharply. 'Where is he?'

'Not here,' Archie said with some bluntness. And as she drew a harsh breath: 'If he's had a hard day, Mistress Philippa, then these rooms are the last place he'd come to. You're the fifth to chap at the door since he shut it.'

'Then where . . . ?' Philippa said, and broke off before the stare of the black, gimlet eyes.

'I gave my word I wouldna let on to a soul, but if you ken

479

my lord count, then perhaps ye ken where he'd find what he wanted,' Archie said. 'Or if not, M. de Montdoré could maybe advise you.'

Pierre de Montdoré was a distinguished mathematician. He was also the King's librorum custodes: the curator of the beautiful library of Charles the Good, housed above the Little Gallery which linked the basse-cour buildings to those of the Oval Court, where lay the royal apartments. From that, it was not hard to guess where Francis had gone to find refuge. To the counsel of dead men. And to solitude.

*

When, presently, Philippa set wide the great double doors of the library, the curator was not in the chamber. The night sky, indigo through the thirteen dormer windows, looked down upon the tiered ranks of fretted shelves, twelve on each side, which held the nine hundred manuscripts lovingly collected by Charles, and the five hundred Greek works left by King Henri's father, along with the others brought him from abroad by his collectors, and looked after for him by Budé. *Go tell my wife*, that curator had said without looking up from his book, when fire broke out and raged through his lodgings. *Go tell my wife. I do not concern myself with domestic matters.*

Montdoré was not in his library tonight, but the silver candelabra were lit at the end of the long shining river of parquet, islanded by lecterns and benches and tables of marble and marquetry, and tall chairs, their fringed velvet stamped with the royal cipher. And at the furthest table, his head lightly propped on one hand, a man sat alone, absorbed in reading. From where she stood, Philippa could see the glimmer of scarlet and gold on the vellum spread under his fingers, and the air was so still that the candlelight lay without tremor on the still, golden wing of his hair.

Philippa closed the door, and Francis looked up, and saw her.

Afterwards, Philippa thought he guessed in that moment why she had come to him. As it was, he dropped his eyes after an interval and laying one hand on the vellum, eased the front board of the book slowly over it and closed both its hasps. A carved ivory boss formed the hub of the thick gilded cover and a band of ouched jewels framed the boards in a coloured rectangle. His fingers still resting on the embossed calf, Lymond rose, and then moving it a little aside, as if to safety, he pushed his chair back and stood where he was, awaiting her.

'Certain comfortable places of the Epistles, namely the Romans,' he said. 'You have brought no one with you?'

'No,' Philippa said. She stopped just short of the table and saw, by the motionless light of the candles, how he had changed in face and manner into something fine-drawn and deliberate, it seemed, in its lack of involvement. She drew a breath and said, 'I have come alone and broken all the rules. The door is locked and Archie is waiting outside to turn any callers away.'

She paused and waited, judging her moment. Lymond said, 'I see. Then, since nothing has changed, it must be for a very good reason.'

'If nothing had changed,' Philippa said, 'I shouldn't be here.'

'Ah,' Lymond said. He added dryly, 'It would sometimes help if Archie's nervous system were less directly attuned to the elephant world.'

Philippa said, 'Perhaps. Sybilla also has asked that you should be taken to see a doctor.'

'So many setters,' he said. 'I thought we understood one another. I thought it was agreed we go our separate ways.'

He had not asked her to sit. She chose one of the velvet chairs and watched herself in his eyes as she seated herself in it. Her skirts, dove-grey for Lent, lay ruched and arrowed about her, and her hair was dressed high and tight-caught with ribbons, save where it lay coiled on her cheek. Pleated cambric covered her shoulders and rose to a high buttoned collar, against which her earrings caught and drifted and swung. She said, 'In the Hôtel d'Hercule, you asked me to make a sacrifice. I am not prepared to see it thrown in the gutter.'

She studied him. Slowly, prudently, one must mount this attack. The world was full of men and women who had tried to bring down Francis Crawford, but none with the advantage she had. And he was tired: more tired, she thought, than on the night she had gone to his room; and his nerves must be bruised, as hers were, with the interminable stress of their meetings.

But as yet, his voice answering her was quite composed. 'For a Somerville, that sounds a little dramatic. Absence is absence, whatever causes it. It is no more or less an affront to you. I did say, as I remember, that I would try to do what you wished me to do. And that you must forgive me if I failed.'

He remained standing. Like herself, he was still in court dress: elegant, close-fitting, impeccable in every detail; and crossed by the black sash of his Order which Austin Grey had torn to the ground.

Philippa said, 'And are you failing? Why?'

He said, 'Because an encounter like this, Philippa, doesn't make it easy to do anything else.' Then he paused and said a little flatly, 'Also, I have been watching you. . . . I did not mean to hurt you so much.'

'I know,' she said. Sitting perfectly still, her hands laid together in her silk lap, she let her eyes speak for her and saw his darken, waiting. She said, 'I thought, too, that it would be kinder to let you think me afflicted with calf-love, or an adolescent devotion, but of course this is not so.' She heard her own voice tremble and stilled it, smiling with her lips only. 'Before God, you are my soul; and till death and beyond, will remain so.'

She saw him catch his breath. One second passed; then two; then three. Then he leaned back his hand and, touching the chair, let himself smoothly into it. He said, 'Then you don't know, Philippa, what I am.'

'I know what you think you are,' Philippa said.

'But not what I am. Will you let me tell you?' he said. And when she nodded, laid his flawless hands on the table and, turning over and over the silk marker lying there, began to speak levelly.

Told in a measured voice, hesitating sometimes; resuming always undemonstratively, it was the story, without colour and virtually without explanation, of all that was ugly in his past. Much of it, as she had said, Philippa already knew. Now she heard also the rest. She heard what happened on his last visit to France; what happened in Scotland; in Djerba; in Russia. She learned the truth about Oonagh O'Dwyer, and Joleta Malett, and of the great courtesan called Güzel. She learned—and did not know she was the first person to be told of it—of the sweet summer's dell north of Hexham where, sick of tragedy and despairing of all the future, he had tried to taunt Richard into knifing him.

And that, in turn, had been after the death of Christian

Stewart, who was blind and who for his sake had ridden to her death over the great Roman ditch by Flaw Valleys, driven to it by Margaret Lennox.

Philippa remembered, far off in her childhood, a red-haired girl being carried, dust-covered and bloody, into Flaw Valleys and laid in the bed with the yellow silk curtains. She remembered Kate's face as Lymond stood by the bed. As the girl died, he had made music for her.

'That was when . . .' Philippa said. There were unshed tears, swelling and pricking under her lashes. But she did not let them fall. In this circus, she was not the victim.

'That was when you were ten years old,' Lymond said. 'And I was an outlaw and an excommunicate, a mercenary and a vagabond already. She died because of me. If I lose my sight, it will only be a kind of rude justice. By releasing you from the net, I pay my debt to her, and to Oonagh and to all the others who died.'

He stopped. His eyes saw the marker, twisted and wrung in his hands, and opening them, he laid it gently down on the marble. Then he lifted his head for the first time and looked at her.

'And I, then, am the son of Abraham?' Philippa said. 'To pay your debts; to salve your pride; to protect your honour, I am to be sacrificed?'

The lash caught him disarmed. He swept his fists from the table and then was still. Then he said, 'Did you not hear?'

'I heard you. It makes no difference.'

'And if it becomes known who my father is?' He could not keep the bitterness, this time, from his voice.

'What is Kuzúm?' Philippa said. 'He is himself. You told me that, once. Embrace whatever stigma you like. My life and birth are both blameless and I am being punished because of your scruples.'

He said, 'Would you rather I had none?'

'No,' Philippa said. 'But I think you must find the grace to forgo them. Otherwise I pay for your sins and you escape, as always.' She looked at him, her brown eyes very open and level. 'I will give you to Catherine. I will not give you to a hole in the ground. I am going to hold you, Francis, to your marriage.'

It was the first time in all the months since Lyon that she had called him by his name. A flame showed, sudden and blue in the depths of his eyes, and then died. The pulse, beating above his drawn brows, told her all at once that he had a headache. 'There is no way you could hold me,' he said.

The wind sighed a little, softly wailing, in the roof windows. The candles burned, repeated over and over in the glazed grilles. The long, empty room filled with the scents of cypress wood and leather and ink harboured them without taking sides, without intrusion, as had the meadow grass on the other occasion when, out of anger, not love, his brother had set out to smash his defences.

'Of course: never against your will,' Philippa said. She rose. Her robe rustled. She moved round the chair and spread her skirts on the arm of it, a little nearer than before to the table. She said, 'Then tell me that what you feel for me is an infatuation. That you object to being tied. That, like poor Jane Shore's lover, you find yourself more amorous of my body than curious of my soul? Then I should agree with you. That I should want to be spared.'

A trickle of wax, occasioned by the draught of her movement, ran like an escaping spirit down the stem of a candle and there stiffened, extinguished as an unwanted emotion. Lymond drew an uneven breath. 'What is temptation, if not that?'

'Then tell me,' Philippa said. 'And make me believe it.'

It was a moment before he replied. Then the shut mouth curled, in something not quite a smile. 'Gould bydeth ever bright ... It would be a pity to cloud it,' he said. 'That is one blasphemy I cannot bring myself to commit. I love you, Philippa, in every way known to man.'

She kept her hands still, and her head; and her buttoned collar hid her throat when she swallowed. She said, 'But you love your vanity more.'

It stung him to his feet; and it seemed a long interval before he removed his gaze and walking across to the bookshelves turned in their shadow, his head gilt against the lustrous bindings. He said, 'Choose your darts better. That means *Put me first*, Philippa. And I don't believe you would ask it.'

She said, 'Do I not come before vanity?'

'I have that, too,' he said. 'But you know the difference between that and conscience. Every other woman since Eve has asked to be loved more than honour. But not you.'

'If you have any,' she said. 'After what you have told me.'
She was standing.

He knew very well now what sort of attack he was under.
He said, 'Even if it is only a chimera, it makes marriage impossible.'

'It seems a pity,' Philippa said. 'But if honour can't make
me the legal occupant of your bed, would it cavil at a private
arrangement? Or do I have to be a fully paid bawd before
you would think it proper?'

He said, 'Don't. That is not a weapon for you. And it
destroys what we have.'

'But I have nothing, yet,' Philippa said. 'And all the nicety
is on your side. Which means I choose any weapon that suits
me. You say I can't hold you to your marriage. Neither I
can. But I can find my way to your room; and to your bed.
Do you think your scruples could survive that? Or I can
come close to you now, like this. The door is locked.'

'*No!*' he said; and then controlled it immediately. 'No,
Philippa. Forgive me, but I'm going to call Archie.' She was
standing only four paces off.

'For protection?' she said.

He said, 'I'm trying to save you. I'm trying to save myself,
if you like. And Catherine. And Austin.'

'They will marry someone else. Perhaps someone who loves
them,' Philippa said. 'Can't you forget what is behind you?
Can't you accept this gift for what it is? Or don't you believe,
don't you see what it is?'

'I see it,' Lymond said. 'It is out of my reach.'

There was an open box on the desk beside Philippa, and
within it a bone pen, and a knife for trimming it. She
stretched out her fingers and lifting the knife, laid it on her
narrow palm. 'Then,' she said, 'if you can slash your wrists
from self-pity, you can hardly keep me from cutting mine,
can you?'

He pushed himself from the grille. 'Stop play-acting,' he
said. His tone suddenly changed, held in it a note that was
quite outside the usual.

Philippa allowed her calm gaze to dwell on him. 'Why not?
I thought we were speaking of death and dishonour? You
would advance to your grave and I should join the ranks of
your numerous dead: Diccon and Salablanca, Tosh and
Christian Stewart; Oonach; Will Scott and his father; Turkey
Mat and Tom Erskine; the dog Luadhas; the child Khaired-

485

din. . . . What shall I say to your son when I meet him? *Don't be surprised: your sire loved me also?'*

The penknife shone in her hand. All he had to do was grasp her and take it. She added, gently, 'It seems a just ultimatum.'

He said, his voice deathly tired, 'You know that if you take one step nearer; if you lift that blade to your wrist, you have beaten me.'

The knife flashed and quivered on her palm. 'I came here to defeat you.' Philippa said. She added violently, 'By any expedient.'

Against the gold and crimson and brown of the books, supported by Ovid and Cicero, by Virgil and Dante and Petrarch, Francis Crawford was standing now very still, as if the air was a burden to him. He said, 'If you bring yourself to do it this way, I don't think either of us could survive it.'

His face had radically altered. As she saw it, he turned to the shelves in a movement wholly involuntary, and the lances of candlelight followed him. He said, 'Let us be ourselves.'

Grief caught her by the throat. Grief and anger.

This was what Marthe had wanted.

The penknife dropped to the ground, and lay shining. Philippa said, 'It is your *life*.' But it was said only in defence, and in protest. After a long time she said, 'Very well.'

But this time he made no reply. Instead she heard a cruel intake of breath, such as a surgeon hears under the scalpel; and she saw that he had lifted his hands to his face, pressing so hard that his fingers were bloodless, with the shadow-wreaths of his collar voile cast on them. She said, 'What is it?'

'Another escape,' he said. His voice shook, like a light bough in a storm just beginning. 'I want you to go.'

She said, 'I did this to you. What can I do?'

He didn't answer. She seized a chair and dragged it up for him. 'Sit. Francis, *tell me what happens?'*

He found the chair with one hand and dropped into it. He was shivering violently. He said, 'Can you go? And send Archie?'

She caught his wrist, intent on finding its pulse; but was defeated. The delicate lace of his cuff covered even the heel of his palm. He drew a breath and said, the rising paroxysm shuttered hard by the bone of his hand, 'Very soon, I shall be extremely sick . . . which will be a very great pity. Archie knows what to do. It would help me . . . if you went away.'

The words followed her as she ran down the long parquet floor and returned, running still, followed by Archie. To the sense of them she paid no attention. She followed behind as, his hand on Lymond's arm, Archie guided him, lightly touching, down the passages to his apartments. And there, it was Philippa who held him when, as he foretold, Francis Crawford was sick, quite desperately so, for a long time. Then she found and measured a potion of sorts under Archie's directions and brought it to the high bed where Archie had already installed his master.

He lay still, sunk in pillows, his eyes heavily closed; and when he opened them as she sat beside him, she saw with a kind of angry despair that they were not clearly trained on her features. *J'irai donc, maugré toy* . . . She wondered if, afterwards, he would remember all he had said this evening.

She said, 'Try to forgive me. But try to remember. . . . There is a difference between absence and death. And you are needed.'

He had no strength and no resistance left; nor any saving stock of the wit and the detachment which had been his most precious qualities all the time she had known him. His lips parted, and his eyes rested open on the place where he thought he might find her.

'Every other woman since Eve,' he said. 'Except you.'

CHAPTER 5

Le prince Anglois Mars à son cueur de ciel
Voudra poursuivre la fortune prospere

There were then twenty days left till the wedding.

How, in twenty days, do you create for a man a new and irresistible motive for his existence? And how, this done, do you preserve him and his family from a blow so devastating as to be, in some ways, worse than self-destruction?

And lastly, how do you achieve all these things while (concealing your grief and your anger) you prepare a spoiled, imperious, charming fifteen-year-old girl for her wedding?

It was noted, in those first days of Easter Week, that the sardonic habit of the young comtesse de Sevigny, refreshing as ever, verged more than usual towards the acid. She had no sympathy with the heated squabble over which two demoiselles possessed the necessary rank, not to mention muscle power, to support the bride's twelve-yard train into the Cathedral Church of Notre-Dame in Paris, although she did supervise the safe, if acrimonious, shuttling between Paris and Fontainebleau of jewels for its embroidery.

A crown was having to be made because the Scottish Commissioners, to everyone's surprise and annoyance, had failed to bring with them the Scottish Crown Matrimonial for use at the ceremony, and refused to send for it.

Richard, tackled about this, had been extremely vague and Philippa, abandoning a private theory thought sheer pressure of work, went off to a stormy rehearsal of the children's share in the wedding banquet entertainment. The twelve wicker unicorns, wheeled but not yet caparisoned, proved only that the makers had no idea of the battering power of small, fat six-year-old princes. The de Guise and de Valois children rammed them at one another while Lord Harry de Valois, sadly and with a slow cry of boredom, fell through his, the red Fleming hair engulfed like a flue brush.

Two hundred masks from Ferrara arrived as a bride's gift to Mary, and instead of being placed in the gift-room, got used at a private and riotous party in the rooms of the Duke of Lorraine, who could not be chastised for it as the King was cultivating him, and he claimed, pressingly, to be in love with Mistress Philippa, anyway.

The Scottish Commissioners agreed to take the oath of fidelity to the Dauphin as King of Scotland after the marriage, which pleased the Dauphin, who had settled in with a household of three hundred and his abominable jester called Chicot, who collected women's garters. The Lyon King of Arms had a smiling discussion with the King of France's principal officer at arms over the manner in which he proposed to quarter the Dauphin's arms with those of Scotland, at the end of which the two herald courts ceased to speak to one another.

It was agreed that the bride's eldest son should be King of France and Scotland, and that her eldest daughter, if she had no sons, should be Queen of Scots only. If the Dauphin were to die, it was settled, his Queen could either stay in France or return to Scotland as a widow, her jointure continuing to be paid whatever happened.

The Seven Planets and the Nine Muses both decided at the last moment to demand new bolts of cloth and different dressmakers, and Mercury's staff disappeared and turned up, to much recrimination, in pawn with the silver snake missing. The Paris Master of Works came three times to consult with the Duke de Guise about the wooden gallery which was to carry the bridal procession to the Church of Notre-Dame, and the staging on which the wedding was to be carried out on the church threshold. The third time he went off and got drunk in a tavern at Fontainebleau and had to be found and carried away by Adam Blacklock, who with Danny and Jerott began to make an appearance, suddenly, in the vicinity, along with a number of other experienced captains.

A firm arrangement was made whereby, at the imprisoned Constable's instigation, emissaries for peace from both the Spanish and French factions would hold a secret meeting almost at once between Péronne and Cambrai. It was decided with reluctance to omit jousting in fancy costume from the wedding programme, at a time when every provident man needed the money for weapons.

The dishes and entertainment for the wedding breakfast in the Bishop of Paris's palace were decided on, and the same for the evening supper and ball in the Palais de Justice, the details being worked out by the Duke de Guise with the help of the Prince of Condé, whose brother, the Cardinal de Bourbon, was to conduct the marriage. It was decreed by his grace of Guise that all Scotsmen of rank, whoever they were, should have entrance to the evening banquet.

It was later decreed, after some tactful prodding, that all Scotsmen of rank should be admitted to the evening banquet, provided they were acquainted with the watchword *Brede and Ale*. The price of the watchword, starting at two sols, had got to ten by the middle of April.

The largest army so far recruited in the King of France's reign began to draw together, paid for by gold newly raised by the Cardinal of Lorraine, and building towards an eventual muster at Verdun, on the Metz road so recently travelled by the comte de Sevigny and his fellow-leaders. The organizing of it, because of the partial preoccupation of the Duke de Guise, fell on the shoulders of M. de Nevers, M. d'Estrée, M. de Sipierre and other veterans of the Calais war, who each in turn found that the bulk of it had already been dealt with by Mr Crawford.

For twenty-four hours following the destructive confrontation in the Library Lymond had not been well enough to go out, but this only Archie knew, and Philippa at a remove, through Archie. After that, he was completely and methodically occupied and much away to the east, in the company of armourers, sappers, masters of camp, harbingers, master gunners and an assortment of experts not usually required for a wedding.

There was a rumour, borne out by the Maréchale de St. André's unusual benignity, that she had confronted the comte de Sevigny with a coy remonstrance over his lack of warmth towards his fiancée, and he had been politely savage in his rejoinder.

That took place, Philippa suspected, as an after-effect of the Library. There was a further rumour that Catherine, running from the room, had cried that she wasn't proposing to marry M. de Sevigny anyway; and certainly her eyes were unusually red for some days. Then, about the middle of the month, her father the Marshal returned for six weeks' parole from his prison at Breda and Lymond was *mon cher*

François again, with St André's hand on his shoulder wherever he went. Piero Strozzi, who had had a diplomatic attack of catarrh as usual during Holy Week, raised less laughter than usual by demanding which of the St Andrés the boy intended to marry anyway.

The Duke de Nemours was put down, with much ribaldry, to partner the prettily pregnant wife of the Duke de Guise in the dances after the wedding breakfast instead of Mademoiselle de Rohan who, as everyone knew, was also plein' comme un oeuf, and bellicose with it.

On 15 April, the same prettily pregnant wife of the Duke de Guise was delivered of a son, six months after the Duke's return from the Italian wars, and no one made any public comment at all, although perhaps for an interval it drew Queen Catherine and Madame de Valentinois imperceptibly closer.

A rumour that the Sieur de Brissac was to return to Piedmont in order to support the Turkish fleet and 12,000 Janissaries in a landing at Genoa was officially scotched.

The Prévôt and échevins of Paris were formally invited to attend what the sieur de Chémault, Master of Ceremonies, had begun to call *the most celebrated marriage ever made* and visited the Cardinal de Lorraine to inquire about dress. Happily, the Cardinal of Lorraine informed them that they were to wear silk robes of the town livery, at the monarch's expense. There followed, among themselves, a long and lethal quarrel on the subject of collars.

A rumour that the Sultan of Turkey entertained hopes of suborning the new French Grand Master in Malta turned out to be true, to the joy of Danny Hislop, in whom was budding a sharp curiosity about the Order.

M. de La Rochefoucauld, calling at the Palais to attend on the King, informed Madame la comtesse de Sevigny that some packets for Lord Grey had arrived at his house from England, and that the courier had expressed a wish to see her. Madame de Sevigny, rising sharply in the middle of a financial discussion on the usufruits of the duchy of Touraine and the comté of Poitou, sat down again, and continued to be bodily present throughout the entire remainder of the dowry conference, but absent as soon as it ended.

The courier, a merry gentleman with a brown beard, gave her some cheerful greetings from Sir Henry Sidney, some others from a Spanish gentleman called Alfonso Derronda and two kisses, which he delivered, from Jane Dormer and Nicholas Chancellor. He also gave her, from inside his pourpoint, a letter from the Sidney seal.

It bore, within it, a brief note from Sir Henry, certifying that the paper inside had come from the banker specified by Marco Schiatti, and represented a document deposited there by one Leonard Bailey of the manor of Gardington, England.

She took it to her room in the Palace to open it, but in the end she found she need not have troubled. For this paper, too, was a blank.

*

Strange to sit in her chamber, among the plotting, the laughter, the fighting, the lovemaking, the dancing, the luxury, the sycophancy and feel alone and afraid, bereft of judgement and confidence.

Stranger still to remember, with a dull and damnable irony, that under this roof another human being was alone and beleaguered, in a sense she had never yet known. And that they could not bring comfort to one another.

For an hour, she had held him between her hands, his hair under her cheek, his racked body gripped and sheltered by hers. The proximity which, half an hour before, would have destroyed him had come and gone disregarded in the landslide of action and anxiety. Afterwards there was no harvest for the long, aching nights: no recollection of the geometry of a lissom back, or of the firmness and warmth of filmed lawn under her steadying fingers. And Francis, she supposed, must be empty-handed as she was.

And now, this further burden, of which he knew nothing as yet.

What to do? Bailey, it seemed, had made no copies of Sybilla's confessions: had trusted to no banker the information which she or the Lennoxes would pay so much to receive. All he had done was to trick her into wasting time.

Where then were the originals? She could try the Hôtel des Sphères, where she had first seen them. Perhaps he had simply replaced them, laughing, in the same desk. Perhaps he had found somewhere to hide them. What he did not know was that she had a key. She would have no trouble in Paris, in finding someone to use it, and to search the whole house for the papers. Someone, that is, who had no skill in reading or writing, but could recognize a seal, and a superscription.

This she could and would do. It was the only thing left. For if the papers were not in the rue de la Cerisaye, there were no means by which she could trace them.

*

The Court moved to Paris. For two hundred years, no heir to the French throne had been married in his own country. Wedding fever and hopes of largesse gripped the populace. On the Tuesday before the marriage, the betrothal ceremony took place in the new Château of the Louvre, at which the Excellente Princesse Madame Marie d'Esteuart, Royne d'Escosse, stated that of her own free will and consent, and by the advice of her lady grandmother the Dowager Duchess of Guise and the Deputies of the Three Estates of Scotland she took the Dauphin Francis for her lord and husband, and promised to espouse him on the following Sunday, 24 April, in the face of the Holy Church.

A ball followed, at which the royal hosts, their relatives and the princes and princesses of the blood performed a number of long, correct dances to the sounds made by a hardworking collection of hautbois, flageolets, viols, citterns, and violins, playing as loudly as possible.

Philippa de Sevigny, standing with the other ladies of honour watching her mistress, did not dance, being on duty.

She did not, in any real sense of the word, serve her mistress that evening either. The previous night, true to her plan, she had dispatched to the Hôtel des Sphères the small and inconspicuous thief someone had found for her. And that afternoon, she had walked out to meet him and with sinking heart, had received his report.

As with every other attempt she had made to sidetrack Leonard Bailey this one had quite failed. Her burglar, who had lost a fortune thereby, was almost more upset than she was.

He had looked everywhere, he said. He had looked in places you would never think of. It was amazing where these old gentlemen sometimes kept their private papers. He had searched the rooms of the servants. He had even gone through the clothes and the chests of the men at arms who slept in the house and that, he said, was something the lady forgot to warn him about.

He had tapped the panelling and tried all the usual places in skirtings and floorboards. He had tested the staircase and the pictures and the fireplaces. He had looked in every pot in the kitchen.

There was nowhere, said Philippa's burglar, where a man could have hidden a paper, and he not know it.

She believed him. He had come to her with the highest reputation. She had paid him well, as he deserved, and only thought as he was leaving to ask one final question. 'The lady housekeeper who lives in the house—Madame Roset. Did you try her chamber?'

'Took it apart thread by thread,' said the small man complacently. 'It wasn't hard, mind, being empty. I don't suppose she could have what you're looking for, could she?'

'Empty?' Philippa said. 'Are you sure it was the house-keeper's room?'

He was offended. 'I always ask, before I get into a house. I knew every room in that place before I went near it. The biggest room, apart from the old man's, it was. And she was away. Had been away a fair time, from the look of it.'

So, she thought all through the handfasting. Leonard Bailey had won. Before she thought to have the house watched, he must have sent Madame Roset away. Perhaps he had told her Lady Culter desired it. But she had gone, where he could find her, no doubt, if the day came when he required her to support his accusation against Sybilla in public.

So, too, with the papers. Someone had them. Someone was no doubt holding them, as he had promised, with instructions to publish what they contained if he came to harm. She had no means now of finding out where they were. She had no means now of stopping him, except by paying. And if he chose to favour the Lennoxes, no means of stopping him at all.

The music ceased, and the rattle of French voices started again, a voice in her ear said, 'What a fine piece, Mistress Philippa! Emeralds, are they not?'

It was Elder, Lady Lennox's secretary, in rallying mood. 'And are you not proposing to spend any of the last hours of your marriage at your brave husband's side? Tell me, is that your husband's brother?'

Across the room, square, quiet and brown in his rich clothing, stood Richard Crawford.

'Yes, it is the Earl of Culter,' Philippa said. She had no desire to introduce him.

'And I believe his lady mother is in Paris, although I have

494

not had the pleasure of meeting her. So regal, I am told. So well thought of at court. I regret,' said Lady Lennox's secretary, 'that I have taken so long to make the acquaintance of this eminent family. I can only claim to know your husband's great-uncle, a gentleman called Mr Bailey.'

'I met him once,' Philippa said. And said it steadily, for the seraglio teaches how to conceal all feeling when you are being tormented. Even when you are being tormented for a private satisfaction that does not know that it has been seen and identified.

'A remarkable gentleman,' said John Elder jovially. 'How he would enjoy meeting your husband's mother once more! Now tell me: who will have your favours when this little marriage of yours come to an end. . . ?'

He had said all he intended to say, and he moved away a little afterwards. It was only a short time after that, as she was bringing sugared plums to present to the Dauphin, that Adam Blacklock put his hand on her arm. 'Philippa? Do you know where Archie is?'

'Why?' she said sharply. The noise was overwhelming.

'For Francis. He had to go out. I can't leave the room. I don't know whether he knows what room Archie is waiting in.'

'There he is,' Philippa said.

Beyond the tapestries and the bright painted frescoes a slight, dour figure appeared in a doorway, loomed over by uneasy ushers; made a signal of appeasement, and left.

'He's got him,' Adam said. And looking at her, frowning, 'You haven't spoken to Lymond tonight?'

'No. I wish the music would stop,' Philippa said. She had found him as soon as she entered the room: one of the smiling, conversing group round the King, and she knew he had been conscious of her. But after that first, headlong glance they had not looked at or approached one another again.

Adam said, 'Then you don't know that Catherine d'Albon has withdrawn from the marriage?'

Her gaze sprang open on his. 'How could she? Her parents?'

'She seems to have defied them. Or at least to have persuaded them that it is in their own interests not to squabble in public. She has agreed not to announce it until after Monday, in case they stop your annulment. Philippa, it's very bad news.'

'I know,' Philippa said. No ties; no duty; no relief. Three filaments gone in the life-thread, fragile as the thread of the silk-moth, which has no organs by which it can nourish itself, but instead is born, and loves once, and then dies.

Adam said gently, 'Then, will you leave him to us? Leave court on Monday, as soon as you sign the annulment. I have had so many letters from Kate. She wants you back badly.'

'You've been writing?' Philippa said.

'When you stopped. She didn't deserve the silence,' Adam said. 'And Kuzúm is forgetting you. Don't leave him.'

She did not realize that she was weeping until she saw the tears on the sugar plums, grey on the white powder, and that Adam had moved, so that his shoulders shielded her from her companions. The new ciphers shimmered, dazzling over them: *M* for Mary and a Greek *Phi* for her bridegroom François.

'This marriage frightens me,' she said. 'I saw Mary Tudor's. Kings, more than other people, have such a hunger for love.'

'Would you wish for them,' Adam said, 'that they lived without knowing such hunger?'

Afterwards, she could not recall having answered him.

Much later, Philippa Somerville crossed to where Richard Crawford was still standing and asked him, without much preliminary, if she might call on his mother next morning. Then, before he had quite finished expressing his pleasure, she asked him if he would be so kind as to enable her to meet Austin Grey at the same time under his roof.

He agreed, as she knew he would: it was a concession easily arranged with the master of Lymond's household. Then she left, and in the peace of her room took the decision to which she now saw there was no alternative. Late that night, without waiting longer, she wrote a message of open supplication to Leonard Bailey.

With the letter, in earnest of her good intentions, she sent the emerald pendant so admired by John Elder.

*

The following morning, in the sunlit parlour of Sybilla's rooms in the Hôtel de l'Ange, Austin Grey arrived for his meeting with Philippa.

Since receiving Richard's summons he had not slept at all, or wanted to sleep. He had come quickly through the spring

496

morning, outpacing his guards to be with her, for it seemed that now she wanted him. Now, with her annulment nearly upon them, she was going to keep her promise: to ask him for his proposal, if he still wished to offer it. And to consent, if he did.

Happiness walked with him into Sybilla's parlour and illuminated all his quiet face. The door closed and his heart beat, seeing that Philippa was alone, her back to the lit, lozenged windows with their achievements. He smiled at the picture she made, her outline childishly austere in her high-necked gown, with all the long, glossy brown hair swept inside an absurd little cylinder.

Then she moved forward. And while he was still assimilating, shocked, the sharp-angled pallor of her face she said, 'Is your arm better? I asked you to come because I have to say something facing you. I can't marry you. I can never marry you. I have wasted three months of your life and I can offer you nothing instead, except possibly the knowledge that I was not worth your trouble in any case.'

The sun turned dark, and there were no lights. Outside, someone was singing.

'Why?' he said. And then, almost at once, 'No.' He made, without thinking of it, a sightless turn round the small room and said, his eyes still trained upon nothing, 'I knew you were in some anxiety. I asked if you would bring it to me as a friend. But perhaps that is too much.'

'No,' Philippa said. 'No. The reasons are very simple. You may not have heard, because it hasn't been made known as yet. But Catherine d'Albon has withdrawn from her marriage to . . . to Mr Crawford.'

A door closing on a black-haired girl through the night in the Hôtel d'Hercule. And a charming voice heard pronouncing, through the raging pain in his arm, *'Even if I were told that Philippa was inflamed with an unlikely love for me, I should still marry Catherine d'Albon.'*

Austin Grey drew a long, uneven breath. 'Now you have frightened me beyond telling. Philippa, think what you are doing. I can see nothing but hurt in this for you.'

'There is nothing but hurt in this for anyone,' said Philippa abruptly. 'I am trying, although you might not think it, to ameliorate it for you.'

He could hear, because he studied everything about her, the effort she was making to keep her voice steady. Austin said, 'He told me he wanted this St André marriage. You said yourself he was interested only in his annulment.'

'I thought it was true,' Philippa said. 'But it isn't. It appears that what I feel for him . . . he also feels for me. As you see, it changes everything.'

This, the second blow, was worse than the first. For a moment he was without words. Then, controlling, brutally, all his dazed senses he said quietly, 'I can see you think it does. When did you tell him, Philippa, that you were in love with him?'

Her pale lips twitched for a moment, wryly. 'I didn't have to,' she said. 'I am not as good at deception as I ought to be.'

'And when did he tell you he felt the same?' Austin asked. And then, seeing her face, said jerkily, 'Or . . . Was it. . . ?'

'Yes,' she said. 'It was the night in the Hôtel d'Hercule when I ran out of his room. I challenged him with being in love with someone else, and he told me. It made no difference, then. He still meant to go through with his marriage to Catherine.'

'If she would still have him, after that evening,' Austin said. 'If not, he had you prepared for the next sacrifice. He is so clever, Philippa.'

She closed her eyes, and opened them again. Under the dark lashes, free of all paint, were blue stains of utter weariness. Then she gave a small sigh. 'He is so clever,' she said. 'It is a pity he cannot manage things better for himself. He acted with honour that night. He made me leave without touching me. Will you believe that?'

'Yes,' Austin said. 'He still wanted the St André marriage. And now? He will cancel your annulment on Monday?'

'He won't,' Philippa said. 'Austin, I think we should stop talking about it. The situation exists. There is no room for a third person in it. Leave me. Hate me, if you like. But best of all, forget me.'

He paid no attention at all. 'I don't understand. He wants your marriage dissolved?'

'Yes,' Philippa said wearily. She moved to a buffet table between the two windows and sat on the corner among the silver, her skirts half-bated, sinking about her. 'I shall try to keep him to it, but I may not succeed.'

'Dear God,' Austin said. 'If he doesn't wish to stay married, how can he love you? Or does he want to be free to find another rich heiress and marry her? What happens if he does annul your union on Monday and marry somebody else? Does he invite you to his rooms again, and this time make you his mistress?'

'He didn't invite me,' Philippa said. Her hands were gripped hard together. 'I have told you. He wants me to leave him. I am the one who is begging him to stay married to me. I am the one who is trying to force him to take me as his mistress.'

'Then you shall be prevented,' Austin said. And walking to the door, flung it open. 'What you mean to do, if you carry it out, could hardly be kept private. Let Lymond's mother and brother be the first to hear of it.'

She said, 'It will only make it worse,' and when he took her arm, he could feel her whole body shaking. But he pulled her none the less to Sybilla's bedchamber and throwing open the door, placed her before him, in front of the Earl of Culter and his mother, slowly rising.

'Your son,' Austin Grey said, 'is striving to make of this lady his whore. Do you approve, or are you prepared to try and prevent it?'

CHAPTER 6

Lettres trouvées de la royne les coffres
Point de subscrit sans aucun nom d'autheur,
Par la police seront cachez les offres
Qu'on ne sçaura qui sera l'amateur.

His elder brother Richard and Austin his prisoner were the first people Francis Crawford saw when he returned that afternoon to the Hôtel d'Hercule, and entered his long, exquisite gallery.

Also waiting him in the quality of temporary hots were his two colleagues, Adam and Jerott. The conversation, it was plain, was not sparkling.

Lymond paused. Though dressed for court he was not, Adam saw, in one of his more extravagant moods. But he came forward readily enough, glanced at Jerott and himself, and then gave all his attention to his brother and his captive, grimly standing together. 'Defective,' he said, 'in affableness, like the natives of Angus. I apologize in advance. What have I done now?'

'I want to talk to you about Philippa,' Richard said. 'I think it had better be done in private.'

Adam rose. So did Jerott, but not to leave. 'What about Philippa?' he said.

Lymond emitted a brief sigh. 'As you see,' he said to his brother, 'the lady is not lacking in champions. Whatever you say to me, I shall simply have to repeat to Jerott afterwards. What is it? You aren't convinced by her story of what happened here last month in my bedchamber?'

'We know what happened,' Richard said harshly.

'I . . . see,' said Lymond. After a moment, he said, 'In that case, Jerott and Adam had better contain their anxiety somewhere else.'

Jerott, unfortunately, was stone sober. 'I don't propose to leave,' he said. 'I'm sorry, Francis. But I warned you.'

'I can't say I remember it,' Lymond said. 'But stay if you

500

wish. I am like the Swiss. I prefer not to fight on a Wednesday.' He indicated, with a lifted hand, the available seats and sat down himself in the master chair, which had once belonged to the Dame de Doubtance.

Adam sat, and then Jerott. Pointedly, Austin and Lord Culter remained standing. To them, Lymond said gently, 'It would be better if you seated yourselves. We are not going to shout at one another over this subject. You have heard, I take it, that my betrothal to Catherine d'Albon has ended. I expect you are concerned to know whether or not I am now going to proceed with dissolving my marriage to Philippa. The answer is, yes.'

'And Philippa?' Richard said. He remained standing. 'What do you plan to do with Philippa?'

The quick, perceptive gaze moved from one stony face to the other. "If you know what happened here that evening, then Philippa herself must have told you.'

'What happened?' Jerott said sharply.

No one answered him.

Austin Grey said, 'Philippa came to see me this morning, to break off all arrangements for our marriage.'

Adam Blacklock, watching the seated man, elegantly disposed under the old chair's refurbished canopy, wondered if the others, like himself, could see that from his throat to his hair he had coloured. Then Lymond said, 'I didn't know. I'm sorry.'

Austin said, 'She says she begged you to allow her to remain your wife, and you refused her. She says——'

'No, by no means, Lord Allendale,' Lymond said, his voice like a sawblade. And as the other man stopped, his eyes burning, Lymond said, his voice level once again. 'You are both here, I assume, to protect a lady's reputation. Kindly try to remember it. Since I doubt, at the moment, whether I can stomach any hysterical verbiage, suppose we simply say what we mean. Lord Grey wishes to marry my wife. I agree it would be an excellent thing for both parties. My wife, at the moment, may wish to remain married to me, but on Monday our union will be dissolved, and she will return directly to England and, I hope, eventual nuptials with the Grey family. I do not intend after Monday to see her again.'

Jerott said in a surprised voice, 'Well, that's all right?' and looked round at Adam.

'Is it?' said Austin Grey.

501

Jerott reddened. 'It's hard luck on Philippa, naturally; and you may have to wait for your wedding, but it's better, surely, than having her tied to Francis.' He bent a fleeting stare of his magnificent dark eyes on the fair, cold face in the chair. 'I'm sorry, Francis, but—'

'. . . you warned me,' Lymond agreed. He was looking at Austin and his brother. 'But like the narration of those who preach to those who do not wish to hear, my story has failed to excite anyone. They don't believe me.'

'Well, they ought to,' said Jerott. 'Of course she's in love with you, but that's not surprising. You've been a figure like Jove to her ever since she was small. She'll get over it. And who could possibly imagine you would want anything to do with her? Your brother knows that.'

He swung round on Richard. 'She's got sense, that girl; and too much backbone to push herself where she's not wanted. Tell her it's no good, and she'll soon see the point.'

There was a disastrous silence.

Lymond stirred. 'Virgil's flude of eloquens,' he said, examining his hands, 'extinguishing the fyr, that in the bedstraw bredeth. Well done, Jerott.'

Annoyed, Jerott looked from Adam to Richard. The big-boned, good-tempered face looked back at him with weary patience.

'That is the point,' Culter said. 'When she knew her love was hopeless, Philippa was content to marry Austin and leave her husband to Catherine. But now Francis is free of the St André marriage. And he has allowed Philippa to understand that he covets her.'

'A mistake,' Lymond agreed. 'But a mistake couched, I must protest, in prettier language.' There was no excess of colour, Adam noted, in his face now.

'Why, in any language?' Austin said. 'You told me yourself you would never live with her. If you don't want her, why do the one thing which will keep her at your side?'

'Because he wants her,' Richard said. He walked forward and kneeling, looked up at the still, passionless face of his brother. 'It has been a long time, hasn't it, since Güzel? Philippa is not the bride who will increase your rank and status in France: you will have to look elsewhere now for that. It shouldn't be difficult. D'Enghien's widow has an annual rental, I'm told, of 40,000 ducats. The King will see to it. But you want your mistress as well. The new Françoise de Rohan is to be Kate's daughter.'

He rose, still staring at his brother's face. Jerott, drawing a hasty breath, was pressed into silence by Adam. Austin said, thickly, 'Is it not true?'

'No,' Lymond said. He returned the other man's gaze, without drama. 'What I told you was true. Married or single, I shall never live with Philippa.'

'Then,' Austin said, 'all you have to do is tell her that you don't love her.'

Their eyes locked. This time, Lymond did not speak. It was Adam who jumped to his feet. 'You fools. How can he. . . ?'

And wheeling, turned on the chair where Lymond, drawing breath, snatched the next words from his mouth. 'How can I? She wouldn't believe me.'

Then he turned to Austin. 'I understand your disappointment. It is not a heroic position to be placed in unawares. I understand also that what you want . . . what we all want is to protect Philippa. We also want, I think, to avoid causing her any more distress. By the time you had extracted this much from her this morning I imagine . . . you were none of you very calm. I have therefore a proposal to make.'

He looked round them all in the manner three of the four present knew so well: the manner of a man whose word was law, briefing his subordinates. 'It is not very difficult,' he said, 'as I rather know to my cost, to remove someone against their own will from a country. The annulment will be signed on Monday, the day after the royal wedding. I promise you that it will be signed. On Tuesday, whether she wants it or not, you should make arrangements for Philippa and Lord Allendale to leave for England. I shall write out for you, before you go, a bond which allots him quite clearly his freedom. Once she is in England, surely you can guard her.'

'And before she is in England?' Lord Allendale said.

'Today is Wednesday. I don't expect to see her again, except at a distance until Monday. But you can make sure of that. Guard her, as you like. Have your friends follow her; stay with her; put a chambermaid to sleep in her room if you wish it. Then the righteous will shine like the sun and run about like sparks among reeds and all of you, I trust, will cease troubling me.'

503

Austin said, "No. I want you to leave France.' His voice was bare with the long tension.

Lymond's smile, replying, was faint. 'How can I? I have to sign the papers on Monday.'

'Then,' Richard said, 'I think we accept your scheme, with one important change in it. You, too, must be watched and followed.'

'And slept with?' Lymond said. 'No. Of course, it is a measure from the pure front against the Devil. Whereby presumption and arrogancy shall be withstanded, malice and contention expelled, and carnal liberty refrained and tempered; especially the latter. So who would do all this?'

'I should,' Richard said. 'Even to sleeping in your own chamber.'

'That I baulk at,' Lymond said. 'The rest you can have. One cock per pen is enough.'

'Dear God,' Richard said, and stood up. 'Can you not dispense with a bawd between Thursday and Monday?'

'You can watch us,' Lymond said. 'The blood of Martyrs serves as manure for the vine of the Saviour. Or if you don't want to watch, you can nail up my door in the evenings. In principle, it seems, we are agreed. Lord Allendale, does all this satisfy you?'

Austin said, 'You are right to taunt. If I had killed you, none of this would have happened.'

'I thought you would realize it sooner or later,' Lymond said. 'Richard?'

'Yes,' Richard said. 'I wonder if there exists any other man, even at this Court, who has to be restrained day and night to preserve a girl's honour?'

''Tis not Anaxarchus but his sheath that you prod?* The word even deserves a monument to itself. If Lord Allendale is returning, will he send your clothes back? Sybilla will long to know why.'

'She knows,' said Richard curtly. 'I should like to go to my room.'

'In a moment,' Lymond said, rising. 'Adam, you will stay please, and Jerott. Lord Allendale . . .'

The door opened on the usher he had rung for. 'Take any of my horses you may need for Richard's baggage.' Lymond paused, the searching blue gaze on the younger man's face. Then he said, 'We've been much at odds, but mostly by accident. If . . . Philippa has lived her childish fantasies through me, she has a great deal that is more commendable to discover in you, and take pleasure in. I have a respect for her as great as yours, I should like you to believe.' He paused again and said, not smiling, 'I didn't think you would fight for her. She is worth any sacrifice.'

Austin was very white. 'That is what she said of you,' he said. 'That is why we are having to follow her like a felon. I am not proud of it. Are you?'

And a moment later, the door closed behind him.

'And now . . .' Lymond said, and turned to Richard.

Adam said crisply, 'Francis. Archie is waiting to see you.'

'Archie,' said Lymond, 'is a pessimist. Twice in two days would be too bloody demeaning. I have, Richard, some Scottish business to discuss with you. If this chair wouldn't offend you, come and read these, if you please.'

The papers he handed Richard as he slowly sat down were in French: so much Adam could see.

He stayed where he was. Jerott, more forthright, got up and walked round to Lymond's shoulder. And Lymond said, 'Adam, I mean you, and later the Commissioners to see.'

And so they read the three scribbled pages together.

The first two missives began with the same words:

Tres haulte et tres excellente princesse, Marie, Royne d'Escosse, presente en personne . . .

'It's by the young Queen,' Richard said. He turned it over and looked at the date. 'Signed on the fourth, a fortnight ago, at Fontainebleau.'

'They were all three signed by the Queen on the same day,' Lymond said. 'It was the Monday of Holy Week. Read them.'

So Richard turned it back and, his hands long-sightedly a little away from his face, held it so that Adam and Jerott could read it too.

Considerante la singulliere et parfaicte affection que les Roys de France ont tousjours eu en la protection et manutention du Royaume d'Escosse contre les Angloys . . . et encores plus le bon traictement qu'elle a eu et receu de la bonte du . . . tres excellent prince Henri, par le grace de Dieu, Roy de France . . .

'It's a bit overdone, isn't it?' Jerott said. 'All this gratitude to Henry by the grace of God King of France? *When* he protected us from the English it was only because he bloody well couldn't afford not to. However. What's she giving him? A

505

falcon? A parcel of stockings? A purseful of river pearls? A box of Aberdeen haddies for every month of his reign?'

Richard's reading, swifter than his, had brought him to the end of the missive. But even then, he could not bring himself to lift his eyes. There was a pause. Then: 'She is giving him Scotland,' said Culter.

It was true. It was there, in line after line for them to read.

'... *advenant le cas qu'elle decedde sans hoirs proceez de son corps—que Dieu ne vueille—elle a donne et donne par ces presentes, par pure et libre donation ... le royaulme d'Escosse ... et telz droictz qui lui peuvent ... appartenir au royaulme d'Angleterre.*

... So that should the Queen die without heirs, she has decreed the King of France should receive in pure and free gift the Kingdom of Scotland, and its rights to the English throne.

Adam said, 'I can't believe it.'

'Then read the second donation,' said Lymond's quiet voice behind them.

The second deposition was clear and brief also: ... *informee des grans fraiz et impenses cy davant employees ... a la protection, tuition et deffence du royaume d'Escosse ... contre les Angloys ... tellement que la conversation en est entierement deue aux Roys de France ...*

'And that's another bloody lie!' said Jerott speaking. 'We don't need a parcel of scented Frenchmen to show us how to push the English back over the Borders. Anyway, what expenses?'

'Shut up, Jerott,' said Adam.

... *Pour ces causes ... ayant pris le conseil de ses meilleurs et plus singulliers amys, mesmement de Monseigneur le reverendissime et illustrissime Cardinal de Lorraine et de Monseigneur le Duc de Guyse, ses oncles ...*

'The de Guise!' said Richard, his gaze jerked upwards to Lymond.

'By the advice of Messeigneurs mes oncles. Who else?' said Francis Crawford. 'Read on.'

'... *Icelle Dame ... ordonne ...* that is she dies childless ... the King of France, present or future, should have and enjoy the Kingdom of Scotland, its fruits, revenues and emoluments, and retain them in full possession until the payment ... God's bones!' Richard said. '... Until the payment and full reimbursement of a million pounds in gold ...'

'From a nation of half a million people to a nation of fifteen million. It's an impossible condition,' Adam said. His mouth was sour.

'Presumably, it is meant to be an impossible condition,' said Richard dryly. He went on reading. '... And until this condition is complied with, she cedes to the King and his successors the Kingdom of Scotland, to enjoy as heretofore stated, without hindrance by any other person whatsoever. Which is accepted by the King through Monseigneur the Cardinal de Sens, Keeper of the Seals of France, and by us, the undersigned, notaries and secretaries of the Crown of France at the request of this lady, who to show her entire approval of this content, has wished to sign with her own hand ...'

'Read the third and last paper,' Lymond said, 'before you comment.'

'Oh Christ,' Jerott said. 'What more can there be?'

'... *Marie, Reine d'Escosse, considerant l'ancienne ligue, alliance parfaite et perpetuelle union d'entre les Rois et Roiaumes de France et d'Escosse* ... above all things wishes to bind, join, annexe and unite the Kingdom of Scotland to the Crown of France ... and to this end, should she die childless, has made certain dispositions to the profit of the Kings of France ...'

'In the previous two documents,' Adam said.

'Yes. Then she says ...' Richard stopped. Jerott, leaning over his shoulder, drew a sudden breath. And Lymond, his voice calm behind them, read, and translated as he read, the third and last document.

'*Toutes fois est de nouvel avertie* ... The Queen is again made aware, by the articles and instructions brought her by the Commission from Scotland, that on the secret cognizance of certain persons, it is intended that her kingdom should pass, should she have no heirs, to certain lords of the country, depriving her, the true Queen, by this means of all liberty of disposing of her own crown, to her great sorrow and prejudice.

Which for the present she has no means of openly preventing, since she is distant from her kingdom, far from her subjects and not in complete possession of the strongholds of her country. If such things were at present to be openly debated, they could create great disturbances and a revolt which might lead to the ruin of her kingdom.

507

'For these reasons, she now puts on record an affirmation that whatever consent or ratification she has given or will give to the articles and instructions sent by the Estates of her Kingdom, to do with the future of Scotland should she die childless, she intends that the dispositions here made by her to the profit of the Kings of France should remain intact and should be fully implemented, having no regard to any other dispositions to which she may give her consent, either in connection with the aforesaid articles and instructions or anything else, which should be regarded as agreements to which she has been constrained, entirely against her wish, will and intention . . .

'This intention, the Keeper of Seals will implement. And the document, for greater effect, is signed not only by Queen Mary but by the Dauphin.'

The clear voice stopped. 'It only remains to add,' said Francis Crawford to his brother, 'that the Dauphin is impotent.'

No one spoke. Beside him, Adam saw Jerott open his lips, and put his hand, hard, on his arm. Lord Culter said, 'Where did these papers come from?'

Lymond walked round and stood looking down at his brother. 'A man who would be drawn and quartered were it known that he passed them on.'

Richard Crawford had not dropped his eyes from his brother's face. 'It is too important for that,' he said. 'If these are genuine, there will be no royal wedding on Sunday.'

'I showed them to you first,' Lymond said, 'because you are intelligent, and moderate, and at the same time inclined by your convictions not to favour France.' He paused.

'If you are asking whether I am a Lutheran,' Richard said grimly, 'the answer is that I am. So are three other members of the Commission.'

'I learned as much at Dieppe,' Lymond said. 'The preacher John Knox had been there, expecting to take ship for Scotland. Then he was told not to come. Do you know why?'

For a moment, it seemed that Lord Culter would not answer. Then he said, 'He is a militant. We hope to receive the concessions we want without open rebellion.'

'Should Mary die childless,' Lymond said, 'the articles she has signed for you provide for the Earl of Arran to reign after her. I am told that he also favours the Protestant religion.'

'You are told correctly,' Richard said.

508

'What then,' said Lymond, 'do you imagine will be his reaction when he hears of this refutation?'

'There'll be a revolt,' Jerott said, 'God, every Lutheran in Scotland will be up in arms. You can't expect anything else.'

'Civil war, then,' Lymond said. 'With the Catholic faction eventually swept to victory by the combined Catholic armies of France, and a French Catholic nominee irrevocably placed on the throne as regent and eventual monarch. The Earl of Lennox, I understand, is a strong contender.'

Adam said, 'How do you know, Francis, it won't come anyway? The present Regent is not only the Queen's mother, she's a de Guise. She's bound to know about this. You say she's given the Lutherans hope of concessions. But is she likely to trouble, after this? And if she doesn't, next time the Lutherans send for John Knox.'

'It may come anyway,' Lymond said. 'But almost any time is better than now. There is a chance that the Queen Dowager will remain tolerant. There is a chance of a Protestant succession in England. There is a chance that France may become too preoccupied with the Huguenots on her own doorstep to have troops and money to spare for Scotland.'

'The Vidame is leaving now, they say, with ten companies of Germans for Scotland,' Jerott said. 'To force us this time, in the Dauphin's name, not to be so backward in attacking England.' He looked at Richard, who had not spoken. 'If the wedding were cancelled, they wouldn't have that extra authority.'

'However many troops they send, they won't get anyone to invade England at the moment,' Richard said. 'That is a minor matter.' He turned to his brother. 'It seems to me that you are suggesting that we connive at this. That we let the royal wedding take place in the face of a betrayal as monstrous as any people has ever experienced at the hands of its own Queen. I am not of the same mind. First, I require to have proof that these papers are genuine. Then I shall take them with my fellow-Commissioners to the King of France and demand the cancellation of the wedding and the return of Queen Mary to Scotland.'

'Then you would have not only civil war, but war with France,' Lymond said.

'Then,' said Richard Crawford, 'you are willing to allow your country to be sold in the market-place in return for the cash for a little girl's bed hangings?'

'I want you to keep the issues clear,' Lymond said. 'And as free as may be of emotion. Mary has signed these, presumably, out of a duty owed to the men who have reared her, and to please Holy Church, which requires Scotland Catholic. She may be unaware that France's main interest in this is not Scotland at all, but her own claim to Catholic England. And that claim, transmitted to someone who is already a contender for both thrones, would give the French a chance to control both countries.'

'You dislike the Lennoxes,' Richard said. 'Is that why you oppose early and frank confrontation? To avoid any risk that the succession should fall to your enemies?'

For a moment Lymond stared at him, and Adam saw his muscles harden, as if he were about to turn and walk away. But instead he folded his arms and said only, 'No. I have not been considering personal issues, either for you or for me. Or I would have mentioned the obvious fact, that the moment you and the other commissioners decide—should you decide—to take action, your lives will be in jeopardy. France won't give up this wedding lightly.'

The long, critical scrutiny of the grey eyes did not alter 'You have considered,' Culter said, 'that if the wedding doesn't take place, France has no claim on England. And, therefore, if that is their first object, they will have perhaps less interest, not more, in interfering with Scottish affairs?'

'It is a viewpoint,' Lymond said. 'I think that if she fails to produce a legal heir, she will make an alliance with Spain and try to take Scotland and England by force. But that is some distance away. At the moment both Spain and England are allied against France, and France is not going to risk having every Protestant in the country up in arms, as Jerott says, against the Queen Dowager; and in alliance with the Protestant faction, and eventually the Protestant monarch in England.

'I think if you use this material, you will start a conflagration that will kill many thousands and may destroy Scotland more surely than a threat already hedged about with a fair number of contingencies. At least, before you talk to your fellows, will you give it grave thought? And I beg you, bind them to the most strict, the most rigorous secrecy. The pride and prestige of the de Guises all depend on this match being ratified.'

'I understand,' Richard said. He stood up. 'I have to ask you again. How did you come by these papers?'

Elsewhere in the household other people, less occupied, were sitting at supper. The faint, savoury smell of hot food entered the gallery and lingered there, mixed with the other scents of cloth and warm metal and sandalwood, the traces of incense; the fragrance of juniper from the fireplace. The afternoon sunlight falling through the long windows latticed the velvet hangings with their flowered coronets; argent, a chaplet proper, debruised by a fess azure, invected ... the device of Sevigny.

And the comte de Sevigny, without moving from where he stood in front of his brother, said, 'They passed through four pairs of hands before they reached mine, and the person who started them on their way I can only guess at. There are many people who don't like the de Guises. There are some who don't want the Scottish wedding. I have had to take these papers on trust, because if I didn't, the people who handled them would be cut off without compunction, and so would you. All I can say is that everything I know points to their being truthful copies of three genuine documents of State, and that the wording bears this out as well. I doubt if anyone outside the French secretariat would have framed them in quite such a way.'

'I remember once,' Richard said, 'you made me march on Annan by telling me that I should go in the opposite direction. I have to think of my country, because I live in it. And I remember that the only other name I have heard shouted in the streets since I came, along with that of de Guise, has been your own.'

He stood, a broad-built man of unshaken purpose and integrity, and said roughly, 'You must excuse me if I malign you. But you preach inaction, and still show me those papers. I think you mean the Commissioners to stop the wedding in order to cripple the power of the de Guise family, regardless of whether these papers are true ones or not; and regardless of what destruction it might mean to Scotland.'

'Wait a bit.' Adam on his feet was not content to stand by any longer. 'Francis made those points himself. You can't have it both ways.'

'My brother is a devious man,' Richard said. He had not moved his eyes from Lymond's face. 'All the points that he made are valid ones, and all the conclusions he reached

511

would have been reached sooner or later by one or other of the Commissioners. Whatever we do, he will receive credit for trying to stop it.'

Jerott Blyth's mouth opened. He said, 'You silly fool, you think *Francis* wants to bring Scotland to butchery?'

Lymond said, 'I don't think we want any testimonials, Jerott, or even any untoward language. Fortunately, it isn't entirely in Richard's hands. The Commissioners will decide what to do. Only, I beg you, watch your step. You are carrying gunpowder.'

For whatever reason, Adam saw Culter suddenly flinch and a moment later Lymond's hands, unfolded, dropped to his sides. Then he said in his usual voice, 'Perhaps you can start guarding me after you have paid a call on the Hôtel de l'Ange and conferred with your colleagues. I promise I shan't leave the house. And this evening a room will be ready for you.'

With some firmness he had drawn to a close a discussion no longer profitable to himself or to his brother. A moment later Culter had taken his leave coolly and gone, the papers folded inside his doublet.

Standing at the glass, his elbows spread high on the casement ledge, his chin upheld by her interlaced knuckles, Lymond watched his brother's progress through the courtyard. Behind him Adam said softly, 'It was Danny who brought you those papers?'

'*Danny!*' said Jerott explosively.

Lymond did not even turn. 'No. It was not Danny,' he said. 'And even if Danny tries to suggest it was, I shall deny it, just as I shall deny this conversation took place today.... There he goes. What do you think he will do?'

'What you want him to do,' Adam said dryly. 'Doesn't he always?'

'No', Lymond said. 'Does anyone—Jerott?—know a nice clean strumpet who doesn't have the pox and will keep in my room tonight to discourage Richard? She needn't stay beyond half an hour, and I don't want to meet her.'

'And that's a bloody waste,' said Jerott belligerently.

'And it's going to stay a bloody waste,' said Lymond tartly. 'I want a little privacy, not to work up a joint reputation as Hophni and Phinehas.'

He abandoned the window, and Adam saw his face and let his lips open.

'Oh, quite.' Lymond said. 'Twice in two days. Once it becomes continuous, I suppose we shall have to tell Richard. Or he will be spending twenty-four hours of every day in my bedroom.'

Then Adam remembered the reason for Richard's vigil: the dragging out into daylight of something of which Lymond had never spoken. And he remembered also, with sudden, raw understanding, a small event of the previous night; when he had heard Francis, his head in his hands, apostrophizing himself mutinously:

> *Plus étroit que la vigne à l'ormeau se marie*
> *Du lien de tes mains, maîtresse, je te prye.*
> *Enlace-moy le corps, maîtresse . . .*
> *Enlace-moy le corps.*

'. . . You never married, Adam?'

He had been startled. 'No.'

'Then don't,' Lymond had said, the words trailing through his muffling hands. 'It makes for very . . . long nights.'

So now Adam touched the comte de Sevigny's arm and said, 'Come. We shall see if Archie can make a short night for you.'

CHAPTER 7

De terre foible et pauvre parentele
Par bout et paix parviendra dans l'empire
Longtemps regner une jeune femele,
Qu'oncq en regne n'en survint un si pire.

At dawn on Sunday, 24 April, since no one had told them to the contrary, the Prévôt and magistrates of Paris rose, broke their fast, put on their robes of crimson and yellow satin and left for the Hôtel de Ville, there to muster at seven in the morning to prepare for the wedding of Monseigneur the Dauphin of France with the young Queen of Scotland. There was a tiff about precedence, which petered out as the air became warmer. It was dry underfoot.

Long before dawn, Philippa Somerville, after a sleepless night, rose from her temporary bed in the Bishop's Palace on the quayside behind Notre-Dame Cathedral, dressed in cloth of silver and proceeded with the other demoiselles of honour to the long task of preparing their mistress for her wedding. She too, like the magistrates of Paris, was unaware of anything which might impede the ceremony.

She remembered, certainly, Richard Crawford returning grim-faced from his brother's house, and the conference of Commissioners which had taken place behind locked doors with, one could hear, a good deal of dissent and even some shouting. What she remembered more clearly, however, was the childish and debasing restrictions Culter and Austin had suddenly placed on her liberty: the withdrawl of Célie and her replacement by a silent woman named, ridiculously, Euphemia, who dogged her every movement and slept in her chamber.

These measures were to protect her, she was told, against Lymond. They also made sure, although no one said so, that she was unable to make any indecorous movements towards Lymond herself. Richard had not spared her an account of the woman who had shared Lymond's bedroom the previous

514

night. He had also taken time, with a slow and bitter reluctance, to place before her the truth of his brother's habit of life, as an outlaw in Scotland, and as a mignon of France six years before, practising all the sensual arts.

She knew it all, since Lymond himself had told her: the reckless degradation for whatever motives, whose stain, like the mud of Paris was indelible. Sybilla had not been in the room while Richard had talked of his brother. Throughout, ever since Austin's outburst, Sybilla had said achingly little. Only from her stillness and the searching blue gaze which followed and rested on her constantly did Philippa guess that only now was she coming to realize, as perhaps few others did, the full dimensions of the doomed relationship between Philippa and her son Francis.

For that, she had to thank Austin, who against all probability was fighting, where Catherine d'Albon had simply withdrawn. And withdrawn sorely hurt, as Philippa knew, although with a pride which would let her smile when Philippa went to see her and say, 'I showed you your face in the mirror. It was not only the face of one who loves, but the face of one whose love is returned. I should rather, Philippa, marry where there is no love than marry and find love turn to jealousy. Don't be sorry. This is a better way than any other.'

And for her, perhaps it was. An heiress finds no shortage of suitors. Since rumour had carried abroad her own rupture with Austin, the four days before the wedding and coming annulment had been made feverishly miserable by the suffocating attentions of all those she had drawn within her circle and especially those, such as the Schiatti cousins, to whom she owed an obligation.

And worse than this, day by day, was the fact that no word reached her from Leonard Bailey; that perhaps no message would ever reach her. Perhaps he had chosen instead to favour John Elder and the Lennoxes, not herself, with the proof of Sybilla's infidelity. Perhaps he had already sent Elder the papers and Elder was moving, smiling and chatting about the royal household, awaiting only his moment to reveal them.

Daily, in those four days of chaos and ritual, she had seen Francis distantly, acting his rôle; and daily had noted the changes in him. The message from Leonard Bailey had be-

515

come, by that Sunday morning, the most important thing in Philippa's life; the most feared and the most hoped for.

There are two things you desire, the astrologers had once told Francis Crawford. *The first you will have. The second you shall never have, nor would it be just that you should.*

It might not be just. But this wish at least she might fulfil for him.

•

The Commissioners for Scotland, chosen by Scotland to decorate the marriage and fortify it with Scottish authority, dressed in the Hôtel de l'Ange and left early for the Episcopal Palace on horseback. The Earl of Culter, who for four days had stayed at the Hôtel d'Hercule with his brother, joined them on the way.

At the Séjour du Roi, Jerott, Adam and Danny, expensively dressed, prepared to leave and take their places in the Cathedral. Danny, who had spent a number of exhausting days attending to his work, analysing a lady called Marthe and baulking every fitful step taken by the Dowager Lady Culter in the direction of the Petit Arsenal, looked as usual, like a spindle of bobbles and fringe from the fripperer's.

Jerott, with the physique of a Knight of St. John and a shrewder eye than most for a good length of tanné velvet, looked little short of magnificent. Under the constant, brutal demands of Lymond's sovereignty, he was learning to forget Marthe and the bottle. Adam, soberly dressed, had not had the heart for Jerott's bitter exuberance. He like the others, had been present when the Commissioners had come to question Lymond; had heard Lymond obstruct every effort to discover the source of the copy, and had then heard the subsequent debate, chaired with incision by Orkney, in which the conclusion that Lymond urged was finally reached: to do nothing: to allow the marriage to proceed, and to act thereafter as the climate of the French court and their own diplomacy would dictate.

It was, as Lymond's exposition had been, a triumph of common sense over emotion, but it was not reached without the airing of harshly opposing views; a venting of small sudden flares which betrayed to the onlooker how uncertain was the ground on which they walked, and how hot the fires beneath. By the Treaty of Haddington ten years before, the Three Estates which comprised the Scottish Parliament had promised that their Sovereign lady should be married with the Dauphin at her perfect age, so that the King of France kept, maintained and defended that realm, the lieges of the same and the liberties and law thereof as he did his own realm of France.

This for ten years France had done. The marriage was due, and Scotland was bound to it. In black and white they had also the agreement of the King of France to the Estates' stipulation: should the Queen of Scotland die without heirs, the righteous blood of the crown of Scotland should suceed without impediment; aided, fortified and supported by the King's majesty and his successors.

This agreement Mary had signed, and rebutted secretly. In addition, the Crown matrimonial had been demanded: the crown which in common usage meant that for his lifetime, the consort would share the powers of the Queen. The crown which, in unscrupulous hands, might be taken to mean that on the Queen's death, the rights to the throne should pass to the blood of her husband.

Orkney had questioned Lymond about the crown. 'I believe,' he had said with his deaf ear cupped, because they were speaking softly, 'that you warned Lord Culter about this. Did you then have prior knowledge of what the French were likely to do? How is it, in fact, that this information came to be passed to you, M. de Sevigny, and not to one of the Commission?'

'In an army, one hears a great deal of gossip,' Lymond had said. 'And as to the papers, perhaps it was thought that I was a likely spearhead of any revolution against the de Guises. I have not been told.'

'And have you decided to enter the lists against the de Guise family?' Bishop Reid asked. 'You have not, I noticed, allowed your gifts in these past weeks to flourish unrecognized. Someone may decide to cure *la piquure du scorpion par le scorpion mesme.*'

'He would be a fool,' Lymond said, 'who would cross the de Guise brothers at this moment. You will take the oath of fidelity to the Dauphin?'

'Yes,' said Lord James Stewart thoughtfully. 'We have the consent of the Three Estates to do so. We accept the sweets of this marriage: and the specific. Let time ahead show whether or not we may digest them.'

517

It was then that Jerott, starting up said, 'How can a country prosper under a Queen who has betrayed it?'

And the Queen's half brother had turned on him those heavy Stewart eyes and said, 'For that, we have so far only the word of your friend the sieur of Lymond and Sevigny. He has explained to us how poor a moment we have chosen to cry patriotism with a shining sword. And I agree. Do not, I pray you, jar the barque of concord.'

They would hold their peace, it seemed; not least because there was no concrete evidence. But, Adam thought, should that proof come, there were those among the nine who would cry patriotism, whatever wisdom counselled. And Richard Crawford would be one of them.

He had watched the brothers through those days, helping with Archie to defend the little left of Lymond's privacy. A reluctant watchdog, Culter held a post of small dignity, vulnerable to a thousand shafts of wit . . . which did not arrive. Francis at his most quiet, his most responsible showed his elder brother the face, Adam thought, his friends sometimes saw. And from that realized that Francis, in those final days, was drawing from obscurity an old friendship, to be remembered later maybe, and recognized.

He did not know that he himself reflected all of this until Lord Allendale, on edge; unmoved by alien weddings which boded ill for England, said, 'Why so despondent? Now you are French and need never go back to cold winds and sour marsh and sodden mutton and kail for your faring. I hear you write to Philippa's mother. Do you tell her all the news?'

Brooding and restless with a sharp edge, in those days, to his tongue, Austin Grey also had changed from the courteous, difficult youth Adam remembered. Adam said, 'I have told Kate all that has happened: yes. As you know, it is hard to get letters back just now, with shipping at war in the Narrow Straits.'

'And you have told her, I hope,' Austin said, 'of the drugs of which your friend avails himself so freely? Perhaps you provide them.'

'No,' Adam said. 'But I should, if it were necessary. He has cared for me, when I needed it.'

'He nursed you, perhaps, when you received the lash you bear on your face?' Austin said.

For a moment Blacklock was silent. Then he said, 'Yes. He sat with me all night.'

'A faithful friend and physician. And who, as a matter of interest, had given you so brutal a lash?' asked Austin Grey.

And Adam, on a long sigh, had looked at him and then turned and left without answering; for it was obvious that he knew the answer, and was tormenting himself as well as his captors. But at least, Adam thought, he did not have to go to the wedding.

*

At nine o'clock, Messieurs of the Town of Paris, variously attired in crimson and yellow and black, mounted mules and left the gates of the Hôtel de Ville, accompanied by all the town bands of archers, arbalesters and hackbutters in their livery, and led by the ten sergeants of the town in particoloured robes pinned by the silver ship emblem of Paris. From there they crossed the Pont Notre-Dame and reached, with difficulty, the parvis, or open space in front of the Cathedral which was jammed by people disputing like starlings.

Above their heads it could be seen that a platform had been erected in front of the west entrance to the Cathedral, with a canopy of Persian blue vlevet studded with gold fleurs de lis and bearing the arms of France and Scotland. On either side of the great doorway were two hangings of the same material. And leading from the platform and round the right hand corner of the Cathedral was a high wooden gallery twined with vine leaves which continued, the town fathers knew, to the doors of the Episcopal Palace. Thus the royal celebrants, when the time came, could reach the church doors by bridging the people.

It was clear how the King of France intended to enter the Cathedral, but not so clear what route was set apart for Messrs the Aldermen, Receivers and Controllers, not to mention their mules.

They tried the doorway near the Church of St Marine and were hustled out by a gentleman usher. To enter the choir, in the end, they had to return to the great door and lower themselves, with a manful absence of imprecation, on to the long bridging ramp which joined the platform at the west door to the furthest interior of the Cathedral.

Like the gallery erected outside, it was laced with leaves

and floored with Turkey carpet and so made pleasant walking except that, in the end, it was discovered that the high chairs to the left to the choir, rightfully those of the Town, had been occupied already by Messieurs of the Counting House and the heads of Justice, leaving only the inferior seats near the door, into which the Town sullenly squeezed itself. The right of the chancel, thick as a poppyfield, was filled with the Court of Parliament in scarlet robes lined with velvet, their furred hats laid on their shoulders. And waiting before them, in a dazzle of massy church gold and painted statuary, was the Reverend Father in God Eustache du Bellay, Bishop of Paris, in his stiffest pontifical habits, flanked by his clergy and awaiting, with grave inclinations of recognition, the arrival of the royal party.

The shuffling footsteps, the long lines of filtering new-comers, the dog-eared flutter of grouped genuflections slowly ceased and the ground-bass of cautious greeting rose to a rumble of titillated self-conceit and excitement. At ten o'clock the noise, suddenly dwindling, allowed to be heard the squeak and the thud of the Swiss Guard with their tambour and fifes, coming to take up their posts by the platform. The Bishop, in a stately glitter of embroidered vestments, glanced about and set off for the porch with his clergy, the Cathedral Cross carried before him, and flanked by two choirboys with lit tapers in silver candlesticks.

The church became rather silent, so that the noise of the crowds in the parvis could be heard, like heavy breathing outside the west door. The sound of trumpets, far away, floated like dandelion quills through the open doors and athwart the south wall of the building. It was eleven o'clock, and the Royal procession had left the Bishop's Palace and was proceeding along the covered gallery to the Cathedral.

To the people filling the parvis and every window and rooftop about it, the Court appeared as a ruching of gold, slowly drawn through a lattice of greenery. Far ahead of the rest, in cloth of gold to his feet, the Duke de Guise arrived on the platform and cleared it, with a sweep of his arm, of all those who obscured the crowd's viewpoint. A great arcade of sound burst from the people, and hard on its heels, a striving outcry of music from trumpets, clarions, hautboys, flageolets, viols, violins, cistres and citterns as the musicians came forth, massed in yellow and red and threw every pigeon flock skywards. Then the procession arrived, and moved from the bridge to the balcony, filling it.

The crowd knew everyone. The cheering overlapped, tossed like faggots of spray into an air stinking of garlic and cheap wine and poverty. They knew the princes with their jewelled berets and doublets and breeches slashed and ribboned and pebbled with gems. They knew why Piero Strozzi was missing, with another attack of catarrh. They knew the bishops, archbishops and abbots, the Cardinals and the Papal Legate, the Cross and the Eucharist carried before him. They knew every famous face of the hundred gentlemen: the King's gentlemen of the chamber, the marshals, the captains, the Chevaliers of the Order, the high officers of State. It pleased him to recognize the war leaders and shout the names of their victories. They did not omit their conspicuous favourite, the angelic Russian for whom the bâton of a Marshal of France was surely waiting.

From the end of the procession, Philippa heard Lymond's name roared and felt her heart hammering. Before her was a thicket of nervous princesses, with in front of them Madame Marguerite, the Queen of Navarre and the Queen of France, led by the Prince of Condé who, though poor, was a prince of the blood and occasionally had to remember it.

Ahead of them was Mary, with the King on one side and the Duke of Lorraine on the other. Philippa could see her crown blaze in the sunshine as she stepped round and on to the platform: it was made of gold clasped with every known gemstone and was a good deal better than the crown the Commissioners had failed to bring from Scotland, having a single jewel worth 500,000 écus in the middle.

In profile, she looked perfectly composed, with her auburn hair bound neatly round it, and her long, slender neck with its collar of jewellery. She was dressed in the colours of Scotland: a white robe, over which fell the difficult train in the same green-grey blue as the hangings, made heavy with jewels and embroidery. It wound successfully round the last of the staging and up, Philippa was happy to see, to the platform. The Dauphin, with the King of Navarre and his two younger brothers, preceded her.

They all came to a halt in the heart of the platform, in the hazy lichenous dusk of the canopy. The end of the procession, scurrying, found its position. Cardinal de Bourbon faced the bridal pair, and with the whole of Paris below, breathless, watching, began to utter the words of the marriage service.

Philippa listened.

Take thou this wilful and lovely young woman, who is the realm, proud and ancient, of Scotland. Take thou this backward and impotent boy, in whom runs great Gaul's royal blood-line. And join them in holy matrimony, whose object is to glorify God, to bear fruit, and to shun adultery.

And who was she, to mock such a marriage, when her own had used the rites of the church for a purpose not one whit more tender? When the union contracted in Turkey had produced neither heirs nor peace nor freedom from lechery . . . ?

Take thou this young man and this girl of different nations who, unmoved on the day of their marriage, may discover in years to come a bond beyond man's understanding. And let it come to them in such a form that they may keep it. . . .

One is permitted to weep at a wedding. There, already ranked on the platform, were the nine Scottish Commissioners, who were not tearful, but whose mien was not that of rejoicing. And on the other side, where she did not have to look to discover him, was Lymond her husband, with the same griefs contained in his stillness.

She had made no effort to withdraw from tomorrow's process of annulment. It made no difference now.

The King of France's ring, slipped on the bride's finger, made her Reine-Dauphine of France. The Bishop of Paris, moving forward, began to intone a long prayer. The Duke de Guise, signing irritably, contrived to move a number of straying figures out of the public's line of vision.

Soon the heralds at arms would come with sacks of coins and throw them from the three sides of the platform, roaring *Largesse:* an act long known to cause hysteria, injury and sometimes even death in the ensuing stampede but which no one, crown or people, dared tamper with. Then turning, the procession would pick its way into the church where Mass would be celebrated in the same style, said the Master of Ceremonies, as all simple brides use for the sacrament.

Once, de Chémault had been a good friend to Francis in London. If she had been a good friend to Francis . . . she would have sent him to Russia. Anything was better than this. Anything was better than the condition which could lead a man to repeat, as he had done that night at Fontainebleau, the words of another, refused by the grim boatman Charon:

J'irai donc, maugré toy, car j'ay dedans mon âme
Tant de traits amoureux et de larmes aux yeux
Que je seray le fleuve, et la barque, et la rame.

The wedding banquet in the Bishop's Palace followed. Messieurs of the Town, who were not invited, dined by prior arrangement in a small house near the parvis of Notre-Dame, which proved inconvenient. After, they made for a bigger house on the Pont au Change, where, until their next assignation, they were able to pull off their robes and take the air over the water.

The royal party, embedded in cloth of gold upon litters, horses and coaches emerged from the banquet and proceeded to the Palais de Justice, making a short detour by the Notre-Dame bridge on the way. Attempting to follow the change of route, the spectators in the rue de Neuv Notre-Dame and the rue de la Calende emptied themselves into the rue du Marche-Palus, a runnel four feet wide in which three drains met, with insalubrious consequences. The royal party, having crossed the Pont Notre-Dame, proceeded a short way down-river among other and cleaner crowds, and then recrossed to the Palais de Justice by means of the Pont au Change, passing Messieurs of the Town, who cheered, anonymously.

There were men in the crowd who remembered the wedding of old King Henri, when the streets were draped with tapestries and carpets hung from every window, and when the Fountain of Ponceau flowed with wine and hippocras. There were younger men who remembered other Triumphs and Ceremonial Entries, when choirs of children had sung at the Hôtel-Dieu and on the Parvis; when the streets were spanned by great arches with living statues, and at every corner there had been stages, with plays enacted upon them, or nymphs waiting with gifts, or gods with heroic poetry.

For the Scotch wedding, it appeared, none of this was considered suitable, when (so the Keeper of Seals let it be known) the country was still at war. There had been largesse, as was right. The belltower of the Palais had led the carillons. There had been a salute, somewhere, of cannon. But even the bird-keepers of the Pont au Change had not been discreetly visited, as was normal, and assured of the King's concrete gratitude if and when they made the traditional gesture when the royal party crossed to the Palais.

The traditional gesture consisted of the release into the air of two hundred dozen birds of all species. Given generous warning, one was assured at least of providing a spectacle. That Sunday, as the bride's procession set foot on the planks of the bridge, the bird-keepers opened their cages; and as peculiar an assortment of bird life ascended the skies as could be seen anywhere outside a bestiary.

The air blackened with wings of all colours, and then blanched with the fruits of their disquietude. On the epaulette of the Archer by Philippa arrived a small portly creature in green, which puked; remarked, *'Hé, petit capitaine de merde!'* and whirred off as he reached up to throttle it.

She was gazing after its flight when a hand, thrust through the crowd, pushed something into her fingers.

The hand had gone before she whirled to look for it. She rode on, gripping her prize, and smiling affably to the jostling thicket of pink, sweating countenances. Then, tilting her palm, she saw what was in it.

A page of paper, tightly balled, bore traces of broken writing. Unfolded a little, it showed her it contained a message. Unfolded a good deal more, it told her that the message was from Leonard Bailey.

At last, on the edge of the river, had been granted the stay she was waiting for.

CHAPTER 8

L'ire insensée du combat furieux
Fera à table par freres le fer luire.

As the Kings of France, like the early Christians, were always
wed in the porch of their church, so they always followed the
Mass with a public banquet at the Marble Table of the Palais
de Justice, attended by the courtiers, the courts of Parliament, Messieurs of the Town and Messieurs of the University, together with the better-bred nationals of whatever nation had received the happy portion of a French spouse.

By five o'clock, when Messieurs of the Town had walked
to the Palais and had been allotted their seats below the royal
covers, the going price for the password *'Brede and Ale'* was
three écues sol and still rising, and the accent in the
strangers' benches was far from predominantly Scottish.
There began, as the ushers realized this, some heavily muffled
engagements.

The gates were fastened. The great seigneurs who were not
princes of the blood entered and took their places. There was
a flourish of trumpets, and the bridal company paced through
the double carved doors and seated themselves, stiff and
smiling as Holy Week images behind the famous table, the
longest, the broadest, the thickest single slab of unbroken
marble in history. Daniel Hislop, sitting four tables down
from this glory, treated Adam over Jerott's suffering head to
a sequence of brilliant strictures, based on a disingenuous
recollection of the court of Tsar Ivan of Russia.

The doors opened again to emit a roll of drums and a
squall of trumpets and clarions, announcing the forthcoming
service. It entered, carried under napkins by two hundred
pairs of gentlemanly hands and preceded by the twelve masters of the royal households, who in turn were led by the heralds of France and Scotland in their tabards, two by two, and
by the dazzling cloth of gold presence of the Duke de Guise,
his bâton of office before him.

On the handsome, scarred face of François de Guise was a

525

smile of perfect complacency. Today, he was Grand Maître d'Hôtel to the King, and had filched at last the Constable's coveted office. Today, without complaint, interference or open impediment, his niece had received with the ring on her finger the rights to three kingdoms. Through her he had laid at the feet of this king the priceless gift of the nation of Scotland, and the larger claim which that throne embodied. Through her, when the time came, the Duke himself might govern three nations, and his brother the Christian cosmos.

The vessel of such superb statecraft, fifteen years old, with the brilliant crown held blazing over her head, received smiling his careful deference. Tiredness hollowed the hazel eyes, but the flush and glitter of pride and excitement still drove aside all awareness of strain. She was the shrine, the fountain, the flame which drew all men's eyes: praise and envy and adulation settled clinging upon her like garlands. Above her hung the French fleur de lis and the lion of Scotland. Her arms and those of France laced through the blue and gold vault of the ceiling. The painted file of arched windows, blazing with the late sunlight drenched the pillars with jewels and burned upon the riches of her subjects in flecks and prisms of colour, bright as soap-bubbles.

Later, when the third service was over and the cressets were lit, the buffet was opened with all its ten shelves laden with the gold plate of France, and the King lifted from it a great quart-pot of red gold for the heralds to carry from table to table, calling largesse. Then the Reine-Dauphine of France and Queen of Scotland was glad, for she could cease appearing to eat a meal for which she had no appetite. Soon, grace would be said and the tables drawn and she could move, and laugh and dance, and be admired all over again.

The demoiselles of honour, who had not been married today, looked more tired than she was. She spoke, twice, to Madame la comtesse de Sevigny, and finally obtained the rosewater and napkin she wanted.

Then the tables were lifted, and the austere replicas of past Presidents, Counsellors and advocates, peering down from the carved pendants and ogives, could see the black and white marble floor bare, where by day the merchants' booths stood, and where the Procureurs of the Court leased their benches. And round the room, in blue and ducat-gold stood, without voicing opinion, the statues of the Kings of France, from Pharamond to Charles IX; the spiritual with arms and eyes uplifted, the less commendable with hands and heads lowered. The Dauphin, his wide-cheeked face suet-coloured, was led away, briefly, by his gentlemen.

The Queen did not want to leave, even temporarily. It was Madame de Valentinois, exerting incredible tact, who finally persuaded her to retire, and Philippa left the room with her, glancing for the last time, as she went, towards the group of gentlemen wearing the silver collar of the Chevaliers of the Order; and in particular at the one Knight of the Order whose shoulder had been turned to her throughout the whole turgid meal.

Adam also had been conscious for the last hour of Francis Crawford, and of the table with the Scottish Commissioners at which he had been sitting. Through all the meaningless vows of the ceremony you could see, if you knew, the anger simmering behind the nine correct faces: but at least up to now the ritual had been ecclesiastical, and familiar.

Here, the perfunctory tinsel was more apparent. Here, the triumph of the six brothers de Guise was quite tangible.

It had been Lymond who had taken in hand, after a moment, the shiftless, fraying web of small talk, aided quickly by Reid, and a little later, quietly by James Stewart. If they could not rejoice, at least they should not look like men stricken by the occasion.

It was accepted that this was a court which enjoyed, whatever the excuse, performing before its inferiors. The gentlemen in bright satin robes, having finished their meal—not lavish, but quite satisfactory—were gathered now at one end of the room and expected to assimilate, dazzled, the grace of blue blood: its wealth and its superiority. And from the masques, the ballads, the mummeries to be impressed, once and for all, with the splendour and consequence of this marriage which, with his usual care for their happiness, their monarch and his seigneurs had arranged for them.

First, the princesses danced; the long, sinuous line led by the Queen of Scots and the King's daughter, Madame Elizabeth. Then, using for dressing-room the gilded Chamber of Pleas, the court proceeded, for two hours, to entertain themselves and their guests with a Triumph, as several Aldermen ringingly said, greater than that of Caesar.

Tact had solved the sartorial problems of the Seven Planets: Mercury's wand bore a snake which looked like silver, even if it was painted hemp, and all sang the verse written for them with fervour and even some accuracy. The children of France, their exhaustion stiffened by arrogance, rode without mishap the twelve willow palfreys, trailing housings of gold and silver.

The white chariot horses did not flinch under the mouths of the clarions, and the singing by each crew, apostrophizing the Dauphin, was such that the noise from their audience abated a little, and faded. *'O Mars, filz de Mars! . . .'*

Three of the singers were not from the King's chapel. 'The young men who so delighted us at your reception. I could wish,' said John Erskine to Lymond, (*Mars, donne nous ce jour où se fait l'aliance/Qui joindra pour jamais l'Ecosse à notre France*) 'that their songs today were of the same order.'

(*O mariage heureux, que Dieu veule lier/Pour faire sous un Roy deux royaumes plier/Et non deux seulement, mais sans meurdre et sans guerre/A la France et l'Ecosse alliant l'Angleterre.*)

It is not difficult, if paid sufficiently well, to find rhymes in French and Latin to extoll the virtues of a match made in heaven, and to proclaim the joy to all men of a union between two brave and ancient countries. None of the main protagonists, including the Scottish Commissioners (*Surgit ab Orcadibus speciosus Palladis autor*), escaped eulogy. But through it all the principal theme, chanted in chorus and proclaimed, thrillingly, by single voices was repeated, hardly varying; glancing from wall to window to pillar to vaulted ceiling, striking back with a thousand tongues from bone and medal and jewel, and ending with the noble Latin of Cassillis' former tutor:

Haec una centum de stirpe nepotes
Sceptriferos numerare potest, haec regina sola est,
Quae bis dena suis includat secula fastis . . .

O royal youth! destined o'er Gaul to reign
Accept a dowry worthy of a King . . .

When history her pride of birth enquires
The race and honours of her ancient sires
She can recount, on Fame's wide spreading wings
One hundred sceptre-bearing martial kings
Sprung from the same august and royal line . . .

When conquered kingdoms were compelled to change
Their laws, and statutes of their sires derange
Scotland alone her liberty retained
And on her ancient base inviolate remained . . .

Hunger to endure beneath a northern sky
The summer's heat and winter's cold defy
Never beneath the tyrant's foot to bend
Without high walls their country to defend . . .

Whate'er of other kingdoms Fame may tell
Scotland still nobler deeds and tales can trace
And from the proudest claim a prouder place . . .

(Icelle Dame a ceddé et delaissé, par ces présentes au Roy et ses successeurs, Roys de France, la possession, vuyde et vacue duy royaulme d'Escosse, pour en joyr por eulx sans ce que aulcun empeschement leur puisse en ce estre faict par personne quelconque.)

It was Francis Crawford, of all the silent circle of Scotsmen, who walked off abruptly and waited, his head bent, his arm on the wainscoting, until the epithalamia had ended.

Then the dancing started again. For half an hour, it was necessary to stand and applaud as the Queen of Scots, her eyes brilliant, her cheekbones pink in her white face, again led the slow chain, her blue-green train, carried for her, interweaving its velvet with the cloth of gold, the silk and the tissue of the princesses.

Two Parliamentary councillors, discovering the Russian commander beside them, began an eager, deferential conversation about trading concessions. When he could, Lymond moved away.

Adam, watchful, saw him twice after that: once with d'Estrée and de Thermes and another gentleman of the Order, the three shoulder-chains of silver cockle shells sparkling fluted together, and once with Perrot, the Prévôt des Marchands, who was reliving, one would say from his hands, the defence of Paris.

He was not difficult to follow. The crimson velvet clasped with rubies and vented with gold was the only brutally vulgar dress Adam had ever seen Lymond wear, but he had known better than to comment on it. Now he watched it progress, constantly impeded, from point to point of the vast salon; now with the Duke de Nevers and some of his captains; now with Madame Marguerite; now with the Marshal de St André, never more attentive than now, when his foolish daughter had broken the formal bond between them. And then, returning laughing to her chair, the bride had called him and was complaining, with mock severity, that he was not wearing her glove.

Mary Fleming, who had a closer view than Adam Blacklock, saw the Queen's hand on Lymond's arm, and the eyes of the Cardinal of Lorraine, watching them. Then someone was brought forward to be presented and unexpectedly the daughter of Jenny Fleming found that the man James admired above all others was standing beside her and asking her, with charming irony, how she was bearing the strain of so many suffocating pleasures.

She answered, and he entertained her, briefly for a moment or two longer before he said, 'Mary: where is Philippa?'

'Did you notice? I don't know,' said Mary Fleming. 'The heat turned her head a little and she slipped away to her room while the tables were being drawn, but she isn't there now. In fact, according to Euphemia, Philippa didn't go to her chamber.'

'If she was dizzy, perhaps she didn't reach it. Have you looked?' said Lymond curtly. And then, seeing her flush, he added quickly, 'I beg your pardon. Of course it has been impossible for you. May I ask a favour of you? Will you take me to her room and allow me to speak to Euphemia? And could you send another page perhaps to look for her, without creating any alarm?'

But Euphemia, yellow of face, had already sent several maids and had been out herself in the network of passages searching for Mistress Philippa, whom she had been enjoined, on pain of a beating, never to let out of her sight. 'And I never did!' wailed Euphemia. 'Day and night, I never did! How could they expect me to get into the King's Grand' Salle to watch her?'

For, it seemed, a cloak was missing. A heavy, enveloping cloak which had been carried, in case of rain, on the short procession from Notre-Dame to the Palais, and must therefore have been removed during the fuss when the Queen was being combed and prinked prior to the banquet. 'She's outside,' said Euphemia, her eyes filled with unbecoming and horrified tears. 'She knew before the banquet she was going out. It is a trick. It is an assignation!'

The gentleman in crimson velvet, whom she did not know, did not rebuke her. He only stood perfectly still and said, 'Do we know where she might be going? Have any messages reached her?'

'None! None!' said Euphemia, horrified. 'She was not permitted to receive messages! Her family ... the Lord Culter is extremely strict!'

'Then,' said Lymond, 'did she send any?'

The woman thought. Mary Fleming shut the door, her heart beating, on the distant noise outside and envied Mr Crawford his composure, waiting. Then Euphemia said, 'There was the letter she sent the Hôtel de Guise, about her boxes.'

He said, 'What was that?'

'Just after we arrived. A letter to one of her grooms, telling him that someone would be calling with mules to take away the four boxes in her chamber, and to help him, as they were heavy.'

'Boxes?' Lymond said. 'What kind of boxes?' And turned as Mary, in spite of herself, drew a quick breath. 'You know?'

'I know the boxes she means,' Mary said. 'They were metal bound, with Nuremberg locks in iron. Philippa has had them with her now for two months. She said they contained books.'

'But you didn't believe her?' Lymond said.

Her mouth for some reason dry, Mary Fleming faced the swift, unaggressive inquisition. 'They were full of money,' she said. 'You could hear the coins move when they were lifted.'

For a moment, Lymond's eyes continued to dwell on her, then he turned back to the woman Euphemia. 'And the gentleman who was to call for the boxes,' he said. 'Did she name him, or describe him in any way?'

That she remembered. 'His name,' Euphemia said, 'was M. Janus, and she said he was an old gentleman, very heavy, with an English accent. She didn't know,' added Euphemia, suddenly frightened afresh by the atmosphere, 'that I read the letter. They said I was to read everything.'

Janus. The two-faced God. The God of Gates, with a key in his hand.

'I see,' Lymond said. 'Thank you. It was not your fault. I know where Mistress Philippa is, and I shall not even trouble

Lord Culter, I believe, with the story. You will have her safely back before long. Mary, will you excuse me?'

But swiftly as he made out of the room, Mary Fleming pursued him. 'Where is she? What do I say? What if someone asks for her?' And then, as he turned, 'You don't know yet, do you?'

'No,' said Lymond. 'But I shall find her. And if you are able, I would ask you not to let it be known, for as long as you can, that she is missing. Am I asking too much?'

'No,' said Mary Fleming. He was asking a great deal, but then, she would have given him a great deal, as once her mother wanted to do.

The last galliard had begun in the hall, and Messieurs of the Town, pleased, well-drunken and wonderfully tolerant now on all matters to do with both collars and precedence were lost in wet-eyed pleasure at the splendour of it all, and in a mood to form loving friendships with every man in the room. Daniel Hislop, having exhausted his larynx, if not his stock of witticisms, had gone to earth among a huddle of somnolent advocates. Jerott, kept remarkably sober by his fellow captains, had found a lady who liked black hair and Lyon velvet, and was skirmishing with her. Adam, uneasy about many things, agreed, for the third time, to become the lifelong blood-brother of a hatmaker and then stepped sharply aside, causing a landslide of creased yellow satin as Lymond's voice spoke abruptly behind him.

'Adam? Is Osias on duty? Or anyone else?'

Adam's heart went cold. 'Not tonight,' he said. 'It was impossible, because of the . . .'

He was not allowed to finish. 'On other days, has Philippa always been followed? I asked that this should be tightened.'

'Always,' Adam said. 'Except for the one time you know about. Francis, what's happened?'

'And on that one occasion,' said Lymond, as if he had not spoken, 'how long was she away from the Hôtel de Guise? Is it known?'

'An hour, Osias thought,' Adam said. 'She crossed the rue St Antoine from the de Guise house, going south. That's all he could find out . . . Francis?'

'She left the palace this evening,' Lymond said. 'So she wasn't going, the other time, to one of the bridges. She didn't leave by the Porte St Antoine, and she had hardly time to get a ferry over the river and back again. And that leaves the Petit Arsenal district.'

'The Petit Arsenal?' Adam said. 'That's where . . .'

'What?' said Lymond.

'Danny was asked by Philippa not to tell you,' said Adam slowly. 'She thought, it seems, that your mother might try to visit a house in the Petit Arsenal district, and if she did, Danny was to prevent her.'

For the first time, Lymond did not speak at once. Then he said, 'And the address?'

'Danny was never told,' and Adam quietly. 'The only person who would know is your mother. If you like, I shall go and ask her. She went some time ago to her room.'

'No. Thank you. I had better do that,' Lymond said.

Long ago, returning from some turbulent sequence of misdeeds, the younger, beloved son of the house of Culter would rap at the door of his mother's chamber, and be admitted, and closing the door, would bend upon her the grave, sweet gaze, made of mischief and love, that melted the bones in her body. Then, sinking to one knee, he would kiss her hand, in obedience and humility.

Now he rapped, and she heard his voice speak her name and, rising, she faced him as the door opened and shut and he stood, his bearing and looks unlike anything she had ever seen in him before, in any extremity. He said, 'I have to find Philippa.' And then, walking into the room, he dropped on one knee and said, 'I will promise anything you wish, to the end of my life, if you will tell me the name of the house that you know of.'

And as she did not answer, staring appalled at his face, he said, 'Philippa asked that you should be prevented from going there. We know it is near the Petit Arsenal. I think Leonard Bailey has found it.'

Blanched by age and by agony, her skin had no colour at all, and her drawn brows this time were no longer those of a beautiful woman. Then she said, her timbreless voice barely audible, 'It is called the Hôtel des Sphères; and it is in the rue de la Cerisaye. . . .

'It is where you were born, Francis.'

He left while she was speaking. He reached the Grand' Salle without thinking, as the quickest way to reach the staircase, and found his way blocked, unbelievably, by the muscular countryman's body of his brother.

'You are very busy,' Richard Crawford said, 'for a man assisting at the nuptial feast of his monarch. Wherever you are going now, I am sure you won't mind if I come along with you.'

Over and over, the same song, the same burden; the obstruction; the battle; the challenge: *if you won't lead, try following, Richard!*

But where he was going now, he could not take Richard. Nor, looking at his brother's face, could he think of any ruse that would serve him. Richard said, 'They tell me Philippa isn't to be found. I don't suppose you would know where she is?'

'No. Ask Euphemia,' the comte de Sevigny said. There were men all about them.

'Don't look round,' Richard said. 'There is no way out there. I would be rather crude, but if I have to, I shall stop you with violence. You are in a hurry, aren't you?'

He was in too much of a hurry not to take all the care in the world with the next move. It was bluff and double bluff: a step, a feint, another step, and a sliding movement which took him out of Richard's grasp just as his own blow, low and accurate, made his brother gasp and desist. Then he was moving as fast as he could through the crowds, with Richard he knew a few bare yards behind him.

He had not gained enough distance to outpace him on the stairs or in the outer rooms and passageways, so he did not attempt it. Instead Lymond turned inwards across the corner of the Grand' Salle and up to where stood the wreathed double doors of the Chamber of Requests, flanked by two Archers of the Royal Bodyguard.

'Monseigneur?' one of them said. He knew them both well.

'I have to assist their graces,' said Lymond. 'The noble earl my brother is not meantime to be admitted.' And did not look back as he stepped through and the doors shut behind him.

The King, with a black silk mask binding his brow, was surprised but instantly welcoming. 'The man we wish to see. Come, you create marvels in the field. Show us how to adjust this galleon so that Monseigneur my son may properly guide it.'

The golden room was full of people, and ships. The ships were ingeniously mechanical, and made of red velvet and cloth of gold, with silver sails as high as a man. The King,

Lorraine, Navarre and Nemours, masked and impatient, were already seated each in his barque. Condé, abandoning his, was kneeling beside the ship of the Dauphin, ferreting within its entrails with a hunted expression to do with a rip in his exquisite stockings. Mars, fil de Mars said, 'It is unsafe. I will not ride in it.'

'Nonsense, *mon fils*,' said the King. 'Is it unsafe?'

'One requires to steer it with caution,' said Condé. He rolled up his eyes, bored, at Lymond, who knelt beside him quickly, and surveyed the mechanism.

'Well?' said the King. 'Our audience, messieurs, awaits us. Is it safe for the Dauphin?'

Lymond rose. 'On any other day, yes,' he observed. 'But on his wedding night—no: I should not trust the Dauphin to any but a perfect vehicle. It would be better to launch five boats instead of six.'

'We can't do that,' Condé said. 'We have to steer round the hall and pick up our consorts.'

It was spoken with the irritation of a man whose consort for the purpose was the Duchess de Guise, ten days over the birth of her untimely offspring. His Majesty said, 'The Dauphin was to have uplifted Queen Catherine. You say the steering will not answer?'

Lymond touched the levers. 'I could make it answer,' he said. 'But that would hardly . . .'

'Then you shall steer it,' said the King heartily. 'François, give him your mask. And the cloak. The height is different but seated, it will not be noticed. The plan, de Sevigny, is to steer twice round the hall. Then I shall pause and take up the Queen of Scotland beside me, while Navarre takes his wife. Lorraine takes my daughter Claude, Nemours takes Madame Marguerite and you, of course, take her grace the Queen. . . . Does it astonish you, to find yourself so acting with the princes of the blood?'

'I am overwhelmed,' said Francis Crawford rapidly, and climbed into the ship. Someone signed to the King's gentleman nearest the door and he opened it, and caught the eye of the trumpets.

The blare of sound warned Richard Crawford that there was no prospect, when the doors opened, of slipping inside and on some excuse, of dragging out his younger brother. Instead he had to stand there, sickened still by the pain of his blow, and see the Archers fling open the leaves and the

535

mechanical fleet of the king come swaying and tacking across the black and white squares of the floor.

The doors closed. Since there was no other exit Lord Culter stationed himself by the entrance, and watched with little attention as, to music and clapping, the royal crew skimmed round the pillars and threw silver light on the statues of past monarchs, long since dead, with their playthings.

It was not until the last graceful ship had passed him twice that he saw that the unsmiling mouth under the mask of the helmsman was longer and firmer than the Dauphin's ever would be; that the chin and throat were mature, and the airy hands on the silk reins were those which had just inflicted on him such careless agony.

Then the barque came to a halt and the captain, rising, smiled and held out his hand while the Queen of France, glancing at him, stepped in and sat down beside him. Her thick lips moved, asking a question, and at the answer she laughed and then sat, as the ship slid into motion and followed the rest down the length of the Grand' Salle and into the depths of the palace. The last Richard saw of them before the crowds closed cheering between them was the Queen's snubbed and inelegant profile turned on her chevalier, a considering look in the shallow, protuberant eyes.

Then, of course, he lost them. Lord Culter turned and, striding, made for the principal stairs.

Those, in his turn, Lymond avoided. Vanishing with remarkable speed from his vehicle he had almost reached the door to the Sainte Chapelle when he was fallen upon by an ancient abbot in his cups. To extricate himself without any means which would be unmemorable took him two minutes: running then, he found the locked doorway and then a porter who did not need the velvet and rubies to tell him who this was.

He was paid for his trouble; and then paid again to provide, as fast as possible, a plain cloak with a hood to cover the gentleman's finery. Then Lymond passed through the door and crossing the balcony of the Sainte Chapelle's upper floor, reached the narrow staircase which led down its side to the street.

He was unaware as he passed, that he had breathed incense and glimpsed the taper-lit glass vaults of the chapel, or that he was treading the steps which, barefoot, Philippa had trodden eight months before. He only saw before him,

536

swirling outside the gates of the Palais, the immense crowds which filled the streets singing, and waiting to cheer the departing guests from the most celebrated royal wedding ever made.

He was recognized twice, reaching the river. The first time his hood was dragged back in the crush and he saw, on the unshaven face pressed nearest to him, the first gaping yaw of astonishment. Then he ducked, pulling the cloth over his face and lost himself as fast as he could in the darkness. Behind him, as he went, he could hear voices calling his name and a ragged cheer rising, but they had not been able to follow his movements.

That and the next time, when a party of wool dyers swept into him near the river, held him up on a journey already fraught with the night-madness of celebration: of bonfires and drinking and dancing, of student songs and acrobats and men who would balance on hemp, and turn somersaults for a penny

The wool dyers wanted him to come and drink with them. He refused, clapping them on the back; scanning the opposite bank where the fires danced red and blue over the water, and the sounds of merrymaking rose and rose, tossed as if in a blanket into the redolent air. Scraps of flame, flocking like birds, shot into the night sky and dispersed, swinging and veering over the river. It was as bad over there, if not worse. He said, 'I need a boat. Who will get me one?'

And so, in the end, he was rowing alone in an old creaking ferry, for which he had paid with one of the Bechistan rubies cut from his sleeve. (*I'd give unto her Indian mole Bokhara town and Samarkand.*) And even there, in the brief, heavy journey upriver, he had to have care, with other ill-guided boats jolting drunkenly against him; with floating debris and mills to look out for and another ferryman, who took exception to his amateur status and wanted to fight it out with him.

But he had had a great deal of practice at rowing, and it was direct, and avoided the crowds. So that, although it felt as sluggish and long as a drug-dream, he had probably saved fifteen minutes by the time he tied up by the Arche Beau-fils by the Célestins.

Then he had only to run. He knew where the rue de la Cerisaye was and had even walked along it to visit the monastery during his days as commander in Paris. The road ended in a high garden wall, and did not contain many houses. He entered it from the rue St Antoine, his feet in kid and velvet soundless on the thin sunken bricks of the road. The third or fourth house he came to, on the left, had a carving of some kind over its doorway which might be a globe. The moon, warmed by the reflected light of distant fires of joy, traced the thin-branched trees which stood between the gates and the delicate outline of the house. Above him, as he tried the lock, a weeping willow fell in cascades of yellow chenille, and a tall chestnut loomed with clutching fingers of half-open leaves. There was a wall of branched candelabra, which were pear trees.

The gates were not locked, and he pushed them open and walked through the garden.

The orchard which lay between himself and the house was of cherry trees, their flowers white as burned ash in the moonlight. And behind them, touched all at once into ghost-life, was the celestial globe over the doorway, with two pensive winged figures guarding it.

The sphere, joining his past with his present. The words of the tomb; the half-caught echo of old enchantments and vows long forgotten:

By these same I swear, by Earth, Sea Sky and the twin brood of Latona and Janus the double-facing, and the might of the nether gods and grim Pluto's shrine: this let our Father hear, who seals treaties with his thunderbolt. I touch the altars, I take to witness the fires and the gods between us. . . .

The house was in darkness, save for a single light in a dormer, high over his head.

He tried the tooled wooden door under the sphere, and it was not locked against him, any more than had been the gates. He thought he heard, for a moment, a whisper over his shoulder; but did not look round.

Only, quite softly and steadily did he push the door open and enter the house where he had been born.

CHAPTER 9

Les deux malins de Scorpion conioints
Le grand seigneur meurtri dedans sa salle.

There was no sound in the Hôtel des Sphères, nor any light in the wainscotted hall, or the parlour which led from it.

The scent of the small room was pleasing. Moonlight limned in grey the story of Psyche on the finely arched window, and alighting within, touched upon nymphs and garlands and roses, and upon lines of silver, glittering by the chimney-piece:

I shall harness thee a chariot of lapis-lazuli and gold
Come into our dwelling, in the perfume of the cedars . . .

Míkál . . . Güzel . . . Where are the links of the chain, glimmering there: joining us to the past? The perfume was pleasing because it was familiar to him. The other presences, in the silence, were older.

No one stirred. If there had been servants, there would be candlelight; the door would have been locked: a cresset left on the stair for the mistress or master.

For the mistress; for this must be the house of Isabelle Roset. The house whose direction her sister had had no chance to give him before dying, blind in a smoke-filled farm kitchen in Fleuvy-le-Martel. Perhaps hers was the voice in his thoughts, saying *Climb* . . .

Dabit Deus his quoque finem. Seek me in the broken hearts and by the crumbling tombs. . . .

'I do not believe in God,' Piero Strozzi had said, 'but I respect His dignity. I shall not visit Him in His house with my presence.' And so had catarrh . . .

Help me to seek.

One knows, when all one's life one has walked in dangerous places, when the silence is that of ambush and when the silence is that of emptiness.

539

This was emptiness. The little staircase, roundly carved, gave upon a passage, and of all the doors in the passage, only one showed a line of light under it.

If one believes in God, but has learned not to pray, one offers only, in silence, one's apologies, and then asks the spirit to do what it can.

Francis Crawford laid on the door the beautiful hand of his father, and pressed the latch, and opened it. And as he did so the candle within flickered and went out.

Inside, the quiet and the darkness were absolute. He stood in the doorway listening, and allowing his eyes, like a cat's, to enlarge again. Slowly, a window opposite grew into his sight, indigo against Indian blackness. And a little flare of light in the sky showed him, glimmering for a moment, the shape of a bed, and tumbled sheets, and a shadow lying upon it.

He had no weapon, except perhaps surprise. Where the candle had been, there must be a flaxbox. He moved noiselessly into the room, guiding himself by his fingertips. A chest; a tall hutch-press; an iron stand with a laver; a chair; a stool, with a candle upon it. Then he felt the box with the tinder and paper, and lifting it, cupped his hands and made a little flame.

What had seemed orderly was an ill-kept chamber, its dusty floor strewn with a man's clothes, rudely discarded. The coverlet dropped to the floor and a pillow, deeply indented, lay there beside it. On the bed, the stained sheets were rammed to the foot of the mattress, one of them torn in half. And upon the mattress, grotesque and naked in the writhing light of the guttering flame, lay the muscular body of Leonard Bailey, lustily spreadeagled in untimely and partnerless death.

The flame burned his fingers and vanished. He did not relight it. He did not want to see again that oxlike body of the powerful old man who had hated him: who had hated all the Crawfords; had spurned their generosity and had spent all his years contriving to ruin them. That gross, elderly body, reaped in the excess of its ardour; dead through no human agency, deprived of life by nothing except its own violence.

He did not want to see that again; or the little kid slippers fallen aside, or the fragile clothes laid on the coffer, with the glint of stiff silver tissue beneath them. The signs, not of a molestation, but of a reckoning formally appointed and now paid to the limit. A tribute to Janus, God of Gates, to prevent that other, deferred payment to Charon.

It was necessary, in any case, to go on. He did, finally, light a candle in order to pass from room to room along the passage. They were all empty. In the silence his own fitful breathing entered his awareness. It was not how he wanted to sound, but if he could hold everything else under his control, that did not matter. He walked downstairs, and through the dark empty chambers and passages, and at last pushed open the door of the kitchen.

Inside it was warm. The great fire, sunk in its embers, still burned rosily on the glimmering brass and latten and copper: on the golden scrubbed wood of Madame Roset's racks and aumbries and table.

Before the fire, barefoot in her torn shift, Philippa lay, her hair spilled on the tiles, her fingers loose, her face invisible. And protected by her outflung arms were two scrolls of yellowed paper.

She was breathing. He knelt where his shadow did not fall on her, and laid two fingers on her wrist. Her pulse was fast and shallow: she was, he thought deeply unconscious. So it must all be done now, and quickly.

It was done then, in a ceaseless flow of quiet movement: the fire made up and water set heating; the shutters closed and the room set in order. He brought a mattress with towels laid upon it and eased it beneath her, touching her as little as possible. Then he drew the ruined shift from her bare body and bathed her, helpless as a young bird, with warm water.

There was room in him for no living trace of desire. He dried her skin and slipped over her hands the sleeves of his own warm lawn shirt. The towels he spread in front of the fire, and in their place on the mattress he laid his borrowed cloak, drawing her within its folds. Lastly, with his small comb he patiently stroked the damp tangle of her brown hair until it lay as it should, a shining scarf over her shoulders. Towards the end she stirred and he moved back at once, and waited. She opened her eyes.

She opened them on his face, at first only half conscious. Then memory came; and awareness. She lay without moving, looking at him; and he received the look where he knelt, without speaking.

Time ceased. At some station within the long, uncounted interval he rose, and bringing a pan poured out some warm milk and gave it to her. He watched her as she drank it, leaning slowly on one elbow and at the end received the cup from her and let her rest, her lids closed, while he remained without moving beside her. From time to time, when she opened her eyes, their gaze blended and held, lightless and still; the surface of the place, fathoms below, of their communication.

He had put a powder of his own in the milk. Perhaps she knew it. At least she sank into sleep without resistance: when he was sure she did not need him he rose and washed the pan and the cup she had used; put away the dried towels; made up the fire and then, taking a candle, went upstairs to the bedroom where Bailey lay.

Let every godly man close the mouth of his stomach, lest he be disturbed.

That night he ruled every organ of his body. He opened the door on the rankness within and set his hand to what had to be done. He cleansed and clothed the thick and stiffening body, restoring the room and replacing foul sheets with fresh ones. He removed every trace of Philippa's presence from the dark bedroom; brought down and burned the stained cloth and salvaged the clothes she could still wear, laying them by her side for when she wakened. He found and took away an emerald pendant he knew to be hers. Then he searched for the boxes of money.

They were near the kitchen, in a locked cellar, whose key he found in Bailey's chamber. They were too heavy to move, so he locked the cellar again and kept the key of it. He also systematically examined the house, until assured that no paper remained which could injure his family. The scrolls from the floor of the kitchen were already in the breast of his doublet together with one other missive: a letter in Philippa's writing which he had not burned.

There were mules in the small stable at the back of the orchard, and saddles. Soon the streets would be cleared of the last celebrants, the wedding party dispersed, the bride and groom bedded, if no more than bedded, beneath the glorious emblems, for ever one, of France and of Scotland.

He returned to the kitchen, and waited; and presently Philippa opened her eyes.

He spoke, then, the only thought which made words unavoidable.

'Come, my wife,' said Francis Crawford. 'We are going to Sevigny.'

Part V

Le corps sans ame plus n'estre en sacrifice:
Jour de la mort mis en nativité:
L'esprit divin fera l'ame felice
Voiant le verbe en son eternité.

CHAPTER 1

Le dix Kalendes d'Apvril de faict Gotique
Resuscité encor par gens malins:
Le feu estainct, assemblée diabolique
Cherchant les os d'Amant et Pselyn.

Kings may mourn the death of a favourite, but his disappearance is viewed as an insult.

By dinnertime on the day appointed for his annulment, it was common knowledge that the comte de Sevigny had left Court without leave or apology, and that Madame his lady had vanished also.

This followed a night-long search prosecuted by Richard his brother, and another fruitless essay, different in the quality of its concern, by the four men to whom Lymond was closest.

Called upon in her chamber by Adam, Sybilla Lady Culter took a long time to answer his query and then gave him, steadfastly, the reply which she was to repeat later to Danny Hislop. She knew of no house in the Petit Arsenal district, and had given no address to her son Francis.

Euphemia, brutally questioned by the stricter member of the Culter family, was rather more garrulous. The protestations of Euphemia together with the puzzled and querulous cries of the Schiatti cousins brought to light one other fragment of information. When the comtesse de Sevigny left, followed later by her husband, she had already withdrawn and sent ahead of her all the wealth she possessed banked in Paris.

It was agreed, in a harsh, one-sided interview between Sybilla and Richard, that Austin, isolated in his room in the masterless Hôtel d'Hercule, should be told nothing meantime, except that the signing of the annulment papers had been deferred. The King of France, summoning the Earl of Culter to the Louvre during a break in the wedding celebrations, questioned him sharply about the possible reasons for M. de

547

Sevigny's absence, and on being satisfied of his brother's total ignorance, remarked tartly that he would be content therefore if M. de Culter would favour the rest of the festivities with his presence, so that the Queen his daughter might not be deprived at one stroke of quite all of her Scottish supporters.

The King was cross. The attitude of the other courtiers tended to echo that of Piero Strozzi, back at court for his daughter's wedding: a mixture of irritation, admiration and envy. The Queen of France said nothing; nor did her demoiselle d'honneur Catherine d'Albon, although it could be seen that she had been weeping.

And the six brothers de Guise said remarkably little either, although the Cardinal was both shot and stinging in his rebuke to the Duke of Nemours who in his presence made light of the matter. To place his private affairs before those of the King at such a time was an insult to France and to Scotland, not to mention an affront to the Cardinal Legate, whose interest to annul this marriage had been solicited with such untiring vigour by M. de Sevigny. He hoped, said the Cardinal of Lorraine, to hear that the gentleman was unwell. It was the only excuse, he believed, which would serve him.

Strangely enough, after her first astonishment and annoyance, the bride herself, it seemed, had not been wholly displeased. Richard, reprimanded by his hosts and conscious of the requirements of his assignation, returned, finally to the ranks of his fellow Commissioners who received him with sympathy below which lay, he could feel, the flatness of disappointment.

Archie vanished.

Servants, returning to a house in the rue de la Cerisaye after a night abroad in celebration of the Dauphin's wedding, paid for by their mistress's guest, were alarmed to find the door unlocked and the English gentleman dead in his bed. A physician, called in hastily, pronounced the death to be a natural one. The only disarrangement in the house or purlieus was the bursting open of the lock of the stables and the theft of a horse and saddle. Arrangements were made for the gentleman's burial and the agent, notified, undertook to do what he could to trace the absent Madame Roset. The matter, of little importance, did not come to the ears of the Court.

The Countess of Lennox's secretary, having attended assiduously all the wedding celebrations, composed a great deal of eulogistic verse and made himself as pleasant and as conspicuous as possible in the Queen of Scotland's circle, grew tired of waiting for a message from an unknown address about a gentleman who had disappeared anyway, and decided that, rather than go home empty-handed, he should attempt a little research on his own account. After waiting therefore for a day on which all the Commissioners and their kinsmen were occupied, Master Elder left the modest lodging he had been allotted and walked through the fine spring weather to the Hôtel d'Hercule, where he asked politely to see the Marquis of Allendale.

On the same morning, a liveried groom arrived at the Hôtel de l'Ange with a packet for the Dowager Lady Culter. It contained two enclosures. One, a letter sealed with the Sevigny crest, was addressed to the Most Christian King of France, and she laid it aside. The other, a single sheet of paper, was a message to herself from Nicholas Applegarth.

They are both here, and safe, although very tired. The enclosed packet, which I am to beg you to pass to his Majesty, contains a surrender of all your son's offices and holdings, other than his house and lands in this Seigneurie. Neither M. le comte nor his wife will be returning to court.

I am asked that this should be made clear to those whom it may concern. On my own account, I beg you to see that all this is accepted so far as possible without discord or argument, and that above all no one should think it necessary to come to Sevigny.

I remain, your obedient servant, NICHOLAS APPLEGARTH.

With that letter in her hands, she sat unmoving until the Commissioners returned. Then, summoning Richard and the three remaining officers of St Mary's to her room, she gave it into their keeping.

To Jerott, to Adam and to Danny, it was the first certain indication that, whatever danger Lymond had feared for her, Philippa was safe; and following her, Lymond had come to no harm.

The news that they were together, and were remaining together, was something else. At that point in their reading Adam looked up and met Sybilla's eyes, his scarred face intent, but he said nothing and neither did Danny, the perpetual talker. It was Jerott who, flushing, said, 'What has he done? What is he thinking of?'

And Richard who answered, 'He has merely broken, as always, every promise he ever made, before man or God.' And then, 'I shall have to tell Austin.'

He did so later, when the other letter had been delivered to its destination and the resulting repercussions had done nothing to sweeten his temper. The discovery, on arriving at the Hôtel d'Hercules, that Master Elder had already visited the English prisoner and had been admitted without sanction did nothing to make him feel better. Lord Cutler had preserved Allendale's peace of mind, he well knew, at the cost of a falsehood. The impact of the truth would be bad enough, without its gleeful and premature delivery by Seton's sycophantic Caithness friend.

He had known it was going to be difficult. But the hostile man who faced him upstairs, exhausted with rage and grief and pacing, over and over, the confines of his room, was something he had not expected. Before he could speak, Austin had rounded on him.

'So much for your promises! The Cardinal Legate has not postponed the signing of the annulment. Philippa has been allowed to run off, and you have permitted your brother to go after her. Perhaps you encouraged him. Perhaps you mean to share her money. If you had told me, I could have paid you more.'

'That bloody, interfering fool Elder,' Richard said. 'We tried to spare you some of this.' He drew a long breath. 'Sit down and get some wine inside you. Losing your head isn't going to help.'

Austin paid no heed whatever. 'If you had nothing to do with it, why conceal it? Why keep me locked in this house, where I could do nothing about it? Twenty-four hours a day, you said you would guard him, and Philippa as well. And they left . . . when?'

'The night of the Queen's wedding,' said Richard. He had found wine and throwing it into as large a cup as he could find, brought it to where Austin stood, braced in a corner, breathing through shut lips rapidly. Richard said quietly, 'Perhaps we were wrong not to tell you, but there was nothing you could have done. I searched the town myself all night and next day as well, without finding them. As for the guard . . . we did our best, but it was the night of the wedding.'

'How clever,' Austin said. He made no attempt to take the wine.

'How clever,' Lord Cutler repeated. 'But then, you know

550

my brother is wily. What successes have you had in your dealings with him? Can you imagine what it feels like for me, to pledge my word to preserve a girl's honour and have it broken for me by Francis?'

'You should have locked him in a room, as I am locked,' Austin said. And then added, 'But I forget. He is too popular and too powerful for that. He can trap a girl like a bird-catcher and then desecrate her, and the Court will only applaud. Then, I suppose, he will leave her.' He stopped, and swallowed, and said, 'Do you ever know if she is alive?'

'Sit down, for Christ's sake,' Richard said, 'and drink that.' And pushing him at last into a chair he thrust the cup into his hand and said, 'He hasn't left her. They are together at Sevigny, and staying there. . . . Drink it, you fool!'

And as Austin, his face grey, leaned against the back of the chair Richard guided the cup to his lips and said, 'They have been together now for long enough to make any annul-ment of the marriage quite impossible. Therefore it is going to stand, and nothing that anyone can do will help it. It is wrong: it is a tragedy; it is a betrayal. I agree with all that. My impulse, too, was to ride off to the Loire and whip him in his own house. But they are legally married. He has not dissolved the union as he threatened to do, so that she could only reach him outside it. And lastly, she loves him.'

Austin said, 'He is very plausible. I believed him when he gave me his oath.'

'Never do that,' said Richard flatly. Then after a moment he said, 'You know of course that you are free. Francis signed your release for the Tuesday you should have left France with Philippa. It is my fault, as I have explained, that we kept you here in ignorance since then. I don't suppose you want to stay. If you will tell me when you want to take ship, I shall ask for a safe-conduct for you for Gravelines.'

'I don't know,' Austin said. He had emptied the cup and the worst of his pallor was leaving him. 'It would do no harm to have the safe-conduct. But I might stay a little.' He looked up. 'Would there be room for me at the Hôtel de l'Ange?'

'Yes,' said Richard. 'But is there any need to stay longer? You will only add to the hurt. And it would do nothing but harm to interfere with them.'

'I should like to know,' Austin said, 'if she is happy.' He paused, and then said, 'Is it true that your father had a natural daughter who is married to Jerott Blyth?'

There was a small silence. Then Richard said, 'I have never met Jerott Blyth's lady. But at court, of course, there is always gossip. I have been told, yes, that she is extremely like Francis. I have even been told that in Lyon he called her his step-sister. More than that I do not know. ... Why do you ask?'

Austin shook his head with a small, irritable movement. 'Master Elder wanted to meet her. I hoped it would not be embarrassing.'

'Not to me,' Richard said. 'I can't, then, persuade you to leave France in the next day or two?'

Austin shook his head again. The outburst of violence had gone, leaving him spent with weariness. He said, 'What if she needs help? You won't be here for long.'

'For long enough,' Richard said. 'In France, it seems, there is almost no term to the celebrations for a Dauphin's nuptials. We have been told to count on a further stay of several weeks: more, if the Narrow Straits are still not safe for shipping. And meantime, we shall have news of Philippa in a very short time. Piero Strozzi is riding to Sevigny.'

'*Strozzi!*' said Austin, his voice cracking. 'But——'

'If you think it is undesirable,' said Richard harshly, 'try arguing with the King and his followers. The more ambitious captains may not want Francis back, but his own men do, and the mercenaries, and the ensigns who fought with him at Calais. The new season's campaign is just about to open in Champagne and King Henri wants Francis there. Strozzi is being sent to tell him so.'

There was a long pause. Then Austin said, 'You will tell me what he says when he returns?'

'He will tell you himself,' Richard said. 'I shall bring him to the Hôtel de l'Ange and he will tell all of us. We deserve that much reassurance, at least.'

*

The French King was hunting when Piero Strozzi returned. He had been hunting, in fact, for ten days largely, it was rumoured, to keep out of the way of prying foreign ambassadors while conducting a war with one hand and a peace conference with the other. As a result, it was the middle of May before Strozzi made his report and was able, on his way back through Paris for his equipment, to call on the Hôtel de l'Ange with his bulletin.

He delivered it, nothing abashed, not only to the Crawfords of Culter and Lord Allendale but to Adam and three of the Commissioners who happened to be in the main salon at the time.

'Well, you are wondering; you ask, did I see him in his asylum of the Muses and I have to say yes, I have seen him. And *quel changement* . . . quantum mutatus ab illo Hectore! Spells, spells has he cast, my enemy and traitor! I take God to record that if the little demoiselle did not look so appealingly, I would have pulled him from his bush of roses with my sword belt, I burn so with jealousy. But who would blame him? Appetite is the stay of life, and it is not given to a man to love and be wise.'

He paused for breath. Richard said flatly, 'Is he coming back to the army?'

'Ah! *Chi mi! Qu'io no pensara di partime!* I lie,' said Piero Strozzi cheerfully. 'At times I hoped very much he was able to leave me. It is not comfortable, when you are a great leader, as I am, and a veteran of many famous wars, to have a second Démétrius appear and sit at your master's right hand. No, he is not returning. He is not planning to throw himself into the King's arms and cry misericordia. He does not wish to take his wife to Lanarkshire, the Paradise of Scotland. He intends to remain where he is, multiplying the fornications and impurities before the idol of Aphrodite like the Agregentines, who gave themselves up to delight as if every day was to be their last. I beg you, Lord Allendale,' said Piero Strozzi, 'do you know of any other young maids from Hexham?'

He was a mischievous man, and not above malice. The Commissioners, having heard what they wanted to hear, movg away. Sybilla said, 'You imply they are much in love. Did you see Mistress Philippa? Did she seem to be happy?'

'I never saw them apart,' Strozzi said. 'They greeted me together, and dined with me together, and waved me farewell together the following morning. I would find that too much. I had a good joke to tell mon petit François and I could find no opportunity. I rode off to Onzain and told it to Lord Grey instead to cheer up his captivity. He is not so badly off as he makes out. He had a wench with him.'

It was Austin who persisted. 'But did he seem happy?' he said. 'Is she well?'

'The wench? Ah, the young maid from Hexham. They never spoke to one another,' said Piero Strozzi thoughtfully.

Sybilla lost patience. 'Signor Strozzi, we are attempting, with some difficulty to distinguish the condition of a young girl of whom we are particularly fond. Did Philippa seem well? Who never spoke to one another?'

Piero Strozzi looked surprised. 'I beg your pardon,' he said. 'Ce beau chevalier and his mignonne. They talked, each of them to me, but almost never to one another. It is true, of course, when I am there, there is no need for others to converse, but some of one's friends are not commonly backward.'

'And their health?' Sybilla said. 'We were told they were both very tired.'

Strozzi shrugged. 'How can one tell? It has changed him, as I have said. He has no wish to hear of the great matters of court, and if I mention the war, I am taken aside and shown horses. You know, I dare say, the intuition one may sometimes acquire, that one is not wanted?'

For the first time, the tension in Lady Cutler's face relaxed a little. 'I do,' she said.

'Well, this I did not have,' said Piero Strozzi simply. 'And yet I knew I was not wanted. There is something formidable in that household of Sevigny.'

Obeying the dictates, perhaps, of just such another presentiment he did not stay much beyond that. Only, just as he was taking his leave and after Austin had left, alone, to go to his room, Sybilla said, 'I wish you would explain something you said. That there was something formidable in that household of Sevigny?'

'Ah,' said Piero Strozzi. 'It does not lend itself truly to words. But you know, perhaps, you, Lord Cutler and you, Blacklock, the *alla sanguigna*, the blue-red shimmer of a sword when it is drawn from the flesh? That is what it was like: the *alla sanguigna*, burning behind all the politenesses. Since also we are here together in small numbers, I may say something else.'

'Yes?' said Richard quietly.

'*Assai sa, chi nulla sa, se tacer' sa.* He knows enough, who knows nothing, and who can keep quiet. It is not a matter which concerns the world,' Piero Strozzi said, 'but I am a curious man, and I notice that much as these two are together, they never touch. There is no embrace. There is no

554

twining of the fingers even. So I ask questions, and I watch, which is difficult, for in that household they are very discreet. But this I must tell you.

'M. le comte and madame la comtesse sleep apart. Their rooms are in different wings. And they do not move from one room to another. Whatever they may wish you to think, Madame, your son and Mistress Philippa are not living as man and wife.'

CHAPTER 2

Un Capitole ne voudra point qu'il regne
Sa grande charge ne pourra maintenir.

The day following Piero Strozzi's visit to the Hôtel de l'Ange, Marthe returned to her husband.

Jerott received no kind of warning. Preparing, with the others, to leave with Strozzi and de Guise to join the army then mustering at Chalons, he was turning out of a back courtyard of the Hôtel du Séjour, his eyes on the lists in his hand, when a familiar voice spoke directly in front of him.

'Whoredom, said Sir Thomas More, is better than wedlock—in a priest. Have you as yet reached any conclusion on the subject, Master Blyth?'

It was Marthe, sweet-sour and golden, in a gown of some Oriental fabric he did not recognize, and a line he had not seen before between her brows.

He killed, with an effort that could seen, the impulse to grip her; to fling himself on her; to press out under his kisses the sight of that mocking mouth. Instead, he said, 'It's a fair argument for returning to the priesthood. Being still in a state of wedlock, I've been trying to keep an open mind.'

'And an open bed?' she said. 'And an open bottle?' She had not changed.

'Suppose you come in,' he said, 'and ask Danny and Adam if they will give me a testimonial.'

'You don't ask,' she said, 'if I can supply one.'

Then he did sigh, looking at her from the open dark eyes in which there was much dignity but no guile, alas, to match hers. 'You know,' he said, 'that with or without a testimonial, you have only to come to be received.'

'Even if I make no promises?' she said.

'I have learned that those, too, are pointless,' he said simply.

*

The Cardinal of Lorraine's first peace conference failed, and he returned to Paris with a quantity of perfumed gloves, pressed upon him by the Spanish. The release from captivity of the Constable retreated a little further into the future. The Duke de Guise's programme for the uniting of the largest army ever mustered by any monarch was tackled by all concerned with exemplary vigour.

During the third week in May, the meadows beyond the Faubourg St Germain in Paris, normally the after-supper pleasance of students, were occupied by an orderly procession of four thousand Protestants singing Lutheran psalms interspersed with anti-Papal invective. In the course of their march, which led them after dark into the city and down the rue de St Jacques, they took with them for protection several companies of horsemen and many on foot with concealed weapons. The composition of the procession was extremely mixed, being drawn from noblemen, plebians and artificers and men of every kind and condition, as well as from women and children. They were not stopped.

The following night they repeated the performance, this time to an immense crowd of spectators. On the third night, a proclamation was issued forbidding the gathering, and when it was ignored, the city gates were closed against them at dusk.

Even then, there was no disturbance. The concourse of ten thousand persons spent the night in the houses of the suburb, or strolling through the meadows in the pleasant mild air, re-entering the town in the morning. On subsequent nights they did the same but omitted, with belated tact, the ballads against the Vatican.

An account of the disturbances being sent to the Court, the Cardinal de Sens, the spiritual Primate of France, issued a severe proclamation in the King's name to prevent further such demonstrations, and by offering rewards for information, succeeded in arresting some hundred persons of no great consequence who had taken part in the singing. Among them were a number of tutors and other officials from the University colleges.

Because of the nature of the times and the danger of civil war, great discretion was used in the case of a number of great persons who openly favoured Calvinism and were known to have attended. The King of Navarre, who had been present only, he pointed out winningly, as an interested bystander, was questioned none the less by the King and by the Cardinal.

François de Coligny, sieur d'Andelot, recently back in Paris after securing the Brittany ports against threat of English invasion, was less fortunate, as it happened, in his perfumed handshake.

He had been seen to attend the demonstrations. He had also, so the Cardinal was able to show, sent for Geneva books during his recent captivity. The King who was fond of him, regretfully summoned him to face his questions, and went so far as to have him warned in advance of their content. A simple lie, there was no doubt, would have saved him. But confronting the King at his supper, the sieur d'Andelot merely replied, with strong rectitude and no sense of discretion that, while owing the French King his absolute devotion, his soul belonged only to God, and lit by the torch of the Evangile, he approved the doctrines of Calvin and thought Mass a horrible profanation and an abominable invention of mortals.

Enraged by the blasphemy, the King snatched a basin to hurl at d'Andelot but, his aim being no better than his son's, instead cracked open the head of the Dauphin. M. d'Andelot, under instant arrest, was marched off with his wife to the bishop's prisons at Meaux, thus freeing the six brothers de Guise of another rival.

The Commissioners for Scotland endeavoured to preserve a unified front behind which, from their various religious convictions, they viewed the passage of events with some little alarm. The presence of the English fleet in the Narrow Seas still compelled them, supposedly, to remain in Paris. The real reasons on both sides were a matter of opinion. If they stayed, they could bring home the terms of the peace or the outcome of the war. They could watch and judge further the honesty or dishonesty of France towards Scotland, as already betrayed by Queen Mary. And, there was no doubt that, by accepting the King's pressing invitation to linger, they were denying the Queen Dowager of Scotland the company of some of her strongest Reformers.

Visiting Lords Seton and Allendale with some frequency, John Elder now knew very well which were the Calvinists and had heard, with admiration, of the fine reception given them by Lord Culter's younger brother. In a comradely and even, one might say, a Christian sense, Lord Culter had been a disappointment, and so had his mother. The Secretary obtained, from Austin Grey, an introduction to Jerott's wife Marthe.

The meeting was not a success. Marthe, faced with a gentle denigration of Lord Cutler for not acknowledging the less fortunate sprigs of his line, remarked merely, with boredom, that she didn't know there were any such. On being reminded, apologetically, of the family resemblance, she merely remarked, irritably, that perhaps then Lord Culter was the bastard. Which, since Lord Culter had been born fully attested many years before anyone else, and the correct number of months after an equally fully attested wedding, was clearly prevarication.

'I beg your pardon,' John Elder had added. 'I felt sure I had heard that M. de Sevigny looked upon you as his step-sister. Could I be mistaken?'

"I don't know,' Marthe had said. 'I suppose it depends on heredity. What sort of mistakes did your parents make?'

He thought of a very good answer in bed that night as he pulled his cap on.

＊

In the continuing absence of Madame Roset, the agent who concerned himself with the Hôtel des Sphères instructed the servants to place neatly within a campaign chest all the money, clothes and other effects of the late Master Bailey, and hand them to the authorities for transmission to England by the first person of that nationality to leave the country. Since the two nations were still officially at war and the traffic was not therefore dense, the chest remained in a bureau in Paris, with a label on it.

A recalcitrant cellar door, forced in the same house by a maidservant, proved to have stacked up behind it four locked boxes clearly containing money. The agent, applied to, took charge of them for his principal.

Sybilla sent for Adam Blacklock and said, 'I've had a letter from Philippa's mother. I can't answer it.'

'I know. So have I,' Adam said. Then as Sybilla added nothing, he said, 'They don't want anyone. I wrote to Applegarth and I wrote to Archie, and they don't answer. I could wring Archie's neck. . . . Nothing happened, did it, about that demonstration?'

'No,' Sybilla said wearily. 'It was not very wise of them to

559

go. But no one seems to have noticed. Why should Archie make you think of that?'

There was no point in lying. 'It was Archie who told me that Lord Culter was a Lutheran,' Adam said. 'Francis found out at Dieppe. You may not have noticed, but all the time you have been here, we have been keeping the Protestant Commissioners so far as possible out of trouble. Only the other night they escaped us. Without Francis at Court, we don't have the warning we usually get.'

'It seems hardly fair,' Sybilla said, 'that you should have had to assume the burden of caring for the Culter family.' Then she said, as if quite against her will, 'I am so afraid. They don't speak, he said.'

'You want me to go,' Adam said. 'But, you know, Francis has always been his own master.'

'He was not his own master when he left Russia,' Sybilla said. 'Nor was he his own master when you brought him to France. He is like a river forced into glass and driven from stem to stem of a conjurer's maze without ever reaching the sea. Would you rather I sent Richard?'

It was an empty threat, but the fact that she was driven to make it was enough. Next day he left.

*

He had forgotten how beautiful Sevigny was. He rode to Orleans through wood-smoke and the song of birds and came to the river, strung like a rosary with its palaces, their bowered turrets stitched in the water like tapestry. He sent no warning before him but spent the night at Blois, and set out with the sun at his back in the morning, past the vineyards and through the spring flowers and between the slender tree trunks gloved in ivy, until ahead of him he saw the wall, and the beeches, and beyond them the château, distinct in the sun as a Cellini tiara.

He was told at first, courteously, that my lord was not at home; and then suddenly Archie was standing before him, his hands on his hips, saying. 'Oh. It's yourself.'

The tone was exasperated. But behind the lined and leathery face Adam caught a glimpse, before it vanished, of an expression which could have been pure relief. Then Archie said, 'Give me your saddlebags. They've been riding. You can wait for them in the parlour.'

'You bloody Indian clam,' Adam said. 'I wrote you.'

'I didn't get it,' said Archie.

'I wrote Applegarth as well,' said Adam angrily.

'He didn't get it either. He's away for a day or two. Jesus,' said Archie, 'are ye not keen to come in? You must be fair wore out with all that writing.'

So whatever there was to tell, Archie did not intend to convey it.

Then, clean and combed, he was waiting rigidly in a tidy, well-appointed room which seemed to be full of books, and the door opened, and Lymond came in.

Quel changement, Strozzi had said, and it was true. The change was there, and not only in the chamois and lawn, replacing the velvet, the rubies, the gold tissue. It was as if all about him had been stripped down and cleansed and reduced, without blurring, to its true structure. And his eyes, which were smiling, were clear.

'Poor Hermes,' said Lymond. 'And without even a winged staff to pawn. Don't look so apprehensive. Someone was bound to try again, once they got Piero to stop talking. O cruell Mars, thou dedly god of war; O dolorous tewisday, dedicate to thy name! We hoped it might be you.' And taking Adam's hand at the same moment to draw him to a chair he turned his head and said, 'And here is Philippa.'

They had walked, for whatever reason along the passage together and, not to embarrass him, were entering separately. *We*, Lymond had said instead of the familiar, imperious *I*. *They've been riding*, Archie had said, without requiring to identify *them*. Such a sovereignty, Adam thought, resentment starting up for the first time in his thoughts. Such a sovereignty, to be pulled down so quickly.

Then Philippa came in, and looking only at himself said smiling, 'I'm sorry. Signor Strozzi said it was like being received by the Dioscuri. Would you rather be entertained by one of us at a time?'

Which was altogether too near the mark to permit him to reply with a truthful assent. So he grinned and said, 'I came to see both of you. Kate has been writing to ask how you are.'

Neither of them queried the excuse. 'Sit down,' Lymond said, 'and have something. I suppose it is too early for anything but Hippocras. Where did you come from, Blois?'

561

And as Adam nodded and he busied himself pouring spiced wine, Lymond said, 'We are as you see. It was not given to us to make this change with proper consideration for our friends, for which you must blame an obtuseness of mine. That it was a change of great ... importance to us, I hope you will understand. Later, I hope you will find us more communicative. When there has been ... what do they call an earthquake?—*a wondernous of earth*, it takes a little time to recover.'

He pressured the wine. 'Now may we leave the subject? You must have seen the vineyards as you came by. We have some changes in the gardens we want to show you presently. And these.' And laying down the salver, he lifted two books of drawings. 'Do you remember my trying to buy these in London?' He did not say how he had now come to them, but Adam saw Philippa lift her eyes, with a smile in them, to his.

It was the key to which all the rest of the long day was tuned: that of tranquil hospitality, filled with small pleasures, carefully designed to his taste, first by one of his hosts and then by the other. All their attention was concentrated on himself and he was enclosed by it, as in a satin box. To his efforts to let in the outside world their response was totally negative and differed only in quality. He mentioned as soon as he could the break-down of the Cardinal's peace negotiations over the twin stumbling-blocks of the future of Savoy and Calais, but before he could speculate about their resumption, or about the honesty of their purpose, he had been led by Lymond's skill into another channel and with equal adroitness denied any chance of returning. Philippa, he found, took no part in such diversions, but would allow an outside topic to die for lack of contribution.

Nor was he more successful on the few brief occasions on which she was absent. At one such time he mentioned Thionville: 'The German levies and the money have come, and we are mustering, all of us at Chalons. De Nemours, of course, and de Nevers and d'Estrée and de La Rochefoucauld and de Thermes and the Vidame and de la Brosse ... d'Elboeuf ... Robertet. It's a damned shame, of course: de Guise and Strozzi are going to sweep in and take all de Vieilleville's credit. You can imagine the comments. With the architect of the Calais victory out of the way, the Duke de Guise wants to make sure of his pedestal. Strozzi——'

'Adam: there must be something which interests you in what we are doing here?' Lymond said. 'We have already, I promise you, had our fill of Piero's views.'

'Piero Strozzi's views, I find, are generally expressed in the form which will best benefit Piero Strozzi,' Adam said. 'I imagine he didn't tell you that——'

'*Enough, Adam,*' said Lymond. The tone was one which any man serving under him would have recognized: he had not used it before, and he did not use it again. A moment later, the door opened, and Philippa came in, obviously unaware of what they had been saying. He had not heard her approach.

Even then, he did not give up, although hour by hour he was beginning to realize the truth in all Strozzi's bizarre statements. Although he knew they did not want him, they continued, one would say, to outdo one another in courtesy towards him.

It was not strictly true to say that they never spoke to one another. Philippa had been reading the *Dialogues*, and at dinner they fell into a discussion about them which ceased, prematurely, when Lymond discovered that Adam had dropped out. About books and ideas they communicated aloud, and at a level which silenced Adam. On trivial matters it was as Strozzi had said: there seemed no need for speech. They appeared to know intuitively the pattern of each other's thoughts and actions. Communication there was effortless as breathing and achieved, in passing, with the eyes. The refreshment they offered himself was part of a climate of carefulness which was continuous, and most of all noticeable in the case of mind they created for one another.

And so it was true, too, that everything about their relationship in public was cerebral. As Strozzi had said, they never even touched fingertips. And when Adam, taking a risk, mentioned that Madame Marguerite was missing her favourite lutenist, and was that a new spinet? no one pursued the subject. In Sevigny, there was something so deep and so dangerous that it could barely be felt. But there was no music. And there was no laughter.

Once, he managed a moment alone with Philippa, as the afternoon drew on and he had only the evening to make his mind felt, before he must sleep and then ride off at daybreak.

Waiting, on their tour of the farm buildings, for Francis to close a gate he said, 'And the headaches? Has the air of the Loire brought an improvement?'

She had found, in a heap of straw, some hens' eggs and was carrying them, brown and smooth, in her palms. One forgot that she was the daughter of a gentleman farmer. It would suit her, this life on Sevigny. Then she turned sober, friendly brown eyes upon him, and said, 'The headaches have gone. It is no credit to the Loire, or my company.'

It was highly improbable. 'Are you sure?' Adam said.

She flushed. And Lymond's voice behind him said, 'Do you think I would mislead her?'

By that time, Adam had flushed also. 'No. I don't think you could mislead her,' he said. 'You think as one person, so far as I can see. But you will have to remember that there is a world awaiting you, when you emerge from your tower. We shall do our best to spin it meantime the way it should go, but it is not easy. There have been Lutheran demonstrations in Paris and Chartres; d'Andelot and his wife have been arrested along with others. Your brother took part in one of the processions. He might very well find himself in difficulties.'

It was one of the rare occasions when, outside an impersonal topic, he saw the eyes of Francis and Philippa meet, and cling. Then Lymond said, his eyes still on hers, 'He is of age.' Then answering, it would seem, some further change in her gaze he said, 'I did not mean the onus to fall on your shoulders. Perhaps my mother could be persuaded to leave, and he to escort her home on the grounds of frailty?'

'Not while Philippa is here,' Adam said.

Then Lymond said, 'I have told you the only solution. The world has turned. We are two families now: two trees; two separate plantings. Tell them that. *And god shall wype awaye all teares from theyr eyes. And there shalbe no more deeth, nether sorow, nether crynge, nether shall ther be eny more payne, for the olde thinges are gone.* And so, too, will be supper, unless we hurry. Come, poor Adam, and eat. You have delivered messages enough.'

He could not enjoy the meal although, as before, it was well cooked and presented. The house, he had already realized, ran like a machine, as it had done for many years under Applegarth's care. There had been nothing demanded of Philippa which needed intrude on this relationship. Nor, except for the books, had there been any change that he could see in the château. It had always been exquisitely furnished but impersonal, and until now Lymond had visited it only rarely. But to this home neither he nor Philippa, it was clear, had brought the detachment of mind which had made of the house at Vorobiovo a casket of brilliant treasures, constructed, chosen, commissioned by Gûzel and Lymond alike to create a setting for their guests' entertainment.

One remembered there, too, the social skills, the fluent ease of host and hostess which obliterated for all practical purposes their personal relationship, so that you did not remember till afterwards that here was a clever and powerful courtesan, and here was the man who possessed her.

This was the same man. It was, one had to believe, the sheer strength of the invisible union which made the bond between man and woman this time such a towering and tangible thing.

Towards the end of the evening, weary himself with the strain of the day, and his journey, Adam saw a tiredness of a different kind begin to touch the hollows of Philippa's face and then, less obviously, betray itself in Francis. Once, visited for a term by a pair newly-betrothed, he had learned to understand the signs. The need, as for a spring in the desert, was for peace in each other's company. He said good night then, as soon as he could, and went upstairs to his chamber.

He was a man, unlike Strozzi, for whom prying was out of the question. It was with no other intention therefore than to admit the night air to his anxieties that he pulled aside the heavy hangings and, opening the latch of his window, stepped out in his shirt among the flower pots on his small balcony.

Below him was the wing of the château he had just left, with the long windows of the grand' salle still blazing. And the comte de Sevigny and his wife were still there, clearly in view from where he was standing.

If there had been anything less than commonplace in their dispositions, he would have turned his back and left the balcony. As it was, he saw that Francis had lodged himself, a book on his knee, in what was obviously an accustomed chair, far to the side of the otherwise empty salon, while Philippa sat close to the fire, also from time to time reading. At other times she simply leaned back, and watched Lymond's

565

downcast eyes and his hand, as he turned the pages of his book. Then he, perhaps feeling the gaze, would look up and smile. So far as Adam could see, they were not speaking.

He stayed there in the mild air, watching, and listening to the clock on the distant stables chime the final hours of the night. Then, across in the other wing, Philippa rose, her book closed in her hand and Lymond, leaving his seat, came forward and opened the door for her. Then, with a smile, she was gone.

With a smile, and nothing else. But, of course, she must know, with the hangings apart and the candelabra burning, that all they did was visible. Presumably, Lymond knew it too. He closed the door at any rate directly after she had gone and returning to his seat, picked up his book and carried it to the chimneypiece. There he stood for a while, studying the embers. Then, the glow underlighting his face he knelt, laying down the thick volume, and began to rebuild the fire with remarkable care, as if erecting a city of gossamer. He remained kneeling by it for quite some time after it was done and then, when the flaring heat must have discommoded him, he rose and wandered to the far end of the room and back, his hands clasped, his eyes on the floor.

An explanation, with two people of different quality, would have been simple: just so might a bridegroom, married a month, await the nightly disrobing of a modest young wife. An explanation which did not even cross Adam's mind as he lingered there, unaware of his fatigue, and watched the owner of Sevigny pass and repass, pacing the length of his salon, diverging sometimes to the fire, to the window, to his book, for the better part of two weary hours. He was still there, gazing down into the fire when Adam saw his head lift sharply and turn. A moment later, the salon door opened abruptly and Philippa stood on the threshold, her long hair tossed over her night-robe.

He had not expected her. His very rigidity made it clear, even seen over such a distance, and from behind. But by the time Philippa had closed the door and come a little way into the room Lymond had backed, and was standing looking at her from the corner in which, hours before, he had been seated. Then Philippa walked forward and confronting him, said something.

Adam saw her stop speaking. For some moments it

566

seemed, nothing occurred. Then with extreme deliberation, Francis Crawford seated himself. And as he did so, Philippa sank on her knees before him, her gaze on his, her robe dragged like a furled sleeve behind her. After a while he unloosed his hands and, withdrawing a kerchief, laid it on the stool beside her, saying something: when she lifted it and held it to her face, Adam knew she must be weeping. Presently she rose and, her fingers still pressed to the linen, moved to the window where she stood in profile against one of the embrasures. Then she lowered her hands and laid the handkerchief, still folded, on the window seat and as she did so Lymond followed her quietly and stood, separated by the window, facing her from the opposite side of the bay.

For a long time they stood there, exchanging sentences occasionally, but more often silent. Then at length, she asked him a question, and he answered. And a moment later, turning, she walked to the door. There, she turned as she had before, and gave a smile of such sweetness that Adam's breath caught. Then she had gone.

Time passed. Between Adam and his high balcony and that blazing range of lit windows below, the night air moved in small breathing stirs. The beeches in the long drive sighed and an owl, unseen, shrieked, twice. Presently Lymond moved in the tall embrasure and taking a silver-gilt snuffer walked slowly from branch to branch of the clusters of tapers, extinguishing them one by one. Then, when the windows were lit by no more than the low dusky red of the fire, he turned and saw his own handkerchief, lying folded where Philippa had left it.

He crossed to the embrasure and lifted it gently. Then with equal care he lowered his hand and replaced it exactly where it had been left. Without looking round, he walked to the door and, opening it, at last left the chamber. A few moments later Adam heard his steps mounting the stairs and then making their way past his bedroom to his own chamber beyond it.

His door opened and closed.

Next morning, when Adam left, they bade him farewell, as they had welcomed him, tranquilly and together.

*

Four days later, Adam Blacklock was back in Paris. To

567

Jerott, to Danny, to Lady Culter, to Richard Crawford, to anyone else who asked what had happened or who talked to him of the Château of Sevigny he had only one answer to make. *For the love of God, leave them alone.*

CHAPTER 3

Avant conflict le grand tombera,
Le grand à mort, trop subite et plainte,
Nay imparfaict: la plus part nagera,
Aupres du fleuve de sang la terre tainte.

On Saturday, 4 June, a week after this, the second mission to Sevigny, the Duke de Guise with nearly two thousand men joined the army already awaiting him before the Spanish-held fortress town of Thionville near the western frontiers of France and settled down, with a total force of twelve thousand, of which three-quarters were German, to besiege it.

There were some who thought he would fail, and there were some who wished that he would. Verses appeared at street junctions in Paris, pointing out that Thionville was not Calais, inhabited only by serfs. The better informed knew that assaults on Thionville had failed on three previous occasions: that the circling walls filled with earth were so thick that two wagons could ride round them abreast; that the ancient castle of the Counts of Luxembourg which guarded it at the edge of the river was so strong as to be proof against battery.

There were others who knew that there was bad blood between the commanders of the French army. As long ago as February, the Governor of nearby Metz had propounded a plan to reduce Thionville while, under de Guise, all the rest of the troops in the north seized the Oye region. Then, by uniting both armies, a complete conquest of the Low Countries was feasible.

Money was short, but he was given general permission to proceed, and with Sipierre and Strozzi and Sevigny had drawn up a plan of attack which began to look astonishingly promising. He collected troops from Thoul and Verdun and made provision for the influx of huge foreign levies. The nobility of Brie, Champagne and Bassigny and of the Duchy of

Orleans came flocking to help until the army was undoubtedly large enough to put the whole Duchy of Luxembourg in the French King's possession.

Before the end of April, the Governor of Metz, M. de Vieilleville, had completed his preparations and was ready to make the assault. He had not perhaps realized that, with the pressure of duties arising from his niece's nuptials, the Duke de Guie had not fully appreciated the attractive conquest appearing on the western horizon. Nor was M. de Vieilleville at that time aware that two of the strongest rivals of the de Guise family had either vanished or were about to vanish: the comte de Sevigny to his château on the Loire, and the sieur d'Andelot in due course to prison. Or he would have been less surprised than he was to receive, on the brink of his attack, a missive, more in sorrow than in anger, from the Duke de Guise, requesting him to cease all operations until the Duke should arrive at Thionville, and adding that as lieutenant-general the Duke would be most distressed if such a thing of honour and importance should occur without him.

By moving at once, M. de Vieilleville afterwards calculated, he could have been inside Thionville in two hours, and in Luxembourg directly afterwards. As it was, in the three weeks it took the Duke to march towards him, Luxembourg fortified itself quite adequately against any assault he might have been planning; and the force inside Thionville under Jean de Caderebbe their Flemish commander aspired to three thousand picked men—twice the number the town would normally contain. The ensigns waiting for M. de Guise greeted him with grim jollity: Let us go, monsieur, and die before Thionville—we have been waiting for you for a long time. And M. d'Estrée the Grand Master of Artillery, supervising the arrival of the thirty-five boats containing the four companies of pioneers, the eighteen cannoneers, the six commissioners of artillery, the guns and the munitions for 15,000 shots, summoned the Duke in sonorous tones to come and see the fine present M. de Vieilleville was making him, while adding in less sonorous tones to his companions that it was very easy for M. de Guise to swallow, when everything else had already been chewed for him.

Danny Hislop, jogging about in his cuirass collecting gems of impolitic vituperation, was consistently busy and happy: so was Blaise de Montluc, who had d'Andelot's command of the infantry. Jerott Blyth, less tolerant of caprice, walked about glowering and being nasty to Adam, who in any case was feeling mildly sorry for himself after all the riding he had undertaken in the past seven days.

When the news came that, after prolonged argument, M. de Vieilleville's battle plan had been entirely changed and the assault was to be made at a different place, Adam experienced no shock of surprise. If Thionville was going to be a glorious victory, then the battle plan would have to be the Duke de Guise's, not that of the Governor of Metz. He moved away from all the bright, lilting voices of the courtiers in the Duke de Guise's train, and heard beside him another voice strongly accented in Italian and belonging to a dark and splendid nobleman in silver-engraved armour with bronze kid buttoned under it.

'Must you look so disapproving?' said Piero Strozzi. 'You Scotsmen: you wish to be like the elephant, hacked to pieces for refusing to bow. You should follow my rule: here am I, supple and amenable as a goatskin glove of Vendôme and pleasant to all, Duke and dotard alike. You did not, I trust, persuade your eminent friend to forsake his bower in favour of these noisome marshes? That would indeed be a case of the punishment being born at the same time as the sin.'

'No. He isn't coming,' said Adam.

'Splendid,' said Piero Strozzi heartily. 'I love him, but I have brethren enough who are trying to climb with a foot on my neck. Do you see that tower over the river?'

'The Tour aux Puces?' said Adam.

'The Tower of Fleas. An adorable fancy. Yes. That is where we are to fire to make our breach, and we have to take the town in seven days: M. de Guise has promised His Majesty so. Once M. d'Estrée has his cannon set up, there is going to be sound enough to make a goat dance. Perhaps, after all, mon petit François has the best of it.'

'He thought,' Adam said, 'that this would be a pioneers' victory, unless M. de Vieilleville could take it by a surprise assault.'

'So does M. d'Estrée,' said Marshal Strozzi. 'But then, they are his pioneers, and all tall old men are hungry for credit. Do you know what Thionville means?'

'No,' said Adam. Jerott had come out of their common tent and was glaring at him.

'It is Villa Theon, the town of God,' said Marshal Strozzi. 'You know the saying, *Ce que Dieu garde est bien gardé?* Fortunately, Master Nostradamus has suggested to His Majesty that good news is on the way, so M. de Vieilleville will be comforted. But of course, you are also a good Christian?'

'Isn't everybody,' said Adam dryly, 'on the eve of battle?' And as Strozzi, laughing, clapped him on the back, he turned and joined the others in his tent.

*

The town of God fell not seven but seventeen days later to its French attackers, leaving eight hundred dead and seven hundred wounded within the fortress, and four hundred French dead outside. And on Friday, 1 July, the news came to Sevigny.

It came in the livery of the royal household and in the form of a troop of bright-armoured horsemen who swept through the royal town of Blois and the vineyards beyond in the trembling heat, and arrived at the château just as the man they were seeking walked down the steps, his fair hair glittering in the sun. Behind him, a young girl with long brown hair in a light silk berline paused and stood still as they dismounted and the leader, a gentleman of the King's bedchamber and therefore a courtier of some considerable distinction, came forward.

'I am glad to see you, M. de Sevigny. I bear you greetings from His Most Christian Majesty.'

This was a different matter from the cheerful exhortations of his fellow-commanders, and all of those present perceived it. When, presently, the King's representative was established indoors with his hosts he lost no time in delivering his message.

'I am to bring you news of the fall of Thionville. It was taken by the Duke de Guise on the 22nd, after a siege of great hardship, and it means that the army may now march north through Luxembourg with good prospects. His Majesty forgives your recent defection. He reminds you that in times such as these, the fulfilment of a gentleman's duty to his king and his Order is a matter of honour. His Majesty therefore refuses all your demissions and requires you instead to present yourself within three weeks to the lieutenant-general of his army. In earnest of which, and of His Majesty's love and good feeling towards you, I am to offer you this.'

Across his two palms the King's representative held an oblong case of gilt leather, stamped with the lilies of France and clasped in gold with the cipher of Valois. M. le comte de Sevigny, rising, accepted it, and placing it on the table, unfastened and laid back the cover.

Inside, banded with gold, was the staff of a Marshal of France.

The girl made a small sound. The comte de Sevigny did not speak at all, with good reason. In France, only four men could hold this office under their Constable, and four men currently did, to his knowledge.

So my lord of Sevigny, his hands on either side of the case, showed no joy but instead broke silence curtly. 'Whose, Monsieur? Whose is the bâton?'

And so, regretfully, the courier answered him. 'It belonged, Monseigneur, to Marshal Strozzi. He was killed at Thionville on the 20th.'

✱

It was Philippa who suggested the day after that, when she knew he had not slept at all, that they should ride southwest to the château of Onzain and visit Lord Grey in his captivity.

Any wish of hers was his also, effortlessly as two pools of a brook reaching parity. She knew he was aware of the reason. That morning, drawn from her own restless bed by her anxiety, she had found him there, within sight of her chamber, waiting as he had done every dawn in those early weeks, restoring to her the gift of his presence.

But this time, unlike those first cruel mornings, she had had to remind herself not to react naturally: by taking his hands as Kate would have done, or offering him the warmth of speechless comfort, as he must have known it once, one supposed, from Sybilla.

That way, that sunlit, gentle path was set with mines, and had at the end of it a chasm she could not contemplate. So she hid her impulse, and did not know, because he was better at concealment than she, that he had noticed it.

✱

They had once before called at the old moated château of Onzain, sct for four hundred years by the Loire on its ridge overlooking the watermeadows.

That had been when she first found casual talk possible: conversations with Nick Applegarth and his steward; encounters with folk on the farms of Sevigny and in the gardens. That was when Francis had brought in, little by little, other elements to replace the first, steady bulwark of the written word, and his presence, all her waking moments beside her.

She had remembered, scanning his charts, what Chancellor had told her about map-making and the arts of navigation, and what she had learned since from Nicholas de Nicolay in Paris. Using his telescope, she learned her way again about the night sky and began to see work they might do together, for they had both travelled far, and had learning enough to apply what they had discovered. A friend of his, a mathematician visiting Blois, was invited with her consent to spend an afternoon with them. This, the opening of the first door upon the outside world was a milestone: as unlike as possible to the paralysis of those two untimely visits, from Strozzi and from Adam Blacklock, when the whole patient fabric of reason and recovery had been upheld by Francis alone, with the willpower which had carried them through these two months.

A willpower exerted now to such prodigal purpose that he could set aside, as an unwanted luxury, the sickness of headaches and blindness, both of which had gone as if they had never existed.

To riding, now that she was recovered, had been added tennis and jeu de paume and pall mall and other sports. Another friend came: a scholar from Strasbourg University; and she paid her first visits to Blois, and then, one day, to the Abbess at la Guiche. And to Willie Grey, who knew, inevitably, the gossip from Paris; who knew that she had flouted Austin and that there was now little hope of the Sevigny money coming to save him. But who had been kind, in the way of a general who makes the best of a failure, and who perhaps was even relieved, a little, for Austin's sake.

So today, in his prison at the top of the keep he welcomed them both, and was prepared to be won from the tale of his grievances.

He knew, as Philippa had hoped, all about Thionville.

Charles de La Rochefoucauld had been there, and the wounded were already returning.

'Glory and fruits of their labour stolen by fortune-hunting princes. That's what d'Estrée said, they tell me, and he had reason. Allowed the fortress to prepare all its defences and then wasted eleven days' ammunition making a breach too exposed to benefit them. You said it and I said it and we were right. It was a pioneers' job and bloody work too, in the shortest nights of the year, however many covering cannon they had. They dug trenches for over three thousand feet, I was told, before they got close enough to take the tower, and the Duke de Guise sent to tell de Vielleville not to let the town surrender until he and his courtiers had a chance to get there and witness it. That doesn't go down well. He should have slept in the trenches, like Strozzi and Montluc. If he'd let Strozzi get on with his work, he'd be there today.'

'How?' asked Philippa. It was cooler within the stone walls than outside, although she could see two of Grey's men on the roof below, taking the air on the battlements. Harry Palmer's wound, they said, had become serious.

'Apparently he crossed the river to change his shirt in his tents, and de Guise insisted on his staying the night there instead of the trenches. He didn't want to. Had a premonition, he said, that something was going to happen. He stayed, and was reconnoitring culverin sites the next morning when the hackbut shot took him above the heart from five hundred paces. So they say.'

Lymond said, 'Why in God's name . . . ?' and breaking off, shrugged.

'Didn't he wear a breastplate? He was just putting it on. But not in God's name. That gentleman,' Lord Grey said without especial rancour, 'was a damned irreligious Italian, although he was reared for the Church. Forced de Vieilleville to retire with the colic, I'm told, the night before he was killed, by promoting a mischievous discussion on what he thought God did before the Creation. De Vieilleville swore he'd never meet him again, and the siege would make an end of him. Which it did, of course.'

'Scusandosi, dicendo, io nol' conosco. I don't need to ask,' Lymond said, 'if he died recanting?'

'You don't,' said Lord Grey grimly. ' "I renounce God; my

hour is over," he said. And when they insisted on reminding him that he would be face to face that day with his Maker: "Morte-Dieu! I shall be with all the rest who have been dying for six thousand years!" the fellow came back with. And gave up his spirit, but to whom, of course, is unknown. He was, I make no doubt, a fine engineer,' said Lord Grey of Wilton.

Lymond said, 'He was also a wit and a scholar. If he had entered the church instead of trying to right his family's wrongs he would be alive today, and you might have kept Calais.'

'And now,' Lord Grey said, 'there is a Marshal's bâton begging. Who will receive it? De Thermes? De Vieilleville?' A royal courier in Blois would hardly escape notice.

'I was offered it yesterday,' Lymond said.'Would you say that in honour I could accept it?'

'It is, of course, the supreme accolade,' William Grey said. 'I suppose you know your own mind if, as a Marshal of France, you are required to take arms against Scotland?'

Philippa, remote in her corner, watched Francis. He said, 'It seems an unlikely contingency. I might as well ask whether you would side with the Scots against England?'

Lord Grey got to his feet and took a turn, without limping, to the barred window. Then he stood, rocking lightly, and faced Francis Crawford 'You are a man,' he said, 'of dangerous acumen. May I remind you that you are also a Knight of the supreme Order of St Michael, vowed to virtue, concord, fidelity, friendship, nobility, grandeur and equality? And I, equally, am a member of the Order of the Garter, with similar requirements of chivalry. You speak of Piero Strozzi who placed his family first. To what do you owe supreme allegiance?'

'To my name,' said Lymond evenly.

'As he did. It is, I suppose, every man's right. And after that?'

From his face, as he sat motionless in his chair, Grey could not have told what Francis was thinking. He said, 'Piero Strozzi had renounced God. But although he took pleasure, sometimes, in tormenting men with small power about him, he never alarmed his men or his superiors by making a public show of it. The task came first.'

'He fought for the Pope,' Lord Grey said. 'In Italy, he kissed the hand of the Pope, and waged war for him.'

576

'They say there are Huguenots among the Knight Hospitallers of St John in Malta,' Lymond said. 'The Grand Prior of France came posthaste to court at the end of May, I have been told, to acquire money to help the Turks attack Italy. How often has Petre changed coat? Or Paget, or Arundel, or Pembroke? Or is it a matter of changing coat, or a matter simply of keeping counsel and pursuing, as best one can, one's chosen objective?'

'Your line of reasoning would appeal to a great many people,' said Lord Grey dryly. 'It all depends of course, on the nature of your objective. The end of successful warfare is victory. The end of victory is the expression of a noble spirit, showing itself in pity and munificence. Such is the aim of each of the Orders to which you and I belong.'

'I observe,' Francis said, 'the spiritual benefits, but they do apply, I believe in other fields also. Meanwhile, battles are fought not by knights, as you well know, but by mercenaries. They are employed, as mastiffs are employed in the boar season, and victory goes to the deepest purse, while the people suffer the cost of them. That is war without pride ruled by chivalry, as the Master of Game rules the hunting field.'

'It has reached my ears,' Lord Grey said, 'that once you spoke otherwise to young Austin.'

She had not known that. Francis said, 'He required, temporarily, a palliative. He spat it out, I am sure, with equal satisfaction when himself again ... There are, surely, other methods of preserving the weak and the good. There are other ways of exercising courage and magnanimity. Fighting preserves a man from wrath and avarice, sloth and gluttony, envy and lechery no more than hunting does.'

'Would you rather men unleashed them at home, or in the council chamber?' said Grey. 'That is the argument for waging war as a exercise; although I agree with you: to kill for such a reason is wasteful. But greed exists, and vanity. How do you propose to control these: with a smile, a prayer, a treaty? This war was begun by the Pontiff.'

'With time,' Lymond said. 'And teaching. And fear of ridicule, if need be. What I cannot control is the stupid man, launched upon a war which is against his material interests. And there is no scavenger of the air, or beast of the earth, or ooze of the sea which will offend nature like two such, opposed to one another.'

577

No one spoke, while the eyes of the two men held one another. Then Lord Grey said, 'I believe you. And it faces us. But what have you done, except run with the mastiffs? You chose to go to Russia, keeping your counsel and pursuing your own objective. In Scotland, of course, to keep counsel is rather more difficult.'

'No more than in England,' said Lymond. And after a moment he added, 'I saw a chance to mould a nation.'

'Your task in your own country, I grant you, would be harder,' said Grey. Then walking to the window he turned and said, 'No. I am unfair. You have had reasons, no doubt, for leaving Scotland, but there is one which any man can distinguish. Amid the teeming millions of Russia, among the hosts of those vying for power in France you have made your mark promptly. I commend you for it. But in Scotland you would have no face that was not a public one. You would be a cock pheasant trapped in a hen coop. They could not afford to leave you alone until they had conned every quill in your belly. A man should be very sure of himself,' said Lord Grey, 'before he set out to face that inquisition. And, as well, you have England to reckon with.'

'Then what should I do?' Lymond said.

Lord Grey looked at him, and then at Philippa silent in her corner. 'I see,' he said. 'I have been brought in to arbitrate. I am to tell your charming wife that you are right. That no man of honour could take high office in a land whose interests may compete with those of the land of his peoples. That since Scotland would give you an ambivalent welcome and Russia is far off and its welcome also in doubt, you would be best to remain as you are, a landed gentleman of title and wealth, employing the passing days hunting with mastiffs. . . .

'Madam, I know your mother. I fought many campaigns with your father and looked upon him as a friend. I tell you that whatever infatuation you have fallen into, you cannot keep that man at your side. He belongs where he belongs and he will arrive there, no matter how deep you bury him. Best free him at once and save the heart ache.'

Francis was smiling. 'Thank you,' he said. 'That was what she was hoping you would say.'

Lord Gray of Wilton looked from one to the other. 'I am a fool? You want to separate?'

'No,' Lymond said. 'We are staying together. But I am none the less grateful for your tribute. Some time, I should like my brother to talk to you about Scotland.'

Lord Grey sat down. 'I should be willing. I make no doubt he is honest. And committed.' He cleared his throat. 'You know perhaps that Austin still stays with your mother?'

Lymond said, 'I did him an injury which no man would readily forgive. But nothing can mend it. He would be better at home.'

'I told him,' Lord Grey said, exasperated. 'I said, you've been made a fool of; they're happy; get off home and marry a good wench from Newcastle.'

'And he didn't?' said Philippa shakily.

'That boy,' said Lord Grey, 'is a bundle of nerves like a kitten. Couldn't stand the sound of cloth tearing. Stuffs himself full of volumes of chivalry, and then comes home heart-broken because some village lout hasn't read them.'

'He believed the harangues,' Lymond said gently. 'For him, the army is wrong, and so is Allendale while his mother lives. He needs a post like Nick Applegarth's at Sevigny, with an estate and some people to practise on. He isn't lacking in fibre. I would have wished it to have turned out differently. In fact,' Lymond said, 'I tried rather hard.'

'I won't ask you to read his letter then,' said Lord Grey. 'I'm afraid it would put you out. He tells me, though, that your men are home again.'

'My men?' Lymond said, Philippa, puzzled, also watched Lord Grey's smooth bearded countenance.

'The men who went missing, I hear, at Saint-Quentin. They were wounded and captured, so Austin says, and now appear to have escaped from the Spaniards. I can't remember their names.'

'Guthrie and Hoddim,' said Francis quietly.

'That's right,' said Lord Grey. 'Well, they're back. Your other men took them in. A party that went on for two days before three of them left for Thionville. They seem to have survived that bungle into the bargain.'

He went on to speak of his ransom. Philippa watched Francis, like herself, fail to listen. She knew from others the endless letters he had sent, the inquiries he had caused to be made in an effort to trace Alec Guthrie and Fergie Hoddim. To join her pleasure to his demanded a gesture ... and here again she must abstain, while even a dog could share its emotion.

But when he turned to her next, the blood risen high under his skin, she had, she believed, banished the thought and was sitting, her hands still in her lap, smiling at him.

CHAPTER 4

Le grand caché long temps soubs les tenebres
Tiedira fer dans la playe sanguine . . .
Et Dame par force de frayeur honorée.

The three weeks of his grace passed, during which the bâton lay untouched in the parlour at Sevigny and, barring once, he did not refer to it.

Coming home from Onzain, she had said, 'You must make your own decision. I do not need you now every day, or even every week, or every month.'

And he had said. 'I have made my decision. I am not going back.'

She did not argue with him because the unspoken issues were clear, and she had already had her case made for her by Grey of Wilton. It was true that she did not need his care now to live; that wit was coming back if not laughter; that they could without fear separate for some parts of the day and find something of interest before, like self meeting self, they joined company again on returning.

They rediscovered trivial conversation over backgammon and pall mall and archery, and talk of another kind with the scholars who increasingly called on them. Francis brought her some books by Thevet and Gilles, and they began, with their gift of tongues, to consider some works of translation.

Poetry she did not attempt, but once, in the bright austere light after sunrise she sat down at the spinet and picked out, within earshot, a short soulless measure in counterpoint. He did not come in, so presently she abandoned it.

Now that he knew he could leave her, he took some time, she observed, to recover his acquaintance with the sun and air and wind which had been his habitat until three months previously. There were men who could engage in rougher sports with him than she could manage. He used the jeu de paume court, often alone, whenever time let him, but when he hunted or shot it was with Archie. For Archie's silence, she knew how much they were both indebted.

Through it all he had taken no solace of drugs or of wine; nor had he offered her any. The therapy had been companionship, through all the day and as much of the night as she needed it, sitting in the long, lit grand' salle until, at length, she could bring herself to go to her chamber. It was in that cruel, brilliant theatre of the salon that she had told him, late one night, that she was not going to bear a child to Leonard Bailey.

By then, they were already so deeply in tune that words were rarely needed, and this was still so. The talking they did do was not in the hearing of others nor, in the early weeks, did it touch on the present or the future. Instead, he sat by her bedside and let her recall, moment by moment, all the long tale of their meetings.

It was then that she found that he had laid flat, himself, every defence against her: that she could, if she wished, enter and be received within this, the long-guarded citadel. And so she discovered, fragment by fragment, what he had never told anyone: the inner truth of all those events which, strung together, made up his unruly life. Then, of his own accord, he brought in Sybilla's name.

'She had ... I thought she had all the virtues: grace and compassion, and laughter, and wisdom. Any lessons I learned to do with justice, with honour, with integrity are lessons I learned at her knee. A child, as you know, makes no allowances.'

Philippa said, 'Another man might have repudiated all she had taught him.'

He was silent. Then he said, 'She thinks, I believe, that I have. She accused me once of excusing myself any vice on the strength of my ... resentment. I think once you thought the same. I suppose you are both right,' he ended.

'Do you? I think it would be truer to say,' Philippa said, 'that both of us at the time had our reasons for hurting you.'

That had been in the first weeks, and her eyes had held unshed tears, her chest ached with the pain of it. But then, the smallest, the most routine human contact had still been beyond her.

From the beginning, intuition had told him not to touch her, and intuition had kept him from speech which would define, like a cobweb in dew, the invisible thing that had hap-

pened. His love showed itself as the air does, by its infinite
space and the life-giving properties of its presence. 'I love you
in every way known to man,' he had said that night in the
Hôtel d'Hercule, and in every way barring one, he had shown
her the truth of it. But he had never spoken of love again.
For in one night she had learned the nature of man's love for
woman, and all poetry and all music had been wrenched
from her.

He understood. She thought that he had hopes of a healing
of the spirit as time went on, although he never spoke of it.
Once, riding with him by the river bank she had heard the
voice of a solitary fisherman, uplifted in a song they both
knew:

> *Ta femme sera de la sorte*
> *Dans les pavois de ta maison*
> *Comme est une vigne qui porte*
> *Force bons fruicts en la saison.*
> *Et tes fils autour de ta table*
> *Arrangé, beaux et verdissants,*
> *Comme la jeunesse agréable*
> *D'un plant d'oliviers fleurissans.*

Then the tears had come, despite herself, and she had said,
'What can I do? Your line will cease.'

And he had turned on her his clear, open gaze and had said
simply, 'Then it will cease.'

And again, his calm acceptance of the situation was not assumed. For him, it was now of no importance, as his place in
the world was of no consequence. He was home, after long
and harsh buffeting. And it was she, who knew his quality as
Grey had done, who had to live with the knowledge that
there was no channel by which it could continue; that for the
purposes of the present world the flourish, so brief, was now
over with.

He was home, one would say. But all that troubled her
came to him, echoing and re-echoing between them. She
knew every shade of his voice; every change in his breathing
and hence, inescapably, when he was hurt, and the reason.
Lacking the crude sturdy signposts of everyday, each had to
find the other in a strange pathless glade of the mind, with
dormant about them, instead of bough and creeper and

trunk, the veils of a thousand threatening mischiefs to trap them.

And basic to them all, the reason why he lived, and had not made his own exit. The act by which, consciously or unconsciously, she had cried out to him: *My love is as great as yours: now will you believe it?* And then: remoter still in her consciousness: *You do not need to believe it for look, I have joined you in your gutter.*

Because of that, he would never leave her. She had meant to set him free and instead had bound him in chains. . . . But that, as well, was too trite an explanation for the thing that had happened. She had granted him moral sanction to bring his love into the sunlight and there, sudden, consuming and devastating to them both, had come this marriage, spirit to spirit, as positive, as devouring as the devotion sought by the monk at the altar rail.

But in the cloister, one does not live and speak daily with the being one worships. For her, with all her senses deadened and maimed, it might have been of little moment. But for her, instead, it was the single source of all misery, since she guessed the one thing he would not show her: the cost of his abstinence.

The summer days passed, ostensibly filled more and more with small and deep pleasures, and with the careful threads of those many affairs which, woven together, were to make them a fit life together. To those about them it seemed the tension was easing. To Philippa, walking with steady feet through the invisible veils of her cloud-forest, the brightness dissolved in the air, darkly filtered.

For how long can one maintain total vigilance? How long before, inattentively, one hurts, and then hurts again without meaning it? And how long, too, can strength of will last, at a pitch such as this, without destroying the structure which houses it?

She knew, from the lights in the salon, how little time he spent in his bed-chamber. She knew from Archie the length of his rides; the violence of the games he played; the prolonged hours of his hunting. Once, returning from Blois, she had found Archie, stony-faced, rubbing down the fine, chestnut Isabela in the stables and walking into the parlour had found Francis asleep there.

She would have been thankful but for the marks of total exhaustion printed under his lashes and about the hard lines of his mouth. Shocked, she moved to his chair and unthinking, found his hand and possessed it.

He opened his eyes; and the trees of the cloud-forest toppled around her. She felt the laceration of his withdrawing fingers, and saw the force of his movements and heard the thud of wood upon wood as the door was flung shut behind him. Then she knelt by the chair, still holding the warmth of his sojourn, and closed her stinging palms over her face as the tears came.

Presently, having removed all trace of distress, she went into the grand' salle and waited.

In an hour he came to join her, the stamp of weariness stark now against a flat pallor, and walking to the window, said, 'Will you forgive me?'

'Why?' said Philippa. 'For suffering what you have suffered for three months?' And felt the veils rend about her, for she had broken the unwritten law: it must not be uttered. It must not be uttered, or they could not bear the pain, mirrored over and over.

So he shook his head, saying nothing; and after a moment chose a chair and sat down, not so far off as usual. An affirmation: *I have strength still. Do not be afraid.* But Philippa said, 'I love you so much.'

All the colour there was left his face. But he only said gently, 'Then next time, you will remember.'

So she must give him the protection he needed and so manage herself that nothing about her, her hand, her dress, her shoulder, should ever approach him. And in such a manner that, one vainly hoped, he might be unaware of it.

For how long can one maintain total vigilance?

For how long can love last, in isolation, without sinking crushed beneath its own presure?

After that she did not go to seek him when he went out, but waited until he was ready to come to her. The fact that he continued to go out told its own story. Some things, then, were now beyond him.

So it was by accident that, one day in mid-July, she left the gardens of Sevigny and chose the path that he had taken, down to the river.

All month the heat had persisted, so that the carp gasped in their pond and the Loire shrank in its wide rushing channel, leaving dry sand and straw at its edges.

It drew Philippa by its coolness. She did not see, until she rounded a bay, that two men she knew stood on the sand, talking. Both were servants of Francis and she saw, from the look of their horses and the cream-tailed Isabela, loosely hobbled near by, that they had been riding hard with him. Then, far out in the river, she saw a wet yellow head in a stream of silver driving towards them, and realized what they were waiting for.

She did not want, at that moment, to speak to them. But she stood, obscured by the alders and was lost for a moment in the beauty of the moving force shearing the water; in the light on the waves and the glitter of the arching hand and arm, repeated over and over.

They were brown. He must have swum many times in the past weeks for the blond skin to take so smooth a tincture on forearm and shoulder and side; on the long line, smooth as a fish, of flank and limbs cleaving the water.

She might have known that here, unlike the steam baths of Baden, he would not only be stripped to the waist. Powerful as a machine, his arm lifted, driving him nearer and with it in her mind rose another arm, masculine also, but with muscles quilted with fat, and a bush of grey hair in its arm-pit. An arm joined by straining muscles to a broad, grey-pelted chest, immovable as a lichened boulder; to a sagging diaphragm and thick, plunging legs, big-boned and ashen. And the suffocating smells: of rotted teeth and stale sweat and old age, and of the voidings of a gasping and effortful maleness.

'She is agog to see him swimming, my Sophie,' one of the servants was saying, 'but I'm not bringing her. I'd have to flog myself to death all night, the bitch, to make believe I was Monseigneur.'

Philippa vomited. Retching and choking, she leaned her weight on a birch sapling and then leaving it, took two steps away from the river and was sick again.

By then, exclaiming and chattering to one another, the two grooms were with her, one of them supporting Madame while the other, on her whispered appeal, brought his horse and held it. She crouched gasping against it, unable to mount, and in the end he jumped into the saddle himself, and taking her up before him, rode off carefully with her back to the château.

She heard, as she went, her husband's voice from the

water, putting a question; and then the other groom's, answering, as he picked up a towel to throw to him.

They would use, to him, the same, jocular reassuring tone in which they had comforted her. 'It comes to the best of wives. Madam. You will make a fine boy, never doubt it!'

While he, listening, would enter her mind, and would know what had happened.

●

Which makes the sound, the hammer or the anvil? Which feels the concussion?

Through her had come the hurt she had feared for him; a stroke neither blunt nor diffuse but direct and most cruelly personal. Lying on her high bed in the heat, with her woman quietly moving about her, she had a long afternoon and evening to ponder it: to realize what she had done, and wonder in what way she could remedy it.

For this time, he did not come to her. She knew, only because she had questioned a maidservant, that he was back in the château and that he had asked for news of her as soon as he entered, and hourly afterwards.

But he did not come nor send any message; for this time, for him, there must be no track left he could follow. Until today, his mind and body, without demands, had existed only to serve her. If even this she could not longer tolerate, then they were both indeed adrift in the wilderness he had spoken of.

Night fell, and her servants left. The sickness was over. Until the next time, when she might deal another man a blow such as that.

But no. That was impossible.

So, in the end, since there was only one thing to do, she rose slowly, and put on the night robe he had seen once before, and brushed her hair over it and walking to the door opened it.

She did not have to search. She knew from the row of blazing windows where he was, in the naked casket which was his protection: the buttress of his self-command: the place where no unseemly emotion could be exhibited, even when alone. It was one reason, she knew, why he remained there, hour after hour, when she had long since gone to bed. The other she also knew: so that he might be within reach, if she needed him.

The last time, she had found him by the fireplace. This time there was no fire when she entered, but the stifling heat of the night, and the candles.

Then she saw him, in a tall chair by one of the windows. His lids were shut, but she could never have thought him sleeping, even had she not seen the arms of his chair, and his hands on them.

She closed the door; and he said, 'There is no need to come any further,' and opened his eyes on her. They were shadowed as if through a long illness, and a golden streak of sweat from the pitiless blaze of the candles ran glinting across his throat and into closed cambric.

It was a matter of anguish that in this heat he should be both fully and formally habited.

Then he said, 'you look so ill. Shall I say it for you? It would be best if I went away, for a short time at least. De Guise is marching north through the duchy of Luxembourg. I could join him, until peace is made.'

It was the only solution, for his sake as well as hers, and he had taken from her, with generosity, the stigma of proposing it. She said, her body trembling, 'If I had not gone to the river, this would not have happened.'

'It might have happened in my arms, Philippa,' he said, and stopped speaking. Then he said, 'The fault was mine that I had to swim; that I had to force you to treat me like a leper; that I couldn't, in the end, give you the spirit without the clay. We had all that two people need, and I have failed you. And . . . I do not know if I can change.'

'It is not you who must change,' Philippa said. And, terrified by what she saw in his face, cried in desperation. 'Oh, my dear: why will you not weep? Or am I not who I am?'

It was the only plea to which he could answer. It forestalled by very little the end of his self-command, and made her witness to something she could neither comfort nor ease, except by the act of releasing it.

After the first moments, he did not know she was there. Agony and anger alike in her mind, Philippa strode to the windows and flung the heavy curtains over the stark glass and left them there, for now their office was over. Then, as summer lightening swayed in the beeches and the thunderclouds, piled high in the night, gave the first low reverberation of the ugly storm sweeping towards them, she fled from the chamber.

❈

Later that night the storm travelled north over Paris, playing a long time over the city and sending many of the uninformed into the churches. While at its height, a flash of lightning struck the Tour de Billy behind the Célestins and exploded two hundred casks of cannon powder, flinging the stones of its wreckage as far as St Antoine des Champs and St Victor and the Terrin of Notre-Dame, to the hurt of the many in shelter there. The Célestins' windows were blown out, as were those of St Paul, St Gervais, St Victor, and St Marcel also. From bank to bank, fish bellies covered the river.

All the houses in the lee of the Arsenal suffered, some being shattered to pieces; and every able man helped to quench fires and pull out the wounded.

It was not until dawn that those digging in the wreckage of the rue de la Cerisaye noticed what appeared to be a shallow grave, partly exposed by the shock of the explosion.

Within it was a woman's body which servants, much distressed, identified as that of their housekeeper, Isabelle Roset.

They notified the authorities in the morning: the same morning on which, before sun-up, Francis Crawford rode from his château of Sevigny.

CHAPTER 5

L'oiseau de proie volant à la semestre,
Avant conflict faict aux François pareure;
L'un bon prendra l'un ambigue sinistre,
La partie foible tiendra par bon augere

When you have gathering under your sceptre one of the largest armies ever mustered by any monarch of France, and also, hopefully, the money to pay for it, there is naturally a strong urge to use it for something.

To King Henri within the fortress walls of the château of La Ferté-Milon came only good news: of the fall of Thionville; of the taking of Arlon; of a string of successes against the English fleet along the north coast; and finally of an unlooked-for victory: the capture of M. de Thermes of the town of Dunkirk, 25 miles east of Calais, together with Bourbourg and Bergues, its small neighbours, with a rich haul of both booty and prisoners.

It confirmed the King in a fond theory: that soon he should take arms in person. They said that King Philip had expressed this wish also, but was held up for want of travelling money. It was a pity that the Dauphin was again unwell, in the care of his Dauphine.

The Duke de Guise, awaiting the arrival of 3,000 more horsemen from Saxony, was lingering in Luxembourg, victualling at the charge of the enemy. Sooner or later he would make his way north, there to join M. de Thermes's victorious army. Meanwhile the King, warmly congratulatory, egged M. de Thermes on to further derring-do.

M. de Thermes, at the head of eight thousand foot soldiers and two thousand horse, marched to the Spanish-held fortress of Gravelines and elated and purposeful, settled down preparatory to surrounding it.

He thought it was lightly garrisoned. He did not know that the Spanish commander and Egmont, the Flemish cavalry leader supporting him, had between them three thousand cavalry and three regiments of German soldiers, two of them in King Philip's service and the other about to embark for England. Seeing this considerable force approaching him, M. de Thermes responded in the only possible way. He mounted his horse and led his army rapidly back across the River Aa on the road leading to Calais.

Unfortunately, the Count of Egmont reached the banks of the Aa just before him, and so did Admiral Malin and twelve ships of the English fleet, standing off at the mouth of the river. Against the shock of Egmont's cavalry and the roar of the broadsides from the naval cannon M. de Thermes's horse turned and tried to escape, but were forced almost immediately to surrender.

The infantry stood the assault for two hours before being totally routed, both M. de Thermes and the Governor of Boulogne being wounded and captured. Of the 8,000 foot, most died by drowning; and the German dead numbered over a thousand.

From Calais, from Montreuil and from Boulogne, the survivors sent news of the calamity to Forté-Milon. The King left quickly for Reims, the Cardinal with him. There, distraught, they awaited the Duke de Guise, the Cardinal's brother, who must now cease his leisured recovery from Thionville and hurry north, yet again, to the rescue of Artois and Picardy.

They were waiting still when Lymond rode into Reims with the company of horse he had gathered in Paris. The King wept as he embraced him, nor did he let him out of his sight all that evening. Within an hour, the work of retrieval had started.

*

On 28 July the army of the Duke de Guise arrived by forced marches just short of Laon on the Champagne–Picardy border, and set up camp on the plain north of Liesse, at a village called Pierrepont.

Two days later, the King of France left Reims to join his army, bringing with him the Duke of Lorraine, the King of Navarre and Marshal of France François de Sevigny, riding beside the now recovered King-Dauphin of France and Scotland.

Waiting to house them two miles south of Liesse was the Château de Marchais, one of the Cardinal's magnificent

591

houses. The comte de Sevigny, overruled sharply by the King, was not able to raise his tents with the rest of his company, but had to wait until the following morning to visit them. On his way to the camp, he called upon the Duke de Guise in his town lodgings. From there, followed by a handful only of his own attendants, the Marshal rode through the long ranks of canvas until he found the pavilion which Jerott Blyth occupied.

Warned by the noise, Jerott was already leaning at his tent door in his shirt, his arms folded, his dark, cynical gaze on the standard of Sevigny, and the group of horsemen approaching him. Then Lymond dismounted, threw the reins to one of his men and said, before Jerott could speak, 'Victories obtained without the master are never complete. Don't glower, my dear man. God and the Immaculate Imáms are with me, and I fear no one. And where is Adam?'

Jerott's arms were no longer folded, and for a moment even his voice failed him. Then, 'Dear Christ, *Francis* ...!' he said; and broke off even before Adam, fully emerging, laid a quick hand on his elbow.

Adam said, 'A lot can change in three months. The others are inside. Have you time to come in?'

'Tact,' Lymond said, 'is the name you should have upon your tombstone; and I shall see you are excused the Kirk Cow and the Upmost Cloth on the strength of it. I have time to come in. I was hoping to see . . .'

But behind Danny Hislop as he entered, Alec Guthrie, grey-bearded and unchanged, was already rising to his feet, with the long face of Hoddim the lawyer beside him, his moustache bracketing the woeful pleats of his smile.

'. . . I hope,' Lymond said, 'you are not expecting your wages. If every candidate for mort-pay turned up eleven months after his demise you would ruin the Kingdom, if the Cardinal hadn't thought of it first. We thought we had lost you.'

'I know,' said Guthrie. After a moment he freed Lymond's hands, and holding him by the shoulders surveyed him up to his face. 'You have something to answer for as well, haven't you?'

'Not at this court,' Lymond said. 'Fergie . . . are you going to raise an action against anyone?'

'Well, no,' said Fergie Hoddim. 'We were captured while pursuing our profession: there's no case for wrongful detention. Forbye, we jouked out of the prison-house anyway, but Alex had a musket ball in his leg, and I had another in a place I'd have to lowse my breeches to show you; and that's why we were slow getting back again. . . . Is it right they've made you a Marshal?'

'Why else do you suppose I've come back?' Lymond said, and sat down on Jerott's campaign bed. 'The Lorde was with Joseph and he was luckie felowe; unlike my unfortunate Piero, qui Fortunam vincit, vincit et invidiam. I hear he is being blamed for all that went wrong at Thionville.'

'Do you?' said Jerott grimly. 'He was as yellow as his shirt with jaundice. It wasn't Strozzi's fault de Vieilleville had to wait three weeks for troops and advice he'd no need for. And he was dead, poor bastard, by the time Montluc took Arlon and the whole town got burned down, including the booty, so the Germans bickered and grumbled all the rest of the marching-time. It wasn't his fault that when we did get word about de Thermes's disaster at Gravelines there was such a panic that we broke the army: sent the bloody German foot and horse off with three months' pay and little gold medals, and then crept along north ourselves with the same troops we'd taken to Thionville with us.

'Forced marches! I tell you, our Guisard friend wants to listen to Montluc: *O mes compagnons, when the King tells you to hurry, don't lose a quarter of an hour*. If we'd made better time north in the first place, Egmont would never have dared keep so many good men at Gravelines. As it was, some-one had to send to Metz and get de Vieilleville to throw twelve companies of legionnaires after us.'

'For that, you can thank me,' said Lymond. 'With de Thermes, we've lost all the best men from Ardres and Boulogne and Montreuil as well as Calais. There are only two ensigns each in Corbie and Amiens and Dourlans. If Egmont had had enough foot soldiers to support his cavalry, we should have had Saint-Quentin all over again in the last fortnight.'

'Christ!' Jerott said. 'What's it like now?'

'Better, marginally. De Sipierre and d'Amville and de Lansac and all the courtiers I could get hold of have gone to Boulogne and Calais. D'Aumale is on his way to Abbeville, and I've sent d'Urfé to Montrueil.'

'Accompanied by Madame Gout?' said Danny. 'But not by overmuch experience.'

593

'One of us will have to relieve him. I should also like to see somebody useful in Corbie and in Dourlans, with seven ensigns at least; and then the rest into Amiens. We shall probably make camp there, once I can get the rest of the army mustered and moving. Philip is marching as well.'

'So you are staying?' Adam said. For good or for evil, the imperious 'I' had returned. What else had been restored to him was not immediately obvious.

'For long enough, I hope, to have this nonsense settled one way or another. All you've said, Jerott, has been echoed in one way or another by Henri. The de Guise family are having a little trouble maintaining their foothold, and that means that the peace talks may prosper. And once a truce is called, the Commissioners can take ship for Scotland.'

Guthrie said, 'That sounds as if you've been busy. You were the King's only senior commander at Reims, then? Which makes you, since St André has gone back to Flanders, and de Brissac is in Italy, one of only two active Marshals in charge here.' His gaze was momentarily searching. 'Why did you take the brevet?'

'Because I was offered it,' said Lymond laconically. 'Aussy tost veu, aussy tost pleust. Also because I dislike untidy wars, as I dislike untidy peacemaking. I am staying in France. Fergie, do you want to go back to Scotland?'

Fergie Hoddim looked surprised. 'I thought the kingdom of France was to be ruinated if I got any wages. I'll have to earn my fare somehow.'

The long mouth twitched in a way that had not changed. 'Alec?'

'Do I take it,' said Alec Guthrie, 'that you want us on the strength here again? I tell you, it's like working under a weather-cock.'

'The answer is yes,' Lymond said, 'provided you can keep Fergie out of the Chambre des Comptes. He'd be a joy on a plinth as Temperantia, embracing his clock and his spectacles.'

He stood up. 'I must go. I'm at Marchais just now, and shall be until the army is mustered, but I shall come back when I can.'

They moved to the doorway with him, talking. As they waited for his horse Adam said, quietly, 'You know Marthe has come back?'

Jerott caught it. He flushed. 'I'm sure he is interested,' he

594

said. 'But we, apparently, are not to ask how Philippa is, or where she is, or why in God's name he didn't keep to his divorce in the first place.' He faced Francis Crawford suddenly, standing stubbornly in his way to the sunlight.

'If I asked you all those things, would you answer?'

There was a little silence. Then Guthrie said dryly, 'I think, mon commandant, that you will have to say something, even if it's only to declare that after all these years, neither your welfare nor Mistress Philippa's should concern us.'

Lymond said, 'She is well. She is at Sevigny, and Archie is with her. If you will tell me, Jerott, why you received Marthe back, I shall tell you why I failed to have my marriage dissolved. The rest, I imagine, is more my affair than that of any other man's, however well disposed he may be. Are you answered?'

'Yes,' said Guthrie bluntly. 'He's answered. Now go, since that is what you have come to do, and advance the glory of the kingdom of France in the terrestrial globe, without if possible permitting the King or the King-Dauphin within ten full miles of the nearest action.'

And to Jerott, as they watched the banners of Sevigny vanishing: 'You will have to change your theory,' said Guthrie, 'unless you have ever met that look on a greedy philanderer. Adam, what do you know, that you are so silent?'

'I know enough,' said Adam Blacklock, 'not to ask a lot of interfering bloody questions and expect them to be answered. If someone builds a bulwark that high, it's for reasons that matter, I take it.'

'I also,' said Alec Guthrie. 'But a bulwark may cut off help, as well as interference. Jerott is right. To measure a ladder against it from time to time is justifiable.'

'Then let's leave it to Jerott,' said Danny. 'The next man with a ladder, I fancy, is going to find himself bounced off and run through the brisket.'

●

The King of France held a review of his army in battle array, the troops numbering 60,000 in all, and comprising the largest and finest force of foot and cavalry the kingdom had ever mustered. The review line was four miles or longer, and it took three hours to march from the top to the bottom and back again. It was a very hot day.

A force of seven ensigns, headed by a captain of Montluc's

595

and Adam Blacklock, left Pierrepont for Corbie, marching for two nights and a day without halting for more than a cat-nap; and entered the town just ahead of the enemy. Danny Hislop departed for Dourlans with three ensigns, and Guthrie, Jerott and Captain de Forcés with seven for Amiens. Fergie Hoddim set off for Montreuil with a small force. With him went de Villars with a larger one, also destined for Amiens.

The comtesse de Sevigny received a letter.

The man who brought it was not known to her, but the su-perscription, small, clear and level, was in a writing now dearly familiar. She slit the wax, alone in her chamber. He had used, instead of the Russian ring, the seal of Sevigny.

The letter inside was direct as the spoken word, and had no preamble. It told her exactly what he was doing and gave, briefly, an outline of his expected movements.

Three lines dealt with business: *I have no reason to expect serious fighting. If I am wrong, Nicholas has control of all my affairs and will see that you are taken home to Flaw Val-leys. What belongs to you in Paris will return to you. Most of my other assets, which have for some time been out of France, will in due course follow you there also.*

The next line said: *I have no premonition about this. It is only necessary to be practical.*

The last lines said: *I have tried not to reach you, in this way or another, by any disfiguring sentiment. You know, I think, that my feelings on this are quite different.*

Below this and above it was an interval, as if with each paragraph the writer had intended to end the letter, but had been brought in, in the end, to add to it.

He had meant, perhaps to leave it unsigned. But below, briefly, he had put the words,

I am thou thy selfe.

And below that, had signed his name: *Francis.*

The courier waited for her reply, which was bright and trenchant and matter-of-fact, as once had been her diary to Kate, written in the Sultan's seraglio; for its purpose, as then, was to strengthen, and not to weaken.

In it she put only her daily news, but with a detail which, unlike his, covered several pages. She found time, as she was writing, to be deeply thankful that love and self-respect to-gether had demanded that her days should be full, so that he should find nothing there to add to his anxiety.

Only at the end did she stop and read again, with painful understanding, the words of his final paragraph, and the appeal which, despite himself, they held in their closing phrases.

So she finished, as he had done, in a brief key which was very different.

I have told you the work of my hands. The place of my thoughts you may know by now. For yours, the door of this kingdom is open by day and by night if you will lend them to me.

The second seal, the one used by Nicholas Applegarth, was still in the desk. She lifted it out, and heating the wax, imprinted it on the folded paper so that the first thing he would see, when he touched it, was his own crest of Sevigny. Then, having delivered it to the courier, she went to her room and, her head in her empty hands, sought for him.

*

In Paris on the same day, Master John Elder took steps at last to obey his mistress, and sail back to England.

He called at the Palais de Justice for his safe conduct. Next, out of malice as well as necessity, he visited the Hôtel de l'Ange, and inquired for Lord Allendale.

Austin was out, but Lord Culter received him. Dealing briefly with his inquiries, Lord Culter observed curtly that his mother was ill in her chamber, and he thought it exceedingly unlikely that Lord Allendale would want to leave France at present, with or without Master Elder.

Master Elder clicked his teeth, his long raw face full of affliction. 'The matter of Mr Crawford. That is, I beg your pardon, the comte de ... Or no. The Marshal, is it not, of Sevigny? A name whose renown, I am sure, will bring nothing but credit to the Crawford family. But of course, mixed with sorrow. ... Mixed, like all great blessings, with sorrow. The young lady, I am told, ran away from him.'

'Indeed?' said Lord Culter. 'Then you have been misinformed. The comtesse de Sevigny is still at her château.'

'I have it wrong,' said Master Elder with contrition. 'It was your brother who renounced all his offices to stay with his bride—a delightful romance: it had all Paris weeping. And then summoned by the King, of course, felt unable to withhold his services. So the Countess expects him to return?'

'I think,' said Austin Grey's voice from the doorway, 'you should absolve Lord Culter from answering. None of us expects Mr Crawford to return, but it would not be polite to say so. Did you wish to see me?'

Master John Elder was not unused to the knowledge that other people were glad to get rid of him. He climbed with undisturbed aplomb to Lord Allendale's room, and once there said, 'I see, since the poor young lady has been deserted, you must feel in honour bound to stay here to help her. I hope you can. I only hope you still can. I hear she is to bear him a child?'

'That is not true,' said Austin Grey harshly. 'Or Lady Culter assures me so.'

'I hope the poor girl fares well,' said Elder sententiously. 'Men of violence are rarely gentle in their dealings with the opposite sex. Children may be denied them. Poor lady. I shall ask Lady Lennox to write to her mother. That is, if you are not to be persuaded to come to England yet? The Commissioners, I am told, are not enjoying the full brightness of the Cardinal's pleasure at present.'

'Their privileges, I suppose, could not continue indefinitely,' Austin said. 'The war has enforced economies, and the unrest has meant firmer measures to protect the public order. As soon as the English fleet ceases patrolling the Narrow Seas they will be permitted to go. I mean to wait at least until then.'

'And, perhaps, take the comtesse de Sevigny back to England with you?' said John Elder warmly. 'How that would delight the Countess my mistress! Then, I have to tell you, the coffer entrusted to you by the Palais de Justice is to be transferred to me. You were about to take home at their instance the effects of a deceased English gentleman, so they tell me? Are they here?'

'In this room. In the corner,' said Austin Grey, nodding. And stood, displeased and astonished as the secretary, bending over the coffer, read the label and straightened with a long, slow and unscholarly imprecation.

'Was this the man who is dead?' said Master Elder. 'A man named Leonard Bailey?'

'Why?' said Austin coldly. 'Did he owe you money? He was a scoundrel, I am told, if not a murderer.'

'What!' said Elder. Then recovering, he folded the shabby skirts of his black robe about him and sitting said, 'Tell me all about him.'

It took five minutes, no more. At the end, 'So that is all

you know?' said Master Elder. 'He was found dead in the Hôtel des Spheres in the morning, having dismissed the servants the previous night, his habit when hiring a woman. On returning, however, the varlets found no sign of a femme usagère, though a horse was missing and later, several coffers of money were found locked, to the servants' surprise, in a cellar. Then the mistress of the house, whose guest the gentleman appeared to be, was discovered dead in the yard, instead of on an extended visit, as Bailey had given out. It was thought that the store of money came to his knowledge, and that having murdered her for it, he died naturally from overstrain and excitement. Do you believe that?'

'Why not?' said Austin Grey.

'And the horse?'

'Someone stole it. The house was empty. There was no one to stop them, and the streets were full. It was the night of the Queen of Scots' wedding.'

'It was the night M. le comte de Sevigny, Chevalier de l'Ordre, vanished from the wedding festivities in pursuance of Madame, his charming wife Philippa,' John Elder said. 'It was the night an elderly gentleman called at Mistress Philippa's rooms and was given, by arrangement, a large sum of money in four coffers, which represented all the gold she had then banked in Paris. . . .

'Suppose a woman did dispose of her person to Leonard Bailey that night. Suppose that, unwisely indulging his appetites he suddenly perished, leaving her in a state of shock and unable to return to her business. Or ailing: so impaired that her husband, Bailey's pander, was forced to remove her from Paris?'

'What are you saying?' said Austin. He was ashen.

'I wonder if you remember,' said Master Edler, 'when we talked of the charming Marthe, who so resembles her *stepbrother* the comte de Sevigny? Did it never strike you as strange that such a resemblance should exist between a brownhaired man's son and his natural daughter, and that both these offspring should have bright yellow hair, while the hair of the eldest, wholly legitimate son should be brown?'

'No,' said Austin. 'I . . . There are surely several possible explanations.'

'Several,' said Master Elder, staring at him. 'But all of them start with the same premise. If Madame Marthe is a bastard, then the gentleman whose colour she shares is almost

599

certain to share her bastardy. I believe,' said John Elder, 'that our eminent friend is not the son of Gavin Crawford. I heard this belief was shared by a distant relative of Mr Crawford's, a great-uncle called Leonard Bailey. One of the reasons I am in Paris this season is that Leonard Bailey promised the Countess, my mistress, to do what he could to obtain documentary proof that Francis Crawford was not what he seemed to be. He was being paid a large monthly fee to look for some original evidence, or even a copy of it. I have been waiting ever since March to hear from him.

'Now I know why I did not hear. He found his originals, did Master Bailey; and he auctioned them. And in return for them, he obtained four coffers of money, a virgin, and a grave in unhallowed ground as a murderer.'

❧

When, later, he broke into her room, Sybilla thought that her courteous young Allendale was gripped, ever-wild, with a sickness. Then she began to distinguish what, in his hoarse shaking voice, he was shouting, and exerting her own clear, scarifying force of personality made him sit down, and lower his voice, and then take in his trembling hands the strongest drink she could find him.

Then she heard him through to the end, although much of his story she had to guess from half-heard whispers and once, for a long time, he could not speak at all. During the recital she herself became very white, but she sat, her back straight, her hands tightly clasped on the long robe before her, and neither drank herself, nor interrupted until it was over.

Then she said, 'Much of this seems to be based on assumption. Have you any real proof?'

'All I need,' said Austin Grey. 'I have just been to the rue de la Cerisaye along with Elder. We found the servants with the help of the Célestins. We found the girl who let Philippa in, one day she called to see Leonard Bailey.' He stopped and then said, 'You see, it explains why your son knew he couldn't get his divorce; because the grounds were to be . . .'

He could not finish. After a bit he went on, with courage: 'And so he had to leave Paris, too, before Madame Roset was found.'

'I thought you said the authorities accused Bailey of killing Madame Roset?' Sybilla said. Her hands shook, and she steadied them.

'Why should he?' said Austin simply. 'Whereas Lymond had every reason, if she knew what Bailey did. Lady Culter ... you have been ill ... and you must forgive me ... but no son of yours could have acted like this, nor, if he did, do I believe you would own him.

'If Lymond is not entitled to the name he bears, then he has married under false pretences, and there are grounds for annulment which never existed before. I beg you, for Philippa's sake, tell me. Who is he? Who is he, if he is not Francis Crawford?'

'He is Francis Crawford,' Sybilla said.

'You would protect him?' Austin said. 'Even yet? Or is it——?' He stopped.

'... myself I am protecting?' Sybilla said. 'Perhaps. Certainly, I am speaking for Richard, and for all his family. If Francis bought the proof, as you say, then it is surely destroyed, and whatever shame you bring down on our kin, you will still be no closer to an annulment. None of this is Richard's fault. Need you ruin him also?' She paused to collect herself and then went on.

'There is something else I want to say. You assume that this was done with my son's connivance. I think that you have guessed correctly. I think that Philippa knew Bailey had those particular papers, and I think that she paid the price he wanted. But, Austin, there is no man on earth who will make me believe that Francis knew it beforehand.'

'But you don't know your son,' Austin said. He looked very tired, with all the violence drained from his face with the colour. 'Then you won't help me?'

'I can't help you,' Sybilla said. 'I can only beg you not to take this to Richard. And to remind you that if Philippa did this thing for Francis, it was a deed of heroic devotion.'

'And so he has left her,' said Austin.

He could not understand it, but he could feel her pain, filling the chamber. Then she said, 'For Philippa, if you love her, you should go home to England now, Austin. Forget us and go home. We have brought you nothing but torture.'

'I shall go home,' he said, 'when I can take Philippa with me.'

❖

It was not to be expected that Lymond's mother would help him. Elder had warned him of that, before he left to take ship for England. 'And remember,' Elder had said, 'I know what this hypocrite is, and so does my mistress. Dig deep, Expose him. Defy all who would stop you. And if, in England or in Scotland, you need a strong arm, you have only to call on us.'

Lymond's mother did not help him, nor did Lymond's sister, although she received him in the Hôtel du Sèjour and listened to all he had to tell her. At the end she said, 'So honour would be satisfied if you can prove that Philippa's husband was not worth her sacrifice?'

The black line crossed his brow, which had come to live there in the past week. 'She is infatuated. He has abandoned her already, for a bâton.'

'As you say. I don't suppose,' Marthe said, 'you could begin to be as enraged as I am by that development. But I don't believe Francis killed Madame Roset.'

'Why should Bailey have killed her?' It was what he had said to Sybilla.

'That,' said Marthe, 'is exactly what I am asking myself. Why should Bailey have killed her?'

CHAPTER 6

Le grand theatre se viendra se redresser,
Les des jettez et les rets ja tendus:
Trop le premier en glaz viendra lasser,
Par ares prostrais de long temps ja fendus.

The Queen of Scotland, learning that the comte de Sevigny had succumbed to the king's inducements, was torn between pleasure and disillusionment. The Queen of France said very little but was as friendly to Madame Valentinois, it was noticed, as she had been on the occasion of the Duchess de Guise's parturition. Mademoiselle Catherine d'Albon was extremely silent, and if she spoke at all, was inclined to be sharp for one of such an equable nature. Her father, receiving the news in Flanders, was not entirely pleased.

The Cardinal of Lorraine, entertaining the King in his château de Marchais, took time to write to Paris, ordering a further and more stringent questioning of some of the college personnel engaged in the recent demonstrations. He instructed a number of qualified theologians to pay a protracted call on the charming wife of M. d'Andelot. And he asked that my lord of Seton, Lord Provost of Edinburgh and senior Lord Baron of Scotland, should be prepared to give him some time when next he found it convenient to ride to Paris.

The Marshal de Sevigny, having assigned and dispatched his advance troops, left Pierrepont himself with a small force of gentlemen and pistoliers, and overtaking that led by Guthrie, de Forcés and Jerott, proceeded to move the 70 miles over the Picardy plateau into Amiens, in readiness to prepare camp for the main royal army.

For the sake of speed, the expedition carried no baggage, except for a light horse-drawn field cannon on four wheels and a couple of wagons. One of these held gunpowder, lead and cord for the hackbuts, while the other contained pioneers' material, including ladders and two light broadbeamed shallops. To ensure their self-sufficiency, they also carried with them, on mules and in wagons, their own bread and wine for the journey.

On the way north, the combined force fought two minor actions, in both of which the German levies were subjected to ungentle discipline.

Already, the large proportion of foreign mercenaries had provoked constant trouble on the march north from Luxembourg. The burning of the Duke de Guise's tent with most of his possessions at Arlon had not been an accident, nor had a similar mishaps suffered by camp-marshal Bourdillon. There had been frequent violent clashes between French and Germans off duty, and on one occasion an outbreak of hackbut fire which had come too close to the Duke's person for comfort.

It was not a situation where reason or soft words had any hope of prevailing. On the first night of the march, after a small but successful encounter with a troop of foraging Flemish cavalry, the footsoldiers from Saxony, elated and hungry for plunder, burst their ranks and made, jumping over the fields, for the village used for the enemy's ambush.

It needed only ten minutes more for a repetition of the scenes the army had endured ever since Thionville: the firing of the straw stacks and thatches, the hysterical barking of dogs and the screaming of women and children; the spread-eagled boys split by pikes and the other, living figures pinned threshing under their predators.

They were half over the fields when Lymond had his trumpeters blow the recall, and three-quarters when his line of hackbutters dropped to one knee and opened fire on them.

Ten of the Duke of Saxony's men dropped in their tracks. The rest hesitated, slowed, and then turning, raised their hands in surrender.

Captain de Forcés rounded them up. Those common soldiers who survived were brought back and whipped; the leaders were hanged from the treetops. Then the force was re-formed, fed, watered and set marching till daylight.

Jerott, extremely uneasy at the quality of their silence, followed an old campaign rule and, dismounting, dropped back and marched beside them. Guthrie, de Forcés and Lymond were already there, each keeping pace with an ensign. He found a group of men with whom he could converse in stumbling Spanish, and listened jealously to the eager, competitive note in the voices round Francis.

The Marshal, from his days as a mercenary, spoke mercenaries' German, as well as dealing out mercenaries' justice. The army and he, it appeared understood one another.

At dawn they found a wood to sleep in, the men in the open and the four chief officers under canvas. It was Alec Guthrie who, missing Lymond, found him alone with his back to a tree, at a place further out than his pickets.

He did not move as Guthrie came up, but despite the dearth of welcome, the older man continued until he stood, hands on hips, looking down at him. 'Remorse?' Guthrie observed.

'No,' Lymond said. His eyes were closed, and he did not open them.

'You want to prove that even after that you won't be found with an accidental knife in your back in the morning?'

'They wouldn't risk it,' said Lymond. 'Not in camp. A shot in the head, perhaps, during the fighting.'

'Perhaps you're right. When did you last get a night's sleep?' said Guthrie abruptly.

This time, Lymond opened his eyes and looked up at him. 'When did I last have peace to get one?'

'You weren't asleep. You weren't asleep last night either. Whatever it is,' Guthrie said, 'that demands this depth of self-analysis, you would be as well to dismiss it while fighting. Men depend on you. Without a routine, you cannot expect to keep healthy.'

He paused, his bearded lips pursed. 'There are various traditional methods of relieving tension. Jerott, I understand, is an expert.'

'If Jerott puts a girl in my tent,' Lymond said, 'I shall kill her.'

He had been expecting something, but the suddenness of it caught Guthrie unprepared. For a long time, his mind busy, he said nothing. Lymond, his eyes closed, was breathing with great regularity. Then Alec Guthrie said, 'I see. And what solution do you propose?'

'The King's Cure,' Lymond said. 'Le Roy te touche. Dieu te guérisse. The problem is not, unfortunately, amenable to communal management.'

'There is no shame in the wine flask, now and then,' Guthrie said. 'It doesn't solve problems, but it makes them a little more tolerable.'

'I have a suggestion in that case,' said Lymond. 'You two have the orgy, and I'll keep the drinker's headache. Assuming, that is, you mean to spend every hour of the twenty-four haunting me.'

He was not getting anywhere, so Guthrie left him. Recounting the incident later, he was quite taken aback by Jerott's reaction.

Late the same day, with forty miles still to cover, they passed the village of Flavy-le-Martel with, beyond it, the enemy-occupied fortress of Ham in which the Marshal himself had once been held prisoner.

No one mentioned it, and they gave Ham an extremely wide berth: the more so that the marquis de Villars had also passed that way, on a march somewhat less orderly.

It was as well that they had brought with them their own food supplies, for the villages they did pass were deserted and many of them in ruins, so that the wide flat countryside stretching far to the east beyond the Somme offered little shelter. In the intense heat much of the marshy ground had dried out, but necessity pushed them once or twice from the more convenient tracks into a network of the small streams which fed the Somme, and there the trestles and boats came into use, and the coils of rope they had brought for dragging both cables and wagons.

They used local guides twice, although these were often double informers, and once hired, were not allowed to leave camp: their news was always checked by Lymond's own outposts which moved back and forth constantly. He knew, at every point, how far de Villars was ahead of him and also the situation at Amiens where d'Estrée and his commissaires de vivres had already started work. His own relay of couriers also arrived at regular intervals from Pierrepont with news of the main army.

Two further letters had come from his wife, one while he was still at Marchais, and the other which he had opened that morning, just before Guthrie came across him.

Each contained a closely written budget of news. 'I gather great princes still make peace sword in hand. The rumour is that Spain won't give in until she has Savoy and Piedmont back; England want Calais and the King of France wants the Constable.

'If peace is made, the Germans will be paid off and the

606

Cardinal, it is thought, will be able to act fairly freely against the Calvinists. Master Knox, in Geneva, has just printed a tract against women monarchs which has made him the de Guises' special favourite. I'm told the church have been investigating the meeting of drapers in the rue Marie-Egyptienne, and hope our mystical friend has not been attending them: he is meanwhile providently predicting nothing but quotable victories.

'Willie Grey is temporarily satisfied in a new-found belief that Onzain communicates with Chaumont under the river by tunnel, and that if he can only find it, he will be a free man, provided he can get out of Chaumont. He says the Duchess d'Uzes has told de La Rochefoucauld who has told de Merguey that Queen Catherine thinks Lord Seton has gone crazy. I have a feeling that you were intended to be at the end of this particular tunnel, so I pass it on for what you can make of it.

'The rest of the news is not mine. On the principle of Fluctuat nec Mergitur, which I hope you approve of, I have solicited all your former correspondents, and new reports are now beginning to come in. There are times, it seems to me, when one needs help in deciphering the recondite secrets of God the Creator . . .'

She had reopened the network which, begun long ago, had kept him apprised before most people of the shifting allegiances of Europe.

The remainder of both letters was occupied with material taken from the incoming dispatches. At the end of each was a paragraph, no more, about her own concerns. The first ended with the words, *You are missed.*

The second, the one he had read in the wood, had been different. In that she had put only her signature. It was not until he turned it over that he saw that there was a separate page.

'*You will have to burn my letters. Shall I tell you exactly when you realized this? Who would believe that I know to the second? Nostradamus?*

"*So I wished to write you something you need not burn.*

'*It seemed to me that a circumscribed love was not love; and it was a reflection on whole love to call it so. But against what you have given me, there should be something to write in the ledger.*

'So let me record it. There is nothing of me that does not belong to you. More than your death I fear mine; because you would be left here to mourn for me. More than your love I want peace for you; so better your need of me died, than that it should become unendurable.

'I want you to know what you have. That is its span. I have no other rod of assize.

'God grant quiet rest. PHILIPPA.'

He had burned the rest of the letter, as she had suggested, after Alec Guthrie had left him. Then, because sleep was a state more and more foreign to him he had stayed there, unmoving in solitude, so that the channel was open. And a little later, like a coming home, he knew her mind was with him.

Just before it was time to rouse the camp he returned silently to his tent and without wakening Jerott took out paper and standish and wrote a quick, careful note to his brother.

Someone had cooked him cabbage on charcoal for breakfast, and found millet bread, and a little pomade, a drink made from apples. De Forcés said, 'If they make a peace, I suppose they'll disband us. Will you go back to Sevigny, mon Maréchal?'

'Yes, of course,' Lymond said. 'But first we have to finish the war.'

They began marching at four, when the worst of the heat should have been over, but the plain still swam with it when they passed Caix four hours after that and their detours were not casued by water, but the need to keep the dry grass, noisy with cicadas, under their feet; rather than the chalky earth which rose funnelling into the air, sharp as desert sand, kicked sparkling into the small fires of evening.

Here and there, adrift in the haze, were small villages, the blue spire of the church set like thorn over the thatched cabins and red and white brick of the houses. Twice, they saw signs of hasty cropping, but mostly rank grass grew in the cornfields, and there were no working horses plodding the meadows, or dappled cows under the fruit trees. Only the birds were the same: a young pheasant, rising underfoot, gave Lymond reason to steady his mare and flocks of short-bodied birds rose and wheeled, as they had on that other journey from Ham. He was concerned, this time, that they should tell no tales to his enemies.

Now, within the ranks, hardship imposed its own discipline. The men marched grimly, eyes bloodshot and seared with the lancing glitter of helm and greaves and cuirass; lips cracked and brown skins opened raw with the sun and napped with clinging dirt. Half the mules had gone, turned back to Laon with their panniers empty, and two vacant wine wagons with them. The field gun, hot enough to flay skin, had been covered, and so too had the wagon of powder: it would be a pity, the Marshal remarked, to reach Amiens vertically.

The horses pulling the wagons were in need of water. Jerott's mind was on that as they neared Caix and saw ahead the reeded banks of the Luce. He noticed the grove of tall chestnuts, hot and gold as syrup in the low light, and thought also how welcome their shade would be for ten minutes. Under his cuirass his buckskin jerkin was stiff with perspiration and, below that, he could feel his shirt oozing water. Beside him, in the outer file of marching men, a soldier fainted, and his companions broke ranks to help him.

Then Jerott saw that he had not fainted, and spurring his horse, sent his stentorian voice ringing along the line of march, bringing all the ensigns to a halt. Before they had stopped, Lymond was with him, looking down at the man in the dust.

'Killed by a crossbolt,' Jerott said. 'From the trees, I think.' Behind him, his lieutenant was pulling the vanguard back out of range. One or two hackbutters, loading quickly in the front line, turned and shot into the thick dusty felting of leaves. A crossbolt struck the ground at their heels as they ran. Lymond backed his horse, still watching the trees, and then turned and trotted with Jerott back to the rest of the company.

'Why draw our attention?' he said. 'Alec?'

'There's a village beyond,' Guthrie said. 'It looked deserted. But while our friends stay in the trees, you couldn't get near enough to tell either way.'

'We don't need to cross near the trees,' Captain de Forcés said. 'We can water the horses downstream just as well.'

'If there's a force in that village,' Jerott said, 'it can't be a very big one.'

Lymond said, 'Big enough to slow us down if it follows us. Big enough to hold us here for a little time if we attack it. I think that is why it is here. To send a scout to Philip's army and hold us until a regiment gets here. A good idea. They've only made one mistake.'

'What?' said Jerott. A pistolier, irritated by the lack of action, walked over the flowering grass and raising his weapon released an explosion in the direction of the chestnut trees. With a brief thud, two returning bolts arrived, one in the grass and the other full on his cuirass, making a white dent the size of a balled fist. He fell, and two comrades scuttled out and hauled him back, gasping.

'Good God,' Lymond said. 'How would you propose to get them out of those trees? Wait till they drop out from famine? We have the field gun, had you forgotten?'

They had the field gun and shot and matches and powder, and they did not need to come within crossbow range to align the cannon on the summer grove, heavy with the langours of August.

Two of the enemy shouted, parting the leaves just before the gun fired and were allowed to climb down and surrender, to be bundled off, their wrists bound up with hackbut cord. Then the gunners touched off the cannon, and reloaded and fired it again, until the grove was a mountainous graveyard of split boughs and dead birds and greenery. Two men were thrown clear, in fragments. For a while they could hear the voice of a third, under the wreckage. Then it faded to silence.

Smoke, rising white into the air thinned and wandered, flushed rose in the sunset. 'And now, *mes amis*,' said the Marshal to the men, brighteyed and alert crowded round him, 'let us see what we have in those houses.'

In the houses were two companies of landsknechts and one of Spaniards, under a young captain from Brabant. The field gun, turned on the wall, breached it with a single ball, and with another brought down all the hovels next to it. Lymond dispatched a trumpet first to call for surrender, and when answered with defiance turned the mouth of the gun on the houses. When he sent his pikemen in, the drums marched with them, the roar of their beating reverberating from all the stone shells and arcades and cellars.

Jerott had once had that done to him, and knew how in a small space it deadened through and sowed panic.

The Spaniards were brave. They stayed where they were

610

and forced men to come in and fight hand to hand in the passages. The Germans escaped into the street and over the roofs, where the hackbutters picked them off, merry as fowlers. Like hot water thrown on an anthill, the fighting seethed, short and sharp for forty minutes. Then it was over; and the only enemy still alive were bound in the wagons.

This time, Lymond had promised his men all the booty they could discover.

The villagers in their flight had overlooked only some hens, some wine, and some onions; and below the rubble in the patched earth were a few vegetables.

Only the Spaniards were better provided. In the blacksmith's house they found flour and biscuit and lard; on the dead bodies fine arms and shirts, money and jewellery; and in a weaver's loft a dozen camp followers, huddled together, who lost no time making themselves pleasant to the conquerors.

The jubilation rose, hurled from building to building, as the evening sky dimmed to turquoise and the cressets flared, bright as animals' eyes in the dusk, leaping from building to black splintered building. De Forcés, before a brilliant fire, collected the booty piled before him ready to apportion in Amiens. Food was distributed. Alec Guthrie, before a locked door, supervised the amount of wine claimed for each ensign.

They had posted sentries and outposts. But the mere fact that they were to be detained there meant a reasonable margin of safety. They fought well, Lymond had said. Give them an hour. Then let's get them over the river.

Some of them were in the river already. Jerott, his thirst slaked, his bodily vigour still driving him at battle pitch, left the village and strode with the rest shouting and singing to the Luce, unbuckling his straps as he went. His sergeant, his points untied, was fondling a girl with her back to the wall in the darkness: as Jerott passed he was having her, neatly and urgently.

A party of Germans, yelling to one another, lit them up with a dangling lantern and began chanting obscenities. Behind them was Jerott's page. Jerott, grinning, began to fling him items of armour as he unfastened them until, in shirt-sleeves and hose, he stood calf-deep in the red surging water, drenched and laughing among the nude hairy flesh which leaped and vaulted and screamed in the spray all about him.

611

A lighted brand, tossed high in the sky, lit the cream mane and tail of an Andalusian mare, and the doublet and bared head of the rider, still as a monument, looking at him.

Someone shrilled. 'Join us, Marshal!'

The Marshal, if he enjoyed the joke, did not answer. But the Isabel flung up her head, as if a goad quite unaccustomed had been used on her. The next moment she had kicked out her heels, and snorting had plunged abruptly into the gathering darkness.

Jerott said to his page, 'Get my horse, quickly.'

❈

A single rider, at dusk, is not so hard to track in open country; the more so if he is quite reckless of pursuit, and of the noise he makes.

Late as he was in the chase, Jerott was saved by the fact that his quarry had no destination. When, discerning the hoofbeats, he first glimpsed mare and horseman streaming like smoke through the meadowlands, he saw the Isabel virtually riderless, and knew his instinct this time was the right one.

There were hedges coming, and the slate-coloured glimmer of ditches and ponds and behind, black on the indigo sky, the crenellated line of a deep band of forest. Jerott, nursing his mount, turned its head to the trees and, converging, asked it to overtake the other uncontrolled horse, far in front of him.

Forty miles on the march had tired the Isabel but, lashed as she had been, she was far too excited to falter. She took a ditch in her stride, and another, and then, her nostrils wide, soared over the thorn hedge which guarded the woodland.

Behind, instead of firm ground, lay a quagmire. Her legs sank into it buckling, and bone jarred on bone and flesh squeezed into flesh as her smooth chestnut flanks struck the earth, twisting. She threshed once, her ribs crushed, and died, almost before Lymond stirred from the spongy ground where she had flung him.

He had broken no bones. What had gone was his bastion: the mindless violence through which thought could not seize him. Without it he stayed where he was, his hair brushing his knees, his folded arms tight as a man with a spear in him.

And so Jerott found him, and obtaining no answers, had

612

to locate for himself what the damage was. There was none that he could find. Only a constant and uncontrollable shuddering; a visible comber of movement running through and through the arrogant body.

Jerott said, 'Oh Christ,' and taking the other man's shoulders held him as if in a vice; in the obliterating grip that itself can sometimes stop thought, and re-form what is shattered below it.

After a long time, the shivering lessened, and Jerott scrupulously slackened his grip and said, 'Francis? There's a tree just behind you.'

And he understood that, for in a little while he pulled himself back and laid his shoulders against it. His lids, in the near-darkness, appeared to be closed, and at no time at all had he spoken.

Stillness descended. Behind them in the wood a bird called and then flew, in a ruffle of wing beats. Something brushed through the grass near the Isabel and then raced away as Jerott shifted. His own horse, its reins knotted, stood heavily, its bridle jangling as its hips altered. Jerott said, 'It's Philippa, isn't it? Philippa herself: not the want of a woman?'

There was the flat silence of extreme exhaustion, both of the mind and of the body. Then, Lymond said, 'Yes.'

'I didn't know,' Jerott said; and the manner in which he said it was the apology he did not think of making. Then he said, 'There is no need for you to be here. I can take this convoy to Amiens.'

There was another silence. Then, 'No' Lymond said. 'No. I shall stay with it.'

'You can't stay with it like this,' Jerott said. And when Lymond made no answer, he said, 'What does it matter? There will be a truce. In a few weeks you can return to her anyway.'

'I can't,' Lymond said. 'I can't. That's the trouble. I don't think I can go back at all.'

He had his palms over his face. 'The marriage is incomplete, Jerott. And there is no way that I can go on with it any longer.'

*

On arrival at Amiens, the Marshal de Sevigny proceeded directly to his business, which was the preparation of a camp

613

in which to receive and lodge, feed and water an army of 60,000 with its arms, munitions and horses; and to arrange, according to the plan of battle, a suitable disposition for the artillery, the sentries and the various companies and their leaders.

It was decided to bring extra cannon from Paris. Jerott Blyth, extremely grim-faced of late, left to arrange it, and bore with him a note from the Marshal de Sevigny to his brother.

This he took to the Hôtel de l'Ange, avoiding Austin Grey but insisting on being seen by Lord Culter who received him, the letter opened and read, with summary courtesy. 'You know what this letter contains?'

'Yes,' Jerott said. 'Francis believes the Cardinal may have guessed that you all know the truth about the dowry papers which signed away Scotland. Have you seen any evidence of it?'

'None,' said Richard Crawford. 'Nor does my brother give reasons for thinking so. Perhaps he is right. Perhaps it would merely suit him to speed our departure, now that he has shown his coat to be so unequivocally Gallic.'

Jerott, his face red, clung to his temper. 'Soldiering is his trade. He merely follows it. In any case, surely common sense alone tells you to leave France. Such things don't remain secret for ever.'

'Particularly,' Richard said, 'if you have a brother as nimble as I have. I'm told that the impossible has occurred, and the Duke de Guise's pedestal trembles. Let Francis only bring down the Cardinal, and the power he wanted is here, with Scotland, no doubt, as his colony. Is anything beyond him now, even a princess? . . . Or no, I forgot. He is, shortsightedly, still legally tied to his Present wife.'

Lacking the finesse to reply, and unwilling to knock the man out of the window, Jerott left him. To Marthe, whose interest he could count on, he eventually was able to relieve all his feelings.

She had no comfort to give him but sent him back, at least calmed, to the source of his anxiety at Amiens. Then, having made sure of her privacy, Lymond's sister prepared her travelling coffers, her mules and her servants and set out for Blois and her house in the street of the Popinjays. From there, she lost no time in calling on Philippa.

*

614

The comtesse de Sevigny was in the gardens when Marthe sought her, and Applegarth had to lead his surprising guest by marble steps and wide paths through arbors and elm bowers, past knotbeds and box groves and walled orchards and water gardens until at last she was discovered, in a grotto canopied by a vine trellis. Before her was a marble sarcophagus, on which lay a number of papers trapped by pebbles, and she was sitting on a low stone bench beside it, dressed in the loose Andalusian robe which had become all the vogue recently, and writing busily.

Nicholas Applegarth, who had not met Marthe before, was sufficiently instructed by rumour to know that it might be wise to remove her from the house, and relied on Philippa's good sense to receive her without warning.

Even so, when he called gently, 'Madame!' and Philippa looked up, he wondered if he had acted correctly. Then Philippa rose and said, 'Marthe. I'm glad you have found your way here. Nicholas, would you look after Mistress Blyth's people, and perhaps send us something cool to take while we talk? Come and sit.'

'I have no one with me. I am staying at the Maison de Doubtance,' Marthe said. And as Applegarth left she said, erect and quite uncompromising, 'Since I am sister to Francis, I should like to know why you are killing him?'

The pen she was holding dropped from Philippa's hand. She knelt after a moment and lifted it. Then, kneeling still, her hair arcading her hands, she said, 'He is ill?'

'Don't you know?' Marthe said. 'According to Jerott, he is working, persecuted by headaches, like a being possessed by the devil; and under a self-imposed regimen which is breaking him. Surely that doesn't surprise you?'

Philippa sat down. She said, 'I thought the headaches had gone.'

Marthe looked down at her. 'But here, he was at the beginning of his trial by endurance. Now he is tired, and in a place where all the demands on him are physical and he is surrounded by nothing but violence and vigour and virility. And he is staying, because there is nowhere else for him to go.'

'Did he tell Jerott that?' Philippa said.

'He told Jerott,' said Marthe deliberately, 'that yours is a platonic marriage, and because of that, he could never return to you. That is all Jerott knows. On the other hand, I know the truth.'

The flowerbeds by the fountains were full of clove pinks. The thick, hot scent of them was stifling, and the sun, reflected from the white marble, dazzled Philippa's sight, so that she closed her eyes and drew a long breath before opening them. Then she said, 'How can you know it? It belongs to me, and to Francis.'

'And to Austin Grey,' Marthe said. 'And to John Elder, and to Sybilla. It will stop there, I imagine, although the Lennoxes are likely to be edified by it. I shall not bore you with the details, but Madame Roset's body was found, apparently murdered by a great-uncle of your husband's. Elder deduced most of the rest from what he already knew, and made sure Austin heard of it. The Marquis, of course, is waiting anxiously in Paris for you to see the light of reason and fly from the arms of your pimping seducer. Are you with child by the old man?' said Marthe.

That took a little while to answer. Then Philippa lifted her head and said, 'No. Marthe, if there is a way out of this, will you leave me to find it?'

'After what you have done?' Marthe said. 'What did you think you were achieving when you marched into that house like Joan of Arc going to the faggots? Saving his honour? The world could learn tomorrow he was the illegitimate son of Gavin Crawford and do no more than crack its jaw yawning. Saving his life? He won't go to Russia, he won't turn his own hand against himself now, that is certain. He will merely die, starved and strangled like a dog on a chain, unable to live with you or away from you. Could you not see it? With all your vaunted care for his life and his name, did you not visualize what would happen?'

'No,' Philippa said; and her voice, even to herself, was unrecognizable. 'I didn't see it. Whatever punishment you think that merits, I am suffering it.' Then after a long moment she said, 'He is not the child of Gavin Crawford, and neither are you. Your father is Gavin's father, the first Francis Crawford. Your mother was Béatris and his was Sybilla. He is a child of incest.'

Marthe said, 'Look at me.'

616

Long accustomed to bastardy, she should have found nothing of great moment in that news. But her eyes, when Philippa looked at her, were open and black as she had sometimes seen those of Francis in great pain, although she was smiling. She said, 'So he is not my full brother. How obstinate ... how obstinate can an old woman get? So the world would not have yawned. But even so, do you think now that he would not have preferred a quick death to this?'

Then as Philippa did not answer, Marthe said, 'A raped woman should go on her knees if her husband will accept her. You talk of suffering. None of this is Bailey's fault, or Sybilla's, or the chiding hand of the One. It is yours. There is no schoolgirl since the spheres were created who has made such a drama out of losing her chastity. You claim to love him. After all he has done for you, can you not grit your teeth and take him, even if you loathe his sex, and all he stands for?'

Philippa, her head high, did not flinch from the angry face above her. She said, 'Do you not think he would prefer a quick death to that?'

'Dissemble then,' Marthe said. 'Kiaya Khatún must have taught you something. Give him what you would have brought to please Suleiman, had he called you.'

Philippa said, 'There is no artifice of Güzel's that Francis does not know. What do you think it would mean to him, to find me using them?'

'Then kill him as you are doing,' Marthe said. 'But it is not a quick death you are offering. Have you not learned from your sensitive swain, there in Paris? Such scruples seldom injure the owner. It is the men like Francis who will allow themselves to be dragged through the marketplace before they will relinquish the code they have chosen to live by.'

She said softly, 'If I owed what you owed to Francis I should go to bed with my farm manager, with Austin Grey, with any functioning male animal of my acquaintance until I knew I could give my husband a love so well simulated he would never question it. I would do it, because I am of his blood. And I tell you, he would do it for you.'

'No,' Philippa said. 'The voice that suggests that is not to be listened to. . . . The Dame de Doubtance was more than

617

an obstinate old woman, wasn't she, Marthe? She ordained that a man of destiny should be born; and when her daughter Beatris produced only a sickly boy, turned her eyes elsewhere for the perfect match for the first Francis Crawford. She found it in Sybilla. But when Sybilla's son came, the stars told her he was not for her grand-daughter.'

'No,' Marthe said. 'It was you he was to marry. She told me. When he lay in Blois after the fire she spoke the name over and over so that his mind would remember it.' She paused. 'She said he was my brother.'

There was sweat on the fair skin. *You should have died with the dog,* the harsh voice had said, speaking through her lips in Lyon.

'But is your half brother, Marthe, he would never have been for you,' Philippa said. 'Gaultier was a nonentity. She took him, and used him, and let him destroy himself. But you are her grand-daughter. Why did she tie you to us? Why did she make you her messenger? It has brought you nothing but misery.'

'Perhaps,' Marthe said, 'so that there will be someone here when you have gone.'

＊

She left soon after that, and Nicholas's servant, returning with refreshments for the Countess's guest, found the grotto empty, and the light of Jupiter's fountain playing on empty marble, denuded of pen and of papers.

Back in the château Philippa had already locked her letters away and after calling her servants and delivering to them, quietly, a series of long and explicit orders, went to find Nicholas Applegarth in his cabinet.

To him she said, 'I have decided to go home to England. I have some correspondence to entrust to you, which I shall explain to you shortly, and I shall also ask you to send me the money which Francis has told you about. I shall need an escort to Paris. After that, I hope to have Lord Allendale's company.'

The kind face of Nicholas Applegarth had become very stern. 'And Francis?' he said.

'It is Francis I am thinking of,' Philippa said.

Since Bailey's death no man had been set to guard her, for

the enemy was now within, and not outside the gates of Sevigny.

The day she left, she wrote the letter that had to be written, and sent it this time with Archie as her courier. Then she set out north for Austin, and England.

CHAPTER 7

Trop tard, tous deux les fleurs seront perdues ...
La pitié grande sera sans loing tarder
Ceux qui donoient seront contraints de prendre.

Between Sevigny and Amiens lay the better part of two
hundred miles, and since he had been told not to hurry, and
had besides a call to make on the way, Archie Abernethy
took a week to cover it, during which time no letters bearing
his own seal reached François de Sevigny.

By the third week in August, when Archie entered the
town of Amiens and sought a guide to take him to the
French camp, the King and his court had been established
for ten days in the Episcopal Palace and all its encircling
buildings to the south and west of the Cathedral, spilling
down into the low town beside the church of St Germaine
and the belfry. With the King was the Dauphin, the King of
Navarre, the Duke of Lorraine and the Duke of Montpensier,
newly ransomed from Spanish captivity, as well as two
children, the sons of the Duke de Guise and his brother, with
their governors and gentlemen.

The rest of the court together with all the King's principal
commanders was outside Amiens, in the camp now spread
for many miles along the banks of the Somme. And facing it,
with fifteen miles of flat ground between them, was the camp
of Philip of Spain, with the King's standard flying over the
royal pavilion, and sixty thousand soldiers entrenched there
under Savoy, Alva and Egmont, the last fresh from his triumph at Gravelines.

In size and quality, there was little to choose between the
two armies. Both were well armed and supplied with munitions. Both were plagued with immense numbers of mercenaries, who had been known, on occasion, to refuse to fight
one another. France had the better leadership, but Spain had
the support of the English fleet, still harrying the coasts and
immobilizing valuable men in the French coastal fortresses.

620

On the other hand, the Spanish army lay within the French frontiers, and on land which had been laid waste for miles to deny them food and forage. Up to the moment of Archie's arrival, every clash between the two forces had been occasioned by the Spaniards' hunger. Dourlans, which was well stocked, was saved by the extra thousand men raced there beforehand by Danny Hislop. But an attack threatened on Montreuil on the Boulogne road, where Hoddim had placed reinforcements. It was clear that the worse his condition, the sooner King Philip's army would be inclined to turn a foraging feint into a true assault in one direction or another. So, day and night, the French camp was held to the alert, with a reconnoitring routine which continued, irrespective of the alarms and counter-attacks which sent them out, in numbers up to six thousand during most nights and often in daytime.

When the sun was at its zenith, however, most leaders lay under their stifling canvas and slept, while the heat haze veiled the blackened Picardy plains and only the great infrastructure of the two vast concourses of men continued to throb with activity.

There was nothing wrong, all the same, with the defence system. Archie counted four challenges before he found himself ranging the tents, identifying them as he passed from the standards and escutcheons, and the livery of those busy about them.

The pavilion of the Duke de Guise and that of his brother d'Aumale were empty, the sides looped up to allow air to enter. Inside both there were carpets and furnishing which would not have disgraced any palace.

Each of the cluster of tents about the flowered chaplet of Sevigny was closed and quiet, evidence of a dawn foray or a tight expedition. Archie, dismounting, saw around him grooms and bodyservants he knew belonging to Jerott Blyth and Hislop, and then a patched saddle he recognized from a great deal further back, owned by Alec Guthrie.

His grooved face softened for the first time since he had left the Loire, and he hesitated. Then someone said, 'Monsieur?' and it was a page in Lymond's livery scrambling up from a patch of shadow. Beside him was the silent central pavilion, its silken fringes and swags hanging heavy and still in the noon-heat.

Archie said, 'I have personal business with the Marshal.

621

Will you tell him Abernethy is here to see him, from Sevigny?'

They were refusing him in whispers when Francis Crawford's voice from within said sharply, 'Amiel! Let him in, please!' And Archie, passing inside, found himself in the suffocating dusk of the master-tent.

Lymond's voice, close to him said, 'Why are you here?' and Archie, sun-dazzled, looked round for him.

He had been resting, his shirt open to the waist, on the high-backed campaign bed, and was just swinging his feet to the ground when Archie saw him. Between the points of the lawn, Lymond's throat and body were burnished with sweat; his hair was bronzed with it, and his brow and cheekbones showed, bright as oil in the twilight. Archie said, 'There's nothing wrong with mistress Philippa. I've brought you a letter.'

There was a little pause. Lymond said, 'Why? Why do *you* bring it?'

So Archie said quietly, 'I am holding it out to you.'

'Then you can probably guess,' Francis Crawford said, 'why I am not taking it. Put it into my hands. Sit down. Tell me why it should be you who carries the letter. And, if you know, what is in it.'

Archie put the letter in his open hand, but did not sit down. 'We heard of the headaches from Mistress Marthe,' he said. 'But not about this. Is it happening all the . . . ?'

'It is not continuous. So Marthe called at Sevigny? Why?'

Archie said, 'You could buff the bristles off a sow's erse wi' my gullet. Have you no drink in the place?'

'Not within reach,' Lymond said. He raised his voice. 'Amiel! A flask of wine and a cup for Mr Abernethy.'

'That is, two cups,' amended Archie.

Lymond placed his elbows on his knees and rested his brow on the heels of his hands. Footsteps passed and repassed on the dry grass accompanied by subdued voices and eventually, the clink of pewter. Archie, standing at the tent door, intercepted a curious Amiel with a laden tray and bringing it in, poured two cups of wine and placed them both by the bed. Lymond said, 'It is worse having to wait, Archie, than being told at once. What has happened?'

And Archie said, 'Mistress Philippa has gone home to England.'

The hands protecting Lymond's face hardened. Archie, with all his senses concentrated on the other man, saw that he was breathing with strict punctuality: short, hard breaths due as much, probably, to the pressures of pain as anything more. Then Lymond said, 'Why?'

'I don't know. It'll be in the letter,' Archie said.

'But I can't read the letter,' said Francis Crawford.

In a little while he said, 'You were right to bring the wine,' and when Archie touched his hands with the cup, took it in both palms and raised it to his lips.

His hands were streaming with sweat. Archie said, 'Can you not get some air into the place? It would give a pain in the heid to a penny-loaf. Or d'you mean to tell me no one knows about this yet?'

The cup was empty. 'Not yet,' said Lymond. It hasn't happened in public. But I take someone with me ... Amiel ... someone ... whenever I do go out. What did Marthe say to Philippa? Do you know that?'

'No ... They spoke in the gardens. For only half an hour, Mr Applegarth said. Mistress Marthe was staying in the old House de Doubtance in Blois. It seems she means to reopen it for business. Mr Applegarth said she spoke of bringing her stock there from Lyon and Paris.'

'If she knew of the headaches ... Of course,' Lymond said. 'Jerott called on Marthe when he was in Paris.'

Archie did not know what that implied, but the silence that followed spoke loud enough. The little man said, 'You'll be able to read it in a couple of hours. Or even one, surely.'

'I know ... I think I know what will be in it,' Lymond said. 'How ... was she going home? Did Mr Applegarth say?'

'By way of Paris. She was to ask Lord Allendale to take her,' Archie said. And added harshly, while Lymond was still looking at him with open, unseeing eyes, 'I didn't think it altogether suitable. I took the liberty on my way here of asking Mr Blacklock to intercept her and go with them. That was two days ago.'

'So that they will have left the country by now? I see. You came very slowly, Archie. I suppose she asked you to.... I'm glad you sent Adam.' He stopped, and said, 'You must be hot and tired. God knows it isn't your problem, or shouldn't be. Go and call on Alec and Jerott. If I lie flat, I shall be functional presently.'

It was obvious now that he didn't want company. Archie

623

left, silent-footed, and crossed the grass to parry Jerott's questions, and to tell him what news of his wife was worth mentioning.

❋

Alone then, Francis Crawford opened his letter, and lay with it in his hands through the long hours so that its grey lines, its indistinct phrases, its capital letters were staging-posts in the slow return to him of his vision.

By the time you read this, because they were expected, were the first words he found he could guess at. Then *I wrote to you once before;* and *peace for you.* And then, later, a single sentence, clearer written than all the others: *All I wrote then is true still.*

The words of love with which she ended were badly written and blurred, so that he had to wait a long time to read them. But by then he knew why she had gone, and what she meant by her message, for he recalled very well the letter of which she reminded him, and all the things she had said in it.

There is nothing of me that does not belong to you.

More than your death I fear mine, because you would be left here to mourn for me. More than your love I want peace for you, so better your need of me died than that it should become unendurable.

One of them had to make the sacrifice. One of them had to suffer the guilt of it.

The first she had done. The return to Sevigny, now so far beyond his powers, did not need to be faced, nor need he inflict the wound of absenting himself. She had made the sacrifice, and even the guilt, if he wished, need not burden him.

With a valour beyond words Philippa had restored to him the free will he had lost, that evening in Paris. She had left him the gift of his life, to keep or cut off as he wanted.

❋

The wind changed, and the chronic fever of Queen Mary of England showed signs of worsening. Both events seemed to the English fleet to constitute an excellent reason for lifting their blockade of the north coast of France for the present, particularly as of recent weeks they had had mixed successes. The climate seemed favourable, at last, for the Commissioners of the Three Estates of Scotland to start for home on their long-delayed passage.

They had already taken their leave of the monarch before his departure to Reims. Since then, with no court to attend but that of their own Queen-Dauphine in Paris, their stay had seemed even more purposeless. The hint of restriction which had crept into their treatment had vanished with the departure of the Cardinal of Lorraine also for the frontier, thereby further depriving of credence the curious letter sent by the new Marshal of France to his brother.

Despite Lymond's warning, there had been no sign during all these weeks that anyone at the French court was aware of a leakage of state information about the future of Scotland. France, having recovered from celebrating its royal wedding, appeared to have dismissed the Scottish question with the greatest facility from its communal mind, and to be concentrating all its money and energies on concluding the present war with as much prestige and property as possible.

Whatever influence the Commissioners might possess, it would be better wielded in Scotland than in France, it was now apparent. So, at last, the gathering together of gifts and gear and coffers began, and of all the party which had left Scotland with such high hopes seven months before, the only one who lingered, and would fain have stayed, was the Dowager Lady Culter.

Until, that is, one day she returned from an outing to the Hôtel de l'Ange to find Austin Grey gone with all his possessions, and a sealed note awaiting her in her room, closed with the signet of Sevigny.

Inside, Philippa had scrawled: *It is over. The blame belongs to me, not to Francis. I have asked Austin to take me to Flaw Valleys.*

Perhaps you would find it possible to leave France soon, with Richard. It may be that we shall need one another.

Lady Culter told her son Richard, since the news was bound to be bandied about, but could not begin to answer his questions. Only, after that, she found she longed very much to go home again.

Just before the Commissioners left, they were given a gracious reception by the Queen-Dauphine at the Tourelles, followed by a final convocation by the Council. They were there subjected to a long harangue by the Chancellor, in which he invited them yet again to deliver the Crown, the

Sceptre and the Sword of Scotland to the Dauphin their monarch.

When they replied, yet again, that such a matter was not entertained within their commission the Chancellor required them to give under their hands their personal consent to the demand, and an undertaking to present it to the Scots Parliament.

This request they refused, as being neither reasonable to desire nor lawful for them to grant. Then, with a smiling hauteur on both sides, the Commissioners for Scotland parted at last from their hosts, and setting out for Dieppe, took ship for the country which was their own, and had some honesty in it.

＊

On the Picardy plain, the army of King Philip decided to move to better foraging territory, and the Duke of Alva with six hundred cavalry issued at dawn to reconnoitre a possible site.

While there, he had a sharp encounter with a French force of pistoliers and hackbutters under the Marshal de Sevigny, at the end of which both forces disengaged to return to camp, with the damage heavily on the Spanish side.

It followed a cavalry sweep of Lymond's own which had lasted half the night, and which was only one of the succession of small expert forays he had conducted ever since the work of settling the great camp had been completed. The only difference now was that he had no need to observe the other half of his self-imposed régime which dictated that, by taking proper sleep, food and medical help where it would be beneficial, he could display what self-respect and maturity he had left, and cause no one to grieve over his negligence.

Habit on that score died hard, even though he was now alone. Also, even a little thought showed that to take what Philippa had given him and turn it instantly to his own private relief would be a paltry way to repay her. And besides, there was the duty he owed the men under him.

So he continued, through all the degradation and pain, with his routine. He reposed without sleep in his bed for the proper number of hours and ate food patiently which his body would not accept, and at first would take nothing, either of drink or of drugs, which would break the invisible pact he had made with himself.

Only when, with lack of food and sleep, he found his skill in the field less than constant did he let Archie bring him an opiate, and some stronger relief for the headaches.

It was known now that, like de Thermes his gout and St André the pox, the Marshal had his weakness, and when he returned to his tent at the end of his tour, he wished privacy. The Duke de Guise sent his own physician, expressing the deepest solicitude, and Lymond admitted him, smiling, and was examined and given a powder, which he delivered to Archie. About the blindness no one else knew except, now, his four officers, and so far it had only struck on his return, in times of exhaustion.

Only, as his strength grew less predictable, the spells of prostration were lengthening. Now, he could rest between actions. But on the day that one of these two great armies finally lost patience and launched a general attack on the other, he would be committed to a command he could no longer justify.

He had said nothing to anyone of that, but he knew it must be in the minds of Jerott and Alec, Danny and Fergie, who had come from their outposts to join him.

News from beyond Amiens still reached him. Applegarth had taken over the bureau of correspondence left by Philippa, and he knew that peace was likely unless something went seriously wrong: that these two armies were here as holding-posts: dog eyeing dog while the statesmen discussed terms elsewhere.

He knew, from a scribbled note sent from Gravelines, that Adam had reached Philippa and Austin in time, and had sailed for England with them; but not, as yet, if they had landed.

He knew that Marthe was still in Blois, and that the Scottish Commissioners had left France, taking ship from Dieppe harbour.

So Sybilla was out of the country and Richard with her. The two village girls who had looked after her all those years ago, Renée and Isabelle, were dead because of her, and because of him; and the house was destroyed with the lines of silver over the mantelpiece.

I shall harness thee a chariot of lapis-lazuli and gold
Comd into our dwelling, in the perfume of the cedars.

A love of sorts, he supposed, had prompted that once. It mattered not at all now, obliterated by what had happened in that dusty upstairs bedroom, with the candle guttering.

On the day he returned from the encounter with Alva's forces, he found Lancelot Plummer waiting for him in his tent, with Archie and the other four of his own men with him.

It was a moment before he recognized, behind the elegant beard, the officer he had left behind in Russia; and he saw from Plummer's face that his own looks clearly had shocked him. He said, 'I'll only believe it if you tell me the Russian for *I can get sandstone from Kama at quarter the cost.* Lancelot! What does this mean?'

Never a boisterous man, Lancelot Plummer, engineer, architect and former member of the Scots mercenary force called St Mary's, stepped forward and shook his hand firmly. 'It means I've left Russia,' he said. 'And you're well out of it. My God, you've got to the rank of Voevoda all over again, they tell me. I hope you can think of someone who's made a lot of money out of this war and is looking for an architect.'

Lymond said, 'I'm sure I can. *Faux conseils et mauvaises testés, M'ont fait bastir ces fenestres?* Or no. That was a lawyer's house. In any case, come and tell us your news. *Le corps sauvé, les branches se reconquesteront tousjours.'*

Archie and Jerott, who had not been in Russia, fetched the wine and put the pots on the board. The others listened to the story of Lancelot's misery: the houses the Tsar had had built but had not paid for; the houses he had half built and knocked down in a rage. His violence in council. His brutal punishments. The crazy scheme to attack Lithuania that year, against the advice of his ministers.

'He's going mad,' Lancelot Plummer said. 'I'm sure of it. You couldn't hold him now, Voevoda. No one could.'

'Not even Prince Vishnevetsky,' said Guthrie dryly.

'Ah,' said Plummer uneasily.

Lymond glanced at him. 'What? We have been placarded as abominable persons on the chancel-rail? We can bear it. We are a long way from Russia now.'

Lancelot Plummer said, 'Güzel is dead.'

No one spoke. Then Lymond said, 'How? How did it happen?'

'She was killed. In April. By Vishnevetsky,' Plummer said. 'You knew . . .'

'I knew they were together. Yes,' said Francis Crawford. For two years, before he had left Russia, he and she had lived together, a Queen and her comfort. It had been Güzel who had enabled Philippa and himself and the child to escape from Turkey safely. It had been Güzel who had sent him on the visit to England from which he had never returned.

'They quarrelled,' Plummer was saying, conscious of awkwardness. 'They were not really suited to one another. No one even knows where she is buried.'

'That seems a pity,' Lymond said.

One of the things he liked least about his present situation was that the others always seemed to know when he was dealing with an attack, and also when he was nearing the limits of his endurance. His later recollection of the next five minutes was somewhat hazy, but he knew that at the end of that time his tent was empty, Plummer having been thoughtfully taken off to dine on some special delicacy of Jerott's. Then Alec Guthrie reappearing like a sentinel in the doorway said, 'Archie is coming in a moment. I'm sorry about the Mistress. She was foolish to trust Baida.'

'She didn't,' said Lymond. He was still sitting, his hands shading his eyes, at the table. 'She thought she was following a course laid down long before, with both of us under some sort of orders. I think she was convinced all along that her life and mine were going to lie apart. I think when she took Vishnevetsky, she knew he was going to kill her.'

'Perhaps you are right,' Guthrie said. 'But we also perhaps saw a little that you didn't see. She may have thought she was guided by fate, but in the end, I think she rebelled against her orders. In which case ... she is likely better dead.'

After that, the loss of vision lasted all night, and the pain and the retching. Also, although he did not lose consciousness he could hear himself speaking, or raving, or discoursing in some fashion.

He tried to stop and succeeded, in the end, in making sensible human contact with Archie, who seemed to be bending over him, which meant his sight must be coming back. He was shivering violently and wringing wet with perspiration, as was the sheet under him. He said, 'It can't go on like this. Archie?'

'No,' said Archie. 'It can't go on. If you're going to survive, you'll have to buy peace. But you know the price of that kind already.'

For a long time Lymond was silent. Then he said, 'You advise it? Will it work?'

'For long enough,' Archie said. 'For a long time, if you're careful. If we can lift the strain, your sight should come back completely.'

'It sounds,' said Francis Crawford, 'as if we have nothing to lose.'

Archie left him. Lymond sat up. The first light of dawn was tinging the cloth over his head and in the distance a bird was singing loudly, to be joined by another. In a moment the whole tissue of dawn song enclosed him. He shivered and, lifting his arms, peeled off the wet shirt and pulled round his shoulders the towel Archie had left by his bedside.

The tent looked and smelt like a hospital. Distaste wrinkled his nose. He got up, his head swimming and walked to the table where he had left his maps, and the orders for next day already written. Archie came in.

The smell of what he carried reached Lymond from where he stood: the pungent, desirable, terrible smell of the drug that had come near to killing him at Volos: from which, with the help of Jerott and Marthe, he had barely emerged with his reason.

Jerott's voice, low and angry from the doorway, said, *'What are you giving him?'*

Archie's hand closed over what he carried.

Lymond said, 'Something to make me sleep. It's all right, Jerott. What wakened you?'

'The sound of Archie opening the drug cabinet,' Jerott said. 'And I saw what he took out from it.' To Archie he said, 'Open your hand.'

Archie looked at Lymond. Lymond said, 'Open it.'

The streaked saffron cake of raw opium lay on his palm; enough for sleep, and sweet dreams and tranquillity for many nights. Jerott struck it; and when it fell to the floor, ground it under his heel in the carpet. 'You bloody fool. You bloody fool, Francis. This is what started it all: don't you remember? Archie didn't hear you screaming at Volos. Archie simply let you have as much as you wanted, whenever . . .'

'Don't lose your head, Jerott,' said Lymond wearily. 'Archie only gave me what would keep me alive till we got out.

He's doing the same now. I shall fight a better battle full of opium than I should without it, I promise you.'

Jerott said, 'Why should you fight a battle at all? A sick commander is excused the field. Go back to Sevigny.'

Lymond looked at him and Jerott paled, and then slowly coloured. He said, 'There must be something else.'

Lymond straightened. He rubbed the towel round his shoulders and then tossing it at a hook walked back and stood before Jerott. Redder still, Jerott held his eyes angrily. Then Lymond smiled.

'A dejective flag of truce. There *is* something else,' he said. 'Forget the opium. I think it is time that the French were reminded of what St Mary's used to be, and what St Mary's still is, and what St Mary's can do that the lanzknechts can't. Would you forgo another night's sleep, if I asked you to?'

'Yes,' said Jerott. He looked a little dazed.

'Good,' said Lymond. 'Then, if you would bring Alec and Danny and Fergie to my tent at midday, we shall plan ourselves a small expedition.'

'And Lancelot?' said Jerott cautiously.

Lymond grinned. 'If you think,' he said, 'that Lancelot is up to it. Off you go. You'll need all the sleep you can manage.'

The smell of the ruined opium filled all the tent. Jerott had gone. Archie said, 'Oh Jesus, lad. Are you sure, are you sure this is how you want it?'

And Lymond said, 'I only know that I want it.' And then, 'It is best done with what one has of pride.'

Lastly, he said, 'I have leave to go.'

'I know,' said Archie.

●

They left camp at sunset: seven men to fight, and four soldiers with crossbows to hide their horses in a quarry just short of the Spanish encampment. In the same quarry they stripped half their armour, and in full darkness set out on the exploit which from Picard farmer to farmer received the name of the *affair of the corn mills of Authie*.

Burdened like a pioneer with shears and mattock, with rope and slow fuse and matches, with a knife and a cavalry bow and a few doctored arrows and last but not, feelingly, least, by a budget of gunpowder wrapped in silk and then canvas, Jerott Blyth said, 'You devil, Francis. I haven't been so bloody frightened since Mdina. Do you remember? There were seven of us then.'

'I prefer, all sutty, blakk and unclene, the present draft,' Lymond said. Because the arrangements had been his, he had not slept during the day as the others had, but like theirs, his face was stained with the dye of the Reiters, and neither his thoughts nor his condition were discernible. Jerott said, 'What is that prayer of Montluc's?'

He had not expected Lymond to answer him, but he did, without mimicking, as he could so easily do, the little man's Gascon accent.

'*Mon Dieu qui m'as créé, je te supplie, garde-moy l'entendement affin qu'aujourd'huy je ne le perde, car tu le m'as donné, et ne le tiens que de toy. Que si tu as aujourd'huy déterminé ma mort, fais que je meure en réputation d'ung homme de bien, laquelle je cherche avec tant de périls. Je ne te demande poinct la vie, car je veux tout ce qu'il te plaist; ta volonté soit faicte, je remets le tout à ta divine bonté* ... It is a fine prayer, if you believe in such things.'

'And do you?' said Jerott Blyth, former Knight of St. John.

'Sometimes,' said Francis Crawford. 'I spread my favours. Tonight I look to Janus the Patron of Portals.'

Soon after that, they were speeding through darkness; sometimes running, sometimes crawling, sometimes lying in ditches until they came within reach of Dourlans and then, to its west, the river on whose upper reaches the town and citadel stood. The River Authie, which skirted the north wall of the fortress and then took its pleasant course north and west all the way to the sea. The river which King Philip would have to cross if, tiring of facing the French, he decided instead to strike north to Montreuil, or to Boulogne or to Calais itself.

The bridge at Dourlans was under the surveillance of the town and citadel, strongly held by the French. But the next bridge fit to take regiments of marching troops and their artillery was only five miles further down the Authie. And it was held at either end, by two companies of Spanish soldiers.

Danny, his voice rather high, had made that abundantly clear at their conference. 'It's a splendid idea. Domine salve nos qui perimus. I'm too young to die on a bridge. Why don't we take all the Germans? Or no. They would all blow their noses on their very large handkerchiefs, and that would bring Philip's whole camp down on us. What's your idea?'

632

'We don't go near the bridge,' said Lymond peacefully.

'Excuse me,' said Fergie Hoddim. 'How can you wreck a fine bridge without going near it?'

'By sending something else near it instead,' Lymond said. 'An ox to Jupiter, a dog to Hecate, a dove to Venus, a sow to Ceres, a fish to Neptune. What, instead of Fergie Hoddim, shall we sacrifice?'

'Boats won't do,' Guthrie said. 'Even if you put stones in them, they won't inflict enough damage.'

'You could put gunpowder in them,' Jerott said. 'But could you be sure of finding boats?'

Fergie Hoddim said, 'But see. You couldna take that amount of gunpowder over the country without being noticed. They'd be shot at, in any case, long before they got to the bridge. They'd either burn and sink before they got there, or just drift up burning, and that's not enough.'

'Wait a bit,' said Lancelot Plummer, poring over Danny's maps. Then he sat up and looked at Lymond. 'Is that what you mean?'

'That's what I mean,' Lymond said. 'What is it to be an engineer. Tell the others.'

Lancelot looked round. 'It's there on the map,' he said. 'Water-mills, two miles upriver from the bridge. One mill, or maybe two, driving down full pelt on the current would make a hell of a hole in a bridge.'

'Especially,' said Lymond, 'if they were burning. In fact, I fancy they would crash right through and perhaps take the next bridge with them. After that, with any luck, they would burn away. I should prefer not to wreck all the bridges joining the coast road to Calais. Lancelot, what do we need? They're held by chain and rope cable.'

'A lawyer,' said Lancelot Plummer indignantly. 'What did I have to come back for? The Tsar only threw an axe at my ground-plans.'

But he not only gave them good engineer's advice, he came with them; which only went to prove, though Jerott with a touch of cynicism, how much he wanted to impress the court if and when he came back to it.

Once they lost sight of the lit city which was the Spanish encampment it was very dark, and they smelt and heard the river before they saw it. Normally, the ground sloping down to the water would have been thick with the hoofmarks of cattle, but it was many weeks since everything edible had been driven off from this stretch of land, and the small farms and cabins that lined the valley were all of them deserted and most of them uninhabitable.

They had expected the little village which lay round the watermills to be abandoned by its householders as well. It was with the stoicism of veteran campaigners that they saw, scaling the rising ground behind, that this was no longer the case. One of the Count of Egmont's foraging parties had acquired half a dozen wagons of grain and were occupying the village in a litter of burning campfires, tethered horse, sacks, chaff, discarded armour and stacked pikes and hackbuts. The floating watermills of the Authie had been in use that day, and were presumably going to be asked to grind the rest of the grain at first light tomorrow morning.

Lymond said, 'They'll have sentries. Danny, go and see how many, and where they are.'

'There's a boat at the water's edge,' Guthrie said. 'But we can't use it now. And if we swim, they'll still hear the blows of the axes, even if they don't see us.'

'There are two sentries,' said Danny, returning. 'And I can make out some of the voices in the village. They're Spanish.'

'That's useful,' said Lymond. 'Now we want the password. Danny, do you think you could deploy your ineffable powers of invention and get the two sentries to challenge one another? And while you are arranging that, show Fergie how to avoid them so that he can get close to the buildings and check how many soldiers there are, with what sort of arms. Lancelot, we want to design an attack from that field there, using the lint and the gunpowder. Show Alec and Jerott what you want done, and then get down into the water and have a look at the mills. I want to know how long it would take to hack two of them free, assuming we can distract the men's attention. Take Archie with you. All of you report back to me here as soon as possible. Who speaks Spanish? You do, Jerott?'

'I can manage,' said Alec Guthrie.

'I used to be rather fluent,' Plummer said. Sweat, like night rain on a window, glittered on his blackened face.

'No, we need you. But if you'll take Jerott's kerchief and mine swimming with you, we ought to be able to clean our faces when you come back. It's in your hands, gentlemen.'

It's in your hands, gentlemen. It was the way he had ended his orders in Russia, although he had not then addressed them by first names. Guthrie grunted; and Danny slipped away, grinning.

'Our belly lyke as it were glude/Unto the earth cleaves fast,' said Lymond's voice, softly disembodied, following him. He had begun to do something, it was clear, with the gunpowder.

> 'Be not so rude and ignorant
> As is the Horse and Mule
> Whose mouth without a rayne or byt
> From harm thou canst not rule . . .

'How long do we have? Two anons and a bye and bye is an hour and a half. Let us bind round our waists the Belt of Endeavour and get there, if we can, before the morning boat of Ra reveals our deficiencies.'

But by that time, probably, he was entertaining himself, for his six companions were already going about their business.

※

There were many people who could have told el capitán Antonio Alcantara to be wary of a blue-eyed Spaniard in a helm which should have been vaguely familiar, erupting through his sentries with an equally plausible companion, and both armed with the night's password and nothing else.

But nobody was with Captain Alcantara but fifty men at arms, already much resentful of being turned into millers and having to spend a night away from the safety of the main encampment. The sight of two fellow-countrymen, disarmed and horseless, their very corselets torn off their backs was alarming enough. But the news that the French troops which attacked them were even now approaching the river was more frightening still.

Firmly, remembering all he had been taught, the captain put out the fires, sent his men for their weapons and posting them and himself hurriedly at all the vantage points above the village, lay waiting for the enemy to make an appearance. He remembered, thankfully, that there was one boat, and that the rest of them, at a pinch, could swim across the river. By that time, surely, the main camp would be roused and would be on the way to the rescue. He had given the junior of the two unfortunate officers his own horse on which to ride and warn them.

There was a short and nerve-racking wait, not at all assisted by the higher-ranking of the two officers who, unable to put his experience behind him, was walking up and down groaning, weeping and recounting, with a detail Captain Alcantara could well have done without, the unpleasant nature of the rout in which he had just been beaten. When without any warning at all a hackbut fired in the dark field ahead of him the captain jumped so sharply that he bit his tongue. Then he was too busy to care about anything but shouting orders, for the shots came cracking, thick and fast from the darkness.

It was the stranger who, yelling 'Charge!', sent them all running, pikes and hackbuts ready, as the firing began to cease and the enemy hung back from the engagement. They charged straight through the field without noting that the unknown officer had already charged in the opposite direction, arriving thus at the water's edge where, with no one to trouble them, the rest of his party had successfully cut free both the floating mills chained to their stakes in the river-bed.

The first mill was already moving gently downriver by the time the Captain and his men at arms had discovered that there were no enemy soldiers anywhere in the field; only a quantity of burned-out flax and packets of gunpowder. And when, looking about them, they thought to run back to the village, it was to see both mills rocking off in the current with the face of Fergie Hoddim, faintly tinged with verd de mer, peering out from one of the windows. They recharged their hackbuts and fired, kneeling: they raced along the river banks, shouting; they even, in some cases, jumped into the river and swam after the swaying edifices, but to no avail. Then all they could do was catch their horses and gallop off downstream as hard as they could, to warn the troops at the bridge what was coming.

The six jubilant men in the second watermill had already had their briefing. One by one they slipped into the water and made for the bank, each taking a pride, before he left, in steering his barque, so far as possible, into the midst of the current. In the dark, it was a simple matter to duck under the water, and to slip past the horsemen strung out along the leafy valley. And to them, the main matter of moment was to warn the bridge and to devise, if they could, some means of stopping the watermills.

It was a pity that because they themselves had to escape in

636

the mills, they had not been able to hold to their original plan to pack them with gunpowder when, of course, one well-aimed hackbut ball would have exploded them. 'If it was in England, now,' said Fergie, emerging with his moustache streaming by Jerott, 'ye'd be entitled tae the Admiral's profits: waifs, flotsam, lagan and deodands, assuming in the first place that the court was willing to accept your definition of a watermill as a seaworthy object. There's Archie. They're all past. We can start on the road back, I should think. We'll need to, to get to the horses while it's still dark. . . . Is that Francis?'

'No, it's Trembling Sancho,' said Danny, climbing up the bank. 'It would be a bloody funny death, being drowned in a watermill. Where is Suo Magnifico?'

'In the first mill,' Jerott said. 'He wanted to take it round the last bend and then set it in line for the bridge. You can see the lights of the bridge if you come up the slope a bit.'

This was true. Straining their eyes from the bowels of the bushes they watched the mill they had just left, a black shape on the slate of the river, give a lurch as someone jumped from it. In a moment, they could see it was Plummer. Guthrie's grey head was already in midstream, sleek as an otter. Jerott, with the others, walked noiselessly along the bank to greet them. Danny said, 'If that's supposed to be a straight line for the bridge, then he hasn't had much practice in steering watermills. Ours is better placed than his.'

'More of us to set it on its course,' Guthrie said. 'When was he going to jump?'

Lancelot Plummer emerged from the water, hawked, and stood up, his face barred with melted black paint. 'After he's set the fuse for the gunpowder,' he said. 'Any minute now, I should think.'

'What?' said Jerott.

'He's madder than the Tsar,' said Plummer cheerfully. 'He swam out with the powder on his head, tied under his chin with kissing strings. His phrase, not mine. The idea was that any hackbut shots were likely to be aimed at the second mill, not the one that got away first. He'll set the fuse when he gets squarely in sight of the bridge and then duck into the river. I left him with the slowmatch in his hand, all lit and ready.'

'The bloody fool,' said Guthrie angrily. 'Hence he wanted

to have the first mill to himself. I don't suppose he is steering it. How could he steer it, if he's got the match already lit . . .'

He stopped speaking suddenly. In the dark his eyes met and found Jerott's. Then he said, 'If he was going to set the powder off, he should have done it by now. Look how close he is to the bridge.'

Jerott Blyth said something under his breath that no one could hear. Then to Lancelot Plummer he said, very clearly, 'Tell me something. Did he ask you to light the match?'"

'Yes,' said Lancelot, surprised. 'I handed it up to him in the mill. He needed a hand to get aboard because he had to keep the gunpowder dry. Then I came back to you. You remember.' He looked round at them all. 'What is it?'

Guthrie said, 'He needed a hand to get aboard because he was blind. Jerott. Jerott, stop. There is nothing you can do.'

*

The Authie was lower than normal, and the current therefore was a busy one, spinning the mills round and round as well as jarring and tilting them.

It needed a strong stomach to handle the buffeting, and a strong head to keep thinking straight in spite of it. To the six men in the second mill, it had been an experience they were extremely glad to abandon. To the man alone in the first, braced against heaving wood with a burning slow match in his hand, it was a matter of assembling all the senses he had left, in the absence of the vital one just denied him.

Half-way through the work of the evening, the headache had begun to beat through all his senses, tightening into the dizzying whiteness of pain which was part of the most grandiloquent kind of seizure. It had been a gamble with providence, all through the highly satisfactory byplay in the village. The bark of the firing, when even the sound of a cough was hard to put up with, had been the signal for the scintillating distortion, and then the blurring he had been waiting for. And now indeed he was the river, the barque and the oars in a manner more autocratic than the poet could ever have dreamed of.

His task was to drive the mill through the main current up to the bridge, without lodging it on either bank or blocking the second mill which must be following him.

He had hoped to use a plank to steer with, as the others had planned, or even his weight, moved from side to side of the frail wooden building. And if he could see nothing, at least surely he could hear the turmoil of midstream, and sense the quiet of the banks and deep pools he should keep from.

What confounded him there . was the racket of the machinery. It was as if some monstrous milling were already in process: a crop of iron grinding between brazen rollers within walls which boomed and echoed like drumskins, crushing his mind with its violence. (*O mill, what hast thou ground? Precious thy wheat! It is not oats thou hast ground, but blood-red wheat* . . .) And if another such was coming behind him, he could not hear it, any more than he could hear the sound of the water, or the shouts of the soldiers, or the distant rap which was the firing of hackbuts.

There would have been a certain splendour in crashing straight into the bridge, except that he did not wish to be rescued unconscious; and in the river he would be his own master. So he knelt, sliding and swaying, and touched the slowmatch to the fuse, keeping it there for a long time to make sure that it caught. Then he blundered purposefully about, thrown from wall to wall of his vessel until he found the open space of the door.

For a moment he stood there, and as once Philippa had done, forbade his mind to fly to its homing.

A fisherman's voice, heard long ago, returned to him with sudden brilliant clarity:

> *Ta femme sera de la sorte*
> *Dans les parois de ta maison*
> *Comme est une vigne qui porte*
> *Force bons fruicts en la saison.*

Then it seemed that an impatient voice said *'Come!'* So he dropped from the mill, and the cold swirling flow of the Authie received him.

He did not know, as the others running along the banks could see, that he was in the path of the second mill, coming lurching along the surface behind him. He did not know either how short a fuse he had given his gunpowder.

It blew up when he was still very close behind, tossing the river into waves and sending out a wall of heat that struck him in the face. Planks fell. Because the charge was small, the mill did not disintegrate. It did, however, begin to burn

639

with great fury and also to move much more quickly, so that to the men on the bridge, it looked like a fiend from hell rushing roaring and rattling upon them.

They ran for their lives. They were mostly in safety when it struck, exploding the four or five culverin. The mill broke through all the supports, dragging out ropes and chains and flinging into the air the boats which had formed part of its structure. Then, unfurling pure flame from its fragments, the mill paused, swung, and then picking up speed moved on downstream, the river slapping its banks in great copper combers behind it.

The shock sweeping back from the bridge caught the second mill for a moment and stopped it. It danced high on the crests, lifting and falling, and finally began to move forward to collide with the bridge in its turn, collecting a streamer of flame as it did so.

In sailing to the bridge, it overran a great deal of wreckage, among which was Francois de Sevigny, who sensibly had stopped swimming because he was hurt, and because at every stroke his head and shoulders and ribs were flailed with tumbling stone and jerking timber. Nor, of course, could he know where to swim.

> ... *Et tes fils autour de ta table*
> *Arrangez, beaux et verdissants,*
> *Comme la jeunesse agréable*
> *D'un plant d'oliviers fleurissans* ...

The voice stopped.
He was already sinking when the mill struck him.

CHAPTER 8

L'ennemi grand vieil dueil meurt de poison ...
Plus ne sera le grand en faux sommeil,
L'inquietude viendra prendre repoz.

The following day the heatwave broke, and the three squadrons of the English fleet which had been standing off the French coast between St Valery and Etaples, eight miles from Montreuil, raised anchor and, after hovering for some time, sailed off for home.

To Philippa, nearing the end of her voyage to Berwick, the change of weather made little difference. The night before her arrival she had been seized by a terror of such a nature that, unable at last to contain it, she had hammered on the door of Adam's cabin and had spent the rest of the hours of darkness dressed, with Adam sitting beside her and all the tapers in the room blazing and swaying with the heave of the vessel.

Adam, himself terrified by the look on her face, could find nothing to comfort her and finally stayed quiet, giving her the support of his repose and his silence until, in the small hours of the morning, she suddenly said, 'Oh put out the candles! Put out the candles! They are burning me,' and burst into stormy sobbing.

He put them out, and gathered her in his arms and held her, until the dawn showed green through the spray-filmed glass. In the morning, he told Austin that Philippa was unwell, and wished to be alone. Then returning to his own cabin he sat for a long time unseeing; but whatever it was she had received, nothing of it came to him.

For the Scottish Commissioners sailing out of Dieppe, the change of weather came three days too late. The wind which had brought the English fleet to St Valery confronted the small Scottish fleet in mid-channel, both with an enemy and with an adversity of weather they could not circumvent. Already one day out on their long-delayed journey home, they were forced to turn tail and run back to Dieppe, there to hope for such lodgings as the Governor could find them until conditions for their departure improved.

The two vessels carrying the nine Commissioners and their immediate suite entered harbour first, followed by the other ships with their remaining servants, baggage and the horses, and lastly the Governor's escorting squadron. Stepping ashore with her son Culter's hand under her arm, Sybilla observed that the five Commissioners on the other ship had not been so ready to disembark; and then, with growing attention, that the traffic to the *La Barbe* seemed at this moment to be more ingoing than otherwise. She pressed Richard's arm, and with John Erskine, also curious, following them, walked past the tangle of ropes and stacked fish creels to the other ship.

They had just reached her when M. de Fors himself appeared at the top of the gangplank, his short cloak swinging about him, and striding down, put each hand on an arm.

'You are to go to your lodging. Don't go up, I beg you. I have no wish to alarm you, but there is a sickness aboard, and we do not yet know what it is. We shall tell you all we can discover shortly.'

'A sickness? In twenty-four hours?' Richard said sharply. 'Who is ill?'

'Who is not ill?' said the Governor grimly. 'Half the servants who came aboard and all your friends. There are physicians with them now, and once we know what we have to deal with, we shall have them taken ashore. Meantime no one is leaving the ship.'

'If it is the plague,' Sybilla said, 'then we are all a danger to you. We have spent every day of the last weeks together with the others.'

'That I should recognize,' de Fors said. 'It is nothing anyone here has seen before. But Dieppe is a seaport. Who knows what sick air travels from the New World and abides in her wharfs and her timbers? I shall give you what news I can, as soon as I can.'

He would perhaps, have turned away then, but his path was blocked by Lord Seton, newly disembarked from the Culter's ship, the Archbishop behind him. Seton said, 'What's this? Illness? A slight affair?'

'A slight affair, Lord Seton? No,' said M. de Fors soberly. 'I am sorry to tell you that there is not a man among your

642

colleagues there who can rely, as you may, on seeing his homeland again.'

✳

Sick men are rarely lodged in great houses. This time, the Scottish Commissioners were not invited to sleep in the House of Jean Ango or in the Governor's Castle, but were given what rooms could be found in those houses which could offer them food and service, for the servants, least well nourished and more overthrown by their fate, began to die first of all those who had sailed on *La Barbe*.

That was on the third day, when it was known that the mysterious illness was not the pest, but something whose symptoms included a gripping pain in the entrails and a burning fever, so that the victim could neither rest nor contain nourishment but called out for water, incessantly.

Of the five Commissioners on the *Barbe* the oldest succumbed the most quickly. Only the two young men, Fleming and Lord James Stewart, were able to keep on their feet; although Fleming made no other progress and moved from wall to wall of his room, suffering bout and remission without recovery.

The Queen's brother, perhaps more worldly or perhaps simply quicker-witted, had drunk salt water at the first onset of sickness and had hung by his heels from his bed, so they said, vomiting out the infection before it had time to breed in him.

It was true, when he came to see Lord Culter at the small house he shared with Erskine that he was weak; but there was no fever in his brain as he lay back in the tall chair they offered him and said, turning his gaze round them all, 'You do not suppose, do you, that this was an accident?'

He was the first to put into words the thought which had been present in all their minds for three days. No one expressed incredulity or even the mildest surprise. Richard said, 'If it was not, why are we not all ill?'

'Perhaps the cooks on the *Soleil* were honest,' Lord James said. 'Or perhaps those of the Roman faith were exempt from the mandate. Were Reid and Fleming not intended to go on the *Soleil* originally?'

John Erskine said, 'I changed with Fleming at the last moment. I wish I had not. He is at the threshold of life.'

'And you are thirty years older. He has a better chance,' Lord James said.

Richard said, 'Does the theory hold? I was never invited to go on the *Barbe*.'

'No,' said Lord James Fleming. 'But de Sevigny is your brother.'

'Perhaps so,' said Richard curtly. 'But it was he who sent us our only warning. I didn't believe him. I may have been wrong.'

'You know him better than I do. I don't believe he had a hand in this poisoning. I do believe he has thrown his lot in with France, and that the de Guises believe they can probably influence all the Culters through him. I have no doubt,' said James Stewart, 'that this was an attempt to get rid of us; or notably, an attempt to get rid of me. Our return to Dieppe was quite unforeseen. We should have sickened at sea and quite probably died there, without suspicion or remedy.

'I shall live to make them regret it. But Robert Reid will never see his garden at Kinloss bloom again.'

&

Robert Reid, Bishop of Orkney, was brought from his ship to the common room of the house in which he had twenty-four hours still to live. Because he had much gear and no servants, as well as a longing to see the faces of friends about him, he had his bed placed there, with his coffers beneath it, and was able to talk, weakly, when Richard went to see him, and Beaton and John Erskine and finally, Lord James, the best-liked and most respected of all the new generation of his antagonists.

It was Lord James who, shocked at the nature of the room, urged him to have himself taken upstairs but Reid, following his lips, only smiled. 'I am well where I am, so long as I can tarry. Long have you and I, my lord, been in plea for purgatory. I think I shall know before long whether there be such a place or not.' And as Lord James began to speak of religion—'No, my lord—let me alone, for you and I never agreed in our life, and I think we shall not agree now at my death.'

'Will you go home?' Lord James said. 'My lord of Cassillis has asked for it.'

'I am a naturalized Frenchman,' Bishop Reid said, 'or so

they tell me, and the years of my learning in France have not been unhappy ones. Why should this carcass not stay here, instead of stinking a ship on the high seas?'

Then he looked up at the young man, his eyes no longer tranquil, but anxious and angry.

'I go to my God, but my heart is torn at leaving my country. Is Satan loose there? Is it a sin to refrain from striking one's brother for the good of his soul? I tell you, there is no war worse than the war when each man is fighting for Paradise.'

'I do not want war,' Lord James said. 'There are others like me. Be at rest.'

'Then you must teach,' Bishop Reid said. 'Point to history. Remind your people of themselves. Remind them of the city-states, small as we are, who because of their smallness could know one another, and rule wisely, and flourish. It is not enough,' Robert Reid said, 'to offer justice. The laws of men, the laws of God himself are not enough unless you know the heart, the tongue, the brain, the gut of your people. . . . I once heard a man speak, who had understanding, and the promise of vision. He was called the Master of Culter.'

'Francis Crawford of Lymond and Sevigny,' Lord James said. 'You may be right. We shall never know. I have just heard from Paris today. He is in Amiens, and dying.'

There was a pause. Then, 'Do you say?' said Bishop Reid. 'I will pray for him. There breaks a crutch Scotland never knew it possessed.'

❋

The Governor of Dieppe imparted the unfortunate news himself to M. le Maréchal de Sevigny's mother and brother and, a good man, was surprised and distressed when it was the brother, the Earl of Culter, who suddenly covered his face with his hands, while the mother said nothing, but sat like one of Master Cellini's goddesses, her face cast in metal.

M. de Fors said, 'If you desire to go to Amiens, then of course I can have post-horses made available to you whenever you wish it. He lies at the Logis du Roi, and there are friends with him. But you may feel the journey too harrowing.'

Then Sybilla looked at him, and he dropped his eyes, reddening. 'If M. de Sevigny can suffer it,' she said, 'then I suppose we, his family, should not find it beyond us.'

*

They had poured sand on the paving bricks outside the Governor's Palace in Amiens, and it bore stamped upon it the tracks of the many horses and men who had passed that way or lingered, watching since François de Sevigny had been brought there.

The sight of the sand, and the people, told Francis Crawford's family only one thing: that he lived as yet. Because they were not expected, they were hindered at the doors of the red and white towered building and it was Jerott Blyth, striding downstairs to silence the disturbance, who stopped in appalled recognition and then, without asking how they came to be in France, gave, sharply, all the necessary orders for the lodging of their retinue and led them without further delay up the turning staircase inside.

Before a doorway on the second floor he stopped and looked at Sybilla and at Richard, his hand supporting her arm. 'Do you know what to expect?'

'They told us,' Sybilla said, 'that he was wounded, and that they believe the hurt to be mortal. That is all that we know.'

Jerott said, 'It happened a week ago, but he did not recover consciousness, and now never will, they tell us. In time, his heart will stop.'

'You look,' Sybilla said, 'as if you have had no sleep since it happened.'

'The King's physicians are here,' Jerott said. 'He has had the finest . . .' He broke off.

Sybilla said, 'What is it, Jerott?'

And Jerott said, 'He didn't mean to come back, and I brought him.'

Richard said curtly, 'You can't be sure of that. He may live to thank you yet.'

In Jerott's dark, deep-set eyes there was an emotion too profound to give rise to either concord or rebuttal. He said, 'You had better see him,' and opened the door.

The silence of the room flowed out like air from a snowfield.

Not that it was cold. The morning sun filled the wide, pleasant chamber, and through the tall double diamond-

646

paned windows the fretted south wall and spire of the Cathedral stood biscuit-coloured against the blue sky of September. An aproned woman who had been seated in the window embrasure rose as the Dowager entered, and a short, bearded man in black cap and robes left the side table at which he was working and came forward, drying his fingers on a napkin.

Jerott said, 'This is Michel de Nostradamus, who has had the ordering of the sickroom over the past week. The Dowager Lady Culter, Master Nostradamus, and my lord count's brother, the Earl.'

'Lady Culter and I have met,' the astrologer said. He stood, the napkin folded between his hands and looked at them with an expression, oddly, more of anger than sympathy. 'I have no good news to give you. His injuries are great, and he already far on his journey. Do not fear to go close, Madame. There is nothing you can do that will disturb him.'

The high bed on which Francis Crawford lay had no curtains at its foot, so that between the bare pillars there was an uninterrupted view from every place in the room of the virgin sheets and the white, creaseless pillowbere and the coverlet, smooth as fresh-fallen snow on a casket. Sybilla, with Richard behind her, walked to the head and looked down on it.

All the linear delicacy of the boy he had once been stood exposed now in the still, blindfolded face of her son. The clinking yellow hair, orderly on the white linen, was the same silk that had veiled her rings when she had smoothed his pillow in childhood; the cheekbone under the bandage had once, fresh and firm, been pressed to her own; the beautiful hands, lying loose on the damask, belonged to him and also to another man, whom she had placed before all others, and always would.

'And so I am punished,' Sybilla Crawford said aloud, and stood looking, with tears silently running down her colourless cheeks.

Richard said, 'Why are his eyes covered?' and then turning suddenly from the bed, rounded upon the physician standing with Jerott silently at the far end of the room. 'Why are his eyes covered? How can you tell if he is awake or if he is dead? Are you doing nothing for him?'

'Put your hand on his wrist,' Nostradamus said quietly. 'As for the bandage . . .' He glanced at Jerott.

647

But Jerott, his face frowning with sleeplessness, was looking at Richard, this powerful man with the brilliant grey
eyes who had not contemplated bereavement with stoicism
but was rebelling, as Sybilla was not rebelling, against what
he had found. He said, 'He was already ill when he went to
Dourlans. It was why he went.'

'Why?' said Richard. 'I know the face of the drug addict. I
know the face of the drunkard. You cannot tell me that what
I see on the pillow is either of those.'

'No,' said Jerott. 'That is the helpless face of blindness.'

For a long moment, Richard did not speak. Then he said,
'It isn't possible.'

'It is,' Sybilla said. She was holding herself, very carefully,
by the back of a chair. 'It is Nature's way—Nature's most
unforgivable way—of preserving a machine past its break-
ing-point. Tell me . . .'

But although she began it, she could not frame the question she wanted to ask. Jerott said, 'It began eighteen months
ago, Lady Culter. He has tried to end his life twice. Once Archie brought him back. Now I have done the same. We have
interfered in what doesn't concern us. He belongs to himself
and is at his own disposal. Or else what are we?'

Richard Crawford, his brother's wrist in his hand, laid it
down gently and turned to him. 'We are,' he said, 'at least no
less than the animals. We are members of a race, and of a
kingdom, and of a family. The world has borrowed his
strength often enough: can we not lend him ours when he
needs it? What can be done? What is wrong?'

The black-robed doctor answered him, the ruddy, chest-
nut-bearded face full of a curious intelligence. 'There has
been a monstrous loss of blood, my lord, with flesh wounds
and burning. Also there is a hurt to the head. The extent we
cannot tell, but it has brought a stupor so deep that nothing
will rouse him. He cannot move, although what liquids we
give him can be swallowed. We bring him what ease we can.'

Richard said, 'You must engage his will. Does he feel pain?
Do you speak to him? There must be something he would answer to.'

'My lord,' said Nostradamus. 'You have heard. He has
long sought this gateway, and at Dourlans he found it. He is
not going to come back now, for me, for you or for anyone.

This time he has found the boatman, and the boatman has taken him over.'

*

At the end of life, parent and kinsman are as a blind man set to look after a burning lamp.

Because, it seemed, the river was wider than anyone knew, he lived in that way for ten days, in a room always peopled with his friends. Between them Alec and Fergie, Jerott, Archie and Danny covered the twenty-four hours at his bedside, with or without sleep, and every day Sybilla was there.

Afterwards, leaving the silent bedside, she would walk out into the free, scented air and pass under the portals of the cathedral, with its pairs of saintly, confiding figures upon whose heads the blue-grey pigeons roosted, preening their malachite neck-feathers. Within, she would not pray, but moved from place to place under the light-dappled vaults of the ceiling, pausing sometimes beside the busy carvings: the handsome, apple-cheeked burghers with their curling beards and draped hats and shoulder capes, where could be read again the sad tale of John the Baptist: *En prison fut Sainct Jhan decapité, Poir avoir dict et presche verité.*

Even here, people came up to her to ask how Francis did. *A good lord, so brave, so sweet, so very debonair.* She came here not for comfort, but to do penance, for she knew the sin she was paying for; she had watched his love die; she had been constrained, in her fear, to turn his own knife against him at Dieppe and thus simply add to a burden which, in the end, had grown too great to carry.

She was in the ambulatory one day, waiting for Richard to come for her, when a cool, contemptuous voice fell on her ears.

'Are you mourning? Seneca says a wise man lives as long as he ought, not so long as he can. You should be pleased. At last Francis has managed to follow his own misguided path without the rest of us consuming time and energy on setting him right.'

Sybilla turned.

Beside her was the face on the pillow, save that here the eyes were open and clear, the lips rosy, the bright hair drawn out of sight beneath the hood of a travelling cloak.

It was Marthe. The hostile, heavy-lidded eyes gazed at Sybilla, and then altered a little as, stepping forward, Jerott

Blyth's wife caught the older woman under the arm. 'Or, I can see, you have been consuming more strength than you should. Sit down. I have no business with you. I have come to help your son, if I can.'

'And how can you help?' said Richard Crawford from behind her. Marthe looked round. And o for the first time, Richard Crawford stood face to face with his grandfather's daughter.

And before her, with open disdain, Marthe saw the brown-haired Scottish countryman in whom the titles and honours of the first Baron Crawford were now vested. A man who, no doubt, could manage a leech or a ploughman: who kept his fishings and cornfields and coney-runs, but had never touched a pen, or a lute, or a brush; or seen an ikon, or a masque in the making. A man to whom the law had given all that she might have been born to, as much as the half-brother who had taken Güzel from her.

Güzel, who was dead.

Richard said, 'I was told that you looked like my brother.' The colour, sapped from his face by the last week, had receded before the same shock as Sybilla's. With some fortitude, he continued, 'I am glad that you have come, but I am afraid that no help is possible.'

She raised her eyebrows. 'But that, as I was saying, is no matter surely for self-reproach. Let the statemongers mourn him. I hear that John Erskine and the Queen's brother are in Amiens wringing their hands. Soon there will be no Protestants left except pregnant Abbesses. . . . You haven't thought of sending for Philippa?'

Sybilla said, 'She couldn't possibly get here in time. Nor could it help matters under the circumstances.'

'I see,' said Marthe, 'that Austin has edified you also with the circumstances. And what is this other story, of blindness?'

Sybilla said, 'That appears to be true.'

'Perhaps,' said Marthe. 'But I can tell you something interesting. The attacks stopped at Sevigny.'

For a moment, Sybilla was silent. Then she said, 'I think he made a great effort at Sevigny. The affliction afterwards was possibly all the worse for it.'

'Is that all it means to you?' Marthe said. 'To me it means there is no disease. It means it's curable, provided you root out the cause of it. Is it not worth an effort? No one would bring back a man doomed to blindness, but what if he isn't?'

Sybilla's blue gaze on hers was long and steady. 'Then tell me,' she said. 'How would you reverse the process that brought Francis here?'

'I?' said Marthe. 'What have I to do with it? You are his mother.'

Richard said, 'You are raising false hopes. If you could offer my brother paradise upon earth tomorrow, you couldn't tell him so. Do you think we haven't tried to rouse him?'

'But if you could reach him,' Marthe said, 'there might be some arguments he would listen to?'

'If I could reach him,' Sybilla said, 'I could keep him alive.'

They both looked at her, Marthe without astonishment, and Richard with a kind of impatient tenderness. Marthe said, 'I think you can waken him. I think you know you can waken him, but are afraid to attempt it. Am I right?'

'For God's sake,' said Richard. 'What are you saying? She has sat hour after hour, talking aloud by his bedside. There is nothing we haven't tried.'

'No,' Sybilla said, and straightened her back. 'There is one thing. . . . How did you know? There is one thing I haven't tried, because it may not rouse him at all. And whether it does so or not, it may kill him.'

'He is going to die anyway,' Marthe said. 'I can't reach him, you see, as she did.'

'As who did?' said Richard.

The edge returned to Marthe's tone. 'I was brought up by an old crone who read fortunes in Lyon. You met her once. She had certain skills. She is dead now.'

'But he has to be awake,' Sybilla said. Her eyes were on Marthe, but she spoke as if she had not been listening. She added, suddenly, 'You came to me, as soon as you heard about Francis. I told you once, I think, that you would need me.'

'Oh, I do,' said Marthe carelessly. 'If only to persuade my furious husband that I haven't butchered your son by driving his devastating Philippa out of the country. You were right. I should really never have gone back to Jerott. Intolerance drunk is bad enough, but intolerance sober is quite insupportable.'

*

651

The house of opium has many rooms, which may be visited every night after the key is first turned in the lock, and every night after it is withdrawn again.

Behind the last door is oblivion. Standing before it, one can go forwards or backwards; but beside it are not the places of exquisite pleasure: the faces of pure ones confined to pavilions, reclining on green cushions and beautiful carpets amid thornless lote-trees and banana trees, one over another; for these have gone with the smoke of the opium.

What remains, four years afterwards, are the haunted rooms of the departed: of a young, vigorous man with red hair and an old man left in his blood in a bothy; of a henchman dragged from his horse with an arrow in him, and another, darker of skin, dead of fighting in a Greek courtyard. Of a man returning from perilous seas to drown, seeking his son, near his homeland; of a girl dying blind behind yellow silk curtains, and another burning at night in an African pavilion. And a child, a son ... an only son ... playing with shells at the feet of the father who shortly would kill it.

One does not, of set purpose, linger long on such a threshold. Sooner or later, the chains must give way; the accusing, querulous voices cease; and the insistent, imperious summons, saying over and over, *'Aucassins, damoisiax, sire! Ja sui jou li vostre amie, Et vos ne me haés mie!'*

He had almost broken free when the tapers were lit: the tall candles set all round the high bed, their wax soaked with the same mandragora that long ago had burned round another bed where he lay ill, between sleeping and waking, with a black-haired woman bending over him.

The scent, the evocative, insidious scent thickened in the still air of the room. The tapers burned, lighting the watching faces: of mother and brother and sister, of sister's husband and familiar spirit: the staunch servant who was the bridge between the room in the Hôtel Moûtier, Blois, six years before and this silent, night-filled room today at Amiens.

Archie Abernethy walked to the bed and looked down, in greeting, in farewell, in pain, with a strange and searching curiosity at the peace which lay there now in the empty carapace of a being who, like the Athenians, had never known rest himself, nor had allowed others to know it. Then he lifted a taper and walking back, held it out to Sybilla.

She did not, as Archie had done, look down at the tranquillity on the pillow. She took the candle and, thrusting it

forth, touched into flame all the hangings about her son's
bed.

❧

The voices screamed, calling his name. The scented smoke
filled his senses: the brooding presence above him changed
and shifted, now to black hair, now to yellow. Someone,
thinly mocking, said, *'Sleep well.'*

But that was the reality, and this was the dream. Or had
that been one of the nightmare furnishings of his opium,
revisited again and again, and was this real?

In his dream she had stood by the door, her black hair on
her shoulders, mocking him. And he had fought the drugged
tapers with fire.

There was fire close to him now. The sound of it beat
across the voices like a strong wind, obliterating them; the
smell of sweet opiates had been pushed aside by stronger
fumes: the hypersensitive surface of his body, long since lost
to his awareness, recorded for him, hesitatingly again, the
sensation of a dry and hovering heat.

So it was happening now, and the Dame de Doubtance
was waiting for him.

Francis Crawford unclosed his eyes.

The flames were there, like glistening silk, rippling up
through the curtains and canopy about him, red and gold as
the tall swirling fires of a Moroccan sunset.

He had defied her then, and must escape. In his nightmare
he had been wounded, and strapped to the bed. He remembered the pain, as he tried to pull himself to the side.

But that had been only a dream, for now he was not conscious of pain when, summoning his willpower, he ordered
his body to move. Instead, holding him immobile was a
lethargy as unsurmountable as the bonds of his imagination.
He drew a short breath and tried once more, aware again of
a shouting: a clamour of voices that used his name, over and
over, except for one, which simply said, '. . . *damoisiax* . . .
sire!'

And that was the one to whom he must respond. He said,
without sound, '. . . *com me plairoit Se monter povie droit*
. . .' and release came. His hand, moving, caught the edge of
the bed and he turned his head, slowly into the pillow to
follow it. Then, it seemed, of no volition of his own but
brought by many hands, he was unravelled from the high

blazing theatre of his isolation and supported, his head on someone's arm, among the shifting airs and cool shadows deep on the floor.

The last time, as now, there had fallen a sudden quiet. Against a pattern of sounds one did not need to interpret, of struck wood and falling water and the pleasant, domestic hiss of a Russian calidarium he was again in a place of silence and falling darkness. The effort was over.

A branch of candles, thrust to within an inch of his face made him, with reluctance, reopen his eyes. The last time, he had been left alone.

The kneeling woman holding the candlestick was not Oonagh, nor the Lady from the same chamber, the chamber which held his dead. It was a face from another room: the room which held the living well of his torment and which, since he left the waters of the Authie, he had not been made to revisit.

It was the face of Sybilla, with upon it an expression he had never known.

The door to the present stood open. All the dark waters of the well rose and moved, deep and glittering towards him. In grief, in fear, in supplication, in total rejection, Francis Crawford closed his eyes. And Sybilla struck him.

The blows jarred Jerott's pillowing forearm and thighs. The force of them, sweeping open-handed first on one side of her son's face and then on the other was shocking because of the lack of resistance. Even the bloodless skin offered no responding colour. Only the bright head turned and the dark-stained closed eyes were no longer tranquil, but lay below clouded brows, awaiting her pleasure.

Sybilla said, 'Francis. My poltroon son. My sickly son. My poor-spirited runt of a scabbed flock: look at me. If, of course, you have the courage.' And laying down the candlestick, she rose to her feet.

So, when he opened his eyes he had to look up and up, to a face that none of them had ever seen as they stared at her: Marthe who had known her only as a well-bred, quick-witted enemy; Archie who remembered her as the dignified hostess of Midculter; Richard who had known her treat only two men with such harshness, and both of them because they had threatened the security of this, her younger son.

Jerott, his throat rigid, watched Francis look at her and saw Sybilla lower her cold gaze on him, snaring his attention.

654

She said, 'I hear you tried to cut your throat—or was it your wrists?—on another occasion. Your childhood is over now, Marshal. Mankind can survive very well without an intimate study of your susceptibilities but not, unfortunately, without your other functions and talents. Do you think I bring any child into the world to live for himself alone?'

'That is unfair,' Richard said hoarsely. Marthe said nothing. Nor, his black gaze unwinkingly on his master's face, did Archie Abernethy. And Jerott, watching Sybilla, saw that the words did not even reach her, even more than they did Francis, his eyes open still on her face.

She said, 'I am not here to watch you disgrace me. I am here because all the Scots who placed themselves here under your protection are dead or dying. Do you hear me? Robert Reid is dead. Gilbert Cassillis is dead. George Leslie is near his end, and so is James Fleming—of poison, with all their servants. You tossed them a warning, and left them.'

She stood, her pitiless stare raking him. 'Is that your whole measure? To shirk what is difficult? To escape to safety, like a strawberry-preacher, when your friends are in danger? My gentleman: if you run from me now, I will brand you and your sister in France, in Scotland, in Midculter and out of it for what you were: *rotten stock*.'

She spat the words at her son. Archie said, on a breath, 'Careful. Oh, careful, ma'am.'

Jerott said nothing, but regardless of cramp crouched on his heels, the sweat pouring through his dark hair, watching Francis.

The coverlet now would not have been still. His heartbeats ran, light as a watchmaker's wheel in the shallow pulse in his throat, as faint as the fluttering stir of his breathing. His eyes on Sybilla were large and sculptured: it was difficult to believe that for so many days they had been sealed, or that they had ever been spared both sight and suffering.

Sybilla said, 'Do you ever keep your bond? You gave me an oath.'

On Jerott's arm, against his knee there was no movement.

'You don't remember?' Sybilla said. 'No. I don't suppose you do. You begged a favour of me, and once it was granted you had no reason to remember your promise. I will remind you. You said, *"I will promise anything. I will do anything you wish, to the end of my life, if you will tell me the name of the house that you know of."*

What that meant, Jerott did not know. What he saw was total recollection pour, flooding, drowning into the distant face below him, so that Marthe pressed her hand suddenly to her mouth and Richard, stretching forward, took his mother hard by the arm and said, 'Enough. Oh, enough.'

'That is what my two younger children said,' Sybilla said. 'And ran away.' And to Francis, from whom her eyes had never moved. 'Now do you remember?'

His chest lifted, and lifted again with the effort. 'Yes,' he said. Across the room, Archie shut his mouth tight.

'And did you mean to honour your promise?' Sybilla said.

The silence this time was terrible, for he had to gather his breath, as one might try to scrape bucket-water from the almost-dry bed of a river. Then, 'Yes,' he said once again.

'Then I tell you,' Sybilla said, 'that you have no leave to die. Nor have you leave to desert the race you belong to. I want your word that from this moment, you live. You live until no device of priest or leech will hold the web of your body together. And when you walk from this room, you turn your back on France and your face towards the place of your life's work. I want your oath that you will come back to Scotland.'

She halted, but there was no mercy in the blue stare. 'Do I have it?'

Jerott did not see the fight to reply, for his own head was twisted away from it. He heard Sybilla say, 'It is not enough. I must have your spoken word, Francis.'

There was a space, during which, of the five men and women standing or kneeling about Francis Crawford, only one watched him. Then Lymond said clearly, 'On my honour. I promise it.'

Sybilla saw the change in his face before Jerott did. She cried out, and instantly Richard flung open the door. Air, light and movement broke into the room, disrupting the tension. Marthe's husband, set aside by many hands, saw Nostradamus had already gained his place, kneeling, with eau de vie and strong, massaging fingers.

Jerott moved back, his limbs shaking, and watched the man on the floor, the busy heads crowded about him.

His eyes were shut and he was unconscious, but in a manner subtly changed from the death-stupor from which they had roused him. Where there had been peace, now there was endurance.

'He will awake,' said Nostradamus. 'You took a great risk, but he will awake, if that is what you want for him.'

It was then that Jerott turned, and caught sight of Sybilla.

Richard got to her first. She relinquished her full weight, choking, against him. Then Nostradamus with surprising agility made for her, and speaking in a low voice swept her, with Richard beside him, from the chamber.

The door closed.

Archie had gone to stand at the foot of the low pallet where the hospitallers, gently working, were still occupied in bringing Lymond to safety. The other bed, drenched and blackened, stood vacant, its tapers darkened: a monument perhaps, but no longer a bier. Marthe said, her face streaked and silvered with tears, 'I could not have done that. I fear nothing and no one. I respect nothing and no one. But *I could not have done that.*'

'You have done it,' Jerott said. 'It is easy to do it, out of hatred. But you are right. I know of no one else on earth who could have done it out of love.

'It was a miracle, and it partook of the first property of miracles. It should never have been performed.'

CHAPTER 9

Celui qu'aura tant d'honneur et caresses
A son entreé de la Gaule Belgique:
Un temps apres fera tant de rudesses,
Et sera contre à la fleur tant bellique.

For three days, Francis Crawford was helped to establish his
hold upon life, and his door was locked to all but his doctors.

On the fourth day the King entered, his hand on the Dauphin's shoulder, and later the Duke de Guise and his brother
the Cardinal. The King spoke of the truce. The brothers de
Guise spoke of the disease which had so tragically cheated
the Scottish Commissioners of their happy homecoming; and
the Cardinal prayed a little.

After that, he saw no one else until next day, when Sybilla
asked leave to visit her son, and Nostradamus, considering,
granted it.

This time, there was no one else in his room.

They had replaced the burned bed with a better one.
Through its light damask hangings the sun lay tawny upon
the carved headboard against which, cushioned in pillows,
Lymond's fair head and shoulders were resting. In the rosy
light his skin was lucent as mother of pearl: his hair burnished, his robe lightly folded over the bandaging. Only he
was perfectly still, and the trenches round his eyes might
have been quarried there.

She shut the door, and walked to the bed. His gaze on her
did not move, or his lips, or his hands lying loosely before
him. She could not tell if his impassivity covered thought, or
if there was nothing there but a shell, only a few days from
death, and still soaked in the tides of its river.

It was clear that he was not going to speak first so, approaching the end of the bed, Sybilla lifted her hand to touch
the garlanded pillar and said, 'You did not have me shown
from the door.'

He did not answer. It was, after all, self-evidence. Sybilla said, 'I thought perhaps you might remember what happened here five days ago.'

'I do remember,' said Francis Crawford.

The wooden acanthus leaves cut into the palm of her hand. She said, harshly, 'How much do you remember?'

'I remember swearing your oath,' Lymond said. 'I shall repeat it, if you like.'

Bodily, the shell was all that was there. But within it a collected mind stood, facing her. Sybilla said, her voice grating again, 'I know, of course, you would rather be dead.'

He gave it a little thought. 'Yes,' he said. 'I don't suppose you want to be here in this room either.'

She could not speak. After a moment he added, 'You called us both rotten stock. Afterwards, I thought perhaps you didn't mean it.'

Her fingers slid from the pillar and sought, with her other hand, the support of the bed. She said, 'I have no proof of goodwill. I came so that you could attack me, if you wanted.'

'But you loved my father,' he said. 'And Eloise's, of course. What was he like?'

'Like you,' Sybilla said.

'And worth all this?' Lymond said.

'Yes,' said Sybilla. 'Don't you, of all people, know what love can do?'

He did not want to pursue that. The silence lasted a long time. Then Sybilla said, 'Whatever touched your honour, four days ago, has been set right with those who heard it. I wanted you to know that, at least.'

'Including my unwillingness to accept responsibility?' Lymond said.

'Your right to die? They accept that already. It is I,' said Sybilla, 'who do not.'

There was another long silence. Then Lymond said, 'That night . . . It must have been hard for you. Almost as hard as it was for Philippa. You know about that?'

Of all things, she had not expected that. 'Yes,' she said.

'I sometimes wonder,' said Francis Crawford, 'if I only exist to be sacrificed to.'

Her heart beating strongly, she watched him. 'Perhaps,' she said. 'But if you accept sacrifices, you must respond with acts of reparation.'

'I see,' he said. He looked very tired, but not so implacably distant as when she had first seen him. 'In Scotland, for my father's sake?'

'In Scotland,' she agreed. She said, daringly, 'Marthe thinks that the attacks of blindness may be cured.'

'It seems,' said Lymond, 'that concussion may have effected that already. If so, I can fight again.'

'Do you want to?' she said.

A faint surprise lingered for a moment on his face. 'Don't you want me to?' he said, without realizing, apparently, that he had not answered her question.

Sybilla said, 'If there are swords, then I suppose you must wear yours. But it is you we need.'

'*We?*' he said.

'Five hundred thousand people,' said Sybilla.

"You have a high opinion of my swordsmanship,' Lymond said. His lips, in the odd hazy light, curled for a moment, it almost seemed, in the way any one of his friends would have recognized, and she most of all. Then she saw that he was indeed smiling a little.

He said, 'It seems we are not meant to be estranged,' and lifting the weight of his arm, held out his hand.

Then she left the carved wood, and drawn by his fingers, bent to receive his light, firm kiss on her cheek.

She was still close when he said, 'I expect Jerott also is wrestling with his conscience. Tell him, from me, that I assume that Archie has already chastised him sufficiently.'

So, although it was more than she ever dared hope for, it was not the same; and never would be.

⁂

The others, not without misgivings, called to see him next day, and were shown the same self-contained will behind the weakness, or the detachment, that kept him immobile. To his own men he spoke entirely of the future. 'You have heard, I'm sure, what has happened in Dieppe. If money or effort or influence can find where the blame lies I shall do it; but I am well marked, and so are you. If I cannot defeat this family on their own ground I may however be able to make myself felt in dead man's shoes. . . . I am going to Scotland. I know Plummer does not want to leave France, and Jerott's business is here. What of the rest of you?'

They had heard, from Jerott, what he had promised. They knew, but were too cautious to count on it, that the disability of his blindness had not so far recurred. Danny Hislop said, 'It's a moot point, naturally; but which side would we be fighting for?'

'You mean,' said Fergie, 'there are only two sides?'

'It makes it simpler to think so,' said Alec Guthrie. 'In fact, I think we are being asked to fight for a nation. Am I right?'

'Not,' said Danny, 'the Queen Dowager all over again, dear hearts. She may think she's the nation, but you should ask Jamie Arran. Or Jamie Stewart, for that matter.'

'I intend to,' said Lymond. 'I am told he is coming to see me, with Erskine. We tried once before, if you remember, to give Scotland a strong arm and a voice of reason, but Graham Malett destroyed them. There will be others like him.'

'They're all in France,' said Danny positively. 'Friends, I shall be glad to get out of France.'

'I dare say,' said Fergie, 'there'll be need of a lawyer. What about it, Archie? No elephants.'

'You'll not have noticed,' said Archie Abernethy. 'But there havena been any elephants since Stamboul, and I've had that many backsides in my face since, that I've never missed them. I've been in Scotland more lately than any of you. I tell you, there are twenty sides in that fight, never mind two, and when they get tired throwing things at each other, they'll all turn and stamp on the mediator. You'll need me tae panse you.'

'Like Danny,' said Guthrie dryly. 'I am tired of France. And I'm curious.'

'It's curiosity,' said Jerott suddenly, 'isn't it, that's taking you all? Is there a man of belief left among us?'

There was a little pause. Then, 'What if there was?' said Lymond quietly. 'Are you suggesting it should affect his behaviour?'

Jerott Blyth went slowly red. He said, 'Then you don't want my services?'

Lymond said, 'If you please, Jerott, not attitudes. You would leave your business and Marthe?'

'She drove Philippa out of Sevigny,' Jerott said. 'Did you know that?'

The fringed lids dropped over Lymond's eyes. Then he said, 'She probably intended to do something rather different. Do you mean to leave Marthe then?'

'Yes,' said Jerott.

Lymond said, with his gaze still on his hands, 'I can have no one who comes out of pique.' He lifted his eyes.

Jerott said, 'If you never met again, your marriage would stand, in the same way that mine never existed. I won't come running back. When do we go?'

'Now,' Lymond said. 'Before you are stopped, and in the same convoy as the Scottish Commissioners. I shall follow as soon as I can.'

'But if you are stopped?' said Alec Guthrie.

'Assuming that I know what the Commissioners knew? They wouldn't dare,' Lymond said. 'In any case, the secret is out. Some of the Commissioners have survived. All the de Guise family can do is hope that it will be kept quiet to avoid bloodshed.'

Jerott said, 'And the poisonings? These were the first men of their nieces's kingdom. Failing proof, do they get off with murder?'

'Failing proof,' said Fergie Hoddim austerely, 'a body: sorner, overlier or Cardinal can get off with murder, and if ye want to suggest otherwise you'll hae me to contend with. You're tied, unless you want to do the same back and hang for it. He's right. Fight them from Scotland.'

'Thank you, Fergie,' said Lymond. 'I can't think how the Court of Session is meeting, on the grass or on the corn, without you. You will be told when and from where the fleet is leaving. I am ... conscious that you are all giving up money and position in France for this.'

'We only came in the first place,' Danny said, open-eyed, 'because you were coming.'

And Archie Abernethy said, 'Then you'll need someone to pack.'

'To pack,' Lymond said. 'But not to come with me. It seems best . . . I have asked my brother to do that.'

*

Later on the same day he was visited by Lord James Stewart and Mr John Erskine of Dun. To them he said simply that he was returning in due course to Scotland, and that meanwhile his men and his mother would travel home, by their leave, with the Commissioners.

Lord James said, 'You believe you are next on the list for assassination? Or have you been converted by danger to Calvinism?'

'Does it have to be either?' said Lymond.

'No,' said Erskine of Dun. 'Come naked of creed or of kind or even of purpose, but bring with you what Orkney saw, all those years ago. We are too small a nation to be able to spare saints to Rome or Geneva, or any other refugees seeking to glorify either the flesh or the spirit. There is no one to understand us, except ourselves.'

'That I know,' said Francis Crawford.

*

Marthe was the last to see him, when he was not in a bed at all but gorgeously robed in a chair near the window, his crossed heels on a cushion, and his eyes dwelling unthinking on the cathedral.

Marthe said, 'You have chosen Richard to escort you home, and he has agreed. What can possibly have reconciled you to one another?'

'Remorse,' said Lymond. 'Give me lilies in full hands: these gifts at least let me lavish on my descendant's soul. You know that Jerott is leaving you?' He turned his head.

'He has, I suppose, a place in the pattern,' Marthe said. 'If an inadvertent one, like the asp who, in order not to hear enchantments, stops up its ears with its tail. He wept tears of knightly rage when he heard what had happened at Sevigny. It was hardly worth explaining that Philippa's departure was quite accidental. I gave her some good advice, but that was not included in it.'

'So that if there is a pattern, you are not entrusted with it,' Lymond said. 'It might be as well to remember that.'

'It moves from vessel to vessel,' Marthe said. 'You know that very well.' She paused and then said, 'Your mother lied to me. She let me think that you and I were the children of Gavin Crawford and the Dame de Doubtance's daughter. We are only half-related.'

Lymond said, 'We do each other nothing but harm. You know that.'

And Marthe cried at him, suddenly, 'Did I do you harm at Volos?'

He did not need to answer. She bore his level gaze for a short time and then said, with a change of direction equally unexpected, 'You know where she is, don't you? All the time. She does not write, but Adam does.'

663

'You know so much,' Lymond said, 'that it hardly seems worth continuing the conversation.'

She had been sitting, still wearing her cloak, in a chair not far from his own. Now she rose, and kneeling quickly by the chimney-piece said, 'What is this? A bouillon? Shall I bring it?'

'I can control both you and the discussion, Marthe, without bouillon,' Lymond said. 'When Jerott has gone, what will you do?'

She stood up, the bowl in her hands, and looked at him. 'What have you brought back from Dourlans? Something your uncouth family won't know how to handle.'

'You hate them, don't you?' Lymond said. 'How uncouth do you think you appeared to Güzel? Don't crack the bowl. That would be very childish of you.'

And when, her eyes cold, she returned the soup with a thud to the fireplace he added, dryly, *Peut-il naître de cette Agar autres enfants que des Ismaëlites et bâtards?*'

'But for Sybilla . . .' said Marthe harshly.

' . . . I should not be here. I asked you. Where are you going?'

She returned, and stood by her chair. 'To Blois, with Master Nostradamus. He says your convalescence does not now require him. Do you remember the night of the fire?'

'I prefer not to remember it,' Lymond said. In his voice, pleasantly concealed, was a warning.

She ignored it. 'Archie told us what you had described to him of the fire in the Hôtel Moûtier. Nostradamus gave us the drugs for the candles. But when you woke, you were not speaking to Oonagh, were you? You were speaking in French.'

'I don't remember,' Lymond said.

'You were speaking the words addressed by Aucassin to Nicolette. You spoke them also six years ago, after the fire, when my . . . grandmother took you into the House of Doubtance and hid you from the King's men who were hunting you. Do you remember that?'

'What are you asking?' Lymond said. 'Do I still think the Dame de Doubtance is there, watching us from her grave? The answer is yes, I do. And unfortunately, it now seems that I am condemned to spend the rest of my life under her patronage. I find your family, my dear Marthe, much more disturbing than mine.'

'You spoke to her?' Marthe said, her eyes alight. 'You spoke to her on the night of the fire? What did she say?'

He looked at her, his head deep among his cushions, and answered calmly.

> *I geid the gait wes nevir gane*
> *I fand the thing was nevir fund*
> *I saw under ane tree bowane*
> *A lowes man lyand bund.*

'She called me back, that was all.'

'It was not, then, Sybilla's voice,' Marthe said. She was smiling. 'It is not yet finished, then. I thought not. How could it be? How could it be, after all I have done?'

'There is no end,' Lymond said. 'There is no rest. There is no answer. But surely, you are now free of me?'

Beside him, on a low table stood a chess set she remembered. The heavy pieces of rock crystal and silver stood, darkly glimmering below the light of the window, and the fire, seeking them, had placed within each a small tongue of living flame.

She said, 'There are not many pieces now left on the board. Who is your opponent?'

'Myself. Who else?' Lymond said. 'Shall we meet again?'

'No one can tell me,' Marthe said. She was very pale. She walked forward and knelt, swiftly, as she had done before, at the side of his chair, her hand on its arm, her fair upturned face just below his. 'How do you take leave, for all time, of a brother?'

'You wish him well,' Lymond said, 'If that is what is in your mind. And you accept from him his understanding, and his pity, and his fellowship as he is driven, as you are, through the world.' He had not moved.

But, her blue eyes on his face, she did not rise.

> *'Lord, is there nothing in the cup for me?*
> *While you were drinking, I was singing to you.'*

The detachment had gone from his face, but not the strength. He shook his head; and rising, Marthe turned and walked from the room.

*

'And good riddance,' said Archie grimly, from the door of his tent.

'I'm glad you think so,' said Danny Hislop. 'A long sea voyage with Jerott spewing drunk on every deck is not my idea of an adequate quid pro quo. Why the hell has Marthe gone to Blois anyway?'

'To set up business there. The Dame de Doubtance left some things she didn't know about, and she wants to look at them.'

'Jerott said that house was empty,' Danny said.

'I know. There was a wee closet,' Archie said. 'I was telling her, when we were talking on the night of the fire. Mr Crawford was hidden in it. The old lady used it for valuables.'

'Including Mr Crawford,' Danny said. He stared at Archie. 'Why should our dear sister rush off so abruptly to look for a problematical room full of valuables? If they've stayed undiscovered for five years, they won't suddenly disappear now.'

'She's keen on money,' said Archie grimly. 'The uncle was an usurer.'

But that isn't sister's style,' Danny said. 'Sister's style is cool and calm and deliberate. So . . .'

'The doctor's gone with her,' said Archie gloomily.

'Who? Nostradamus?' Danny said. 'I thought he was needed . . .'

'Well, he isna,' said Archie. 'Mr Crawford hasna had a megrim since Dourlans, and that's because of a bang on the heid from a billet, and no thanks to Master Nostradamus. Astrologer! He wouldna so much as keek at the lines on my loof,' said Archie bitterly. 'That's no way to give a man confidence in his future. I offered him my recipe book, even.'

'He probably doesn't keep elephants,' said Danny absently. 'Archie, did Lady Culter know where Marthe was going, and why?'

'No. She left for the coast yesterday,' Archie said, surprised, 'because the litter would take longer than we would. I thought you knew. We're all ready to go except Mr Crawford and his brother, and they'll follow as soon as Mr Crawford is able. Why?'

'Archie, my man,' said Danny, 'I've changed my mind. You're all going, but I'm sailing later as well. There is a little errand I want to run before I leave this banquet of delight, this beadroll of glory, this fair and flourishing country of France. Keep Jerott happy.'

'Aye,' said Archie. "Shall I tell him right away you're at Blois with his wife, or wait until he sets foot in Scotland?' And ducked as Danny, cursing, swiped at him.

＊

About that time, the last of the heat left the fields, and the days began and ended with mist. Finally the rains came, dissolving the two camps and the scarred land between them into mud. In Spain, far from the great theatre of his victories and his blundering son, at half-past two before dawn on a still day in the third week of September Charles V, once King of Spain and Emperor of Germany, ruler of Sicily and the Low Countries, conquerer of Peru and of Mexico, gave up his soul to his God.

Of the brave party of Scots who had come to France seven months before to represent the realm of their Queen at her wedding, four living men sailed from Dieppe with the herald court and their depleted retinue. With them went a fifth, to his burial. And behind, in Dieppe and in Paris, they left one man in the crypt of St Jacques; and two others dying.

Lord Culter did not travel with them, although his mother was taken on board with the help of Archie Abernethy, who in his time had served all the Crawfords. There sailed also, without leave from their camp, three captains who had not come from Scotland in February. M. de Fors, Lieutenant-Governor of the castle of Dieppe and Admiral of the fleet, leaving for Scotland, did not regard it as his business to inform anyone of the circumstance.

At Amiens, two days after they sailed, the Marshal de Sevigny presented himself, with his brother, at the levée hour at the Episcopal Palace.

He had told Alec Guthrie that he was in no danger. Until he saw the manner of his return to Court, Richard would hardly have accepted it. But even on the short walk to the Cathedral they excited attention. Men called to them. The Archers and the gentlemen of the household greeted the comte de Sevigny in ways which conspicuously lapsed from the formal. And in the Audience Chamber the elect, awaiting admission, were openly boisterous.

Watching his brother among them, Culter could pick out the mignons de couchette—the Vidame de Chartres, the Prince of Condé, the Prince de la Roche-sur-Yon—whose interest in Francis Crawford over the years had not been im-

667

personal. And those with whom, presumably, he had shared his campaigns: de Nevers, Saxony, Ferrara, and d'Estrée, the gaunt Gascon whose guns never blew up, or needed vinegar. And the brothers de Guise, the Duke, the Cardinal, the Duke d'Aumale and the rest who did not advance upon him as the others did, but waited, smiling, to congratulate him on his recovery and to suggest, with amusement, the means by which he might add substance to the fair vehicle his body, so cherished by many.

But for that, and M. le comte's extreme delicacy of complexion, one would have said it was a court occasion like any other. And when the doors were thrown open and the King was seen, in his shirt, rising from his prie-Dieu, the open pleasure with which he turned and greeted his returned commander had a significance readily apparent in that court of small, shifting allegiances. Ah, M. Tête de Fer, you have returned to us, fragrant with Tartar musk and peonies, I note, in place of reeking of Egyptiacum. I have been surrounded by invalids—M. de Guise, M. de Ferrara, M. de Bouillon there. You have infected my army.'

He sat down and thrust out a foot. The Duke de Guise, receiving a silken pile from the hands of a gentleman of the chamber, began to draw on the royal hose. The triple tuck of a little tabor, playing a pavane with two recorders in the back of the room, barely disturbed the murmuring quiet.

> Belle qui tiens ma vie
> Captive dans tes yeulx
> Qui m'as l'âme ravie
> D'un soubzris gracieux,
> Viens tost me secourir
> Ou me fauldra mourir . . .

'I have had,' the King said, 'to prohibit skirmishes after your little exploit, or we should have found ourselves, so eager for glory are my commanders, in the thick of a general engagement. So you have lost no opportunities by your absence. Indeed, affairs have moved. The bridge which you destroyed with such superbité may now prove an inconvenience when dispatching our emissaries to Cercamp for peace talks.' He put down the other foot and stood up. M. d'Aumale, holding the royal pourpoint, moved forward.

'I must beg your grace's pardon,' Lymond said. 'The next

bridge I destroy I shall leave fitted with spriggs and spelkin nails, fit for rebuilding. So there is a truce to be made?'

'It seems so,' said the King. He slid his arm through the second ribboned sleeve and waited while the garment was smoothed about him. The fire, scented with rosemary, threw its gentle light on the red and chestnut and gold of the Cordoban hangings and the pavane entered its second verse:

> *Approche donc ma belle,*
> *Approche toy mon bien,*
> *Ne me sois plus rebelle*
> *Puisque mon coeur est tien*
> *Pour mon mal appaiser*
> *Donne moi un braiser.*

'Col de Dieu, you play better than that, mon ami. If you will not take the cremorne, and I know you will not,' said the King, 'have them give you a lute and let us have some music worthy of the name. Yes, I shall soon be disposing of my troublesome Blacksmiths, and the Bishop of Ely and the Earl of Arundel are on their way from England for peace talks. You know them both, as I remember. I shall look to you to give me advice.' He pressed his feet into his velvet slippers and leaned forward to choose his rings.

'May one ask what the terms are likely to be?' Lymond said. He received the lute someone brought him and walking a step or two, adjusted his weight against a gilt and marquetry table and began, his head bent, to tune it softly.

'We shall dictate them,' said the Cardinal of Lorraine, smiling. The firelight, burning on the vermilion robes, lit the golden hair and beard and the kind, light grey eyes. 'The Duke of Savoy, naturally, wishes Piedmont and Nice and Savoy returned to him. The King of Spain wishes to have restored Thionville and the other great towns which have been captured from him. And the English want back Calais and Guînes and the rest of the Pale. They will not receive them, but they have no redress; money is far too short with King Philip. He will return to Spain, the Duke of Savoy to his own business. The Duke of Alva, they tell me, is already licking Flemish boots in the hope of being given the Regency. The war which opened so inauspiciously for us last August with the sad defeat of Saint-Quentin is ending in victory.'

No one dissented. The lute, in an extremely low voice, dictated a brilliant account of a melody Richard Crawford recognized instantly.

> *Margot labourez les vignes*
> *Vignes, vignes, vignolet*
> *Margot labourez les vignes bient tost.*

De Nevers said, 'Perhaps M. de Sevigny has not heard. Fray Carlo de Santo-Hieronimo is dead. King Philip's father. The Queen of England, it seems, is sinking. Even Cardinal Pole has a double quartain ague and is not likely, they say, to survive. As his grace has said, there has been a mortal sickness abroad these past weeks which touches us all."

'And if God were to call the Queen to her account, King Philip would have a new bride to seek,' Lymond said. 'A versatile commodity, death; except for those suffering it. My brother's colleagues at Dieppe were also among the unfortunate.'

As if unrelated to the musician, the song of the lute continued to dance:

> *En revenant de Lorraine*
> *Margot recontray trois capitaines,*
> *Vignes, vignes, vignolet.*

The King's cap was set on his head and, as he stood, his sash, his chain and his Order added, followed by his furred surcoat. He said, 'I made sure, M. de Sevigny, that every Scotsman with a complaining tongue in his throat would come running to you: I am glad to hear that your door has been closed to them. No one regrets the unfortunate sickness of your poor countrymen more than I do. M. de Culter your brother will, I am sure, tell you what trouble we have taken to trace the disease and to help the poor sufferers. My daughter your Queen has been quite overset by it. I hope they will have a happier landfall in their own country, those that now return.' He turned, and receiving a silver goblet of hippocras drank half, quickly, and then touched his lips with the silk napkin offered him by the Cardinal.

'But these are sad affairs, and we must rejoice. The summer is over and we are here in good health, to begin all the pleasures of winter. You shall see, you Russian Scotsman, what we mean in France by the chase. M. de Nemours will challenge you again to ride up the Palais de Justice steps and down them as well: you will beat M. le Vidame at jeu de paume and caress us with your lute and teach the Dauphin—here he is, eager to learn—how to sledge and to slide in the snows, as you did in Muscovy. Do you now long for the winter?'

❧

Ils m'ont salué vilaine
Margot je suis leurs fievres quartaines,
Vignes, vignes, vignolet
Margot labourez les vignes bient tost . . .

. . . said the gay lute; and stopped. 'Forgive me, your grace, but I shall not be at court,' Lymond said.

The King put down his cup, the black eyes glancing at Culter's impassive face and then back to his Marshal again.

'A few days: I can understand. You must recover your strength: you have family business no doubt to discuss. But I require,' said the tres-hault, tres-puissant, tres-vertueux et magnanime Prince Henry, in a voice which did not match the last of his attributes, 'that you should be present for the banquet of the Order on Thursday. And that, M. de Sevigny, is a command.'

Francis Crawford of Lymond and Sevigny laid down the lute. Then walking foward, he knelt very slowly at the King's feet and lifted his head to speak to him.

'Once before, sire, I asked you to accept my honours and you refused them, for France, you said, had need of my services. That time is over. You may hunt without my aid, and M. de Nemours may ride up and down the steps of the Palais de Justice with other companions. I contracted to stay in France for a year, and I have done so. I beg now to be allowed to leave the light of your presence.'

Outside in the courtyard a group of bored noblemen were playing a game of *cheval fondu*. The noise rattled the leaded panes in the windows. Someone spoke in a low voice outside the door.

The King said, 'What do you lack?' I have treated you *en naturel françois*. There is no privilege you have not received from us. Is this to be our recompense?' He gave no sign that M. Crawford should rise.

Lymond said, 'You have honoured me far above my

deserts. You will appoint a Marshal of France and a Chevalier of the Order without difficulty ten times more worthy. My collar and my bâton are both here in the hands of your officers and I now resign the sash into your keeping.'

He slipped it over his head as he spoke and held it between his hands, the green and gold of the Little Order sparkling on it. The King said, 'You have misread the rules of this Order. It is one you resign with your life.'

'Then my life is in your hands,' Lymond said.

In a slow glimmer of vermilion, the Cardinal of Lorraine moved forward a trifle. 'I think,' he said, 'M. le Maréchal should be permitted to stand. His Majesty will recall that he is speaking to a sick man. And perhaps, sire, you would allow me to ask M. de Sevigny what employment he has in mind, that exceeds in honour and consequence that of a liegeman to the Most Christian King of France?'

If it had been possible to continue kneeling, thought Richard grimly, no doubt Francis would have done so. But instead he rose, his manner a little more studied than usual, and said, 'M. le Cardinal is thoughtful.' To the King he said, 'I go, sire, to no other master. My family affairs call me home to Scotland, and I hope to sail there shortly with Lord Culter and, once there, to live privately on my estate.'

No one, in a matter as crucial as this, risked interfering except the family whom it touched most closely. The Duke de Guise gave an easy laugh. 'Sire: may I interpret the Marshal's wishes to you? He desires to command your Majesty's army in Scotland, and knows no other way to set about it.'

Lymond said, 'I wish to command neither the King's army, monseigneur, nor that of the Queen Dowager your sister. My mother, as you have seen, is no longer young, and I have been many years from home. She has asked me to come back and I have agreed.'

'To do what? To spend a lifetime at your sewing?' said the Duke of Guise. 'Your mother already has your excellent brother, M. de Culter here, to look after her concerns. What career is there for a nobleman and a man of honour except war?'

'But the war is ending.' Lymond said. 'A peace between Spain and France will encompass both England and Scotland, I am sure. And if I am to hunt, saving His Majesty's incomparable presence, the hunting is as fine in Scotland as in France.'

'On that score,' said the Duke de Guise, 'monsieur, I beg to differ. Perhaps your wish is to return to your wife and son, although I believe both are in England, not Scotland. Even so, I cannot see what loyalty you would place before His Majesty, what comparison you can make between a nation of sixteen million persons and a country which holds in all its lands no more than the population of Paris. Is that to be henceforth your kingdom?'

'I exchanged Russia for France,' Lymond said.

'And for what will you in time abandon Scotland?' said the Cardinal gently. 'For Fort Coligny in the new world, perhaps, with M. de Villegagnon?'

'Enough,' said the King. His colour, naturally pale, was high above the brushed black beard; under the freshy placed hat with its impeccable tilt. 'We do not cajole. You have chosen to inform us publicly that you are leaving. I shall therefore dismiss you publicly. As you say, there are many valiant men, lovers of France, who are worthy of the Marshal's bâton you are laying down. To one of these, it will be given. As to the Royal Order . . .'

He paused. 'This is not confined, as you know, to knights of France. Your own King bore it once. I wish you to know that you have not served a mean king, although your service has been ended meanly. The Order you may keep, in token of the victories you have won for France, and in the expectation that one day, realizing what you have cast aside, you will return to her. Replace the sash, M. de Sevigny. It is still yours. Your presence in this palace, however, is no longer required.'

He had moved back, away from his retinue. It was surprising therefore that, at the last moment, he held out his ringed hand and that Francis Crawford, after hesitating for a moment, walked forward and, kneeling again, was permitted to kiss it.

They all saw the King's lips move. But not even the brothers de Guise, nearest to their master, heard the words that he spoke.

'*Adieu, mon compère. Dieu vous doint bonne vie et longue.*'

Then Lymond rose and, retreating slowly, performed in silence the triple obeisance due to royalty before he turned and walked swiftly at last from the room, with Richard moving beside him.

They were stopped twice in the antechamber: once by the Prince of Condé, waspishly upbraiding, who ended, his face suddenly clearing, with the remark, 'Well at least, mon cher, if we no longer have your sweet company, I can have Madame Marguerite de St André's undivided attention.'

The second time it was the comte de La Rochefoucauld who slipped from the royal chamber and, pausing beside his former colleague in war, placed a thin packet in his hand. 'Our friend at Onzain wished me to give this to you,' he said. 'I would advise you to read it in privacy.' Then, raising his voice he said, 'I fear you have disappointed us M. le comte. Give our greetings to your sour land and all its sour inhabitants.'

Richard's hand tightened on his belt but Lymond drew him aside and walked on.

Richard said, 'Of course you knew, when you made that promise to Sybilla, that this was what it would mean?'

'So did Sybilla,' said Lymond. 'Do you think she is a novice in the way of courts? It could have been much worse. There are certain safeguards.'

'I am glad you think so,' said Richard, his voice agreeably quiet. 'Because, my dear comte de Sevigny, I think you are about to require them.'

❊

The men at arms who blocked the exit of the former Marshal de Sevigny and his brother from the Episcopal Palace were perfectly polite but quite immune to persuasion. My lord of Culter, with their assistance, was to be escorted to his lodging, there to complete his arrangements to leave Amiens. As for M. de Sevigny, their orders were to convey him elsewhere.

M. de Sevigny, extremely splendid in Shemakha silk and wearing once more the black taffeta cross-sash of the Order showed no sign of alarm. 'Naturally,' he said. 'My time is yours. I have two amendments to make. I go nowhere without my brother. Nor do I move from the palace without an escort supplied by Monseigneur the Cardinal of Lorraine. You may arrange if it you please. If not, I shall do so.'

There was a pause. The sergeant in charge said, 'My lord ... we are carrying out the Cardinal's orders.'

'Then where is your livery?' said Lymond. 'Fine someone of good character who can identify you. Perhaps it would be quickest to ask the Cardinal himself to step into the courtyard?'

It took less than five minutes to have the men at arms publicly established, to Richard's silent admiration. Then, very soon after that, he found himself in a room he did not know, in a building he did not know, with swift footsteps following along the passage. Then the door opened and Charles de Guise, the second, and cleverest and the most dangerous of all the brilliant princes of Lorraine, entered and closed the door.

'M. de Culter,' he said. 'In this court, as no doubt in that of Scotland, there are many eminent noblemen of opposing views who may yet be of great value to the crown if their views are not openly flouted. For that reason, interviews are sometimes best conducted in privacy. What I have to say concerns M. de Sevigny but may be positively harmful if overheard by a third person. I would therefore ask you to have the goodness to withdraw. I shall not detail your brother long. You may wait for him below.'

It was not a day on which Richard was to be allowed a great deal of initiative. He opened his mouth.

'Monseigneur,' Lymond said, 'what you wish to say to me may also be said before my brother. I can vouch for his perfect discretion.'

'I have no doubt,' the Cardinal said. Unlike his monarch, he met resistance with no more than sweet tranquillity. 'But this, M. de Sevigny, touches your honour. Do you wish to continue before the head of your house?'

Richard moved. 'I should take it extremely badly,' Lymond said, 'if after that, my brother felt constrained to leave. You have heard the King dismiss me and I am anxious, monseignuer, to set out for Paris.'

'To pay your last respects, as I suppose, to my niece,' the Cardinal said. 'Both she and my master, M. de Sevigny, are over-lenient towards those who please their fancy. This I am sure you have noted in the years you have spent here during the building of your career. It has always been my duty and that of my brother to prevent either the Queen or his grace the King from having their kindness imposed upon. I speak to the point, as you will see. I wonder if you, or your brother, recognize this ring?'

It lay on the table between them, a heavy gold ring Richard had seen many times on his brother's hand. He kept silent. Lymond said, 'Where did you find this?'

'In the possession of a youth,' the Cardinal said. 'What would you say, my lord of Culter, should be the penalty for impersonating a prince of the church?'

Richard said, 'I think, monseigneur, I should require to know the details.'

'Would you?' said the Cardinal. 'Then you will require to ask your brother. What then, would you say should be the punishment for the concealment of lewd and heretical meetings, and the abetting of those attempting to escape justice after such orgies?'

'I should say,' said Richard, 'that it first requires to be proven.'

'Ah,' said the Cardinal. 'But the proof is not in doubt. And the punishment, one would say, should not be less than the punishment which has already attended those malefactors who have already been brought to justice, despite the impassioned appeal on their behalf put forward by this impudent Scotsman. . . . What is his name, M. de Sevigny? You stayed together in Dieppe, I am told. You even approved the manuscript of the blasphemous articles he has just published against the name and rank of your Queen. Knox, is it not?'

'You have the name correctly,' Lymond said. Richard, staring at him transfixed, saw that there was no surprise on his face; nor indeed any expression other than a hardness about the eyes which matched the Cardinal's own. Lymond added, 'We have never met. I have read his writings, but have not given sanction to them.'

'You have never met? But he claims to be your admirer,' the Cardinal said. 'Certainly, you stayed with the widow Bouchard, his staunch hostess in Dieppe, where you had your first secret meetings with the Protestant lords who came over so boldly as emissaries to my niece's wedding. You may well have attended further meetings of the sect in the rue Marie-Egyptienne in Paris. Certainly, your wife was there. And both of you, with a daring unparalleled, entertained the dregs of the Reformers and their adherents at an occasion in which you took care to involve your innocent Queen.

'You were not a participant in the Protestant processions, M. de Sevigny, but your brother here was. You were on campaign, and it has been clear which of our court has found most favour with you: M. d'Estrée, M. d'Andelot, M. de Fors, the Prince of Condé, the King of Navarre. . . . Do those names surprise you, my lord of Culter? Or have you been able sufficiently to develop your Calvinist sympathies to identify those in this country of France who are about to bring her to ruin? I am told that one-third of the people of this country think as you do. It is my task to uproot these poisoned shoots, to raze the temples and make sweet sewers of heresy. It is also my task to remove from the land any who may set themselves at the head of this devilish army, and lead it further to flout the Lord.'

He picked up the trinket from the desk and turned to Lymond. 'You are such a man. That is your ring. These are your deeds. You have accepted the King's bounty and spat in the face of the Evangile.'

'You surprise my brother,' said Lymond quietly. 'Most of the occurrences you mention came about, as you must know, by pure chance.'

'Was the gathering of Reformers in the presence of your Queen in the Hôtel d'Hercule by pure chance?' the Cardinal asked.

'Yes,' said Lymond. 'In so far as most of them, including my wife, had been invited by Marshal Strozzi.'

'Marshal Strozzi! Why should he trouble to do such a thing?' the Cardinal asked. 'And of course, alas, he is not present to vouch for you.'

'Alas, as you say,' Lymond said. 'His purpose, I am sorry to say, was probably to discredit me.'

'To discredit you! His friend?' said the Cardinal of Lorraine. 'But the quibble is of no importance, so much exists in evidence against you. I have all these papers, M. de Sevigny. They lie locked in my cabinet: evidence against a foreigner who came here and travailed to solicit the love of a King, while working to wrest a people from their salvation.

'Do you know the worst punishment that can befall a man who would take from another his body? I see you do. What, then, would you recommend for a man who purloins the soul of a nation?'

'A hearing,' said Lymond. 'Otherwise you make a martyr of him.'

A trace of colour this time had risen in the Cardinal's pale-skinned face. For a long moment he met the other's gaze, grey to blue; then slowly, he shifted his eyes to the older man. To Richard he said, 'You are fortunate to leave France with your life. Quit this country as soon as you can and do not return. Till your fields and care for your tenants and leave the cultivation of the soul to those who are skilled in the arts. Above all, I suggest that you constrain your brother to do likewise.'

To Lymond he said, 'The King has told you to leave France. It is not for me to darken his mind with the truth of this sojourn of yours, which seemed at the beginning so felicitous. Nor will I dismay those who fought and risked their lives for you. I shall merely add a promise to what his grace the King has already said. You will leave this country of France, not to return. If ever you cross the frontier, you will be brought to me, and I shall place before the ecclesiastical courts the papers I have prepared about you. They will condemn you. And your punishment, I promise you, will do justice to the nature of your error.'

'I should try,' said Lymond, 'equally to rise to the occasion while wearing, I assume, my sash of the Order which may only be relinquished on death. The situation is understood and has, I think, been laboured enough. We may leave?'

'You may leave. I do not,' said the Cardinal, 'wish you to call upon the Reine-Dauphine in Paris.'

'Your pardon. I have already written her requesting an audience, and have her answer granting it. Do you wish me to tell her,' said Lymond, 'that you have rescinded it?'

There was a pause. Then, 'No, M. de Sevigny,' said the Cardinal. 'In that case you may continue with your arrangement to see her. But I would ask you to be very careful, both in your dealings with the Queen's grace, and in your doings when you return to Scotland. I have a long arm.'

'Monseigneur: you have no arm at all,' Lymond said, 'unless England allows you a sleeve for it.'

*

Outside, Lymond said, 'I do not, as it happens, wish to swoon in the public street. There's a tavern.' And after that, did nothing to help except walk, after a fashion, into the private room Richard got for him. Some time after that, he read Willie Grey's letter.

'What was it?' said Richard, who had needed the flagon of wine almost as badly as his brother.

'A warning, from Lord Grey of Wilton. Much along the

lines we have heard. If I don't behave, they'll have me indicted for heresy.'

'But they daren't,' said Richard.

'They daren't,' Lymond agreed. He put away the letter. 'The diatribe we just heard was for your benefit, my Lutheran friend, not for mine.'

'Maybe,' said Richard. 'But they've tried to use poison already. I really don't think we need, do we, to move around like the new moon in the arms of the old quite for ever: they can't try it twice. In any case, who am I running from?'

'Raveand Rhamnusia, Goddes of Dispyte,' said Lymond acidly. 'I am trying to get you home, vide the shiten shepherd and the clene shepe, with your woolly chops spotless. The only drawback to date is that the bloody sheep is going to have to carry the shepherd, so far as I can see.'

But he walked, and suffered no nerve-storms; and next day, by easy stages, he and his brother set off for Paris.

The Cardinal, who saw everything and heard everything, watched them go. Then, calling his secretary, he gave into his care a letter, carefully sealed, addressed to her grace the Countess of Lennox at the castle of Settringham, England.

CHAPTER 10

Le changement sera fort difficile,
Cité, province au change gain fera:
Coeur haut, prudent mis, chassé lui habile,
Mer, terre, peuple son estat changera.

In the comfortable manor house called Flaw Valley, set
among its yards and its gardens in the valley of the Tyne in
northern England, Philippa Somerville lived through September, motionless as a lead suspended in busy waters while her
mother, deeply troubled, watched her in silence.

From France had come back a courtly woman who kissed
but did not throw herself into the arms of her relatives;
whose elegance was beyond anything she had acquired at
Hampton Court or at Greenwich, but whose conscious mind
was as far beyond communication as that of a bird lying
stunned in the reeds.

With her had come Austin Grey, the charming, diffident
boy one remembered from long ago, cosseted by his mother
in the tall old house in the next valley. One supposed, in the
absent years, that some eligible men had been known to pay
court in their fashion to Philippa. Austin Grey treated her
like a sick goddess, and it was painful to watch the carefulness with which she was polite to him. On Austin's side,
there was worship. On Philippa's something one could only
begin to guess at.

One knew something from Adam Blacklock's letters. Six
years before, Philippa's mother Kate had observed Blacklock
among the men of St Mary's: the artist with the long, lean
frame and the halt in one leg who had possessed some insight, she thought, denied to others of that brilliant band.
Since then, he had fought in France and in Russia. She knew,
from some of Philippa's earlier letters, that he was receiving
a captain's pay under the French crown, but that was all.
Then when Philippa's letters had ceased just after Sybilla and

Richard reached France, the first diffident communication had arrived, signed *A. Blacklock*.

It had been no more than a short bulletin of the minor affairs at court in the weeks before the wedding, and conveyed the impression, with some skill, that the news was indirectly from Philippa herself, who was at present too occupied to write to her mother. From it Kate had learned—a piece of news Philippa had not thought to tell her—that Francis Crawford was affianced to a French heiress and would marry her as soon as the Queen's wedding was over, and his own marriage to Philippa had been dissolved. She also knew that Austin Grey was in Paris, a prisoner of war, and that he was said to be a serious suitor of Philippa's.

Then had come the information, embedded in some detail of little consequence, that the French heiress had withdrawn from the prospective marriage, but the annulment was to proceed. And after that, the two letters she would never forget.

In the first, Mr Blacklock had written, *Philippa will shortly be on her way home. Please be understanding. From her long acquaintance with Mr Crawford it seems, has grown something none of us would have wished for her, least of all Lymond himself. He is to continue with the divorce, but she will sail home, much against her will, as soon as the royal wedding is over. She is not a child and her feelings are not superficial, but we see no other solution, nor do Mr Crawford's mother and brother. Lord Allendale will be coming with her.*

And almost immediately after that: *I have to tell you that Philippa and her husband have left Paris and are living at Sevigny. There is now no question of a divorce.*

That was all. No letters followed that, from Blacklock, or from Philippa or even from Sybilla and Richard. The next news she had was from Adam Blacklock in person, standing on her doorsteps with a curious scar on his face, saying, 'Mistress Somerville? Allendale and I have brought Philippa home.'

One did not ask questions then of this self-contained, exhausted creature. One installed her in the bedroom she had known from childhood, and entertained, as best one could, the two men who had brought her, with such trouble, all the way from France. Then, when Austin had left for his home, one was able to turn to the man Blacklock and say, more viperishly than perhaps one had intended, 'All I gathered from that is that Francis Crawford is a raging harlot, and I am only doubtfully adequate to touch the hem of my daughter's extremely expensive farthingale. I look to you to tell me what has happened.'

And Adam, confronting the sharp brown eyes of the small, untidy, vivid person he remembered all those years ago from the days of St Mary's, had answered, 'I don't know. All I can tell you is that, superficially, Francis was offered the rank of Marshal of France and took it, leaving Philippa at Sevigny. And that she then left for Paris, and asked Allendale to bring her home.'

'And a little deeper than superficially?' Kate had said.

Then he had had to say, 'I don't understand what Allendale is implying. He knows something, I think, that Philippa has not told any of us. What I have found out is difficult enough to put into words.'

'Can I guess?' had said Kate abruptly. 'She learned her affection was not adequately returned? No? Then, she was deliberately led to believe that it was not adequately returned?'

'I think that was true,' Adam said. 'For a long time.'

'But not at Sevigny?'

'No,' said Adam. 'I saw them at Sevigny.' He stopped and then said, without looking at Philippa's mother, 'As the pen needs the penknife, they are made for one another. And they know it.'

He could feel how still she had become. 'But . . . ?' said Kate.

'But it is of the spirit only,' Adam said.

The width of her surprise, it seemed, filled all the room. 'Why? Why?' said Kate. And then, 'No. Of course, it is not fair of me to ask you. But what then was Austin . . . ? No, you didn't know that either.' Staring at him, her sunburned brow was lined in her perplexity. 'Then why did they part?'

He had known he was going to be asked that question. He answered it with the truth. 'Because Francis could not support it,' he said.

*

For more than three weeks Adam Blacklock stayed at Flaw Valleys, and during that time was sometimes the only company Kate had, for Philippa seemed to find the society of others for many days quite beyond her.

It was strange for Kate, after eight years of widowhood, to have another likeminded human being waiting, quietly, to be talked to and to give advice when she wanted it. In fact, she did not realize how much of the past they shared, until the first morning after his arrival she knocked on his door, and taking in the small offering of food and drink she had prepared for him, had seen his eyes widen at the sight of her companion.

'Ah,' said Kate, 'late night, you were too late to meet each other. Master Blacklock, this is Khaireddin Crawford. He prefers to be called Kuzúm.'

'And I prefer to be called Adam,' Blacklock said. He held out his hand. 'I know your father.'

Kazúm, his yellow hair brushed for the occasion, returned the handshake cordially. 'He rides horses very well. I expect you ride horses very well too. Were you in Russia?'

'Yes,' said Adam. 'He rode on sledges in Russia. He was very good at that as well.'

'We tried to ride on sledges last winter,' Kuzúm said. 'But I was only six, so I didn't get on very well. I'm going to see Fippy. You brought her home, didn't you? She isn't my mother, you know.'

'I know,' said Adam. His throat was aching.

'Aunt Kate says she is going to cry,' Kuzúm said, gazing at him with those very blue eyes. 'And I am not to mind, because it is only because she is a girl, and tired after her journey. Men don't cry.'

'Don't they?' said Adam.

'Well, only sometimes. I broke my arm once, in the apple orchard. My father doesn't cry.'

'No,' said Adam.

*

On the third day when, for once, she had let Kuzúm out of her sight, Philippa said to her mother, 'What has Adam told you?'

At last, Kate sat down, and then got up again because it was a good chair, and she had butter on her skirt. 'He was very discreet,' she said. 'But I think I gathered that you have a fine marriage but not a complete one.'

'That *was* discreet,' said Philippa. 'And what did Austin say?'

'Austin was biased,' said Kate firmly. 'You know he has called twice a day?'

'I shall see him tomorrow,' Philippa said, as she had said for three days. 'In any case, what did he say, including the bias?'

'It partook,' said Kate, 'of the nature of a full-scale cursing against one Crawford of Lymond, but whether for sins of omission or commission is not entirely clear. You wouldn't like to clear up the point?'

'No,' said Philippa. 'If you don't mind.'

'I do,' said Kate. 'I don't care to have my second-best bedroom looking like the den of a hibernating bear. In fact, I am beginning to feel like the gentleman who killed his sister with his bare hands for weeping for a private loss on a day of public rejoicing. What is wrong?'

'I don't know,' Philippa said. "I have to know what is happening.'

'And you know what is happening, shut up in this room?' Kate said. And knew, As soon as the words left her lips that, of course, she had hit on the truth.

'Yes,' said Philippa. 'On the ship . . .'

'Adam told me that you were upset on the ship. You thought that Francis was in trouble?' said Kate.

'I thought he was dead,' Philippa said. 'You see, I released him to do as he wished.'

'I see,' said Kate slowly. She sat down, the butter forgotten. 'And this is why you are waiting?'

'Yes,' said Philippa.

Kate said, 'Philippa. What frightened you? Why couldn't this be a complete marriage?'

But Philippa's eyes, the candid brown eyes she would have trusted to tell the truth, however unpalatable, would not look at her, and her daughter turned her head, shaking it. Then Kate said, equally gently, 'Then why hold to the marriage, my darling? Why not obtain your divorce and release him and yourself in that way?'

The silence this time continued for a very long time, so that she could hear the new kitchen maid break a bowl, and the puppy bark, and the high, clear piping of Kuzúm's voice, speaking to Adam. Then Philippa said, 'Because the grounds for the divorce were to be lack of consummation.'

And then she turned her face so that her dark circled eyes

locked with Kate's and Kate, pale herself, was wise enough this time not to ask any more.

After that, the only really unbearable incident happened in the third week, when Philippa had begun to join them, very quietly, in the main part of the house and to stop the habit, so disconcerting both in herself and Adam, of thinking and speaking primarily in an idiomatic French which drove Kate to irritable despair.

By then, also, she had begun occasionally to entertain Austin, if only, Kate thought, to show some helpless return for the gifts of sweetmeats and flowers, of fruit and music and little, bound books which arrived daily and, it seemed, sometimes hourly from the next valley.

Only that night he excelled himself, and sent musicians.

Kate, more than warned by the barking of all the dogs far up the road, had already sent her steward to investigate and then dispatched a swift, conciliatory message round all the servants' quarters before tapping on her daughter's door and saying, 'Philippa? Don't undress in front of the candles: there's an oboe in the flowerbed.'

In fact, there were also two recorders, a rebec and a cittern, sadly flattening her marigolds; and something else made Kate, peering unseen out of the window in company with her daughter, moan with silent apprehension. 'You remember the hombull bee who handyld the horne pype, for ham fyngers wer small? He's sent a cremorne, darling. The dogs will never stand for it.'

'I think we should send them away,' Philippa said. Her hand, from the first moment, had detained her mother and had not released her since.

'I think so too,' said Kate. 'After the first offering, anyway. Open the casement and lean out, glowing. All they want to do is report to Austin that you listened to them without apparently having a seizure.' Adam tapped on the door, made an inquiry and, reassured, returned to his room. To a chorus of resonant barking, the instruments proceeded to adjust themselves into tune. A billy-goat, alarmed, aroused his harem, and distantly a muffled lowing broke out.

Philippa said, 'Oh dear. It must have cost a fortune. Did Gideon ever do this to you?'

Kate thought. 'No, but I did it to him. He hadn't called to see me for a week, so I sent eight bell ringers to serenade him

685

at cock-crow and his mother's parrot dropped dead, quoting Luther.'

'What did it say?' Philippa said. Sitting on the sill, with her long brown hair falling over her night robe, she looked, in the darkness, like the daughter who had come back from Turkey: calm and smiling and soignée.

'Music is a fair and lovely gift of God, and deserves to be extolled as the mistress and governess of the feelings of the human heart,' said Kate, surprised. The sound of Philippa laughing mingled with the first notes of the consort below, the cremorne snoring manfully among the rest of its brethren:

> *Tant que je vive, mon cueur ne changera*
> *Pour nulle vivante, tant soit elle bonne ou saige*
> *Forte et puissante, riche de hault lignaige*
> *Mon chois est fait, aultre ne se fera.*

'No!' said Philippa. 'No! No! No! No! No!'

The casement slammed on the wood, breaking the glass. And Philippa, her hands rammed over her ears, fled gasping from the window and crouched, her sobs rising in pitch against the bed while Kate, her breath stopped, dragged the hangings over the window and finding the bed knelt and hugged her, suppressing the noise with her closeness.

They were like that when Adam, running, found them and left, without words, to stride downstairs and tell the prayers, surprised and more than little displeased, to remove themselves. He gave them all the money he had, and excuses. Then, slowly, he went back into the house and stayed in his room until all was quiet.

Much later Kate, looking very tired, scratched at his door. 'She's sleeping,' she said.

He looked at her over the candlelight, and the flame stood in both pairs of eyes. 'It can't go on. Poor Austin,' he said.

'Yes,' said Kate. 'Thank you, Adam, for what you did.'

He bowed his head a little. She gave him a small smile and then moved slowly out of his sight, with the light of the candles.

*

Upon them, in the first week of October came Sybilla, with Jerott and Archie, on her way home at last to Midculter.

They were within sight of the tall rose-red chimneys of Flaw Valleys, the short cavalcade bobbing behind them of servants and laden baggage mules in the familiar housings and liveries of azure and silver, when Sybilla put her hand on Jerott's arm and said, 'Help me down. I think she is coming.'

So she was standing, with Jerott beside her on the dusty slope of the hill, when the long-haired girl flying towards them came nearer, and slowing, walked until she was close enough for the travellers to see that this was indeed Philippa. Then Sybilla spread her hands and called, her clear voice spanning the distance between them, 'He is safe.... He is safe.' And the next moment, Philippa was there, and she was holding her.

❋

One phrase upon which, as it turned out, the welcome of three wayfarers could be fuelled until at length, restored and refreshed, Sybilla could sit in Kate's parlour and looking at the sober faces about her say, 'You have been forbearing enough. Ask your questions. Jerott will have told you that Mr Guthrie and Mr Hoddim have gone to the keep at St Mary's. Master Hislop is to sail later. My two sons are also in France.'

'Together?' said Adam.

'Together,' said Sybilla. She turned her wise eyes. 'Philippa. You gave your husband a brevet to absent himself from his responsibilities. I have cancelled it.'

Adam looked at Jerott and then at Archie but neither, it seemed, was willing to meet his eyes. Philippa said, 'He was ill.'

'He was dying,' said Jerott Blyth, his hollow eyes still on his hands. 'Lady Culter persuaded him not to give up.'

'In September?' said Philippa. 'On a Monday? On a Monday in September?'

Archie was looking at her. 'Yes,' said Sybilla. 'It reached you, then. And you think me wrong, perhaps, as Jerott does. But it seemed to me that he has work to do which was not finished yet. Once, he made me a promise to do anything, to the end of his life, that I asked him. I held him to it.'

'And?' said Adam. Philippa was staring, her pupils enormous, at Lady Culter.

'I made him promise to live,' Sybilla said. 'And to come back to Scotland.'

'I think,' said Philippa, 'you have made it very hard for him.'

Kate said, 'Philippa, you have been waiting for four weeks with your heart in your eyes, to hear whether he is alive.'

'I know,' said Philippa. 'Do you think I want this for myself?'

'He is one of many good men,' Sybilla said. 'Would you put him first? Of if he has work to do, should he not do it? He is not blind: they say because of a blow on the head. But I think that, for some reason, he no longer needs his headaches.'

'Or doesn't care enough,' Philippa said, without timbre. 'Lady Culter, why can't he stay in France?'

Jerott said, 'The de Guises can't afford to keep him in France. He went out of his way to become a popular idol. You saw him.'

'He had, I think, a reason,' Sybilla said. 'And then when the reason no longer mattered, it was too late. The effect stands. He cannot stay in France. And Russia is closed to him. The Tsar has changed to other favourites and the woman he lived with is dead.'

'*Güzel?*' said Philippa. After a moment she said, 'Does he know?'

'My God, he knows,' said Jerott Blyth. 'It drove him to . . .'

'. . . I don't think,' said the soft voice of Archie, cutting across, 'that yon incident has any bearing. Mr Blacklock won't have heard about the Commissioners.'

'They're landing in Montrose,' said Adam. 'Aren't they?'

'Some of them,' Jerott said. 'Four of them won't land anywhere any more. Someone, somewhere must have got to know that Queen Mary's secret bond had become known to us. They tried to poison all the Commissioners at Dieppe, as they were sailing.'

'Who? Not Richard?' said Kate.

'No. Francis is keeping Richard with him, for safety. Orkney and Cassillis are dead; Rothes and Fleming probably dying. And most of their servants. Nothing can be proved and no one accused, but four men have gone who won't trouble France any longer.'

'I don't understand,' Kate said. 'Were they so dangerous that France had to poison them?'

Adam said, 'The fewer leaders we have, the better France will be suited. But there is a second reason. Will you add yet another state secret to all those with which Francis must have entrusted you? The Queen of Scotland has signed three bonds, arranged with her uncles of Guise, by which Scotland is to belong to France if she dies childless. The Commissioners were told of it by Francis. To make it public would have meant civil war, or an annihilating struggle with France. So they took Lymond's advice, which was to do nothing meantime. He also warned them to hold their tongues, for their lives.'

'I had a warning through Willie Grey,' Philippa said. 'I passed it to Francis, but I didn't know what it was. I think Lord Seton perhaps was indiscreet.'

'I see,' said Sybilla. 'A friend of England, and a friend of the Lennoxes. It isn't unlikely. Do you agree, Philippa, that the world has need of her men of judgement? We cannot belong to ourselves, or to one person only.'

Adam said, 'When is Francis coming?'

'He and Richard should sail in a few days.'

'And ride to Midculter?' said Philippa.

'To his own house of St Mary's,' Sybilla said. 'I need not tell you. Unless matters change, you should not meet.'

She left with Jerott next day, leaving Archie, as so often before at Flaw Valleys, and carrying with her Kuzúm, her cherished grandson. To Philippa, and to Kate, it was as if the windows had darkened.

Before they left, Philippa found Jerott alone and asked him for news of his wife.

'I thought you knew,' Jerott said. 'She's gone to her house in Blois. We are tied, I suppose, but the marriage is over. It should never have happened. She drove you out of Sevigny. But for that . . .'

'What would it have changed?' Philippa said. 'And she didn't drive me, Jerott. I left to save Francis from trying to join me. She came to Sevigny to persuade me to take him back.'

Jerott said, 'He chose you, and it seems you are not made as other women. He was true to you—do you know that? Everything he did, good or bad, was for your sake only.'

'I know,' said Philippa. 'I know. I gave him his release and his mother has snapped shut the fetters again. What am I to do? I cannot even go myself without leaving him to bear the burden of it.'

There were no tears in her empty face. All the rage in Jerott died, and the contempt, and the bitter anxiety.

You don't know what love is, either of you. And God help us and you, if you ever find out.

He said, 'I believe it is out of our hands, and his as well. I think we must wait till he comes. Then perhaps we shall be shown what to do.'

✳

On the fourth of October Francis Crawford of Lymond, comte de Sevigny, Chevalier of the Order, left France to return as he had promised to his own country.

Before he sailed he was received by his young Queen in Paris, and laid before her the guerdon she had given him long ago, when he saved her from death. He said, 'I have to leave, your grace, to look after the affairs of my family. I return you the glove, for my allegiance henceforth is to Scotland.'

Seated before him in her small cap and her stiff, high-necked gown she was not at all pleased. 'The two countries are the same, M. de Sevigny. It is we and our marriage who have made this possible. We do not understand why you have to leave. Is it to follow Mme la comtesse, who left us so abruptly?'

He did not reply to that. Instead, 'What causes you to think, madame, that the two countries are one?' Lymond said. 'Does it seem so from here? It is not the common impression in Scotland.'

'Among the heretics, perhaps not,' Mary said. 'But my people want union. They begged for it, at Haddington. They have accepted naturalization. They have agreed that my children should rule them. They have made Monseigneur my husband their King. Do the Three Estates count for nothing?'

'They have agreed,' Lymond said, 'that the Dauphine should be King during your lifetime. But after your death, which please God will be long distant, there is no man in Scotland, of the established church or the new one, who would agree to the rule of a Frenchman.'

'I do not believe it,' said Mary. 'Would the faithful suffer a king or a regent who professed heresy? Would they consent to be ruled by a heretic queen from over their borders? These are the alternatives, M. de Sevigny. I am surprised you do not see them.'

'If a Brazilian dancer came to you in his paint,' Lymond said, 'and proved to you that he was a true Catholic, and appointed a judge in his country, would you allow him to condemn and burn your heretic brother?'

'You are saying,' Mary said, 'that the ties of the blood are more important than the state of the soul?'

'I am saying,' Lymond said, 'that the bond of race is a deep one, and of a dimension which gives it nobility. I am saying that the salvation of each man's soul lies within himself, and is not a matter which concerns even his brother.'

'So,' said Mary, 'you would condemn the human race to hell, for want of enlightenment?'

'Why not?' said Francis Crawford. 'It has nothing to fear, surely, from hell.'

*

He saw that day many people in Paris, from Mary Fleming to Madame de Valentinois; from the King's sister to Madame la Maréchale de St André. He saw Nicolas de Nicolay and, last of all, the Queen of France, who made him sit by her, the goitrous eyes smiling, and said, 'You are to leave for Scotland? I hear a curious rumour, that a number of other Scottish gentlemen have also broken camp at Amiens for that purpose. I suppose now our sister of Scotland may expect many stout arms to help her in Edinburgh?'

The blue eyes of M. de Sevigny, turned upon her, were perfectly calm. 'I return for family reasons,' he said. 'With peace now certain, I trust there will be no need for armies.'

'And if there were?' Catherine de Médicis said. 'Perhaps we might tempt you back to France.'

Lymond smiled. 'I have been told that might be unwise.'

'By whom? By the King?' said Queen Catherine. 'You must not listen to the threats of underlings. I hear my Nostradamus healed you well.'

'I was grateful,' Lymond said, 'for his services.'

'I see, however, little value from them in other directions. He was unable to save your unlucky compatriots.'

'There is a saying,' Lymond said, *'Mal sur mal ne font pas santé.* There is no purpose served in having a few deaths followed by many. But the results of this blow will be felt in France and in Scotland. Sometimes, when there is good warning of the obstacle, the ship may be steered round it.'

'You are more hopeful, M. de Sevigny, than I should be. I shall watch you,' said the Queen. 'You were well thought of by my late cousin ... by both my cousins. The Marshal Strozzi in his will left me his library. I have set aside from it three manuscripts I wish you to take to Scotland. Perhaps, if you will not keep the guerdon of the Reine-Dauphine my daughter, you will accept a gift of simple goodwill from me?"

'I am honoured,' said Lymond.

'It is no more than you deserve. We shall miss you. Now you may take your leave. I shall ask Mistress d'Albon to guide you.'

He bowed at the doors, and when they were closed, stood until Catherine d'Albon joined him. 'You are leaving,' she said.

She had not changed, except perhaps in a firming of the contours of her face, and a little exaggeration in her colouring which had not been there before.

Lymond said, 'I am riding to Dieppe with my brother. We should be there on Tuesday.'

'You should take longer,' she said, 'They say you have been gravely ill. I can see it.'

'We go slowly,' said Lymond. He did not avoid her eyes. 'If I had come to you that night in the Hôtel d'Hercule, none of this would have happened.'

'One thinks of these things,' Catherine said. 'If you had not spoken harshly to your mother, Madame de Sevigny would not have gone to your room. If you had not wanted a divorce, you would not have stayed in France. . . . Why did you accept your marriage in the end, and then break it? They say you are fickle.'

'And you are not. You withdrew because of Philippa, am I not right? Then you might like to know that if you made a sacrifice, it was not in vain.'

'Then you are going to join her?' Catherine said.

'No,' Lymond said. 'I don't expect to see her again. But I shall never marry again, nor I think will she. I hope you will find one day what we had. Even if it lasts only an hour, it is worth it.'

'I am glad then,' said Catherine, 'that there was nothing between us, rather than mediocrity.'

And from the hornes . . . of Unicornes . . .

'There was kindness,' he said. 'And that was a great deal.' Then he kissed her hand and left, to find his brother.

*

The journey to Dieppe, as he had said, was slow, because he was not strong. He did not speak much as they travelled and in the evenings he retired early to his tavern room, although this was difficult, as everywhere they went he was recognized. He wrote, Richard saw, a great many letters, some of them to familiar addresses: to Lord Grey at Onzain; to Nicholas Applegarth at Sevigny. To Gravelines on behalf of a man called Harry Palmer, who had died. Nearly every day, also, there was a call to make, or several, upon friends on the way. For a total of many years now, one realized, France had been Lymond's home.

And the weather was kindly on this last journey north: the trees hardly tinged yet with russet, and meadowsweet and white columbine in the meadows where sun-gilded cattle grazed.

In place of the bitter wildness of winter, the mellow ripeness of autumn moved past them. In the townships there were full blown roses still, and vines on the trellis, and white geese, and sunflowers, and the pallid blue velvet of cabbages. Ploughed fields, and slender stemmed trees with their leaves embroidered sharp on the skyline. The latticed pattern of wood stacks, and the slow stride and swift trot of water. Crows, and hay barns, and a bank of bracken like chiffon against the low sun. A farm with a dovecote, and hens and dogs and hives and sheets on a line; the weeping arrows of willows. An orchard of apples, jade as the rose window of the Sainte Chapelle, past which he had escaped on his way to the Hôtel des Sphères.

The pretty house in the rue de la Cerisaye, now quite gone. The empty, ruined old house in Lyon. The graves of two old women; and a strong and vigorous man; and an old and vicious one. A sister lost, a lover lost, an escutcheon taken from him, and two nations he had made temporarily his own. And Philippa.

At Dieppe, the captain at the gate greeted them, and Richard, his attention attracted at last by the sheer exhaustion in his brother's face, was reminded of the last time Francis must have made this identical journey, and wondered if he remembered it.

693

M. de Fors was still in Scotland, so they were received in his absence by one of his lieutenants, who gave them a bed for the night, and next day saw that their luggage, their servants and their horses were safely loaded on the *Réal*. Richard stayed on deck to watch the steep white-pleated cliffs sink into the sea, but Francis had gone below, and did not return.

Richard left him alone. By her own curious alchemy Sybilla had obtained what all these years he had desired of his brother. He was on his way home, to fulfil the duties of rank and family; to bring his talents at last back to Scotland. Whatever had caused the quarrel with Sybilla, it seemed to be over. Whatever had made him long to leave Europe and return to Russia had vanished also. He was still married to Philippa, and Philippa was only a ride away, on the English side of the Border. Perhaps that would mend itself also.

It was hard to say therefore why he did not go below, and rally his brother, and encourage him to let the past fade, and look forward to what lay before him. Unless, in his heart of hearts he recognized as Lymond did that what lay around him were shut gates; and what lay before him was nothing.

CHAPTER 11

Coq verra l'Aigle, l'aesle mal accompli
Par Lyon mise sera en extremité

Up the twisting stairs of the house called Doubtance in the rue des Papegaults, Blois, the dusty rooms were little more habitable then they had been a year before when Philippa, helped by Nicholas Applegarth, had searched them.

The sparse furniture Marthe had brought stood untended against the peeled stucco, and the clocks, the instruments, the ancient artefacts of her business lay unopened still in their cases. So it was a simple matter, watched by the short, bearded figure of Nostradamus, for Marthe to push aside the single chair in the room once occupied by her grandmother, and probing with her long fingers along the wainscoting, to press the boss Archie Abernethy had told her of, which opened the way to the treasure house.

At first, it stuck. Marthe had to push with both hands, disregarding the smears on her gown, to force back the thick sliding door in the panelling, and then to stop and take time to light a lamp, before she could step into the small hidden room in which the Dame de Doubtance had kept the cream of her collection and once, Francis Crawford.

So finely had the wood fitted that only a light film of dust dimmed the objects which lay stacked on the shelves, or spilled from the caskets stored in the little dark cabinet. The yellow of ivory smiled at her, delicately wrought on its plinth, and the glint of thick, opaque jewellery, and the gleam of rich tissue, a trifle disturbed from its wrappings. A marble cupid gazed at her over his shoulder, and a visage much older, with arched, spidery brows and bent finger.

It was that face she moved towards, her neck bent and her yellow hair brushing the ceiling; and for a moment knelt before, looking. From the doorway the sonorous Jewish voice said, 'Was she like that?'

695

'Yes,' said Marthe. 'She was more beautiful.' And then, turning, followed the slender, bent finger to its destination.

And there on the floor was a little casket, as old as the ikon and painted like it in deep, vibrant colours in which the blue-shadowed angled heads and long faces followed each other in silence from panel to panel.

The heavy lid was not locked. Inside it, as she had expected, was a thin roll of parchment, bound in blue silk and sealed with the pheon and phoenix of Culter. She lifted it out, and a voice from the doorway said, 'I doubt, Mistress Marthe, if birth or any other sanction gives you authority to read that particular document. Why not let me have it? I'm a very good friend of the owner.'

It was the little sandy-haired Scotsman who had followed her to the rue de Marie-Egyptienne, and had then brought Lady Culter to plague her. Handing his way courteously past the astrologer, Danny Hislop stood in the doorway to the treasure chamber.

The parchment cracked in her clenched hand. She could not even stand fully upright. Marthe said, 'This is no business of yours. Get out of my house.'

'I'm sorry. A wholly vulgar reaction,' said Danny Hislop. 'I'll give you another, in two syllables, if you press me. It isn't your house, nor are any of the objects within it. They belong to Lymond.'

'Then bring him in,' Marthe said. 'And I will give them to him.'

The pale, clever eyes turned up. Their owner quoted Surrey at her. *'And of ech thought a dout doth growe/Now he comes, will he come? alas, no, no! ...*

'On the other hand,' said Danny Hislop, 'I can take it to him.'

He moved backwards as she advanced and stepped into the daylight, leaving the lamp set behind her. 'Do you know what it is?' said Marthe softly. Master Nostradamus, his back to the window, had said nothing.

'Lyk an aspen leef he quook,' said Danny defensively. 'Don't tell me! A little knock with a wakener? A knife for the shoulderblades?'

'Oh come, Mr Hislop,' said Marthe. 'You knew from the beginning at Lyon that Philippa was hunting for some papers exposing the Crawford family. They came to light in Paris and she and Francis suppressed them. Lord Allendale told me he thought there was another copy, and here it is.'

'Forgive my lack of surprise,' Danny said. 'It is, I assume, a document certifying the poor bastard's bastardy, if I may so refer to your brother. Since he's on his way home, there seems little point in flourishing it now. I can either take it to him, or help you burn it.'

'I am sure,' said Michael Nostradamus, 'that Mistress Marthe does not mean to dismiss any course of action that seems reasonable. But it might be sensible to discover first what you are burning.'

The silk had already been slipped from the scroll and Marthe, her long fingers parting the fold, was about to break open the seal. She was smiling at Danny as she did so. 'At least,' she said, 'my authority is greater than yours. What did your Scottish king say? Marry never a priest's get?'

'I never heard of anyone worth the name who got the chance,' Danny said. 'I give you instead Daniel Hislop, who said that bastards should only marry each other. Can you make it out, or do you want me to read it to you?'

'I can make it out,' Marthe said. She was looking at the astrologer.

'And what are you going to do with it?' said Danny Hislop.

'Publish it where it will hurt most,' said Lymond's sister. 'I am going to show it to Richard Crawford, and watch him thrust it in front of his mother. Did you not know that the stately Sybilla has committed incest?'

'No,' said Danny.

'Or that our eminent Marshal is the child, as I am, of the first Lord Culter, Richard's grandfather? Perhaps,' said Marthe, 'if I hold the paper like this, both you and Master Nostradamus may read it and satisfy yourselves about the true nature of this little family. Don't you think, Master Hislop, that I shall enjoy Lord Culter's next visit to Paris? I don't think on that occasion I shall be expected to skulk in an attic.'

Danny had reached the bottom of the parchment. He said, *'Christ in heaven,'* and then started again from the top. At the end he looked up and met the chilly blue eyes of Marthe. He was not smiling.

'And this is your revenge for bastardy?' said Danny Hislop. 'How long, in this world, can a woman remain a bloody juvenile? You've knelt in the dirt, and so have I before the

697

Bastard of France and the Bastard of Scotland ... my God, we all watched Jenny Fleming produce one. You and I can't hand on our money—openly; we can't hold some kinds of high office—openly; but the rest of it doesn't matter a damn, least of all to you. You're as hard as cooled steel, Madame Marthe, except in one direction. You resent what Lymond's family did to him, and you want to watch them suffer for it. What you don't see, you stupid bitch, is that what hurts Culter and his mother hurts Francis.'

'Even after your spirited dismissal of the stigma of bastardy? Marthe said. She had rolled the parchment and replaced the silk on it. Nostradamus, who had not accepted her invitation to read, remained standing where he was by the window.

Danny said, 'I didn't tell you the other side, because you know it. You and I don't have a family. They have. They were brought up together. They need each other, and support each other. It's too late to change any of that. Whether he ever marries again or not, Francis has that; and if anything happens to him, the rest of the family have each other. You won't get him now, Marthe,' said Danny Hislop. 'Now that you want him. He belongs to them. It's too late. And I don't think you would be allowed to try it.'

The eyes of Marthe, looking past him, had met the steady look of the silent astrologer, and stayed on him. 'Allowed?' said Marthe. 'I have finished with asking permission for what I do and what I think. I have finished with being dispatched scurrying from errand to errand. I am my own mistress now. I am going to move the pieces. I am going to direct the end of the game.'

Her voice was raised, as if in anger, but the voice of Nostradamus, answering her, was perfectly calm. 'If you wish to carry this paper from France and deliver it into Lord Culter's hands,' he said, 'I know of no power which would stop you, unless an earthly one.'

'And that,' said Daniel Hislop, 'is the first totally accurate prediction I have ever had the pleasure of listening to. Give me that.'

'No,' said Marthe. 'No. You will get hurt. It is none of your business. You fool, if I can deal with Jerott, don't you imagine I can defend my own ...'

He nearly had the paper then; his finger and thumb on her outflung wrist; his other hand hard on her neck. Then she brought out her left hand, with the dagger in it, and struck him once, and twice, and three times, until he fell.

She stood gasping, while in a flutter of black, Nostradamus knelt quickly and touched him. The blood, silvered with dust, jumped and slid over the floorboards. Marthe said, 'I had to.'

'A knife for the bloody shoulder-blades,' said Danny's voice thinly from beside the astrologer's knees. 'You and your brother. You don't have to be so God-damned thorough.'

Marthe looked down, the hilt gripped hard in her fist. Beneath the floss of fine hair, the freckles overcast Danny's white face like flotsam; but it was not the face of a man who was dying.

'He was wearing steel under his shirt,' said Nostradamus. 'But he won't walk for a while, or use his shoulder.'

'I never trust bastards either,' Danny said hoarsely. 'Marthe. You owe me something. Take the advice of a well-wisher. Leave that paper alone.'

'I had to,' said Marthe again. She looked at Nostradamus. 'You could look after him? That is . . . You are staying?'

'I am not leaving France,' said Nostradamus. 'My part in the prophecy is fulfilled. Yours has still to come. Whatever made you think you were free?'

'And the end?' Marthe said. 'Do you know it?'

'We all die,' said Nostradamus. 'The man you love. The man who loves you. The man you married. But because of you there will be something, I promise you, by which men will know Francis Crawford has been.'

*

She left in an hour, alone, in the plain clothes of a merchant, with a merchant's safe-conduct in her saddlebags. And in the breast of her shirt was the scroll from the house of Doubtance, freshly packeted, and sealed, in bitter whimsy, with the crest of her husband's ring.

On the week-long ride to Dieppe no one followed her, and no power of heaven or of earth prevented her sailing, although storms delayed her departure and drove her ship finally from port after port, before stranding her in the roads outside Dover. There her patience ran out, and when they sent a boat to the town for fresh water, she had herself and her bags put ashore by it. She was engaged in buying a horse when two customers, strolling up, asked her to come with them into their office.

Searchers and customers are not always honest men, and she took thought for her saddlebags, but not for the paper she carried. Nor could she have known, unless the Lennoxes had told her, that wherever she had made landfall, one man or two would have stopped her, and thrust her, as now, into an empty cell, and turning the key, made her their prisoner.

*

The storms which delayed the *Réal* on her journey north were more erratic. After the fourth unexplained sojourn in harbour, Richard Crawford sought out the master and demanded an accounting. He had not known his brother was on deck until, halfway through the seaman's obliging explanations, Francis said agreeably, 'When did the wind change?'

The more uncommunicative gentleman, who looked fragile, had not so far engaged the master's attention. 'Eh?' he said.

'When did the wind change? It's been south-south-west for thirty-six hours, but you've adjusted the foremast and the staysail twice already this morning. Are we a training ship?'

'No,' said the master.

'... my lord,' said Lymond.

'No, my lord,' said the master. 'Only honest seamen who serve their trade faithfully. She's an old vessel, and seen a few flights. You have to gentle her.'

'Thank you,' said Lymond. 'I should prefer sailing her. Do I have your permission?'

The master gazed at him. 'I can't see my owners liking that, my lord. I'm sorry. But perhaps you or the other gentleman would like to take the helm for a little?'

'Would you like to take the helm for a little, Richard?' Lymond said. It was as inconsequential as any of his conversation had been, on the rare occasions during the voyage when he had sought company. Once, in his sleep, he had spoken Philippa's name, but never at any other time.

'Not unless you want to swim to Leith,' Richard said.

'Or, like the Turks' diabolical iron galley, ride under the water for ever. It would pose, one should say, certain problems of steering.' He raised his voice just a little, and threw it aft, '*M. le timonier? Pouge un peu, s'il vous plaît. Et puis il faut larguer les voiles.* Master?'

The master had gone very red. 'My lord, there can only be one who commands on a ship.'

'That is correct. And you have kindly handed me your authority for a day,' Lymond said. 'Go and sleep. I shall give you your ship back at nightfall.'

His jaw jutting, the master turned on Lord Culter. 'I will stand security for him,' said Richard gravely. 'If he chips the shaft of an oar, I shall pay for it.'

He was not at all sure that it was wise, but it seemed to be what Francis wanted, and that he should want anything was of moment. He was aware that the master, although overborne, was still there, on the long rambade, watching. Then Lymond walked to the poop, and, turning, his hands clasped lightly behind him, said, *Ecoutez, tout le monde ...*' and talked on in short, carrying phrases, while the stern post arched to the sky and plunged again into the sea just behind him.

The men near Richard were grinning, but he did not know the common language of galleys, and so missed the cause of it. He could tell the orders, however, from the pitch of his brother's voice and watched, holding hard to the rail as lines of men came and went, in a rush of bare feet. Above his head, soles dangling, they were doing something to the brails on a yardarm. The sea hissed and the coast, grey in the drizzle, began, quickening, to unroll towards them.

The ship was trim in an hour, and then there was nothing to do. Richard said, 'Chancellor. I had forgotten the voyage from Russia.'

'Had you?' Lymond said. He had come in for food, his skin with colour in it, and his hair blowing and damp. 'Oh, yes. Russia, and all the Levantine seas and Malta. And of course, my years at the oar.'

'You prefer the sea to the land?' Richard said. The possibility had never struck him.

'Sometimes,' Lymond said. He had eaten, but with no obvious appetite. 'I don't like to see things done badly on either. At the moment, I am tired of journeys. It is time I arrived somewhere.'

'And when you do?' Richard said. 'I've tried not to force you to talk of the future, but your men are in Scotland ahead of you and that means that you have to find them employment. And this time, you cannot be neutral. You have to make up your mind whether you are going to support or oppose France. You have to make up your mind whether you are going to support or oppose the new religion. And even if

701

you and your officers try not to commit yourselves, your men will, when and if you start recruiting them.'

He tried, and failed, to collect Lymond's eyes. He added, a little brusquely, 'I wanted you to come back to Scotland for Sybilla's sake; not to defend any cause of mine.'

'I know,' Lymond said. 'But my calling is war: even if I wanted to retire to the farm or the cloister, do you think I should be allowed to? As soon as I set foot on Scottish soil, rumour will make me the centre of every conspiracy.'

'What then?' said Richard.

'If I knew, I would tell you,' Lymond said. 'There will be no recruiting for St Mary's. I should like to think there need never be. I stopped Graham Malett from leading a power crusade in the name of religion. It would be the ultimate irony to be forced into doing the same thing myself. Hoddim and Guthrie and Blyth and the rest are in Scotland because they are men of great experience, with counsel to give and the ability to answer force with force, if it does become necessary. We don't know yet what your fellow-Commissioners are going to say or do. If word of the donations leaks out, if accusations of poison are made openly, then trouble may start before anyone is ready for it.'

'They know what is at stake,' Richard said. With pained perplexity, he stared at the downbent head, propped on one hand, of his brother. 'You were taken to Russia, expecting little. Perhaps you will find a purpose here.'

'Oh, Christ, Richard,' Lymond said. 'You don't need to remind me what country I belong to.'

Richard drew a deep breath, his eyes suddenly open. 'Then——'

'Then I am making a gift to her of the men I have trained,' his brother said. He had removed his hand from his head and, looking up, met Richard's eyes with tired resignation. 'I have been told to live in Scotland, and I shall do it, but I doubt if it will be to Scotland's benefit. There are handicaps, I have found, more crippling than blindness. Even the part of me that did not come back from Dourlans would hardly have made you a whole man. . . . But one would like to spare Sybilla the realization of it.'

And Richard was silent, for the truth Jerott had seen touched him, too, for a moment before he thrust it aside. He said, instead, 'Once, I returned, by mistake, a present you gave me.'

As when he had come in, fresh from the wind, surprise and pleasure roused, for an instant, all the colour in his brother's face. Francis Crawford said, 'I have kept it, in case one day you might want it. If you do ... It makes worthwhile this part, at least, of the journey.'

*

That evening, as he promised, he handed his command to the master, who was good enough to comment, gruffly, on the speed he had made. Then, as was usual during this convalescence, Lymond went below and drifted quite early into the deep, empty sleep of physical weariness.

He was not awake, therefore, when the vessel tacked, in the night, into the roads outside Berwick where two small English ships were hovering, waiting to take her.

The noise of the boarding broke Richard's sleep, and presently that of his brother. But by that time the *Réal* was firmly under escort, and sailing into the mouth of the Tweed in captivity.

There, neither the master nor the crew of the *Réal* was invited to come ashore. Only the Earl of Culter and his brother with their servants and their belongings were transferred briskly without explanation from the riverside to the brooding heights of Berwick castle.

The room to which Richard found himself taken, with Lymond following, was that of the Lieutenant-Governor of the castle; but Lord Wharton, it seemed, was either asleep or absent that evening. The officer who turned and greeted them, shaved, accoutred and quite impeccably groomed, was Austin Grey, Marquis of Allendale.

Richard spoke to him. Without even glancing at him, Austin Grey said, 'Our two countries are still at war. Any objections you may have will be noted. You will not find your stay here unpleasant, Lord Culter.'

He was looking at Francis. Then, turning, Richard saw that his brother was white as a pargeted board. He remembered then, with abrupt nausea, the disastrous encounter in Paris with Allendale, after Lymond had broken his word and escaped from the wedding with Philippa. In Francis, there was so much that was admirable; and the flaws were so great. Yet one forgot them.

Austin Grey had not forgotten. His brown, austere face, its nostrils a little distended, told that; and his open stare of

703

hatred and loathing, focused without words on Lymond. Then Lymond said, as if he could not wait any longer, 'Where is she?'

'Haven't you been able to have her watched?' Austin said. 'Or has your spy forgotten you? Or . . . No. I forgot. You have been on the high seas for quite some time, haven't you? You wouldn't even know if she was dead.'

*

Except by pleading, there was no possible answer. The anguish of it got to Richard, or a shred of the kind of perception one still had not learned to expect of him. Richard said, 'You heard my brother. Where is Mistress Philippa?'

It gave Austin pleasure, clearly, to prolong the silence. He said, at length, 'In Flaw Valleys, with her mother. She wrote me two days ago, to say that since she would never remarry, it might be better if we did not continue to meet. An abrupt quittance, don't you think, for the girl she once was? Or could she have been preparing for your arrival?'

Francis Crawford had experienced this form of antagonism before, and when well, was fully qualified to withstand it. Now, nothing was especially easy. The hammer-beats of relief made him unsure for a while of his stance on a floor which still swayed like a sea-deck. He said, 'Philippa didn't know I was coming. I am on my way to my own house. I have no intention of seeing her.'

'I thought I would make sure of that for you,' Austin said. 'Lord Culter will, I am certain, be transferred fairly easily, after due negotiation over the Border. Your own stay will, I think, be rather longer. A Marshal of France, a man whose ingenuity wrested Calais and Guînes from us and placed my uncle in such harsh captivity, will not soon, I'm afraid, be forgiven. Nor would it be reasonable to expect your conditions of imprisonment to be any less strict than those of my uncle. I am speaking, after all, to the man who tricked us so ably at Douai, at Flavy-le-Martel, at Ham, at Calais . . . and, of course, in the matter of his personal bond in Paris. Lord Culter, you will be lodged here.'

He rang a bell and the door opened. 'And my brother?' Richard was saying.

'He will be in private hands,' said Austin Grey. 'Where, it is not for me to tell you.'

Richard, a strong man, was resisting the guard who, entering, had gripped his arms to remove him. 'I demand to know where,' he said. 'I demand to be lodged in the same room. Bring Lord Wharton.'

'Lord Wharton is away,' Austin said. 'Take him out.'

The fool was still resisting. Lymond said, 'For God's sake get out, Richard. If you do what they want, they'll release you.'

It got home, evidently, for Richard hesitated, and then turned and walked out. The door closed.

'You knew we were coming,' Lymond said.

'Obviously. There are some powerful people in France,' said Austin Grey, 'who dislike you nearly as much as I do. I do not think you quite realize yet what you are dealing with. I know what happened to Philippa in ... in the Hôtel des Sphères in Paris.'

The power to cerebrate every physical response had long since left Francis Crawford. He sat down. He said, 'How do you know?'

'It was an evening of quite some violence,' said Austin. 'Didn't you imagine it might become a matter of public knowledge?'

Lymond said, 'I know it's not a matter of public knowledge. I have just come from Paris.'

'It hardly counts now anyway, does it?' said Austin. 'Now you have left France. Do you still tell me you are not going to join Philippa?'

Whatever he said, he was not going to be believed, but he did keep looking directly at Austin, so that the other man could see his eyes. He said, 'I left Philippa because I don't want to be near her. She left me because she doesn't want me beside her. If you ask her, she will tell you this also.'

'You devil,' said Austin Grey in a low voice. 'Oh you devil, what have you done to her?'

'Everything, I think except kill her,' said Francis Crawford. There was nothing it seemed worth while adding. Eventually, he said, 'I think you should tell me what you are going to do with me.'

'Nothing,' said Austin Grey. 'I couldn't make you suffer enough. I haven't the skill. But I know someone who has.

'I am going to walk out of the door, and send in the four men who are to take you to your place of imprisonment. I shall not come back. I do not expect to see you again. I hope, when what is about to happen happens to you, that you will think of me. And crow. Crow on your bloody dunghill, if you can still do it.'

The four men who came in were heavily armed, down to mail coat and steel gloves and morions. They wasted no time on speech but advanced on him. He stood up.

He had no weapons other than his hands, and against the steel they were of little use. He managed to break someone's nose, and mark another unshaven face with his knuckles before he was beaten half-stunned to the floor and kicked senseless.

They shackled him all the same, and put him into a cart, and took him to his destination while he was easy to manage.

*

It was the piercing cold, penetrating and even overwhelming the pain of his stiffened body which brought him finally back to consciousness. He lay with his eyes closed for a long time, as his training taught him to do, seeking the augurs of danger. He was lying, stripped to the waist on stone flags and stuck there, so far as he could feel, by the dried blood from recent contusions. He was not fettered.

After a while, when it was fairly certain that he was alone, he opened his eyes and found himself in a bare, circular room, served by two doors and one window, barred and set high in the wall. One of the doors, securely locked, gave probably on to a staircase. The other he was grateful, for the sake of dignity, to find led to a primitive office of necessity. Within the room itself, there were no furnishings.

He was in an unused tower, and it was daylight, but how far advanced into the day he did not know, nor if the tower was part of a habitable building. The window was too high to look out of, and the floor too cold to lie upon, so he sat, curled like a cat in the corner under the window, and concentrated all his senses on listening.

After a long time he did hear some sounds far below which indicated that there was life of some sort in the building. And that therefore he had not perhaps been abandoned to starve. At first, this seemed a matter for relief; and then, when he thought about it, of little consequence. When, several hours later, footsteps sounded quite clearly mounting the staircase, and there came the rattle of keys, and the sound of men's voices, echoing, he was shivering so uncontrollably that his teeth rattled if he closed them. He stood up, slowly, as the door opened, and John Elder entered the chamber.

He was smiling; the raw smile one remembered from all the tedious receptions preceding Queen Mary's marriage. Behind him were the four armed men he had met before, one of them with his nose in a plaster. Lymond gazed at it, pursing his lips, for a long and insolent moment, and then turned his attention to Elder.

'M. le comte de Sevigny,' said the secretary. His smile had grown, if anything, wider. 'I am happy to see you. I am to ask you if you will have the goodness to come downstairs and join the Countess of Lennox directly.'

*

They gave him his shirt back for the occasion, but his fingers were too cold to lace it, and for Margaret Lennox, in any case, there were well-defined limits to the trouble he would take. From her jealous concupiscence at twenty-seven for a boy eleven years younger had come all the ills that had dogged him.

He wondered if she had ever come to regret that seduction, as again and again his life had collided with hers, and alway to her detriment, or that of her husband, or her husband's family. Through him, her husband's brother had been brought to ruin at the French court; her father's Scottish inheritance had been denied to her. Restored to Scotland, he could baulk all her family's hopes of ruling there. He could do more. Once her lover, he could cast doubt on the very legitimacy of her heir, the boy whose claim to both the Scots and English thrones was far from negligible.

It was small wonder that Margaret Lennox had paid a fortune to have him discredited, or that now she had brought him here, her captive at last to enjoy her victory. It should be a brief one.

Nothing of what he thought showed on his face. He found to his pleasure that the main part of the house was quite warm, and that his muscles therefore would obey him in a gentlemanly fashion. His gratitude did not stretch to making any concessions in his appearance. Then they rapped on a wide, four-panelled door, and when a woman's voice spoke, opened it and sent him in.

She sat, modishly dressed, by a blazing log fire, the splendid woman born of an English king's sister, in whom the hopes of two thrones, kept alive through three reigns, were still burning secretly. The woman of whose eight children only Harry Darnley and Charles still survived, precocious pupils of their tutor John Elder. Lymond said, 'Alone? A somewhat disagreeable cop in its coppeweb?'

She had always been glorious, with her green-fair hair and regal stature, and in the eighteen months and more since last they met she had ripened, it seemed, in the sun of royal and Catholic favour, her skin sumptuous, her eyes dark and rich as her jewels. Lady Lennox said, 'There are four men you know of on the other side of the door.'

He had expected her to assail him with words. 'And Matthew?' he said. '*Gai comme un bonnet de nuit?*' He did not intend to walk halting towards the saving heat of the fire, so he stayed where he was.

'My husband is in Settrington,' Lady Lennox replied. I might have had you brought into Bridlington Bay, but I preferred to have you dealt with more distantly, and without Matthew being involved.'

'Also, young Allendale could put the matter on an official footing,' Lymond said. So they were, as he had guessed, not too far south of Berwick. He added thoughtfully, 'I came quite to like Willie Grey. If anything happens to me, won't there be repercussions?'

He saw then, from her eyes, that she knew a little more than he had bargained for. 'From whom?' Margaret said. 'France has no interest in you now. The English Council don't want a prominent mercenary bought into the anti-Catholic factions in either Scotland or England. I can think of no one who will mourn you, Francis, and a great many who will be much comforted to learn that God has otherwise disposed of you. Provided it is done with discretion.'

'Oh, I can see the advantages,' Lymond said. 'The Cardinal's gratitude: the help of the de Guises to get back your lands in Scotland, and perhaps even to work towards better things. Matthew for Regent, and Harry for King. What do you do about Richard?'

'Show him your grave,' Margaret said. 'When finally we agree to allow him to visit you. Unless you have a particular resistance to cold?'

He said, 'Evading excessive heat so far has been my speciality.' A plaguing thirst and a growing light-headedness made him aware that he had lost rather more blood than he could afford to.

Margaret said, 'So I would gather. I am told that you encouraged an old great-uncle to perform his business of the night with your wife, and that you haven't bedded her since. It seems a pity. Green wood, they say, makes a hot fire. Can you afford such fastidiousness?'

He had not expected that, either. 'I don't suppose I can,' he said. 'Now that the field has shrunk so alarmingly.'

'And I rather doubt,' Margaret said, 'if I am in any danger. Don't move. I want to see how long you can stand there. Allendale tells me your poor child-wife is most unhappy. You have a heavy hand, have you not, for girl children? I remember the young lady who could not see. What was her name? Joleta?'

'You have my conquests confused,' Lymond said. 'I have the same trouble. Joleta was the sister of that charming hypocrite I am sure you remember: Sir Graham Reid Malett of Malta?'

'I gave myself the pleasure of telling Lord Allendale about her.' Margaret Lennox said. 'He knew about Graham Malett. Have you not realized yet that he regards you as a man of that stamp? You are his holy war, Francis.'

'And yours?' he said.

He could see, in the swimming heat of the fire, that she was smiling. 'Just war,' she said. 'Come, where is all that insouciant ribaldry? Smile, M. le comte! Is this all the wit you can bring to my salon?' And derisively, she quoted softly:

> Cy gist qui pendant qu'il vivoit
> Fit tout meistier de gueserie
> Il soufloit, predisoit, rimoit
> Et cultivoit Philosophie ...

'What is your name, M. le comte de Sevigny?'

'Patience,' said Francis Crawford. He had postponed total humiliation, with regret, by backing two paces and leaning his shoulders against a tall cupboard.

'It is as good, I suppose, as any other,' Margaret said. 'And what name would you have me give your mother? I hired Master Bailey, did you know?, to trace her mistake and identify it for me.'

'And did he?' he said.

709

'I didn't think of trying your methods. If I had that information,' Margaret said, 'what would you pay me to keep it secret?'

She had held back, deliberately, until she had nothing to fear from him. He said, the words soft in his dry throat. 'What do you want?'

'Beg,' she said.

He could barely stand upright. But he gave, in spite of himself, a short hoot of laughter, 'Oh Christ, Margaret,' he said. 'That's old King Henry, my dear. That's ten whole years out of date.'

She stood up. 'You won't?'

'No, I won't. I won't bend my knee, or kiss your charming shoes either. I may possibly fall flat on my face, but that will be quite inadvertent.'

'You will stand there and let me refer to Madame la putaine your mother? You will watch while I call my sergeant in to listen while I brand you bastard?'

'No,' said Lymond. One could, as he had proved, concentrate the willpower. One could lease five minutes' strength, or perhaps less, and hold it until now, when she was standing smiling, her beautiful hair aureoled by the fire.

It took three long, silent strides to reach her; and one hand to seize her dress and another her hair.

The gown ripped, as he had meant it to, through the bodice and the embroidered chemise under, until she was bare to the waistline.

The hair came away in his hand, leaving beneath it an unkempt, strong-smelling nest. The head, prematurely grey, of a forty-three year old woman who stood, her painted neck blotched by his hands, too vain to shriek out in protest.

So he summoned help for her, walking erratically to the door and opening it gently, so that the four men leaning outside stood and stared at him, and then at what they saw past his shoulder, as their prisoner stepped aside and encouraged them cordially to enter.

There was a certain satisfaction in it, but that was all, for they did not kill him outright: merely returned him after another crude beating to his tower room. His only conscious thought, as he struck the floor and rolled over, was that this time, ripped though it was, they had left him his shirt.

He was collecting the strength to lift his limbs from the stone when the man with the broken nose entered, grinning, and shot a pailful of icy water over his head and body. Then they left him, and did not come back.

When you die, Margaret Lennox had said to him once, *When you die—and I shall be there—it will be an experience which no man has savoured.*

Ironic that now, without food, without water, without warmth, one should watch the day give way to night and the night give way to day, knowing that the gift Philippa had left him, which Sybilla had taken away, might be returned him in the end at this woman's hands, who wished him nothing but mischief.

He did not want to live. As the condition of life does, so the condition of death should depend on one's choice. The wise man lives as long as he ought, not as long as he can. Democrites fell on his sword; Aruntius killed himself to fly both the past and the future; Crates said that love would be cured by hunger, if not by time; and whoever disliked these two remedies, by a rope.

All these were barred to him because of the vow he had made to Sybilla. Because of it, he could not resign himself to what, easy or difficult, was coming; but instead had to turn again to his lessons: the long, bitter schooling thrust at him, for no purpose, throughout every twist of his lifespan.

In rebellion he made his preparations; and in rebellion composed himself, as the Shamans do, to reduce the shivering husk of the body to one spark of life, conserving what it has; feeling cold and hunger and thirst no more than a plant does, laid in its sap on an icefield.

It was all he could do; and would extend his life, he supposed, by a day or so. For what came after that, his only regret lay in the Lennoxes' triumph. And that death should come without grace, instead of the way he had planned in the Authie, in the open air among men, in a moment of verve and of freedom.

What ties the fool to his body? somebody said.
A promise.
I shall send gems of lapis lazuli: I shall make her fields into vineyards, and the field of her love into orchards.
Philippa.

*

He did not want to be roused when Wharton's men broke into the room, and even when they laid him before the warm

711

fire, from which the Countess of Lennox had been removed, crying indignantly, an hour earlier, he tried to avoid them. Then he came to himself, and remembered.

What ties the fool to his body?'

A promise.

∗

Before he left, Lord Wharton came to see him. 'You think you can ride? I'll send my men part of the way with you; then you'll have no more trouble. Your mother is with the Somervilles at Flaw Valleys. So is Lord Culter. I do not want him, in these difficult times, to appear further south. They're waiting there for you.'

He had changed less than anyone else: This small, elderly, hardbitten man who had crossed his path first eleven years before, in the English war, in Annan. Thomas, first Baron Wharton, knew the north and its problems better than any man, even William Grey of Wilton. But he took Grey's advice on political matters. And Grey, even from far off on the Loire, had advised him.

One knew this was likely. One hoped that Richard, ransomed or somehow released, would get hold of Wharton and force him to take a hand in the affair. What was surprising was that it had all happened so easily. 'Who will mourn you?' Margaret Lennox had said. 'Not France. Not the English Council.' Yet when he had wakened fully, it was to find Margaret gone, with all her servants, and in their place the doctors and servants of Thomas Wharton, Governor of Berwick and Warden of all the Marches.

So now he said, 'I have to thank you, sir, for my life. How did it come about?'

The scarred, uncompromising soldier's face stared at him. 'You had a key. Did you not recollect? Your brother did.' And when Lymond shook his head, Thomas Wharton pulled forward the pocket of his cloak and drew from it something he threw on the table.

It was a glove: a gauntlet of padded silk embroidered over and over with colours and fine gold, and in the centre, where the wrist would lie, an elaborate initial, enclosed in a cartouche.

'You collect them, I believe,' said Thomas Wharton. 'It was in your baggage. Lord Culter brought it to me.'

'Then——' Lymond said.

712

'Mary Tudor is dead. Her sister Elizabeth is Queen of England. The house of Lennox has fallen,' said Lord Wharton abruptly. 'And Francis Crawford of Lymond, who has Elizabeth's guerdon, as he once had that of a child, is not a man who can be held prisoner with impunity by anyone, far less a Catholic with a claim to the thrones of England and Scotland. Lady Lennox has gone back to Settringham, and you are free.'

'The term is relative,' Lymond said. He looked up into the weatherbeaten face. 'You love your country?'

'I have served it a long time,' Wharton said. He waited, curious.

'Then,' said Lymond, 'you will remember the autumn of '42, when the eldest son of every Scottish nobleman worth the name was in London, compounding for his freedom, promising Henry of England to further his church, his son's marriage to Mary, his claims to the overlordship of my country. Is it not going to happen again?'

'Because there is a Protestant monarch?' Wharton said. 'Perhaps. Is it a bad thing? Then, your noblemen bargained, as they fought, out of self-interest or devilment. Now they do it from conviction. If you met Grey, he has told you how the Reformed church is growing in England. I don't need to tell you it has happened in Scotland as well. The ties with France are going to slacken, and when they do, don't you think it is time Scotland looked to the ally over her Borders who has the same faith, and the same language and the same blood in her veins?'

'So Lord Grey thinks,' Lymond said.

'And you?'

'England or France?' Lymond got up suddenly from the seat where he had been resting. 'Of course, England is the old enemy. Eleven years ago the English occupied our forts and we hated them, whereas the French, from whatever self-interest, have sent us their gold and their generals: French ships have foundered for us; Frenchmen died on our ramparts. But we're small; we are a cockpit; sooner or later every ally turns into an overlord. Today the French are in Dumbarton and Leith instead of the English and tomorrow, instead of being grateful, we may with reason have to throw them out, or be swallowed.'

'Then you must choose,' Wharton said, 'the nation with the

713

greatest affinity; the ally which will serve you best. Does the Church count for nothing?'

Francis Crawford did not look at the English warden. Instead he wandered to the high window and, gazing down on the mild English countryside, said soberly, 'Affinity? French blood runs in both England and Scotland; their tongue is no barrier. As for religion ... Identity of faith is small recommendation. Freedom of faith, surely, is what must be sought for: tolerance between every sect and its neighbour; clemency from every government. Otherwise you have men fighting from conviction who might as well be fighting from devilment: the thing has no more sense in it than your young Allendale's cocks, slashing each other to death only because one will not give way to the other. And if there is to be tolerance, where do you think we may look for it? To England? Or to France, rather?'

'I recommend you my nation,' said Wharton. 'I tell you also to look about you as you make and unmake alliances. The board is clearing. The old game is almost played, and the pieces broken. The Emperor is dead and Suleiman ageing. Russia, which you nearly saved, is being dashed to pieces in the madness of her Tsar. Mary Tudor has gone, and her church with her. Philip, free of his English bondage, may well abandon the sad Flemish morass he has floundered in, and France is sinking: all Italy lost; all her conquests squandered in a silly peace, made for the return of an old man to his monarch.'

'Except for Calais,' Lymond said.

'Except for Calais,' Wharton agreed. 'The King of France won't give up Calais. But he has given up Thionville, they tell me.'

Lymond did not speak. Wharton said, 'You were young at Annan.'

'Was I?' Lymond said. After a moment he added, 'I am thirty-two.'

'And I am sixty-three,' Lord Wharton said. 'Who else does your country have? There is a new game about to begin. Will you leave it to others?'

'As you will leave it to your son,' said Francis Crawford. 'It is all I find I can do.'

*

He left, with Wharton's armed escort, later that day. And Lord Wharton himself, riding preoccupied back to his castle of Berwick, was only roused from his speculations by the sight of his new, quiet lieutenant, confronting him in his own chamber.

'I am told that the comte de Sevigny has been released,' said Austin Grey, Marquis of Allendale.

'He should never have been arrested,' said Wharton. 'Don't you know better than to trust the Lennoxes?'

Austin said, 'He commanded the French army. He took Calais. He captured my uncle.'

Thomas, first Baron Wharton of Wharton, sat in his chair. 'Boy,' he said. 'Listen to me, and learn the first lesson of man, the political animal. When you wage war, you wage it for ever. When war is over, it has never existed. There is a truce, and there will shortly be a peace between England and Scotland. Crawford of Lymond is the Queen's friend, and my friend, and your friend.'

'I am glad,' said Austin Grey, 'that you told me. My lord, I have some business at home, and my spell of duty, as you know, has been a long one. Could your lordship allow me a brief leave of absence?'

Lord Wharton, who rarely took leave, agreed crisply. And within the hour, his young aide had left Berwick.

*

To go to Flaw Valleys had been far from Lymond's intention. But the file of men escorting him there could not, being English, cross the Border, and he was tired; and he had to rest somewhere. So, after his initial protests Francis Crawford ceased planning, and rode north and west from the cold prison he had stayed in to Kate's pretty manor near Hexham.

He thought, in his self-deception, that Philippa would not mind, since he was so weary; and today his love, like hers, was of the mind only.

He did not look to see if anyone followed him.

CHAPTER 12

L'oeuvre ancienne se parachevera.

In Flaw Valleys itself few people slept easily the night before Lymond was expected. After losing his temper all day, Jerott was sent striding off to bed by Sybilla, who then retired, looking suddenly weary. Richard stayed an hour or so longer, and then in his turn climbed the stairs, followed by Adam. Archie had made himself scarce from the outset.

Kate walked round with her lamp, testing locks. Upstairs, she stopped by Philippa's door and laid her warm cheek for a moment against it. But there was no sound inside; and after an interval she touched the timber in sombre caress and then left it. Philippa heard her but did not speak, or rise from the windowseat.

She had been there since Lord Wharton's messenger had come to tell them that Francis was coming. She had retreated there stage by stage since the first good-humoured reports had come in from Newcastle: did Mistress Somerville know they had caught a French ship, with two Scottish nobles on board her? And then Jerott arriving, grim-faced, with Sybilla: Richard was in Berwick being held to ransom; and Francis had been taken, no one knew where, into England. Then the messages from Richard himself, and the delay while they located Lord Wharton. Then Richard, in person, with the laconic news that Francis had been found, and they were to wait for him.

'Unless matters change, you should not meet,' Sybilla had said; reflectively, as if it were a slight affair, and open to contingency.

The last time she and Francis had met was on the night of a summer thunderstorm, when she had flung the dark curtains across the eight blazing windows at Sevigny.

How could it begin again: the anguish of touch and withdrawal; of unspoken words and unanswered silences; of absence and sleeplessness and unending suffering?

Adam knew it: she had seen the look in his eyes when Sybilla came back with that quiet pronouncement: 'I made him promise to live, and to come back to Scotland.'

She thought even Jerott knew it; although she had heard what occurred at the Authie, and knew that it was Jerott's hand which had drawn him from the water, as Sybilla's from the fire.

Fire, and water. Where had she heard that before?

So, he was coming. And if there was a way out for them both, it was for her to find it. And alone: since the night on her voyage to England he had not tried to reach her. But that, of course, would be because of his promise.

Towards dawn, she left the casement over the gentle garden where the oboe had stood; and lying still on her bed listened, and watched, but heard and saw nothing.

*

The next morning she kept to the music room. From there you could see clear down to the gatehouse, and to the moors lifting beyond, bleached under the pallid blue sky of November. On the first rise, a planting of firs, straddled like peacocks, bore under its plumes the pale lilac bloom of new woodsmoke.

Philippa stared at it. Today a single man would ride over the fall of the moor. She would not be at the gatehouse this time, intent on his betrayal; although perhaps Kate would stand here again, watching, unable to avert what was coming.

There was a book of music propped on the harpsichord. Her mother had been here, then, with Adam. It was easy to see why, from lending a man's strength in the manor, Adam had come to linger, and why Kate had found it so grateful to discover beside her, at last, a human being whose hand she could take. With the insight particular to her nature she had moved through each day as it opened for her, and had hidden nothing from Philippa's eyes. Only, in her hearing, neither Adam or Kate had touched the lute or the spinet or the harpsichord which had belonged to Gideon, and which Francis had made his own, before music, too, had betrayed him.

Towards noon, the man Richard had posted came riding downhill to tell them that Mr Crawford had been sighted.

717

Philippa heard the bustle. A moment later the door of the music room opened.

It was not Kate, or Adam, but Archie Abernethy. Forbidding; wrinkled; authoritarian as the menagerie keeper he had once been in Saint-Germain, in Rouen, in Stamboul, in Tarnassery, he said, 'Lord Culter and Mr Blyth are for riding over the moors now to meet him. I'll take ye, if ye want to go with them.'

Philippa turned and looked at him. 'You know him,' she said.

The unwinking black eyes looked back at her. 'There'll be ae thing in his mind: how ye are faring. If he sees you, he will know. Forbye . . .

'. . . Forbye,' said Archie Abernethy gently, 'he has been sick and will be low, I dare say; and in need of friends.'

It was what she had wondered, all through the night. He had said he did not think he could change. But he had been sound then. She said, 'Yes. Tell them to wait. I will come with you.'

They left Sybilla at the gatehouse with Adam and Kate to keep her company and cantered up the long rising slopes: Richard and Jerott first, with Philippa and Archie following. The wind on their faces was bright and sharp and the horses' shoulders worked, polished velours in the shallow sunshine; while Philippa's cloak scudded like a green sail behind her, with her shining brown hair as its ensign.

*

A Marshal of France, the Veovoda of all Muscovy, is never alone.

It was a long time since he had ridden like this, with no valets, no footmen, no grooms, no harbingers at his heels, and no luggage, and no retinue of gentlemen lances. The last he had had until a moment ago, and had not been sorry to leave them.

He was tired, but not in distress, for the ride was a hag on the post; a moment to record, as the ride through France had been an act of ritual. . . . A free and gentle reminder of a familiar book, with the wide skies of Northumberland over him, and the wind, and the moors, yellow and brown, rising to Scotland.

Tomorrow, he would go there. Today, in Flaw Valleys, he

718

would see Philippa again. He would learn, looking at her, how she had borne the weight of this deadly separation, and would read in her eyes the understanding which no one else living could offer him. And receive so much more: her clear, cool judgement on all that had happened since Sevigny, from the great issues down to those most desperately minor and personal.

He would see her.

He would see whether she painted her lashes in the same way; and her brown eyes could encompass the same horrendous range of expression: from freezing superiority through scathing correction to untrustworthy whimsy when she was attacking him, or tormenting him, or holding her own in violent argument.

He would see whether the sardonic, curling lips seemed as soft, and the high brow as round and sweetly polished and the slender body as lithe, with its budding sweetness now all come to ripen.

> *When her loose gown from her shoulders did fall*
> *And she me caught in her arms, long and small,*
> *Therewith all sweetly did me kiss*
> *And softly said, 'Dear heart . . .'*

His horse stumbled in the tussocky ground and made him realize, then, how thoughtlessly fast he was riding . . . how thoughtlessly fast he was thinking.

Nothing had changed. Every passion was low, every appetite dull except one; and it seemed now that it would never leave him. They had been wise: they had taken care for each other once. How could he burden her again? How could he go to Flaw Valleys?

His mare was weary. Unlike his mount at Dieppe she obeyed him unquestioningly when he laid his reins against her neck and nudged her into the turn; the slow sweep which would take him away from the pain that could not be borne and towards the emptiness that held only pain that was bearable.

Someone shouted, then, from a belt of trees on the hill just ahead of him. He had been going to ride on, but it was not a place in his life where he would deny help to any man. So instead he turned the mare's head, and putting her into a gentle trot, rode up and over.

*

Richard shouted twice, smiling. They had not quite reached the trees when they had seen, far off, the moving horse with its bareheaded rider who turned, hearing his voice, and then after a moment put the horse at the sloping ground which led to the pine grove.

With Jerott alongside, Culter laughed aloud and kicked his mouth into a gallop. Just before the two horses drew abreast of the wood, a man walked out of it.

A dark young man, too well dressed, one could see even at this remove, to be a cottager. A man with something dark in each hand, who paid no attention to the two horsemen approaching behind him, but looked only in the other direction, where the single rider, slowing a little, was unawares nearing the hilltop.

And so the amber hair of Francis Crawford's father, which all his life had marked him out: for hurt, for passion; for treachery; performed its last destined office in the sunshine and fresh winds of England that morning. A single rider, a sober doublet and cloak might have escaped notice. But not the bare, golden head.

Austin Grey had left Berwick with a longer journey than Lymond to make. He counted on the slowness of the armed escort, and perhaps some weakness in Lymond himself to give him the advantage he needed. And riding faster than he had ever done in his life, he reached before Lymond the point just short of Flaw Valleys where their two paths must intersect.

Then, it was merely a matter of waiting.

He knew he was about to act outside the law, as his own executioner. No other man would do it. No other man could see, it seemed, the rottenness under the enchantments; the hypocrisy within that plotting brain, that graceless tongue. The greed, the lust, the careless arrogance that had broken Philippa.

He had learned, at Gûnes, to kill his man to save others. When his quarry, unsuspecting, had moved within range Austin Grey walked steadily forward and lifting the first of his pistols, took aim with it.

Riding flat out, Richard might have reached him in time. It

was Jerott, his face white as ghost coal, who seized his reins and his sword-arm and hindered him, the horses stamping and plunging. And it was Jerott who cried out as, amazed and distracted, Richard fought him, 'No. Oh Christ, no. It should have happened long ago. Don't stop it. *No one else could do it for him.*'

While he was speaking, the pistol in the trees fired, and then its neighbour; and in a screaming rush, the birds left the woodland.

At pointblank range, there was no possibility of missing. He aimed into the fair, weary, rancourless face, and then at the heart, and both balls found their mark and brought death in the end, not with the sweet ambiguity of an arrow but with the finality which frees the earth at once of body and soul, and all that was good or bad in either.

Either ball would have killed. The second also injured the horse which fell, dying. Archie Abernethy said, 'Don't look!' thickly as Philippa half slid from her horse; and kneeling, cradled her on the grass, her eyes blinded against his jerkin. Then Jerott dragged out the pistol he, too, carried, and dismounting walked towards Austin.

The young Marquis of Allendale made no effort to evade him. It was an execution. Allendale was not afraid to answer for it to Lymond's rotten cohorts. Only the smile on his lips wavered when he saw Philippa: and he was not sorry to die when Jerott, weeping, lifted his weapon and fired it.

After that, Archie could not hold her; but by then the horse was still, and Richard had flung his cloak and Jerott's over the carnage. She lifted only a corner; and after a long while unclasped her own cloak and laid it, green as young turf, over the others.

Richard said, 'There could have been no quicker death. And in the open, with friends not far off.'

'Because of me,' Philippa said. 'Austin killed him because of me.'

Richard lifted and held her. His hands were shaking. 'You heard what Jerott said. No one else could do it for him.'

'But for me, he would not have needed it done at all,' Philippa said. Then she added, 'I think Sybilla is coming.'

That made Richard leave her, to walk back over the hill. After a moment Jerott rose and walked back also, to meet Adam and Kate and say what had to be said to Sybilla. That now she had one son only living. That Francis, the best loved of the three, had now left her.

Philippa stood. Someone sobbed. Someone said, *'It is finished. Remember me no longer; or my children; or my children's children.'*

But something remained. *You have a brain. Use it.* He lived in her, his disciple. For her to think, now, as he would have done. And to act always thereafter.

For him, the gateway had opened, and the loss was hers to bear: that at least she could do, and honour his teaching. She could remember what he was and what had died with him: all the virtues and vices of Scorpio: *In manners well dignified. In feats of warre and courage invincible. Contentious: challenging all honour to himself. Valiant lover of warre, hazarding himself for all Perils.* And that other he had: a capacity for human love so great that its denial in Sybilla had changed his life; and its power, once unleashed for herself, had been more than he could manage.

What had he left behind him? Herself, whom he had never touched. Kuzúm, who might not be his. Men throughout Scotland and over the narrow seas who lived different lives because they had known him. One does not need to have children to see continue one's work, and one's doctrine. No one, once they had met him, could remain the same.

So spoke the brain. The heart cried aloud, to the empty air, *'Is it for this thou wast created?* You were mistaken, Jerott. And Sybilla was right. Every day he lived mattered. He belonged to life: it should have been allowed him.'

'My dear, look up,' said Archie.

She could hear, from distant voices, that Sybilla had come. Someone shouted, and there was an answering call from the gatehouse, remote over the folds of the moors. She looked up.

Beyond the last of the trees, a rider was breasting the slight hill towards them. As she watched, he slowed his horse from a trot to a walk and then, after what seemed to be some hesitation, slipped his feet from the stirrups and dismounted altogether.

Behind her, the murmuring voices had stopped.

The world ceased. Only the spirit stayed, watching.

This was not a man with pistols in his hands. He stood, with the wintry boughs swaying and swaying, frail as leaf ghosts behind his fair head, and his person as still as the tree-stems.

And she had crossed, now, the boundary she wanted to cross; for the face was the one which, before God she loved; and the look was the one upon which she had opened her eyes, lying within the folds of his cloak in the desecrated house where he had been born.

Then he said, 'Philippa?' in the key she had come to learn at Sevigny; which was not the light, charming voice which had drawn her from her warm home here at Flaw Valleys, and had taken her through deeper seas and over crests more steep than her spirit alone would ever have striven to conquer.

And if they were on the same side of the boundary, it must be real; for Sybilla was standing beside her, and Kate and Jerott and Richard . . . all of them, silent as she was, and gazing. So she began to walk forward.

He stayed where he was; and after a little it became clear that she was going to reach him, and touch him.

Then she started to run.

He did not move even then until the last second, when her hands reached his shoulders and he flung his own hands out from his sides, and kept them there. Then those left behind saw Philippa lift her palm and turn her cheek over and over against his, like someone blinded.

On that his hands locked, imprisoning them both. He held back one moment longer. Then he slid his fingers into her hair and bending his head, sought her mouth as a man withered by sun might seek water.

They are made for one another, and they know it, his wise friend had said. Kate turned from watching, to Adam.

Jerott Blyth also turned; and walking slowly, knelt by the green cloak; and after a moment, dropped his face in his hands.

My beloved is unto me as a cluster of camphire in the vineyards of Engedi.

My beloved is dead.

CHAPTER 13

L'arbre qu'estoit par long temps mort seché
Dans un nuict viendra à reverdir.

They set off that evening to take Marthe Crawford to the home of her fathers, which she had never known. And behind them, in care of Flaw Valleys, left Philippa, and Sybilla and her younger son, who could not easily travel.

To Jerott's question of *'Why? Why?'* Sybilla could only say, 'She was coming, perhaps to find you. Jerott, what will you do?'

'Bury her at Midculter, if you will allow me,' he said. 'And then leave.'

'For France?'

'For Malta, I think,' Jerott said. 'It is different, now. I should rather fight than be a merchant. Danny Hislop, perhaps, would come with me.'

Only Richard, as they were preparing to move off, said to his mother, 'She couldn't have been coming to Jerott.'

'No,' said Sybilla, 'But it will do him no harm to think, in years to come, that he was in love with her and she with him.'

'Why, then?' said Richard.

'I think,' said Sybilla, 'to follow Francis. Someone took her for him on the way and delayed her: there is a note of indemnity in her saddlebag. Also a letter for Francis. I shall give it to him in the morning. Today is his.'

Today had been his, and nothing could touch him. They had arranged, without him, the decent bier which would carry Austin to his home, and the account they would give there of the chance enemy shot that had killed him. He had stood for a long time beside the closed coffin that held the broken bones and golden hair of his sister; and then had closed the door on it to find Philippa waiting, as he used to wait outside her room, to join with him her hands and her warmth and her comfort.

In one stride indeed, the wall had been scaled and the boundary crossed. Death had sprung the trap; shock brought the release; desire, broken now from all bondage, had excavated clean with its torrent all the poisoned gulf which had lain between them. To be apart, in those hours, was more than they could bear; and to touch a thing of sweetness and anguish. She moved all day, lightly, in the shelter of his arm.

Then, standing at the gatehouse with Francis, she kissed Kate, who was weeping, and watched Jerott and Adam take their leave also.

Richard said, 'You will come soon? We need you.' And Francis said, 'We shall both come.'

Archie Abernethy was the last to go from Flaw Valleys.

To him, Francis gave no easy farewell, but set his hands lightly on the wiry shoulders and said, 'How much of it did you see, back in Rouen?'

'Not as much as the auld besom,' said Archie. 'She had a grip of me long before that, looking for you. It's been a fair upgang. It's a bloody sight easier with ...'

And Lymond laughed, his eyes brilliant. 'I know. But I can't offer you a zoo at St Mary's. Can you make do with what I have?'

'With Hoddim and Guthrie and Blacklock? What you have is a zoo,' said Archie Abernethy; and shook his hand, and turned his thin leather back on Flaw Falleys.

Then Sybilla retired, in broad daylight, and Francis said, in the empty upper reaches of the house, 'It seems that if there is a room set aside for me, no one knows where it is.'

'There is my room,' Philippa said; and freeing her fingers, laid them on the latch of a door. 'Here it is.'

He made a little movement, turning his face into her hair. '*Asik; Durr-i Bakht; Yunitsa* ... my dear, my dear ...

'I am in love-desire, and unless you take me now, I shall fall in pieces ... but I do not think I can be moderate. Forgive me, forgive me ...'

But her breathing was as changed now as his, and all order retreating before the strength of the living force beating about them. She pressed the latch, and set the last door to lie open.

'*Khush geldi:* welcome: thou art come happily,' she said gently, and let him come, where he belonged, within her governance.

And so, incontinently, the striding flame that consumed

them, without words, without courtship became, instead of the echo of lust, the cauterizing fire which expelled it for ever. For in the total extremity of need, with the fine mind overturned and subjugated for once by the overwhelming desires of his body, there still remained, drowned and helpless but there, the shadows of grace, and care, and courtesy, caught fast like stars in the deluge.

It would have been enough, were she still the crippled Philippa of Sevigny, to have swept her with him. But although she marked them, rejoicing, she did not need them, for by then she, too, was part of the torrent.

*

He slept half the night through after that, motionless in her arms in the kind of peace he had probably not known since childhood. She wept a little, from happiness and from pity for him, and then herself sank into slumber.

So that he had the felicity of wakening her; and the first thing she knew was the exquisite drift of his hands, and his voice saying, 'Qedeshet, Mistress of all the Gods, Eye of Ra, who has none like her. . . . Come and let us beget all kinds of living things.'

And then his true courtship of her had its beginning; and to the worship of his body, he joined the fairest garlands from the treasure-house of his mind, and made a bower for her.

Adored; caressed into delight; conducted by delicate paths into ravishing labyrinths where pleasure, like carillons on glass, played upon pleasure, she leaned on his voice, and sometimes answered it.

> *. . . You mee embraced; in bosom soft you mee*
> *Cherished, as I your onely chylde had bee . . .*
>
> *. . . Quhen I wes hungry, ye me fed*
> *Quhen I was naikit, ye me cled*
> *Oftymes ye gave me herberye*
> *And gaif me drynk, quen, I was drye*
> *And vesyit me with myndis meik*
> *Quhen I wes presonar, and seik . . .*

And once, triumphantly, 'And Harald went with his host out to Jerusalem-land, and sithence up to Jerusalem-town,

726

and wheresoever he fared over Jerusalem-land, all towns and castles were given up to his wielding.'

And that was when she realized that laughter, which they had lost, had come back to them and they were whole again.

*

Sleep overcame them far into the day and the November light was falling grey through her windows when he woke her to joy again, laughing. 'Amis, art thou asleep? My lyves loy, myn hertes plesance . . . The world knows all our affairs. It is tomorrow, and nearly the day after tomorrow, and we have neither eaten, nor dressed, nor gone to visit Sybilla . . .'

'I have eaten,' Philippa said.

And then the blue eyes, with gentleness, scanned all her new-made body and came to rest on her eyes. 'I have begun to eat,' said Francis Crawford. 'And I have begun to slake my thirst. But in you I have found a banquet under the heavens that will serve me for ever.'

*

Sybilla was in her room when they tapped on the door and stood there, robed like children, with Philippa's long hair on her son's shoulder.

This time, it was Philippa who ran to her, and knelt, and put her head, smiling, on Sybilla's lap.

Sybilla kissed her, and then taking her by the hand rose herself, and crossed the room to where Francis stood, his eyes grave, his face so changed that it took her breath away. He said, the deep blue eyes smiling at her, 'They gave me some medicine.'

Then he held out his hands and, when she came, bent and kissed her.

She said, 'I asked you to come when you woke, for I had something to show you.'

She glanced at his feet and then, quizzically, up at his face. 'Can I send you on an errand?'

He flushed, Philippa was delighted to see; and then laughed. 'Within limits. I am sky-clad like the Digambaras.'

'Then you will simply have to risk upsetting the servants,' said Sybilla. 'Lace that garment properly. Then go to the music room and take from the little desk at the wall the letter you will find just inside it. Here is the key.'

Both Francis and Philippa looked at her. He said, 'A letter?'

But Philippa, meeting his eyes, walked forward and taking the key said, 'Let me get it. I know where the desk is.'

'So do I,' Francis said; but did not explain. And in a moment Philippa was back, with in her hand a long packet bearing the seal of Jerott Blyth.

'That was found in Marthe's baggage,' said Lady Culter. 'It is addressed to you, Francis, and there seems to be another letter within it. Take it, and read it.'

He took it from Philippa's hands, his thoughts still, she saw on something else and not on the letter. Philippa said. 'You may give me a brooch. A sapphire one.'

'Ah,' he said. 'But will you take care of it?'

Her smile was a very private kind of answer. Then he looked down and broke the seal.

Inside was, as she said, another letter, with this time the wax already ruptured. Then he saw what the crest was, and lifted his eyes.

Sybilla said, 'Jerott tells me that Marthe went to Blois. My guess is that she found this document there, and was bringing it to you. Or if not to you, to all of us at Midculter.' She had seated herself again in her stiff leather chair by the fire. There was just enough light from the window to read by.

Lymond said quietly, 'I don't think I want to read this. You may have it.'

'If it had been addressed to me,' Sybilla said, 'I would have withheld it. But we must keep faith with whoever is leading us. It is yours. Read it.' And so he bent his head, reading.

At the end, he did not show his face even to Philippa. Instead he walked to the window, the paper still in his hand, and Philippa, who had thought, enchanted back into childhood, that there was an end to all pain heard his breathing and knew that whatever it was, it was not the old story. It was not another confession of petty fault, bought back by shame and by barter. Then he said, 'Will you tell Philippa?'

The fire lit only one side of Sybilla's face. The pretty profile, with its tilted nose and soft lips and large, thick-lashed eyes for a moment looked less than its seventy years: looked perhaps almost as it had looked when she spent such a night as that with a man as beloved; and from which had been born Francis Crawford.

Sybilla said, 'What Francis is reading tells him for the first

728

time that the castle Richard lives in, its lands, its estates, its wealth and all its properties belong to him, along with the title of Culter.'

At the window, Francis did not move. Philippa said, in a dry void of utter bemusement, 'How? How can it be possible, when Richard's birth followed your marriage?'

Sybilla said, 'Richard's birth followed my marriage to Gavin. Francis is the son of Gavin's father, the first Francis Crawford.'

'We know,' said Philippa quietly. 'We know, too, that Eloise was his daughter.'

'You know that,' said Sybilla evenly, 'because it is as much as Leonard Bailey intended you to know. There was a very good reason why he did not sell my secret to anyone else ... the same reason, I suppose, that compelled him to put Isabelle, who knew it, to death.

'Francis and Eloise were the only children born to me and to Francis, Lord Culter.

'They were legitimate. What Francis has in his hand are my marriage lines.'

Philippa sat down. Then, as no one spoke, 'Please?' she said. 'I can't understand.' At the window, Francis had turned.

'There is no need to make a long story of it,' Sybilla said. 'We married in France, secretly, and then he was lost at sea: swept overboard sailing home to Scotland with Albany. I had loved him. . . . Perhaps you know, or can guess, how I loved him. I had nothing left. I went back to Scotland. And there was the castle he had made, with his books in it, and his clothes and his music, and all the men who had known him ... and his son, importuning me to marry him. . . . If Francis had died yesterday instead of Marthe,' said Sybilla suddenly to the girl, 'could you have brought yourself one day to marry Kuzúm?'

'Yes,' said Philippa. Her mouth was dry.

'I was seven years older than Gavin,' Sybilla said. 'Then after illness and imprisonment, Francis—my husband—came back to France. He had forgotten his marriage. He had a child, Marthe, by the Dame de Doubtance's daughter, whom he had also known before he met me.'

'He also had a son by her earlier,' Philippa said. 'Didn't he? A sick boy who died.'

'A sick boy, and a daughter. So it seemed to the Dame de

729

Doubtance that her great scheme was going to fail: to breed a son from Francis Crawford who would carry his blood and do what the times had been wrong for the first baron to do. Therefore she brought back to him the recollection of our marriage, and he came back to Scotland, and found Gavin in his place, and Richard a young boy of nine.'

'That was when he threw Bailey out,' Philippa said.

'Yes,' Sybilla said. The room had become very dark.

'But not Gavin? He didn't expose your marriage to Gavin as bigamous, and Richard as . . .'

'Gavin Crawford was a vicious and venomous man,' Sybilla said. 'But I had wronged him very deeply. He chose to remain my husband in appearance, and to have Richard reared as his legitimate heir. In return, I received the discretion to visit France when I wished and my children, when they were born, were brought up as Gavin's.'

Francis said, 'Why? Why did you not . . . ?' and broke off.

'Disown Gavin and make it all public? For Richard's sake,' Sybilla said. 'And when he came back to me, Francis—my Francis—had only four years of life left to him.'

'And all the rest you spent in that castle, tied to his son, putting up with threatened disclosures from Bailey, watching Francis . . .' Philippa choked.

'I had given my word,' Sybilla said, 'to both men that I would never tell Francis or anyone else what had happened. And I had committed a sin. To marry a man and his son is not permitted.'

'So Francis suffered,' Philippa said.

And Lymond said, 'No. I understand. You had given your word. And it was more than that. Every step of the way, the signs have been laid for us, haven't they . . . even yesterday?'

'For much of the way,' Sybilla said. 'Camille de Doubtance knew me when I was at la Guiche. Through her I made the journey to Ireland where Richard met Meriotta; and Mariotta had cousins who knew Oonagh O'Dwyer.'

'Every astrologer in France seems to have been her intimate,' Lymond said. 'And . . . Kuzúm?'

Sybilla returned his look steadily. 'May be Oonagh's child,' she said. 'Or may be Joleta's. Marthe knew.'

'And is dead. Poor sister. A pawn more helpless even than . . .' He broke off.

'It is as well, you see, that we do not know,' said Sybilla. 'And Kuzúm will always have Kate, and of course, Archie.'

He had forgotten Archie. His brow cleared. 'And, of course, Archie, everyman's keeper. Christ,' he said despairingly. *'Faire d'une mouche un elephant.'*

Philippa turned her head and saw Sybilla look too, and the lines on her firelit face ease a fraction. What this meant to Francis struck her, suddenly, for the first time. She looked at the paper, still held in his hand.

As if she had spoken, he looked down as well. Then walking forward, smiling a little, he held it to Philippa. 'Read,' he said, 'so that you will know what your children might have been. Then give it to Sybilla.'

'Might have been?' Sybilla said.

He dropped by her side and laid his hand over hers, where it gripped the chair arm. 'What did you think I would do?' he said. 'Rush to Midculter and bastardize all my nieces and nephews? These are yours. Keep them. Burn them, if you wish. It is over.'

'John Dee made a prophecy,' Philippa said. 'Do you remember it? He said that now you knew what you wanted. The first thing you would have, but the second you would never have; nor would it be just that you should.'

'I was thinking of it,' said Lymond. 'The first thing was you, my Lady bricht ... The second, it seems, was my heritage.'

'Do you regret it?' said Sybilla. 'I would have kept it for you if I could. I did not know, you see, what you were to be.'

He lifted his fingers, and looking at her, kissed them. 'With the Dame de Doubtance to blame,' her son said, 'you are absolved of all responsibility. . . . My dear, there is no blame, where there lives a passion like that: do we not know it? Rest at peace. We are your children; and we love you.'

*

Much later, when they had left her, she sat in her room and saw beneath her door the lights blazing from the wide oaken porch to the music room.

She did not know when they found their way there; and at first the music she heard was only tentative. A harp sang, and then someone picked out a low, gentle tune on the harpsichord. And through it all their voices murmured, talking and talking.

Then, at some point, what they learned must have been put

731

behind them. She heard her son's voice lilting in some mimicry, and Philippa's laughing, and then more laughter, and their voices declaiming together. Then the harpsichord found its major habit and suddenly spoke, firmly and well, and a lute joined in, and was discarded for the guitar, cleanly executed. Then the music mounted, and altered.

Sitting still in the dark, Sybilla listened to the condition of love, transmuted into brilliant sound, rolling, surging, ringing through all the quiet house. And then her son's voice, formally speaking:

'So cler and so light hit wes, that joye ther was ynough. Treon ther were, ful of frut, wel thikke on everich bough. Hit was evere more dai, hi ne fonde nevere nyght; Hi ne wende fynde in no stede so moch cler light . . .'

In the bright room, had she seen him, he was sitting, his arms leaning on the harpsichord, looking at Philippa. He got up.

> 'He wald upon his tais stand
> And tak the sternis downe with his hand
> And set them in a gold garland
> Above his wyfis hair . . .

'I love you. I love you . . .'

There was a broad praying stool at his side. He saw it, and smiling knelt, and held his palms up to Philippa. And she, kneeling opposite, closed them, palm to palm, with her own.

'Camille de Doubtance, and whoever may be your master . . .

'We are here. We will work together for what purpose seems to us right. We will work with calm, and with tolerance and, please God, with saving laughter.

'We know something of men. We know of evil, and of sloth, and of self-seeking ambition. We accept it, and will use what we have of wit and good faith to overcome it.

'And if we do not overcome it, still we are the road; we are the bridge; we are the conduit. For something have we been born. For something have we been brought here. And if we hold firm, the men who peopled our earth need not be ashamed, when the reckoning comes, to say, *we worked with all we had been given; and for one another.*'

732

He closed her hands with his own and spoke to her, holding them.

'We have reached the open sea, with some charts; and the firmament.'

28 February 1974
EDINBURGH

Excellent Fiction by *Joyce Carol Oates*